NOBEL PRIZE LIBRARY

ASTURIAS

BENAVENTE

BERGSON

Nobel Prize Library

PUBLISHED UNDER THE SPONSORSHIP OF THE
NOBEL FOUNDATION & THE SWEDISH ACADEMY

Miguel Angel Asturias

Jacinto Benavente

Henri Bergson

ALEXIS GREGORY, *New York*, AND
CRM PUBLISHING, *Del Mar, California*

CONTENTS

Miguel Angel Asturias

1967

"For the vividness of his literary

work, rooted in national traits

and Indian traditions"

Illustrated by FONTANAROSA

PRESENTATION ADDRESS

By *ANDERS ÖSTERLING*

PERMANENT SECRETARY
OF THE SWEDISH ACADEMY

THIS YEAR the Nobel Prize for Literature has been awarded to the
Guatemalan writer Miguel Angel Asturias, a prominent representative of
the modern literature of Latin America, in which such interesting developments are now taking place. Born in 1899 in the capital of Guatemala,
Asturias became imbued, even as a child, with the characteristically
Guatemalan love of nature and of the mythical world. He devoted to this
native heritage and to its libertarian spirit a fervor which was to dominate
his whole literary production. After studying law and folklore, he lived
in France during the twenties and for a time represented his country in
the diplomatic service. He condemned himself to a long exile after the
antidemocratic coup d'état of 1954, but returned when the legitimate regime took office again. He is presently [1967] the Guatemalan ambassador in Paris.

During the last few years, Asturias has gained international recognition, as his most important works came to be translated into various
languages; today they can be read even in Swedish. His first work was a
collection of Guatemalan legends, strange evocations of the Mayas' past,
a treasure of images and symbols which has ever since been the inexhaustible source of his inspiration. But he did not get his real start as a
writer until 1946, the year of the publication of the novel *El Señor Presidente (The President)*. This magnificent and tragic satire criticizes the
prototype of the Latin-American dictator who appeared in several places
at the beginning of the century and has since reappeared, his existence
being fostered by the mechanism of tyranny which for the common man
makes every day a hell on earth. The passionate vigor with which

[3]

Asturias evokes the terror and distrust which poisoned the social atmosphere of the time makes his work a challenge and an invaluable aesthetic gesture. The narrative entitled *Hombres de maíz* (Men of Corn) appeared three years later. It might be considered a folk tale whose chief inspiration is in the imagination but which nevertheless remains true to life. Its motifs came from the mythology of that tropical land where man must struggle simultaneously against a mysteriously beautiful but hostile nature and against unbearable social distortions, oppression, and tyranny. Such an accumulation of nightmares and totemic phantasms may overwhelm our sensibilities, but we cannot help being fascinated by a poetry so bizarre and terrifying.

With the trilogy of novels begun in 1950—*Viente fuerte* (*Strong Wind,* 1950), *El Papa verde* (The Green Pope, 1954), and *Los ojos de los enterrados* (The Eyes of the Interred, 1960)—a new topical concern appears in Asturias's epic work: the theme of the struggle against the domination of American trusts, epitomized by the United Fruit Company and its political and economic effects upon the contemporary history of the "Banana Republic." Here again we see the violent effervescence and the visionary vehemence which stem from the author's intense involvement in the situation of his country.

Asturias has completely freed himself from obsolete narrative techniques. Very early he came under the influence of the new tendencies appearing in European literature; his explosive style bears a close kinship to French surrealism. It must be noted, however, that he always takes his inspiration from real life. In his impressive cycle of poems entitled *Clarivigilia primaveral* (Bright and Awake in Spring, 1965), on which a Swedish critical study has just appeared, Asturias deals with the very genesis of the arts and of poetic creation, in a language which seems to have assumed the bright splendor of the magical quetzal's feathers and the glimmering of phosphorescent insects.

Latin America today can boast an active group of prominent writers, a multivoiced chorus in which individual contributions are not readily discernible. Asturias's work is nevertheless vast, bold, and outstanding enough to arouse interest outside of his own literary milieu, beyond a geographically limited area situated far away from us. One of the Indian legends Asturias alludes to evokes the belief that dead ancestors are forced to witness, with open eyes, the struggles and sufferings of their offspring. Only when justice is reestablished and the stolen soil restituted, will the dead finally be able to close their eyes and sleep peacefully in their tombs. It is a beautiful and poignant popular belief, and we can easily imagine that the militant poet has often felt upon him the gaze of his ancestors and has often heard the silent, symbolic appeal reaching to his heart.

Mr. Ambassador—You come from a distant country; but do not let this fact make you feel today that you are a stranger among us. Your work is known and appreciated in Sweden. We take pleasure in welcoming you as a messenger from Latin America, its people, its spirit, and its future. I congratulate you in the name of the Swedish Academy, which pays tribute to the "vividness of your literary work, rooted in national traits and Indian traditions." I now invite you to receive your Prize from His Majesty the King.

ACCEPTANCE SPEECH

By MIGUEL ANGEL ASTURIAS

MY VOICE on the threshold. My voice coming from afar. On the threshold of the Academy. It is difficult to become a member of a family. And it is easy. The stars know it. The families of luminous torches. To become a member of the Nobel family. To become an heir of Alfred Nobel. To blood ties, to civil relationship, a new consanguinity is added, a more subtle kinship, born of the spirit and the creative task. And this was perhaps the unspoken intention of the founder of this great family of Nobel Prizewinners. To enlarge, through time, from generation to generation, the world of his own kin. As for me, I enter the Nobel family as the least worthy to be called among the many who could have been chosen.

I enter by the will of this Academy, whose doors open and close once a year in order to consecrate a writer, and also because of the use I made of the word in my poems and novels, the word which, more than beautiful, is responsible, a concern not foreign to that dreamer who with the passing of time would shock the world with his inventions—the discovery of the most destructive explosives then known—for helping man in his titanic chores of mining, digging tunnels, and constructing roads and canals.

I do not know if the comparison is too daring. But it is necessary. The use of destructive forces, the secret which Alfred Nobel extracted from nature, made possible in our America the most colossal enterprises. Among them, the Panama Canal. A magic of catastrophe which could be compared to the thrust of our novels, called upon to destroy unjust structures in order to make way for a new life. The secret mines of the people, buried under tons of misunderstanding, prejudices, and taboos, bring to light in our narrative—between fables and myths—with blows of protest, testimony, and denunciation, dikes of letters which, like sands, contain reality to let the dream flow free or, on the contrary, contain the dream to let reality escape.

Cataclysms which engendered a geography of madness, terrifying traumas, such as the Conquest: these cannot be the antecedents of a literature of cheap compromise; and, thus, our novels appear to Europeans as illogical or aberrant. They are not shocking for the sake of shock effects. It is just that what happened to us was shocking. Continents submerged in the sea, races castrated as they surged to independence, and the fragmentation of the New World. As the antecedents of a literature these are already tragic. And from there we have had to extract not the man of defeat, but the man of hope, that blind creature who wanders through our songs. We are peoples from worlds which have nothing like the orderly unfolding of European conflicts, always human in their dimensions. The dimensions of our conflicts in the past centuries have been catastrophic.

Scaffoldings. Ladders. New vocabularies. The primitive recitation of the texts. The rhapsodists. And later, once again, the broken trajectory. The new tongue. Long chains of words. Thought unchained. Until arriving, once again, after the bloodiest verbal battles, at one's own expressions. There are no rules. They are invented. And after much invention, the grammarians come with their language-trimming shears. American Spanish is fine with me, but without the roughness. Grammar becomes an obsession. The risk of antigrammar. And that is where we are now. The search for dynamic words. Another magic. The poet and the writer of the active word. Life. Its variations. Nothing prefabricated. Everything in ebullition. Not to write literature. Not to substitute words for things. To look for word-things, word-beings. And the problems of man, in addition. Evasion is impossible. Man. His problems. A continent that speaks. And which was heard in this Academy. Do not ask us for genealogies, schools, treatises. We bring you the probabilities of a world. Verify them. They are singular. Singular is the movement, the dialogue, the novelistic intrigue. And most singular of all, throughout the ages there has been no interruption in the constant creation.

EL SEÑOR PRESIDENTE

By MIGUEL ANGEL ASTURIAS

Translated by Frances Partridge

PART I

The 21st, 22nd and 23rd of April

CHAPTER I

In the Cathedral Porch

"Boom, bloom, alum-bright, Lucifer of alunite!" The sound of the church bells summoning people to prayer lingered on, like a humming in the ears, an uneasy transition from brightness to gloom, from gloom to brightness. "Boom, bloom, alum-bright, Lucifer of alunite, over the somber tomb! Bloom, alum-bright, over the tomb, Lucifer of alunite! Boom, boom, alum-bright . . . bloom . . . alum-bright . . . bloom, alum-bright . . . bloom, boom."

In the frozen shadow of the cathedral, the beggars were shuffling past the market eating-houses as they made their way through the ocean-wide streets to the Plaza de Armas, leaving the deserted city behind them.

Nightfall assembled them, as it did the stars. With nothing in common but their destitution, they mustered to sleep together in the Porch of Our Lord, cursing, insulting and jostling each other, picking quarrels with old enemies, or throwing earth and rubbish, even rolling on the ground and spitting and biting with rage.

This confraternity of the dunghill had never known pillows or mutual trust. They lay down in all their clothes at a distance from one another, and slept like thieves, with their heads on the bags containing their worldly goods: left-over scraps of meat, worn-out shoes, candle-ends, handfuls of cooked rice wrapped in old newspapers, oranges and rotten bananas.

They could be seen sitting on the steps of the Porch with their faces to the wall, counting their money, biting the nickel coins to see if they were false, talking to themselves, inspecting their stores of food and ammunition (for they went out into the streets fully armed with stones and scapularies) and stuffing themselves secretly on crusts of dry bread. They had never been known to help each other; like all beggars they were miserly with their scraps, and would rather give them to the dogs than to their companions in misfortune.

Having satisfied their hunger and tied up their money with seven knots in handkerchiefs fastened to their belts, they threw themselves on the ground and sank into sad, agitated dreams—nightmares in which they saw famished pigs, thin women, maimed dogs and carriage wheels passing before their eyes, or a funeral procession of phantom monks going into the cathedral preceded by a sliver of moon carried on a cross made of frozen shin-bones. Sometimes they would be woken from their deepest dreams by the cries of an idiot who had lost his way in the Plaza de Armas; or sometimes by the sobs of a blind woman dreaming that she was covered in flies and suspended from a hook like a piece of meat in a butcher's shop. Or sometimes by the tramp of a patrol, belaboring a political prisoner as they dragged him along, while women followed wiping away the blood-stains with handkerchiefs soaked in tears. Sometimes by the snores of a scabby valetudinarian, or the heavy breathing of a pregnant deaf-mute, weeping with fear of the child she felt in her womb. But the idiot's cry was the saddest of all. It rent the sky. It was a long-drawn-out inhuman wail.

On Sundays this strange fraternity used to be joined by a drunk man who called for his mother and wept like a child in his sleep. Hearing the word "mother" fall more like an oath than a prayer from the drunkard's lips, the idiot would sit up, search every corner of the Porch with his eyes and—having woken himself and his companions with his cries—burst into tears of fright, joining his sobs to those of the drunkard.

Dogs barked, shouts were heard, and the more irritable beggars got up and increased the hubbub by calling for silence. If they didn't shut their jaws the police would come. But the police wanted nothing to do with the beggars. None of them had enough money to pay a fine. "Long live France!" Flatfoot would shout, amidst the cries and antics of the idiot, who became the laughing-stock of the other beggars in the end,

simply because this scoundrelly, foul-mouthed cripple liked to pretend to be drunk several nights every week. So Flatfoot would pretend to be drunk, while the Zany (as they called the idiot), who looked like a corpse when he was asleep, became more lively with every shriek, ignoring the huddled forms lying under rags on the ground, who jeered and cackled shrilly at his crazy behavior. With his eyes far away from the hideous faces of his companions, he saw nothing, heard nothing and felt nothing, and fell asleep at last, worn out with weeping. But it was the same every night—no sooner had he dropped off than Flatfoot's voice woke him again:

"Mother!"

The Zany opened his eyes with a start like someone who dreams he is falling into space; he shrank back with enormously dilated pupils as if mortally wounded and the tears began to flow once more; then sleep gradually overcame him, his body became flaccid, and anxious fears reverberated through his deranged mind. But no sooner was he thoroughly asleep than another voice would wake him:

"Mother!"

It was the voice of a degenerate mulatto known as the Widower, snivelling like an old woman, amid bursts of laughter:

". . . mother of mercy, our hope and salvation, may God preserve you, listen to us poor down-and-outs and idiots . . ."

The idiot used to wake up laughing; it seemed that he too found his misery and hunger so amusing that he laughed till he cried, while the beggars snatched bu-bu-bursts of la-la-laughter from the air, from the air . . . la-la-laughter; a fat man with his moustaches dripping with stew lost his breath from laughing; and a one-eyed man laughed till he urinated and beat his head against the wall like a goat;

while the blind men complained that they couldn't sleep with such a row going on, and the Mosquito, who was legless as well as blind, cried out that only sodomites could amuse themselves in such a fashion.

No one paid any attention to the blind men's protests and the Mosquito's remark was not even heard. Why should anyone listen to his jabber? "Oh yes, I spent my childhood in the artillery barracks, and the mules and officers kicked me into shape and made a man of me—a man who could work like a horse, which was useful when I had to pull a barrel-organ through the streets! Oh yes, and I lost my sight when I was on the booze, the devil knows how, and my right leg on another booze-up, the devil knows when, and the other in another booze-up, knocked down by a car the devil knows where!"

The beggars spread a rumor among the people of the town that the Zany went mad whenever anyone mentioned his mother. The poor wretch used to run through the streets, squares, courtyards and markets, trying to get away from people shouting "Mother!" at him from every side and at any hour of the day, like a malediction from the sky. He tried to take refuge in houses, but was chased out again by dogs or servants. They drove him out of churches, shops and everywhere else, indifferent to his utter exhaustion and the plea for pity in his uncomprehending eyes.

The town that his exhaustion had made so large—so immensely large— seemed to shrink in the face of his despair. Nights of terror were followed by days of persecution, during which he was hounded by people who were not content to shout: "On Sunday you'll marry your Mother, my little Zany—your old woman!" but beat him and tore his clothes as well. Pursued by children, he would take refuge in the poorer quarters, but there his fate was even worse; there everyone lived on the verge of destitution, and insults were not enough—they threw stones, dead rats and empty tins at him as he ran away in terror.

One day he came to the Cathedral Porch from the suburbs just as the angelus was ringing, without his hat, with a wound in his forehead, and trailing the tail of a kite which had been fastened to him as a joke. Everything frightened him: the shadows of the walls, dogs trotting by, leaves falling from the trees, and the irregular rumbling of wheels. When he arrived at the Porch it was almost dark and the beggars were sitting with their faces to the wall counting their earnings. Flatfoot was quarreling with the Mosquito, the deaf-mute was feeling her inexplicably swollen belly, and the blind woman was hanging from a hook in her dreams, covered in flies, like a piece of meat at the butcher's.

The idiot fell on the ground as if dead; he had not closed his eyes for nights, he had not been able to rest his feet for days. The beggars were silently scratching their fleabites but could not sleep; they listened for the footsteps of the police going to and fro in the dimly lit square and the click of the sentinels presenting arms, as they stood at attention like ghosts in their striped *ponchos* at the windows of the neighboring barracks, keeping their nightly watch over the President of the Republic. No one knew where he was, for he occupied several houses in the outskirts of the town; nor how he slept—some said beside the telephone with a whip in his hand; nor when—his friends declared he never slept at all.

A figure advanced towards the Porch of Our Lord. The beggars curled themselves up like worms. The creak of military boots was answered by the sinister hoot of a bird from the dark, navigable, bottomless night.

Flatfoot opened his eyes (a menacing threat as of the end of the world weighed upon the air) and said to the owl:

"Hoo-hoo! Do your worst! I wish you neither good nor ill, but the devil take you all the same!"

The Mosquito groped for his face with his hands. The air was tense as though an earthquake were brewing. The Widower crossed himself as he sat among the blind men. Only the Zany slept like a log, snoring for once.

The new arrival stopped; his face lit up with a smile. Going up to the idiot on tiptoe he shouted jeeringly at him: "Mother!"

That was all. Torn from the ground by the cry, the Zany flung himself upon his tormentor, and, without giving him time to get at his weapons, thrust his fingers into his eyes, tore at his nose with his teeth and jabbed his private parts with his knees, till he fell to the ground motionless.

The beggars shut their eyes in horror, the owl flew by once more and the Zany fled away down the shadowy streets in a paroxysm of mad terror.

Some blind force had put an end to the life of Colonel José Parrales Sonriente, known as "the man with the little mule."

It was nearly dawn.

CHAPTER II

The Death of the Mosquito

The sun was gilding the projecting terraces of the Second Police Station (a few people were passing along the street), the Protestant church (one or two doors stood open) and a brick building in process of construction.

It always seemed to be raining in the patio of the Police Station, and groups of barefooted women were sitting on stone benches in the dark corridors waiting for the prisoners, with their breakfast baskets in the hammocks made by their skirts between their knees. Their children clustered round them, the babies glued to their pendulous breasts and the bigger ones threatening the loaves in the baskets with hungrily opened mouths. The women were telling each other their troubles in low voices, crying all the while, and mopping their tears with the ends of their shawls. A hollow-eyed old woman, shaking with malaria, wept copiously and silently as if to show that as a mother she suffered more acutely than the rest. The evils of life seemed without remedy here in this dismal place of waiting, with nothing to look at but two or three neglected shrubs, an empty fountain and these sallow-faced policemen cleaning their celluloid collars with saliva. They must put their trust in the power of the Almighty.

A ladino* policeman came by, dragging along the Mosquito. He had caught him at the corner by the Infants' School and was pulling him along by the hand, shaking him from side to side like a monkey. But the women did not notice anything comic in this; they were too busy spying on the movements of the jailers as they carried in breakfasts and returned with news of the prisoners: "He says . . . not to worry about him, things are looking up already! He says . . . you're to buy him four *reals*-worth of mercury ointment as soon as the chemist opens! He says . . . not to count on what his cousin told you! He says . . . you're to get a lawyer for him; best look for a student, he won't rook you so much! He says . . . don't go on like that, they've got no women in there with them so you can't be jealous; they brought in one of *them* the other day and

---

* Of mixed white and Indian blood.

he soon found himself a boy-friend! He says . . . send him a few *reals*-worth of purge or he can't shit! He says . . . he's fed up with you for selling the cupboard!"

"Hey, you!" the Mosquito protested, indignant at the way this copper was knocking him about. "What d'you think you're doing? No pity, eh? Just because I'm poor? Poor but honest. Listen to me: I'm not your kid, nor your fancy-boy, for you to treat me like that! A find idea to keep in with the Yankees by nabbing us and carting us to the workhouse! What a dirty trick! Like turkeys for the Christmas dinner! And it's not as if you even treated us right! Not you. When Mister Nosey-Parker got there we'd been there three days with nothing to eat, looking out of the windows dressed in blankets as if we were nuts . . ."

The captured beggars were taken straight to one of the narrow dark cells known as the "Three Marias." The Mosquito was dragged in like a crab. His voice was drowned at first by the noise of the keys in the locks and the curses of the jailers, who stank of sweat-soaked clothes and stale tobacco, but afterwards it echoed loudly through the underground vault:

"Oh my God, what a copper! Holy Conception, what a bastard! Jesus Christ!"

His companions were whimpering like sick animals and sniveling with horror of the darkness (they felt they would never be able to free their eyes from it again), and with fear (so many other men had suffered hunger and thirst here till they died); they had a growing conviction that they would be boiled down and made into soap like dogs, or have their throats cut and be given to the police to eat. They seemed to see the faces of these cannibals, lit up like lanterns, advancing through the shadows, with cheeks like buttocks and moustaches like slobbered chocolate . . .

A student and a sacristan found themselves together in the same cell.

"I think I'm right in saying you were the first here. You and then me, isn't that so?"

The student talked for the sake of saying something, to get rid of the knot of anxiety which constricted his throat.

"Yes, I think so," replied the sacristan, trying to see the other's face in the darkness.

"Well, I was just going to ask what you're here for."

"For political reasons, so they say."

The student was trembling from head to foot as he enunciated with great difficulty: "Me too."

The beggars were hunting about for their inseparable bags of provisions, but everything had been taken away in the office of the Chief of Police, even what they had in their pockets, so that not even a match should be allowed in. Orders were strict.

"And what about your case?" went on the student.

"There's no case against me. I'm here by orders from above!"

The sacristan rubbed his back against the rough wall as he spoke, to scratch his lice.

"You were—?"

"Nothing," interrupted the sacristan violently. "I wasn't anything!"

At this moment the hinges of the door creaked as it opened to admit another beggar.

"Long live France!" cried Flatfoot as he came in.

"I'm in prison . . ." declared the sacristan.

"Long live France!"

". . . for doing something that was purely an accident. You see, instead of taking down an announcement about the

Virgin of La O from the door of the church where I was sacristan, I went and removed a notice of the President's mother's anniversary."

"But how did he find out?" murmured the student, while the sacristan wiped away his tears with his fingers.

"I don't know. My own stupidity. Anyway, they arrested me and took me to the offices of the Chief of Police, who hit me once or twice and then gave orders for me to be put in this cell in solitary confinement—as a revolutionary, he said."

The beggars were crumpled up in the darkness, crying with fear, cold and hunger. They couldn't even see their own hands. Sometimes they relapsed into lethargy, and the heavy breathing of the pregnant deaf-mute could be heard circulating among them as if seeking a way out.

No one knew what time it was, perhaps midnight, when they were taken out of their dungeon. A squat little man with a wrinkled, saffron-colored face, an unkempt moustache combed over his thick lips, a rather snub nose and hooded eyes, informed them that he was investigating a political crime. And he ended by asking them, first all together and then separately, whether they knew the perpetrator or perpetrators of the murder in the Cathedral Porch, committed the night before on the person of a Colonel in the army.

The room to which they had been taken was lit by a smoking lamp, whose feeble light seemed to be filtered through lenses full of water. What was happening? What wall was that? And that rack bristling more fiercely with weapons than the jaws of a tiger, and that policeman's belt full of cartridges?

The beggars' unexpected reply to his questions made the Judge Advocate General jump up from his chair.

"Tell me the truth!" he shouted, opening basilisk eyes behind his thick spectacles and banging his fist on the table he used as a desk.

One by one they repeated in the voices of souls in torment that the assassin had been the Zany, and described in detail the crime they had witnessed with their own eyes.

At a sign from the Judge Advocate the policemen who had been listening outside the door fell upon the beggars, beat them and pushed them into an empty room. From the almost invisible center beam a long rope was hanging.

"It was the idiot!" screamed the first to be tortured, eager to escape by telling the truth. "It was the idiot, sir! It was the idiot! Before God, it was the idiot! The idiot! The idiot! The Zany! The Zany! It was him! Him! Him!"

"That's what they told you to say, but lies won't cut any ice with me. The truth or death, do you hear? Get that into your heads if it's not there already!"

The Judge Advocate's voice faded away like the roaring of blood in the ears of the unfortunate wretch, who was suspended by his thumbs with his feet some way off the ground. He went on shouting:

"It was the idiot! That's who it was! I swear to God it was the idiot! It was the idiot! It was the idiot! It was the idiot! . . . It was the idiot!"

"Lies!" declared the Judge Advocate, and then, during a pause: "Lies! You're a liar! I'll tell you who murdered Colonel José Parrales Sonriente, and we'll see if you dare deny it; I'll tell you myself. It was General Eusebio Canales and Abel Carvajal, the lawyer!"

A frozen silence followed these words; then there was a moan, and after a pause another moan and finally a "yes." When the rope was unfastened the Widower fell to the floor unconscious. Dripping with sweat and tears, the mulatto's cheeks looked like coal wetted by the rain.

When they went on to interrogate his companions, who were trembling like dogs poisoned by the police and dying in the street, they all confirmed what the Judge Advocate General had said—all except the Mosquito. His face was contorted by a rictus of fear and disgust. They hung him up by the fingers because he went on insisting from the ground—seeming indeed half buried in the earth as all legless men do—that his companions were lying when they accused unknown persons of a crime for which the idiot alone was responsible.

"Responsible!" The Judge Advocate pounced on the word. "How dare you say an idiot is responsible? You see what lies you tell us—an irresponsible idiot responsible!"

"It's what he'll tell you himself—"

"He must be beaten," said a policeman with a woman's voice; and another struck him across the face with a lash.

"Tell the truth!" shouted the Judge Advocate as the whip lashed the old man's cheeks. "The truth, or you'll hang here all night!"

"Can't you see I'm blind?"

"Then stop saying it was the Zany."

"No, because that's the truth and I've got the spunk to say so!"

Two strokes from the lash covered his lips in blood.

"Listen, even if you are blind you can tell the truth like the rest."

"All right," agreed the Mosquito in a faint voice, and the Judge Advocate thought he had won. "All right, you clot, it was the Zany who did it . . ."

"You fool!"

The Judge Advocate's insult was lost to the ears of this half-man who would never hear anything again. When they loosed the rope, the Mosquito's dead body—or rather his torso, for he had lost both his legs—fell to the ground like a broken pendulum.

"The old liar, how could his evidence

be any use when he was blind?" said the Judge Advocate General as he walked past the corpse.

And he hurried off to take the President the news of the first results of the inquiry, in a ramshackle cab drawn by two thin horses, and with its lamps shining like the eyes of death. The police flung the Mosquito's body into a garbage-cart on its way to the cemetery. The cocks were beginning to crow. Those of the beggars who had been set free went back to the streets. The deaf-mute was crying with fear of the child she felt moving in her womb.

CHAPTER III

The Flight of the Zany

The Zany fled through the narrow twisting streets of the suburbs, but his frantic cries disturbed neither the calm of the sky nor the sleep of the inhabitants, who were as alike one another in their simulation of death as they would be different when they resumed the struggle for life at sunrise. Some lacked the bare necessities of life and were forced to work hard for their daily bread, others got more than enough from the privileged industries of idleness: as friends of the President; owners of house-property (forty or fifty houses); money-lenders at nine, nine and a half and ten per cent a month; officials holding seven or eight different public posts; exploiters of concessions, pensions, professional qualifications, gambling hells, cock-pits, Indians, brandy distilleries, brothels, bars and subsidized newspapers.

The blood-red juice of dawn was staining the edges of the funnel of mountains encircling the town, as it lay like a crust of scurf in the plain. The streets were tunnels of shadows, through which the earliest workmen were setting out like phantoms in the emptiness of a world that was created anew every morning; they were followed a few hours later by office workers, clerks and students; and at about eleven, when the sun was already high, by important gentlemen walking off their breakfasts and getting up an appetite for lunch, or going to see some influential friend, to get him to join in the purchase of the arrears of starving school-masters' salaries at half-price. The streets still lay deep in shadow when their silence was broken by the rustle of the starched skirts of some townswoman, working without respite—as swine-herd, milk-woman, street-hawker or offal-seller—to keep her family alive, or up early to do her chores; then, when the light paled to a rosy white like a begonia flower, there would be the pattering footsteps of some thin little typist, despised by the grand ladies who waited till the sun was already hot before they left their bedrooms, stretched their legs in the passages, told their dreams to the servants, criticized the passers-by, fondled the cat, read the newspaper or admired themselves in the looking-glass.

Half in the world of reality, half in a dream, the Zany ran on, pursued by dogs and by spears of fine rain. He ran aimlessly, with his mouth opened and his tongue hanging out, slobbering and panting, and his arms in the air. Doors and doors and doors and windows and doors and windows flashed past him. Suddenly he would stop and put his hands over his face to defend himself from a telegraph pole, but when he realized it was harmless he burst out laughing and went on again, like a man escaping from a prison with walls made of mist, so that the more he ran the further they receded.

When he came to the suburbs, where the town gave way to the surrounding country, he sank on to a heap of rubbish, like someone who has reached his bed at last, and fell asleep. Above the dunghill

was a spiders-web of dead trees, covered with turkey-buzzards; when they saw the Zany lying there motionless, the black birds of prey fixed him with their bluish eyes and settled on the ground beside him, hopping all round him—a hop this way, a hop that way—in a macabre dance. Ceaselessly looking about them, making ready for flight at the smallest movement of a leaf or the wind in the rubbish—a hop this way, a hop that way—they closed in upon him in a circle until he was within reach of their beaks. A savage croaking gave the signal for the attack. The Zany got to his feet as he woke, prepared to defend himself. One of the boldest birds had fastened its beak in his upper lip piercing it right through to the teeth like a dart, while the other carnivores disputed as to which should have his eyes and his heart. The bird which had hold of his lip struggled to tear off the morsel, caring nothing that its prey was alive, and would have succeeded had not the Zany taken a step backwards and rolled down a precipice of garbage, sending up clouds of dust and chunks of caked debris.

It was growing dark. Green sky. Green countryside. In the barracks the bugles were sounding six o'clock, echoing the anxiety of a tribe on the alert, or a besieged medieval town. In the prisons the agony of captives who were being slowly killed by the passage of the years began anew. The horizon withdrew its little heads into the streets of the town, a snail with a thousand heads. People were returning from audiences with the President, some in favor, some in disgrace. The lights from the windows of the gambling-dens stabbed the darkness.

The idiot was struggling with the ghost of the turkey-buzzard which he still seemed to feel attacking him, and also with the pain of a leg broken in his fall—an unbearable, black pain, which tore at his vitals.

All night long he whined like an injured dog, first softly then loudly, softly and loudly:

"Ee, ee, ee . . . Ee, ee, ee . . ."

As he sat beside a pool of water among the wild plants whose lovely flowers had been engendered by the filth of the town, the idiot's brain was brewing gigantic storms within its small compass.

"E-e-eee . . . E-e-eee. E-e-eee."

The steel fingernails of fever were clawing at his forehead. Disassociation of ideas. A fluctuating world seen in a mirror. Fantastic disproportion. Hurricane of delirium. Vertiginous flight, horizontal, vertical, oblique, newly-born and dead in a spiral . . .

"Eee, ee, ee, ee, ee."

Curveofacurveinacurveofacurvecurveofacurveinacurveof Lot's wife. (Did she invent lotteries?) The mules pulling the tram were turning into Lot's wife and their immobility annoyed the tram conductors, who, not content with breaking their whips on their backs and throwing stones at them, invited the gentlemen passengers to use their weapons. The grandest of them carried daggers and made the mules go by stabbing them . . .

"Ee, ee, ee."

INRIdiot! INRIdiot!

"Ee, ee, ee."

The knife-grinder sharpens his teeth before he laughs! Smile-sharpeners! Knife-grinder's teeth!

"Mother!"

The drunkard's cry roused him.

"Mother!"

The moon was shining brilliantly between the spongy clouds. Its white light fell on the damp leaves giving them the gloss and texture of porcelain.

They're carrying off—!

They're carrying off—!

They're carrying off the saints from the church to bury them!

Oh what fun, oh they're going to bury them, they're going to bury them, oh, what fun!

The cemetery is gayer than the town and cleaner than the town! Oh what fun! They're going to bury them!

Ta-ra-ra! Ta-ra-ra-boom!

And on he went, through thick and thin, taking great leaps from one volcano to another, from star to star, from sky to sky, half awake, half asleep, among big mouths and little mouths, with teeth and without teeth, with lips and without lips, with double lips, with moustaches, with double tongues, with triple tongues, crying: "Mother! Mother! Mother!"

Toot-toot! He took the local train to get away from the town to the mountains as quickly as possible; the mountains would give him a leg-up to the volcanoes, beyond the wireless pylons, beyond the slaughter-house, beyond the artillery fort —a *vol-au-vent* stuffed with soldiers.

But the train returned to its point of departure like a toy on a string; and when it arrived—chuff-chuff, chuff-chuff —a snuffling vegetable-seller with hair like the withies her baskets were made of was waiting in the station, and cried out: "Some bread for the idiot, polly parrot? Water for the idiot! Water for the idiot!"

Pursued by the vegetable-seller who was threatening him with a gourd full of water, he ran towards the Cathedral Porch, but when he arrived—"Mother!" a cry, a jump, a man, night; a struggle, death, blood, flight, the idiot . . . "Water for the idiot, polly parrot! Water for the idiot!"

The pain in his leg awoke him. He felt there was a labyrinth inside his bones. His eyes grew sad in the daylight. Sleeping lianas covered in beautiful flowers invited him to sleep beneath their shade, close to a cool spring which moved its foaming tail as if a silver squirrel were hidden among its mosses and ferns.

No one. No one.

Once again the Zany took refuge in the

night of his closed eyes and fought against pain, trying to find a position for his broken leg, holding his torn lip in place. But whenever he raised his burning lids, blood-red skies were passing above him. Between flashes of lightning the ghosts of caterpillars fled away as butterflies.

He turned his back on the alarum bell of delirium. Snow for the dying! The ice-man is selling the viaticum! The priest is selling snow! Snow for the dying! Ting-a-ling! Snow for the dying! The viaticum is going by! The ice-man is passing! Take your hat off, you dribbling mute! Snow for the dying!

CHAPTER IV

Angel Face

Covered in bits of paper, leather and rags, skeleton umbrellas, brims of straw hats, saucepans with holes in them, broken china, cardboard boxes, pulped books, pieces of glass, shoes curled up by the sun, collars, egg-shells, scraps of cotton and food—the Zany went on dreaming. Now he saw himself in a large patio surrounded by masks; soon he realized that they were the faces of people watching a cock-fight. The fight blazed up like paper in a flame. One of the combatants expired without pain before the spectators' eyes, which were glazed with pleasure to see the curved spurs drawn out smothered in blood. A smell of brandy. Tobacco-stained spittle. Entrails. Savage exhaustion. Somnolence. Weakness. Tropical noon. Someone was tiptoeing through his dream so as not to wake him . . .

It was the Zany's mother. The mistress of a cock-breeder who played the guitar with flinty fingernails, she had been the victim of his jealousy and his vices. The story of her troubles was endless: at the mercy of this worthless man and a martyr to the child born to her under the "direct" influence of a changing moon,

so the midwives said, in her agony she had connected her baby's disproportionately large head—a round head with a double crown like the moon—with the bony faces of all the other patients in the hospital, and the expressions of fear and disgust, the hiccups, gloom and vomiting of the drunken cock-breeder.

The Zany became aware of the rustle of starched petticoats—wind and leaves—and ran after her with tears in his eyes.

He found relief in her motherly bosom. The entrails of the woman who had given birth to him absorbed the pain of his wounds like blotting-paper. What a deep and imperturbable refuge. What abundance of love! My pretty little lily! My fine big lily! How I love you! How I love you!

The cock-breeder was singing softly into the hollow of his ear:

Why not,
Why not,
Why not, my sugar-plum lollypop,
For I am a cock lollypop
And when I raise my foot lollypop
I drag my wing lollypop!

The Zany raised his head and without speaking said:
"I'm sorry, Mamma, I'm sorry!"
And the apparition stroked his face tenderly and replied:
"I'm sorry, my son, I'm sorry!"
From a long way off he heard his father's voice, emerging from a glass of brandy:

I was hooked
I was hooked
I was hooked by a white woman,
And when the yucca grows well
Only the leaves are torn up!

The Zany murmured:
"I'm sick to my soul, Mamma!"
And the apparition stroked his face tenderly and replied: "I'm sick to my soul, my son!"

Happiness does not taste of flesh. Close beside them the shadow of a pine tree lay kissing the earth, as cool as a river. And in the pine tree a bird was singing, a bird that was also a little gold bell.

"I am the Rose-Apple of the Bird of Paradise, I am life, half my body is a lie, the other half is truth; I am a rose and I am an apple, I give to everyone one glass eye and one real eye; those who see with my glass eye see because they dream, those who see with my real eye see because they are looking! I am life, the Rose-Apple of the Bird of Paradise; I am the lie in every truth, and the truth in every fabrication!"

Suddenly the idiot left his mother's lap and ran to watch the circus go by: horses with long manes like weeping-willows ridden by women dressed in spangles; carriages decorated with flowers and paper streamers reeled along the paved streets as unsteadily as drunkards. A troupe of squalid street musicians, trumpeters, fiddle-scrapers and drum-beaters. Floury-faced clowns were distributing bright-colored programs announcing a gala performance in honor of the President of the Republic, the Benefactor of his Country, Head of the Great Liberal Party and Protector of Studious Youth.

The idiot's gaze wandered round the high vaulted roof. The circus performers left him alone in a building standing above a bottomless abyss the color of verdigris. The seats were hanging from the curtains like suspension bridges. The confessionals went up and down between the earth and sky like lifts carrying souls, operated by the Angel of the Golden Ball and the Devil with Eleven Thousand Horns. The Virgin of Carmel came out from her shrine through the wall of glass enclosing her, just as light passed through a window, and asked what he wanted and whom he was looking for. And he was delighted to stop and talk to

her, to the owner of the house, the sweetest of the angels, the reason for the existence of the saints and the poor people's pastrycook. This great lady was less than three feet tall, but when she spoke she gave the impression of understanding everything like a full-grown person. The Zany explained by signs how much he enjoyed chewing wax; and half-smiling, half-serious, she told him to take one of the lighted tapers from the altar. Then, gathering up her too-long silver cloak, she led him by the hand to a basin full of colored fish and gave him the rainbow to suck like barley-sugar. Perfect bliss! He felt happy from the tip of his tongue to the tip of his toes. It was something he had never had in his life: a piece of wax to chew like copal, peppermint-flavored barley-sugar, a basin full of colored fish, and a mother who sang as she massaged his injured leg: "Get well, get well, my little frog's bottom, seven little farts for you and your mamma!" All this was his as he slept on the garbage.

But happiness lasts no longer than a shower in the sunshine . . . Down the path of beaten earth the color of milk leading to the rubbish-dump came a wood-cutter followed by his dog; he carried a faggot of sticks on his back, his coat folded over it and his machete in his arms like a baby. The gulley was not deep, but the falling dusk had plunged it in shadows and shrouded the rubbish piled up in its depths. The wood-cutter turned and looked back. He could have sworn he was being followed. Further on, he stopped again. He sensed the presence of some hidden person. The dog howled, with its hair standing on end as if it saw the devil. An eddy of wind lifted some dirty bits of paper, stained as with women's blood or beetroot juice. The sky looked very far away, very blue, decorated like the vault of a very high tomb with sleepily circling turkey-buzzards. Suddenly the dog raced off to the place where the Zany was lying. The wood-cutter trembled with fear. He followed the dog cautiously, step by step, to see who the dead man was. He was in danger of cutting his feet on broken glass, bottle-ends and sardine-tins, and had to jump over foul-smelling excrement and nameless patches of darkness. The hollows were full of water, like harbors among the garbage.

Without putting down his load—his fear was a heavier burden—he caught hold of one of the supposed corpse's feet. and was astonished to find a living man, whose panting breath combined with his cries and the dog's barking to make a graph of his distress, like wind when it is laced with rain. The footsteps of someone walking through a little wood of pines and ancient guava-trees near-by agitated the wood-cutter even more. Suppose it was a policeman! Oh well, really, that would be the last straw!

"Quiet!" he said to the dog. And as it went on barking he gave it a kick. "Shut up, you brute, be quiet!"

Should he run for it? But flight would be a confession of guilt. Worse still, if it were a policeman. And turning to the injured man:

"Here quick, I'll help you get up! My God, they've half killed you! Quick, don't be scared, don't shout; I'm not hurting you! I was just coming along, and saw you lying there . . ."

"I saw you digging him out," interrupted a voice behind him, "and I turned back in case it was someone I knew; let's get him out of here."

The wood-cutter turned his head to reply, and nearly fainted with fear. He gave a gasp, and would have made off except that he was supporting a man who could barely stand. The man who had spoken was an angel: a complexion of golden marble, fair hair, a small mouth and an almost feminine appearance, in strong contrast with the manly expression of his black eyes. He was wearing gray. In the fading light he seemed to be dressed in a cloud. In his slender hands he held a thin cane and a broad-brimmed hat which looked like a dove.

"An angel!" The wood-cutter couldn't take his eyes from him. "An angel," he repeated, "an angel!"

"It's obvious from his clothes that he's very poor," said the newcomer. "What a sad thing it is to be poor!"

"That depends; everything in this world depends on something else. Look at me; I'm very poor; but I've got my work, my wife and my hut, and I don't think I'm to be pitied," stammered the wood-cutter like a man talking in his sleep, hoping to ingratiate himself with this angel, who might recompense his Christian resignation by changing him from a wood-cutter to a king, if he so wished. And for a second he saw himself dressed in gold, with a red cloak, a crown on his head and a sceptre set with jewels in his hand. The rubbish dump seemed far away . . .

"Strange!" remarked the new arrival, raising his voice above the Zany's groans.

"Why strange? After all, we poor men are more resigned than other people. And what can we do, anyway? It's true that with the schools and all that, anyone who learns to read gets ideas into his head. Even my wife gets sad sometimes and says she'd like to have wings on Sundays."

The injured man fainted two or three times as they descended the steeper part of the slope. The trees rose and sank before his moribund eyes like the fingers of Chinese dancers. The remarks of the men who were now almost carrying him zigzagged in his ears like drunk men on a slippery floor. There was a great black patch before his eyes. Sudden cold shivers blew through his body, setting ablaze the ashes of his burning fancies.

"So your wife wants wings on Sundays?" said the stranger. "Wings! And if she had them they'd be no use to her."

"That's right; she says she wants them to go out with, and when she's fed up with me she asks the wind for them."

The wood-cutter stopped to wipe the sweat from his forehead with his sleeve, and exclaimed:

"He's no light weight!"

The new arrival said:

"Her legs are quite good enough for that; even if she had wings she wouldn't go."

"Not she; nor yet out of good nature neither, but because women are birds who can't live without their cage, and because I carry home too few bits of wood to go breaking them on her back"—he remembered at this point that he was talking to an angel and hastily gilded the pill—"for her own good, of course."

The stranger was silent.

"Who can have beaten up this poor chap?" went on the wood-cutter, changing the subject out of embarrassment at what he had just said.

"There are plenty . . ."

"It's true, some people'll do anything, but this chap looks as if—as if they'd had no mercy on him. A jab in the mouth with a knife and off with him to the rubbish dump!"

"He's probably got other wounds."

"Looks to me as if the one in his lip was done with a razor, and they chucked him away here so that the crime shouldn't be found out, eh?"

"But what a place!"

"Just what I was going to say."

The trees were covered with turkey-buzzards making ready to leave the gulley. The Zany's fear was stronger even than his pain, and kept him mute; he curled himself up like a hedgehog in a deathly silence.

The wind ran lightly over the plain, blowing from the town into the country, delicate, gentle, familiar . . .

The stranger looked at his watch, and after putting some money in the wounded man's pocket and bidding the wood-cutter a friendly goodbye, he walked quickly away.

The sky was cloudless and resplendent. The outermost houses of the town looked out at the countryside with their electric lights burning like matches in a darkened theater. Sinuous groves of trees were beginning to appear out of the darkness near the first houses: mud huts smelling of straw, wooden cabins smelling of ladino, big houses with sordid front yards stinking like stables, and inns where it was usual to find fodder for sale, a servant girl with a lover in the barracks, and a group of muleteers sitting in the darkness.

When he reached the first houses the wood-cutter abandoned the injured man, after telling him how to get to the hospital. The Zany half-opened his eyes in search of help, or something to cure his hiccups; but it was on shut doors in a deserted street that his moribund gaze fastened itself like a sharp thorn. Far off bugles could be heard, testifying to the submission of a nomad race, and bells tremulously tolling thrice for the souls of dead Christians: Mer—cy! Mer—cy! Mer—cy!

He was terrified by a turkey-buzzard dragging itself through the shadows. The creature had a broken wing and its angry complaints sounded to him like a threat. Slowly he moved away, step by step, leaning against the walls, against the motionless trembling of the walls, giving moan after moan, not knowing where he was going, with the wind in his face, the wind which had bitten ice before it blew at night. He was shaken by hiccups . . .

The wood-cutter dropped his bundle of wood in the courtyard of his hut as usual. His dog had got home before him and received him effusively. He pushed it aside, and without taking off his hat opened his coat so that it hung on his shoulders like a bat's wings; then he went up to the fire in the corner of the room, where his wife was cooking pancakes, and told her what had happened.

"I met an angel on the rubbish dump."

The light from the flames flickered on the bamboo walls and the straw roof, like the wings of other angels.

From the hut there emerged a tremulous stream of white, vegetal smoke.

CHAPTER V

That Swine!

The President's secretary was listening to Doctor Barreño.

"I must tell you, Mr. Secretary, that I've been visiting the barracks daily for the last ten years, as military surgeon. And I tell you I've been the victim of an unspeakable outrage; I was arrested, and my arrest was due to—but I must tell you about it. This is what happened: a strange disease suddenly made its appearance in the Military Hospital; every day ten or twelve men died in the morning, ten or twelve in the afternoon, and ten or twelve more in the night. Well, the Chief of Military Hygiene commissioned me and some of my colleagues to inquire into the situation and find out what was the cause of the death of individuals who had been admitted to hospital the day before in good health, or nearly so. Well, after five autopsies I succeeded in proving that these unfortunate men had died of a perforation in the stomach, as big as a small coin, produced by some external agent that I didn't recognize, and which turned out to be the sodium sulphate they had been given as a purge—sodium bought from the soda-water factory, and therefore of

poor quality. Well, my colleagues didn't share my opinion, and presumably for that reason were not arrested; in their view it was a new disease which needed further investigation. I tell you a hundred and forty soldiers died, and there are still two barrels of sulphate left. I tell you that in order to enrich himself by a few pesos, the Chief of Military Hygiene sacrificed a hundred and forty men, as well as those still to follow. I tell you . . ."

"Doctor Luis Barreño!" shouted one of the President's aides-de-camp from the door of the secretary's office:

"I'll tell you what he says to me, Mr. Secretary."

The secretary took a few steps towards the door with Doctor Barreño. Humanitarian considerations apart, he was interested by the picaresque style of his story, built up step by step, monotonous and gray, in harmony with the grizzled head and dry beef-steak face of a man of science.

The President of the Republic received the doctor standing, his head held high, one arm hanging at his side in a natural position, the other behind his back, and without giving him time to greet him, he declaimed:

"Please get this straight, Don Luis: I am not going to stand the good name of my government being deprecated by gossiping medical quacks, even to the smallest degree. My enemies must be careful to remember this, because I'll have the head of the first man who forgets it. You may go! Get out! . . . and go and fetch that swine!"

Doctor Barreño went out backwards, hat in hand, his forehead wrinkled tragically and his face as pale as it would be the day he was buried.

"I'm done for, Mr. Secretary, I'm done for! The only thing I heard him say was: 'You may go! Get out, and go and fetch that swine!' "

"I am that swine!"

So saying, a clerk got up from a table in a corner, and went into the President's room by the door Doctor Barreño had just shut behind him.

"I thought he was going to hit me! If you'd only seen—if you'd only seen!" gabbled the doctor, wiping away the sweat that was streaming down his face. "If only you'd seen! But I'm wasting your time, Mr. Secretary, and you're very busy. I'm going now. And thank you very much."

"Goodbye, my dear Doctor. Don't mention it. Good luck."

The Secretary finished writing out the dispatches which the President would sign in a few minutes' time. The town was soaking up the orangeade of dusk; it was clothed in pretty muslin clouds and a crown of stars like the angels in a prologue. The shining steeples let fall the Ave Maria like a life-belt into the streets.

Barreño went home, his world crumbling round him. How could he have parried such a treacherous blow? He shut the door, looking at the roofs from which murderous hands might descend and strangle him, and hid himself at the back of a wardrobe in his bedroom.

His coats were suspended in a solemn row like the corpses of hanged men preserved in naphthaline, and their funereal appearance reminded Barreño of the assassination of his father, many years ago, when walking alone at night. His family had had to be content with a fruitless judicial inquiry; and after crime came melodrama in the form of an anonymous letter couched in more or less the following terms: "My brother-in-law and I were returning along the road from Vuelta Grande to La Canoa at about eleven o'clock at night when we heard a shot some way off; another, another, another—we counted five. We took refuge in a little copse near by. We

heard horses coming towards us at full gallop. Riders and horses almost touched us as they went by, and after a while we went on our way again. Then all was silence, but soon our horses began to rear. While they were shying and whinnying we dismounted, pistol in hand, to see what was the matter, and there we found the dead body of a man lying on his face, and a little further on a wounded mule, which my brother-in-law put out of its pain. We immediately went back to Vuelta Grande to report our discovery. At Headquarters we found Colonel José Parrales Sonriente, 'the man with the little mule,' and a group of his friends, sitting round a table covered with wine-glasses. We took him on one side and told him what we had seen. First the shots, then . . . He listened to us, shrugged his shoulders, turned his gaze to the guttering candle-flame and replied deliberately: 'Go straight home—I know what I'm talking about—and never mention this matter again!' "

"Luis! Luis!"

One of his overcoats slipped from its hanger like a bird of prey.

"Luis!"

With a quick movement Barreño stepped into his library and began turning the pages of a book. How frightened his wife would have been if she had found him in his hanging-cupboard!

"It's really past a joke! You'll kill yourself or go crazy with all this studying! I've told you so from the first! Can't you understand that it's tact rather than knowledge you need if you want to get on? What good does all this studying do you? None whatever! It won't even buy you a pair of socks! It's really too bad! It's too bad!"

Daylight, and his wife's voice restored him to calm.

"It's the last straw! Studying, studying . . . What for? So that when you're dead they'll say how learned you were, just as they always do about everyone. Pooh! Leave studying to quacks; you don't need it—that's the point of having a degree; you've got knowledge and don't have to study. And don't look so cross! Clients are what you need, not a library. If you had a patient for each of these useless books, this house would be a healthier place. As for me, I'd like to see your clinic full up, hear the telephone ringing all the time, see you summoned to consultations—getting somewhere, in fact . . ."

"What do you mean by getting somewhere?"

"Well—be a success. And don't go and tell me that you must wear your eyes out reading for that. Other doctors get along with half of what you know. They're content to elbow their way to the front and make a name for themselves. The President's doctor here, the President's doctor there—that's what it means to get somewhere."

"We-e-ell." Barreño dwelt on the word as if to bridge a little gap in his memory. "Well, my dear, you'd better stop hoping; I suppose you'll fall over backwards when I tell you that I've just been to see the President. Yes, to see the President."

"Oh, my goodness! And what did he say to you? How did he receive you?"

"Badly. The only thing I heard him say was something about cutting my head off. I was afraid, and what was worse I couldn't find the way out of the room."

"He ticked you off? Well, you're not the first nor the last. He's pitched into plenty of others!" And after a long pause she added: "Timidity has always been your undoing."

"But, my dear girl, show me somebody who is brave when he meets a wild beast."

"No, my dear, that's not what I mean; I'm talking about surgery, since you can't

manage to be the President's doctor. And for that the important thing is to lose your timidity. What a surgeon needs is courage, I tell you. Courage and determination in using his knife. A dressmaker who isn't ready to waste material will never succeed in cutting out a dress properly. And a dress is worth something, you know. On the other hand, a doctor can get his hand in by practicing on the Indians in hospital. But don't worry about what's happened between you and the President. Come and have lunch. He must have been in a bad temper because of that horrible assassination in the Cathedral Porch."

"Be quiet, will you—or I'll do what I've never done before and slap your face. It wasn't an assassination, and there's nothing horrible in the death of that odious brute who killed my father on a lonely road—an old, defenseless man!"

"Only according to an anonymous letter! What an extraordinary man you are! Who takes any notice of anonymous letters?"

"If I paid attention to anonymous letters . . ."

"It would be unworthy of you . . ."

"Will you let me speak? If I paid attention to anonymous letters you wouldn't be here with me in my house." Barreño searched feverishly in his pockets with a tense expression. "You wouldn't be here in my house. Hear, read that."

Pale-faced, with no color but the chemical vermilion on her lips, she took the paper her husband handed her, and ran her eyes quickly over it:

"Doctor, please console your wife, now that 'the man with the little mule' has gone to a better place. The advice of friends who wish you well."

With an anguished laugh—a laugh which splintered and filled the test-tubes and retorts in Barreño's small laboratory, like a poison to be analyzed—she returned the paper to her husband. A maid had just come to the door and announced:

"Lunch is served."

At the Palace, the President was signing papers with the assistance of the little old man who had entered the room as Doctor Barreño left, and whom he had referred to as "that swine."

"That swine" was a poorly dressed man with a pink skin like a young mouse, hair of inferior quality gold, and worried blue eyes lost behind bright yellow spectacles.

The President signed his name for the last time, and the little old man, trying to blot it in a hurry, upset the ink-pot over the signed sheet.

"SWINE!"

"Sir!"

"SWINE!"

A ring at the bell, another, another. Footsteps, and an officer appeared at the door.

"General, see that this man gets two hundred lashes, at once, at once!" roared the President, and immediately went into his own apartments. Luncheon was ready.

The eyes of "that swine" filled with tears. He said nothing because he was incapable of speech and because he knew it was useless to beg for forgiveness: the assassination of Parrales Sonriente had put the President in a furious temper. In the mists before his eyes he saw his wife and children begging for mercy for him: a hard-working woman and half a dozen thin children. With a claw-like hand he searched in his coat pocket for a handkerchief—if only he could relieve his feelings by crying!—he did not think, as anyone else would have done, that the punishment was unjust, but on the contrary that it was right he should be beaten to teach him to be less clumsy—if only he could relieve his feelings by cry-

ing!—and to be more efficient and not to spill ink over documents—if only he could relieve his feelings by crying!

His teeth projected between his tight lips like those of a comb, combining with his hollow cheeks and his anguished expression to give him the appearance of a man condemned to death. His shirt was glued to his back with sweat, and this caused him special dismay. He had never sweated like this before! If only he could relieve his feelings by crying! And the nausea of fear made him . . . him . . . him . . . shiver.

The President's aide-de-camp took hold of him by the arm; he was stupefied, sunk in a macabre torpor, his eyes staring, a terrible emptiness in his ears, his skin heavy as lead, his body doubled up, weak, growing ever weaker . . .

A few minutes later in the dining-room:

"May I come in, Mr. President?"

"Come in, General."

"I've come to tell you that that swine was unable to stand the two hundred lashes, sir."

The President was at that moment helping himself to fried potatoes, and the maid-servant holding the dish began to tremble.

"Why are you trembling?" her master scolded her.

Then turning to the general who was standing at attention without blinking, his kepi in his hand: "Very good, you may go!"

Still holding the dish, the servant hurried after the aide-de-camp and asked him why the man had been unable to stand the two hundred lashes.

"Why? Because he died."

And, still holding the dish, she went back to the dining-room.

"Please, sir," she said to the President almost in tears, as he calmly ate his lunch, "the General says he couldn't stand it because he died!"

"Well, what of it? Bring the next course!"

CHAPTER VI
A General's Head

Miguel Angel Face, the President's confidential adviser, came to see him after the dessert.

"Please forgive me, Mr. President," he said as he appeared at the dining-room door. (He was as beautiful and wicked as Satan.) "Please forgive me if I'm late—but I had to go to the assistance of a wood-cutter who had found a wounded man on the rubbish-dump, and I couldn't get here sooner. It was no one you know, Mr. President—a low sort of fellow!"

The President was dressed as usual in the deepest mourning: black shoes, black suit, black tie, and the black hat which he never took off; he concealed his toothless gums beneath a grizzled moustache combed over the corners of his mouth; he had thin pendulous cheeks and pinched eyelids.

"And did you take him to hospital?" he asked, allowing his frown to subside.

"Sir . . . ?"

"What's this you're telling me? A man who prides himself on being the friend of the President of the Republic surely doesn't leave a poor wretch lying in the street, wounded by some unknown hand!"

A slight movement at the dining-room door made him turn his head.

"Come in, General."

"With your permission, Mr. President."

"Are they ready, General?"

"Yes, Mr. President."

"Go yourself, General; offer my condolences to his widow and present her with these three hundred pesos in the name of the President of the Republic, to help her with the funeral expenses."

The General, who was standing at attention, cap in hand, without blinking and almost without breathing, bent forward and took the money from the table, turned on his heel and was seen to leave a few minutes later, in a motor-car with the coffin containing the body of "that swine."

Angel Face hastened to explain:

"I thought of going to the hospital with the injured man, but then I said to myself: 'He'll be better looked after if I get an order from the President.' And as I was coming here at your request, and also to tell you again how horrified I am at the treacherous assassination of our Parrales Sonriente—"

"I'll give orders . . ."

"That is only what one would expect from a man who they say ought not to be governing this country."

The President started as if he had been stung.

"Who says so?"

"I do, Mr. President—the first of many who believe that a man like you ought to govern a country like France, or free Switzerland, or industrious Belgium or wonderful Denmark! But France—France above all. You would be the ideal man to guide the destinies of the great race to which Gambetta and Victor Hugo belonged!"

An almost imperceptible smile appeared beneath the President's moustache, as he polished his spectacles on a white silk handkerchief without taking his eyes from his friend's face. After a short pause he embarked on a new subject of conversation.

"I asked you to come here, Miguel, because of an affair which I want to have settled tonight. The competent authorities have given orders for the arrest of that scoundrel General Eusebio Canales, and it is to take place at his house first thing tomorrow. For special reasons, although he was one of Parrales Sonriente's assas-

sins, it doesn't suit the Government for him to go to prison, and it is essential that he takes to flight at once. Go and find him, tell him what you know and advise him to escape tonight, as though the idea were your own. You may have to help him do it, because like every professional soldier he believes in honor and would rather die than run away. If they catch him tomorrow he'll be executed. He must know nothing of this conversation; this is between you and me. And take care the police don't find out you've been to see him; arrange matters so as not to arouse suspicion and so that the ruffian escapes. You can go now."

The favorite left with his face half hidden in his black muffler. (He was as beautiful and wicked as Satan.) The officers guarding their master's dining-room instinctively gave him a military salute—or perhaps they had heard that he held a general's head in his hands. Seventy despondent people were yawning in the audience-chamber, waiting for the President to be at liberty. The streets surrounding the Palace and the President's House were carpeted with flowers. Groups of soldiers were decorating the front of the neighboring barracks with lanterns, little flags and blue-and-white paper chains, under instructions from their commanding officer.

Angel Face took no notice of these festive preparations. He had to see the general and make plans for his flight. Everything seemed easy until the dogs began barking at him in the monstrous wood which separated the President from his enemies, a wood made up of trees with ears which responded to the slightest sound by whirling as if blown by a hurricane. Not the tiniest noise for miles around could escape the avidity of those millions of membranes. The dogs went on barking. A network of invisible threads, more invisible than telegraph wires, connected every leaf with the Pres-

ident, enabling him to keep watch on the most secret thoughts of the townspeople.

If only it were possible to make a pact with the devil, to sell one's soul to him on condition that the police were deceived and the general escaped! But the devil does not lend himself to charitable actions; although almost anything might be at stake in this strange undertaking. The general's head—and something else. He uttered the words as if he really held in his hands the general's head—and something else.

He arrived at General Canales' house in the district of La Merced. It was a large corner house, almost a hundred years old, whose eight balconies on the front and big carriage entrance on the back gave it something of the majestic appearance of an ancient coin. The favorite decided to listen outside the door and knock for admission if he heard anyone moving inside. But the presence of police patroling the opposite pavement forced him to give up this plan. He walked quickly past, glancing at the windows to see if there were anyone to whom he could make a sign. He saw no one. It was impossible to stand about on the pavement without arousing suspicion. But on the corner opposite to the house was a disreputable little tavern, and the safest way to remain in the neighborhood was to go in and have a drink. A beer. He exchanged a few words with the woman who served him and then, with the glass of beer in his hand, turned his head to see who was sitting on a bench against the wall; he had glimpsed a man's silhouette out of the corner of his eye as he came in. His hat pulled down over his forehead almost to his eyes, a handkerchief round his neck, the collar of his coat turned up, wide trousers, high boots with the buttons unfastened, made of rubber, yellow leather and coffee-colored cloth. The favorite raised his eyes absentmindedly and looked at the bottles standing in rows on the shelves, the luminous S in the electric light bulb, an advertisement for Spanish wines (Bacchus astride a barrel among pot-bellied friars and naked women), and a portrait of the President, outrageously rejuvenated, with epaulettes like railway-lines on his shoulders, and a cherub crowning him with a laurel wreath. A portrait in the best of taste! Every now and then he turned and glanced at the general's house. It would be a serious matter if the man on the bench and the barkeeper were more than friends and made any trouble. He unbuttoned his jacket and at the same time crossed one leg over the other, leaning his elbows on the bar as if he were in no hurry to leave. Suppose he ordered another beer? He ordered it and paid for it with a hundred peso note to gain time. Perhaps the innkeeper had no change. She opened the drawer of the till with a cross expression, rummaged among the grimy notes and shut it with a bang. She hadn't any change. Always the same story! She would have to go out and get some. She threw her apron over her bare arms and went out into the street, after a glance at the man on the bench, as if to warn him to keep an eye on her client: to take care he didn't steal anything. A useless precaution, because at that moment a young lady came out of the general's house as if she had dropped from the sky, and Angel Face was off like a shot.

"Señorita," he said, walking beside her, "would you tell the master of the house you've just left that I have something very urgent to say to him?"

"My papa?"

"You're General Canales' daughter?"

"Yes."

"Then, don't stop; no, no . . . Keep on walking; we must keep on walking. Here's my card. Please tell him that I shall expect him at my house as soon as possible; that I'm going straight there

now and will wait for him, that his life is in danger. Yes, yes, at my house as soon as possible."

The wind blew his hat off and he had to run after it. Twice or three times it escaped him. At last he caught it with the wild gesture of someone catching a fowl in a chicken-run.

He went back to the bar, on the pretext of picking up his change, but really to see what impression his sudden exit had made on the man on the bench, and found him struggling with the barkeeper; she had her back to the wall, while his eager mouth sought a kiss from hers.

"You miserable policeman, you! *Bascas** is the right name for you!" she cried when the man from the bench let go of her, alarmed by the sound of Angel Face's approaching steps.

It suited Angel Face's plans to intervene amicably; he took away the bottle the innkeeper was brandishing and looked indulgently at the man.

"Take it easy! Take it easy, Señora! Heavens, what a to-do! Here! Keep the change and make it up. You won't gain anything by kicking up a row, and the police might come along; besides if our friend here . . ."

"Lucio Vasquez, at your service."

"Lucio Vasquez? *Sucio Bascas*,† more likely! The police! It's always 'the police.' Let 'em try! Just let 'em try and come in here. I'm not afraid of anyone and I'm not an Indian neither, d'you hear? so that he can't frighten me with his Casa Nueva prison!"

"I'll put you in a brothel if I want to!" mumbled Vasquez, spitting out something he had swallowed the wrong way.

"Come on, man, make it up! That's enough!"

"All right, sir, I wasn't saying anything!"

---

* Vomit.
† Filthy vomit.

Vasquez had a disagreeable voice; he spoke like a woman, in a small affected falsetto. Deeply enamored of the barkeeper, he used to struggle with her day and night for one freely-given kiss—that was all he asked. But she refused on the grounds that giving him a kiss would mean giving him everything. Entreaties, threats, little presents, false or real tears, serenades, lies were all of no avail against the barkeeper's stubborn refusal, and she had never given in nor let herself be wheedled. "Anyone who tries to make love to me," she used to say, "knows that he's in for a free fight."

"If you've finished," went on Angel Face, speaking as if to himself and rubbing with his forefinger at a nickel coin nailed to the counter, "I'll tell you about the young lady opposite."

And he began to tell them that a friend of his had asked him to find out whether she had received a letter, when the barkeeper interrupted:

"Anyone can see that you're the one who's after her, you lucky bastard!"

The favorite had an inspiration . . . After her . . . say that her family was against it . . . pretend to kidnap her . . .

He went on rubbing his forefinger on the nickel coin fastened to the counter, but more vigorously now.

"That's true," said Angel Face, "but the trouble is her father doesn't want us to marry."

"Don't talk to me about that old man!" put in Vasquez. "The sour faces he makes at a chap, as if I could help being ordered to follow him everywhere!"

"That's the rich all over!" commented the barkeeper disagreeably.

"That's why I'm planning to run off with the girl. She's agreed. We were talking about it just this minute and we're going to do it tonight."

The barkeeper and Vasquez smiled.

"Let's have a drink," said Vasquez,

"that's better." Then he turned and offered Angel Face a cigarette. "Smoke?"

"No thanks. Well—I don't want to be unfriendly."

The woman filled three glasses while they lit their cigarettes.

A moment later, after the fiery liquid had burned its way down his throat, Angel Face said:

"Then I can count on you both? Whatever happens I shall need your help. Oh, but it must be today!"

"No good after eleven tonight; I'm on duty. But this one here . . ."

"*This one* indeed! I like your cheek! Watch out what you say!"

"La Masacuata here," said Vasquez, turning to look at the barkeeper, "she'll take my place—she's worth two men—unless you want me to send someone else; a friend of mine's meeting me in the Indian quarter tonight."

"Why must you always drag that milk-and-water Genaro Rodas into everything?" asked the woman.

"What's this about milk-and-water?" inquired Angel Face.

"It's because he looks half-dead. He's pasty-faced."

"What does that matter?"

"I don't see anything wrong with him . . ."

"Yes there is; I'm sorry to interrupt, sir. I didn't want to tell you, but Genaro Rodas' wife Fedina has been telling everyone that the general's daughter is going to be godmother to her child; so you see your pal Genaro isn't the chap for what this gentleman wants done."

"Poppycock!"

"Everything's poppycock to you!"

Angel Face thanked Vasquez for his amiability, but told him it would be better not to count on his milk-and-water friend, since (as the woman had said) he could not be considered neutral.

"It's a pity, Vasquez my friend, that you can't help me this time."

"I'm sorry too not to be in on it; if I'd known I'd have got leave of absence."

"If money would help fix matters . . ."

"No; that's not my game. It can't be done." And he put his hand to his ear.

"Well, it can't be helped. I'll be back before dawn, about a quarter to two or half past one, because in love affairs you must strike while the iron's hot."

He said goodbye and went to the door, lifting his wrist-watch to his ear to see if it was going—how portentous is the tiny tremor of that isochronous pulsation!— and then hurried away with his black muffler pulled up over his pale face. He was carrying the general's head in his hands—and something else.

CHAPTER VII

Archiepiscopal Absolution

Genaro Rodas stopped by the wall to light a cigarette. Just as the match scratched the side of the box, Lucio Vasquez appeared. A dog was vomiting against the grille of a shrine.

"Curse this wind!" growled Rodas when he saw his friend.

"Hullo there!" Vasquez greeted him, and they walked on together.

"How goes it, eh?"

"Where are you off to?"

"Where am I off to indeed! Are you trying to be funny? Didn't we fix to meet here then?"

"Oh, I thought you'd forgotten. I'll tell you about your affair, but come and have a drink. I could do with a drink, I don't know why. Come on, let's go by the Cathedral Porch and see what's doing."

"Nothing much, probably, but we'll go if you like: ever since they stopped the beggars sleeping there there's not a cat stirring."

"All the better, say I. We'll go through the close, shall we? What a devil of a wind!"

Ever since the assassination of Colonel Parrales Sonriente, the Cathedral Porch had been constantly occupied by the Secret Police. The toughest men were chosen to keep watch there. Vasquez and his friend traversed the Porch, climbed the steps at the corner of the Archbishop's Palace and went out by the Hundred Doors. The shadows of the columns lay on the ground occupying the places where the beggars had once slept. A ladder, and another and another, bore witness to the fact that a painter was going to rejuvenate the doors and windows of the building. And in fact, among the Municipality's plans for showing their unconditional support of the President of the Republic, the first on the list was that of painting and repairing the building which had been the scene of the odious assassination, at the expense of the Turks who kept a bazaar there redolent of burning rubbish. "Let the Turks pay they are in a way responsible for the death of Colonel Parrales Sonriente, because they live in the place where the deed was done," was the stern decision of the aldermen when the subject of money came up. And as a result of this vindictive arrangement, the Turks would have ended up poorer than the beggars who used to sleep on their doorsteps, had it not been for the help of influential friends who managed to pay for the painting, cleaning and improved lighting of the Cathedral, with receipts from the National Treasury bought at half their value.

But the presence of the Secret Police worried them. They asked each other in a whisper what could be the reason for such vigilance. Hadn't the receipts been converted into pails of white-wash? Hadn't paint-brushes as broad as the beards of the Prophets of Israel been bought at their expense? They prudently increased the number of bars, bolts and padlocks on the doors of their shops.

Vasquez and Rodas left the porch by the side nearest to the Hundred Doors. The silence swallowed up their heavy footsteps. Further on up the street, they slipped into a bar called The Lion's Awakening. Vasquez greeted the barman, ordered two glasses and a bottle of wine, and sat down beside Rodas at a small table behind a screen.

"Well, what news have you got for me?" asked Rodas.

"Cheers!" Vasquez raised his glass.

"Cheers!"

The barman, who had come up to serve them, added mechanically: "Your healths, gentlemen!"

Both drained their glasses at a single gulp.

"Nothing doing." Vasquez spat out the words with his last mouthful of liquor diluted with frothy saliva; "the assistant director put up a bloke of his own, and when I spoke up for you they'd already given the job to the lousy fellow."

"You don't say?"

"But when the captain commands, the sailor has to do as he's told, you know. I let him see you were keen to join the Secret Police, that you had plenty of guts. Every trick I knew!"

"And what did he say?"

"What I've told you: that he already had a man of his own, and then he shut me up. I can tell you it's more difficult now than when I joined to get into the Secret Police. Everyone has spotted it as the career of the future."

Rodas shook off his friend's remarks with a shrug of the shoulders and an unintelligible comment. He had come there in hopes of getting work.

"Don't take it to heart! As soon as I hear of another vacancy you shall have it. I swear by God you shall have it; especially now that the place is becoming a regular ants' nest and there are sure to be more jobs going. Did I tell you . . . ?" Vasquez looked about him nervously. "No—I'm not a blabber. Better not!"

"All right, don't tell me; what do I care?"

"It's a tricky business . . ."

"Look, old chap, don't tell me anything; do me a favor and shut up! You don't trust me, I see! You don't trust me!"

"I do, old chap, how touchy you are!"

"Look here, shut up, will you; I don't like this suspiciousness. You're just like a woman! Who's been asking you anything, that you go on like this?"

Vasquez stood up to see if anyone could hear, and spoke in a low tone, going close to Rodas, who listened to him sulkily, still offended by his reticence.

"I don't know if I told you that the beggars who were sleeping in the Porch on the night of the murder have already blabbed, and now there's not a single soul that doesn't know who did in the colonel." And raising his voice he asked: "Who do you think?" He lowered it to a pitch suitable to a State Secret. "Blowed if it wasn't General Eusebio Canales and Abel Carvajal, the lawyer."

"Are you telling me the truth?"

"The order for their arrest went out today. There, now you know the whole thing."

"So that's how it is," said Rodas in a more conciliatory tone; "so the famous colonel who could shoot a fly at a hundred yards and was such a devil of a fellow, wasn't finished off with a revolver or sword—he just had his neck twisted like a chicken! You can do anything in this world if you make up your mind to it! The murdering swine!"

Vasquez suggested another round of drinks and called out:

"Two more short ones, Don Lucho!"

Don Lucho, the barman, displayed his black silk braces as he refilled their glasses.

"Knock it back!" said Vasquez; then he spat and added between his teeth: "Hurry, or the bird will have flown! I hate to see a full glass, you know; or if you don't know you ought to. Cheers!"

Rodas had seemed preoccupied, but now he drained his glass hastily, and removing it from his lips exclaimed:

"The devils who sent the colonel into the next world won't be such fools as to come back to the Porch. Not bloody likely! It's not worth waiting for them; or is it for love of the Turks the Secret Police are there?"

"What the Secret Police are up to in the Cathedral Porch has nothing to do with the assassination. I promise you it hasn't. You'll never guess what we're doing there. We're waiting for a man with rabies!"

"Come off it!"

"You remember that scoundrel people used to shout 'Mother!' at in the streets? Tall fellow, bony, with twisted legs, who used to run about the streets like a loony. Remember? Yes, of course you do. Well, it's him we've been waiting for in the Porch these last three days, ever since he disappeared. We're going to pump him full of lead . . ." and Vasquez's hand went to his pistol.

"Don't be funny!"

"No, I'm not joking; it's true, I tell you, he's bitten a whole crowd of people and the dose the doctors have ordered is an ounce of lead injected into his skin. What do you say to that?"

"What d'you take me for? No man alive could make me believe it. I'm not such a fool as all that. The Police are waiting in the Porch for the men who wrung the Colonel's neck."

"God, no! What a stubborn mule you

are! It's for the dumb chap, do you hear? The dumb fellow with rabies who has been biting everyone! Have I got to say it all over again?"

The Zany's moans filled the street, as he dragged himself along, sometimes on all fours, helping himself with the toes of one foot and scraping his stomach on the stones, and sometimes supported on the thigh of his good leg and one elbow, while pain tore at his side. At last the square came into view. The wind buffeting the trees in the park seemed to bring with it a sound of turkey-buzzards. The Zany was so terrified that he became almost unconscious for some time, his anguish manifested in the dryness of his swollen tongue, like a dead fish in the ashes, and the sweat-soaked scissors of his pants. Step by step he clambered up to the Porch of Our Lord, hauling himself along like a dying cat, and lay huddled in a shady corner with his mouth open, his eyes glazed and his ragged clothes stiff with blood and earth. The silence blended together the footsteps of late passers-by, the click of the sentinels' rifles and the sound of stray dogs padding along, noses to the ground, poking about for bones among the bits of paper and leaves the wind had blown to the foot of the porch.

Don Lucho refilled the large wine-glasses known as "two-storeys."

"Why the hell won't you believe me?" said Vasquez in a sharper voice than usual, between two expectorations. "Didn't I tell you that about nine this evening—or perhaps half-past nine— before I met you here, I was making up to La Masacuata, when into her bar comes a fellow and asks for a beer? She serves him one quick. The bloke asks for another and pays for it with a hundred peso note. She's got no change and goes out to

get some. But I kept my eyes open, because as soon as I saw him come in I
smelled a rat—and just as if I'd known it
beforehand, a tart came out of the house
opposite, and she'd hardly got her foot
outside when this chap went after her.
But that was all I saw, because just then
La Masacuata came back, and then, you
see, I had to get my hands on her again
. . ."

"And the hundred pesos?"

"Wait and I'll tell you. We were hard
at it, she and I, when this fellow comes
back for the change; he finds us hugging
each other, so he gets confidential and
tells us he's crazy about General Canales'
daughter and he's thinking of running off
with her this very night if possible.
General Canales' daughter was this tart
who came out to meet him. You've no
idea how he went on at me to help him;
but what could I do with this business of
the Porch on my hands?"

"What a story!"

Rodas accompanied this remark with a
jet of saliva.

"And the funny thing is I've seen this
chap often over by the President's
House."

"Well I'm blowed, he must be one of
the family!"

"Not him. That's not the way the land
lies. What I'd like to know is: why such a
hurry to kidnap the girl today? He knows
something about the general's arrest and
thinks he'll get away with her while the
soldiers are nabbing her old man."

"You've hit it, and no mistake."

"One more little drink, and then we'll
show 'em!"

Don Lucho filled the two friends'
glasses, which were quickly emptied.
They spat on to the gobbets of spittle and
stubs of cheap cigarettes covering the
floor.

"What's to pay, Don Lucho?"

"Sixteen, and four . . ."

"Each?" put in Rodas.

"No—the lot," the barman replied,
while Vasquez counted out the notes and
four nickel coins.

"So long, Don Lucho!"

"Be seeing you, Don Luchito!"

Their voices mingled with that of the
barman, who came to the door with
them.

"Oh Christ! it's damned cold!" exclaimed Rodas, thrusting his hands into
his trouser pockets, as they went into the
street.

Walking slowly, they reached the
shops by the prison, at the corner nearest
to the Porch of Our Lord, and there they
stopped at Vasquez's suggestion; he was
feeling happy and stretched out his arms
as if to rid himself of a load of sluggish-
ness.

"This is the lion awakening, all right,
with his curly mane!" he said as he
stretched himself. "And what a job it
must be for a lion to be a lion! Cheer up
a bit, d'you mind? because this is my
lucky night; this is my lucky night, I tell
you, this is my lucky night!"

And by dint of repeating these words
in a piercing tone, increasing in shrillness
each time, he seemed to transform the
night into a black tambourine decorated
with gold bells; to be shaking hands with
invisible friends in the wind, and inviting
the puppet-master of the Cathedral Porch
and his marionettes to come and tickle
his throat till he burst out laughing. He
laughed and he laughed, and tried out a
few dance steps with his hands in his
waistcoat pockets, and then his laugh
suddenly died and became a groan and
his happiness turned to pain. He doubled
up to protect his mouth against his
stomach's revolt. He was suddenly silent.
His laughter hardened in his mouth like
the plaster dentists use for their models.
He had caught sight of the Zany. His
footsteps pattered through the silent

porch and the old edifice multiplied them by two, by eight, by twelve. The idiot was whining, now softly now louder, like a wounded dog. A yell rent the darkness. The Zany had seen Vasquez approaching, pistol in hand, to drag him by his broken leg towards the flight of steps leading down to the Archbishop's Palace. Rodas watched the scene without moving, breathing heavily and damp with sweat. At the first shot the Zany rolled down the stone steps. Another shot finished the job. The Turks cowered and flinched between the two explosions. And no one saw anything.

But a saint was looking out from one of the windows of the Archbishop's Palace and helping the unfortunate man to die, and just as the body rolled down the steps, a hand wearing an amethyst ring gave him absolution and opened the door to the Kingdom of Heaven to him.

CHAPTER VIII

The Puppet-Master of the Porch

Immediately after the pistol shots, the Zany's yells and the flight of Vasquez and his friend, the streets ran one after the other, all scantily clad in moonlight, and not knowing what had happened, while the trees in the square twisted their fingers together in despair because they could not announce the event either by means of the wind or the telephone wires. The streets arrived at the crossroads and asked one another where the crime had taken place, and then some hurried to the center of the town and others to the outskirts, as if disorientated. No, it wasn't in Jew's Alley, which wound and zigzagged as though traced by a drunkard's hand. Nor in the Alley of Escuintilla, once famous because some younger sons of a noble family had revived the days of chivalry and muske-

teers by fleshing their swords in the bodies of some scoundrelly police there. Nor was it in King's Alley, frequented by gamblers, where it was said no one could pass without saluting the King. Nor in Saint Theresa's Alley, a steep hill descending through a dismal neighborhood. Nor in Rabbit Alley, nor near the Fountain of Havana, nor the Five Streets, nor in the Martinique district.

It had been in the Plaza Central, where the water flows ceaselessly through the public urinals with a suggestion of tears, where the sentinels never stop presenting arms and the night turns and turns around the Cathedral under the icy vault of the sky.

The wind throbbed fitfully like the blood in temples wounded by shots, but could not blow away the leaves fixed like obsessions to the heads of the trees.

Suddenly a door opened into the Cathedral Porch and the puppet-master peered out like a mouse. With the curiosity of a fifty-year-old little girl, his wife pushed him into the street, so that he should see what was happening and describe it to her. What was up? What had been the meaning of those two reports, the second so soon after the first? The puppet-master did not care about showing himself at his door in his underwear to satisfy the whims of Doña Venjamon,* as his wife had been nicknamed (presumably because his name was Benjamin), and thought it indelicate of her to be so carried away by her desire to know if one of the Turks had been killed that she buried her fingers between his ribs like ten spurs to force him to poke his neck out as far as possible.

"But I can't see a thing, woman! What do you expect me to tell you? What's all the fuss about?"

"What d'you say? Was it over by the Turks?"

_____

* Literally "Come ham."

"I tell you I can't see a thing, and that all this fuss . . ."

"Don't mumble, for heaven's sake!"

When the puppet-master left his false teeth out, his mouth was drawn in and out as he talked, like a suction valve.

"Ah, now I see! Wait a moment! I see what it is!"

"But, Benjamin, I can't understand a thing you say!" she said, almost whimpering. "Don't you understand? I can't understand a thing you say!"

"I can see now! I can see now! There's a crowd collecting over there at the corner of the Archbishop's Palace."

"Come away from the door if you can't see anything—you're no good at all! I can't understand a word you say!"

Don Benjamin made way for his wife, who appeared at the door in a dishevelled state, with one of her breasts hanging out of her yellow cotton nightgown and the other entangled in the scapulary of the Virgin of Carmel.

"There—they're bringing a stretcher!" was Don Benjamin's final contribution.

"Oh, good, good! So it's over there, not by the Turks as I thought. Why didn't you say so, Benjamin? Well, of course, that's why the shots sounded so close."

"Look, don't you see them bringing the stretcher?" said the puppet-master. His voice seemed to come from the depths of the earth when he spoke from behind his wife.

"Be quiet! I don't know what you're talking about. You'd better go and put your teeth in—without them you might be talking English!"

"I said I saw them bringing the stretcher."

"No, they're bringing it now!"

"No, my dear girl, it was there before!"

"I tell you they're bringing it now! I'm not blind, am I?"

"I don't know, I'm sure, but I saw it with my own eyes . . . !"

"Saw what? The stretcher?"

Don Benjamin was hardly three feet tall and as slender and hairy as a bat; it was impossible for him to see what was interesting the groups of people and police over the shoulders of Doña Venjamon, a woman of colossal build, who required two seats in the tram (one for each buttock) and more than eight yards of material for a dress.

"But you're the only one who can see," Don Benjamin ventured to say in hopes of escaping from this state of total eclipse.

It was as if he had said: "Open sesame!" Doña Venjamon whirled round like a mountain and seized hold of him.

"Jesus Maria! I'll lift you up!" she cried. And she picked him up in her arms like a child and carried him to the door.

The puppet-master spat green, purple, orange and every other color. While he was kicking his wife's chest and stomach, four drunken men were crossing the far side of the square carrying the Zany's body on a stretcher. Doña Venjamon crossed herself. The public urinals wept for the dead man, and the wind made a noise like the wings of turkey-buzzards in the pale dusty-colored trees in the park.

" 'I'm giving you a nurse not a slave.' That's what the priest should have said on our wedding day—damn him!" growled the puppet-master as his feet touched solid ground again.

His better half let him talk—better half was hardly the word, for she would have made more than a whole grapefruit to his half tangerine. She let him talk, partly because she couldn't understand a word he said without his teeth and partly out of respect.

A quarter of an hour later, Doña Venjamon was snoring as if her respiratory organs were fighting for their life within

[35]

this barrel of flesh, and he was still cursing the day he married with flashing eyes.

But this unusual event brought pros-
perity to his marionette theater. The puppets took the tragedy as their theme, with
tears oozing drop by drop from their
cardboard eyes, thanks to a system of
little tubes fed by a syringe and a basin
of water. Hitherto the marionettes had
only laughed, or if they wept it had been
with smiling grimaces and without the
eloquence given by the tears now trickling down their cheeks and falling in
streams on to the stage which had been
the scene of so many cheerful farces.

Don Benjamin thought that the painful element in the drama would make the
children cry, and his surprise knew no
bounds when he saw them laugh more
heartily than before, with wide open
mouths and happy expressions. The sight
of tears made the children laugh. The
sight of blows made the children laugh.

"Illogical! Illogical!" decided Don Benjamin.

"Logical! Relogical!" Doña Venjamon
contradicted him.

"Illogical! Illogical! Illogical!"

"Relogical! Relogical! Relogical!"

"Don't let's quarrel!" Don Benjamin
suggested.

"Don't let's quarrel!" she agreed.

"But it *is* logical . . ."

"Relogical, I tell you! Relogical, recontralogical!"

When Doña Venjamon argued with
her husband she always added syllables
to her words, like safety valves to prevent
an explosion.

"Illolological!" shouted the puppet
master, nearly tearing out his hair in his
frenzy.

"Relogical! Relogical! Recontralogical!
Recontrarelogical!"

However, the little puppet went on for
a long time using the device with the
syringe, and making the marionettes cry
to amuse the children.

CHAPTER IX

Glass Eye

The smaller shops of the town used to
shut at nightfall, after doing their ac-
counts, taking in the newspaper and serving the last customers. Groups of boys
would amuse themselves at street corners
with the cockchafers blundering around
the electric lamps. Each insect they
caught was submitted to a series of tortures which were prolonged by the more
vicious through lack of anyone sufficiently merciful to put his foot on the
creatures and finish them off. At the
windows, young couples could be seen,
absorbed in the pangs of love; while
patrols armed with bayonets or sticks
ranged through the quiet streets in single
file, keeping step with their leader. However, there were evenings when everything was different. The peaceful tormen-
tors of cockchafers played organized
games, waging battles whose duration depended on the supply of missiles, for the
combatants refused to give in while there
were stones left in the street. As for the
lovers, the girl's mother would appear,
put an end to the amorous display and
send the young man running into the
street, hat in hand, as if the devil were
after him. And the patrol would fall on
some passer-by for a change, search him
to the skin and carry him off to prison,
even if he was unarmed, as a suspicious
character, vagrant, plotter or (as the
leader of the patrol said): "Because I
don't like his looks."

At this hour of the night, the poor
quarters of the town made an impression
of infinite solitude, grimy poverty and
oriental decadence stamped with religious
fatalism. The gutters carried the moon's
reflection at ground level, and the water
dripping from the drinking fountains
measured out the endless hours of a race

who believed themselves condemned to slavery and vice.

In one of these poorer quarters, Lucio Vasquez was saying goodbye to his friend.

"Goodbye, Genaro!" he said, his eyes enjoining secrecy. "I'm off to see if it's not too late to lend a hand with kidnapping the general's daughter."

Genaro stood still for a moment with the undecided expression of someone hesitating to say a last word to a departing friend; then he went up to one of the houses—he lived in a shop—and tapped on the door.

"Who's there? Who is it?" said a voice from inside.

"It's me," replied Genaro, bending his head as if speaking to a very small person.

"Who's me?" said the woman who opened the door.

His wife, Fedina de Rodas, raised her candle to the height of his head to see his face; her hair was dishevelled and she was in her nightdress.

As Genaro went indoors, she lowered the candle, put back the bars of the door with a loud bang and went into the bedroom without a word. Then she set her light down in front of the clock, so that the reprobate should see at what time he had come home. He stopped to stroke the cat sleeping on the counter and tried to whistle a gay tune.

"Well, what's happened to make you so cheerful?" cried Fedina, rubbing her feet before she got into bed.

"Nothing!" Genaro replied hastily from the darkened shop, anxious lest his wife should detect the worry in his voice.

"You and that policeman with the woman's voice are thicker than ever these days."

"No!" interrupted Genaro, going into the back room where they slept, with his slouch hat pulled down over his eyes.

"Liar! You've just this minute left

him! Oh, I know what I'm talking about; a man who talks in a little voice—neither cock nor hen—like that friend of yours, is never up to any good. You go about with him because you want to get into the Secret Police. A lot of lazy brutes! They ought to be ashamed of themselves!"

"What's this?" asked Genaro, to change the subject, taking a little dress out of a box.

Fedina took the frock from her husband like a flag of peace, and sitting on the bed began to tell him excitedly that it was a present from General Canales' daughter, who had been asked to be godmother to her first child. Rodas hid his face in the shadows surrounding his son's cradle, and without hearing what his wife was saying about the arrangements for the christening, he put up his hand irritably to ward off the light of the candle from his eyes; then he quickly snatched it away, shaking it to cleanse it of the red light which clung like blood to his fingers. The specter of death arose from his child's cradle as if it were a bier. The dead have to be rocked, like babies. The specter was the color of white of egg, with cloudy eyes; it had no hair, eyebrows or teeth, and it twisted itself spirally like the inner convolutions of the censers used in the funeral service. Genaro heard his wife's voice coming to him as if from a long way off. She was talking of her child, of the christening, of the general's daughter, of inviting her next-door neighbor, the fat man opposite and the one who lived on the corner, the pubkeeper, the butcher and the baker.

"Won't it be lovely?"

And then, sharply:

"What's the matter, Genaro?"

He started.

"Nothing's the matter."

His wife's voice had brought out a number of little black spots on the specter of death, little spots which made it stand out against the dark corner of the room. It was a woman's skeleton, but no feminine attributes remained to it except the sunken breasts, limp and hairy like rats, hanging over the framework of the ribs.

"What's the matter, Genaro?"

"Nothing's the matter."

"That's what comes of your going out. You come home like a sleep-walker, with your tail between your legs. Why the devil can't you stay at home, you miserable man?"

His wife's voice dissolved the skeleton.

"No, nothing's the matter."

An eye was traveling over the fingers of his right hand like the circle of light from an electric bulb. From the little finger to the middle finger, thence to the ring finger, from ring finger to index, from index to thumb. An eye . . . A single eye. He could feel it throbbing. He tried to crush it by closing his hand hard, till his nails sank into his flesh. But it was impossible; when he opened his hand, there it was again on his fingers, no bigger than a bird's heart and more horrifying than Hell. Beads of hot sweat, like beef broth, broke out on his forehead. Who was looking at him with this eye, which rested on his fingers and jumped about like the ball of a roulette wheel to the rhythm of a funeral knell?

Fedina pulled him away from the cradle where her son was sleeping.

"What's the matter, Genaro?"

"Nothing."

And a little later he sighed several times and said:

"Nothing; there's an eye after me! I'm being pursued by an eye, an eye is chasing me! I can see my hands—no! that's impossible! They're my eyes, it's an eye . . ."

"Commend yourself to God," she advised him between her teeth, without comprehending this rigmarole.

"It's an eye—yes, a round, black eye with eyelashes, like a glass eye!"

"You're drunk, that's what's the matter with you!"

"How can I be, when I've had nothing to drink?"

"Nothing? Why, your breath reeks of it!"

Though he was standing in the middle of the bedroom alcove—the other half of the room was occupied by the shop— Rodas felt as if he were lost in a cellar full of bats and spiders, snakes and crabs, far from all possible help and comfort.

"You must have been up to something," went on Fedina, between yawns; "it's the eye of God watching you!"

Genaro took one leap on to the bed and got under the sheets fully dressed, shoes and all. The eye was there, dancing beside his wife's body, her fine young woman's body. Fedina put out the light but that was worse; in the darkness the eye grew rapidly bigger and bigger, until it covered the walls, the floor, the ceiling, roof, the houses, his whole life, his child . . .

"No!" he replied in answer to a remark from his wife, who had relit the candle when she heard his terrified cries and was wiping the cold sweat from his forehead with one of the baby's napkins. "No, it's not the eye of God, it's the eye of the Devil."

Fedina crossed herself. Genaro told her to put out the light again. The eye became a figure of eight as it moved from the light into darkness, then a thunderous noise came from it, it seemed as if it must break against something, and almost at once it did break against the footsteps echoing in the street.

"The Porch! The Porch!" cried Genaro. "Yes! Yes! Light! Matches! Light! For the love of God!"

She stretched her arm across him to reach the match-box. There was a sound of distant wheels. Genaro had his fingers in his mouth and spoke as if he were choking: he didn't want to be left alone and called to his wife, who had thrown on a petticoat and gone to heat him up some coffee.

Hearing her husband's cries she came back to the bed in alarm.

"Is he ill—or what?" she said to herself, watching the flickering candle flame with her beautiful black eyes. She thought of the worms they had taken from the stomach of Henrietta—the girl from the inn by the theater; of the fungus they found where brains should have been in an Indian in the hospital; of the dreadful creature called the Cadejo, which prevented one from sleeping. Like a hen which flaps its wings and calls to its chickens when she sees a sparrow-hawk, she got up and hung a medallion of St. Blas round the little neck of her new-born child, reciting the words of the trisagion as she did so.

But the trisagion shook Genaro as though he were being beaten. He got out of bed with his eyes tight shut, found his wife beside the cradle and fell on his knees embracing her legs and telling her what he had seen.

"He rolled down the steps, yes, right to the bottom, bleeding from the first shot, and he never shut his eyes again. His legs apart, his eyes fixed in such a cold, glassy stare, I never saw anything like it! One of his eyes seemed to take in everything like a flash of lightning, and how it gazed at us! An eye with long eyelashes, which won't leave me, won't leave my fingers, here, oh my God, here!"

A wail from the baby silenced him. Fedina took the child from its cot, wrapped it in flannels and gave it her breast, without being able to get away from her husband, though she felt disgusted by him as he knelt there, grasping her legs and groaning.

"The worst thing of all is that Lucio—"

"Is the man with the woman's voice called Lucio?"

"Yes, Lucio Vasquez."

"The one they call 'Velvet'?"

"Yes."

"And why in heaven's name did he kill him?"

"He was ordered to; he had the rabies. But that's not the worst thing of all; the worst thing is that Lucio told me that a warrant for General Canales' arrest had been issued, and that a chap he knows means to kidnap his daughter tonight—"

"Señorita Camila? My child's god-mother?"

"Yes."

On hearing this unbelievable news, Fedina wept with the facility and abundance with which women of the people weep over the troubles of others. Her tears fell on her child's little head as she lulled him—as warm as the water grand-mothers take to church to add to the cold holy water in baptismal fonts. The baby fell asleep. The night passed, and they were still sitting as if under a spell when dawn drew a gold line under the door and the silence of the shop was broken by the baker's girl tapping on the door.

"Bread! Bread! Bread!"

CHAPTER X

The Princes of the Army

General Eusebio Canales, alias Chamar-rita, left Angel Face's house with the bearing of a soldier at the head of his army, but as soon as the door had shut behind him and he was alone in the street, his military stride was transformed into the scuttling run of an Indian going to market to sell a hen. He was aware of eager pursuers close at his heels. He kept his hand pressed against a hernia in his groin, for the pain from it sickened him.

He was gasping out disconnected words and broken exclamations of despair, while his heart gave wild leaps, contracted and missed several beats, by turns. With vacant eyes and his thoughts in suspense, he pressed his hands against his ribs as if it were a broken limb and he could force it to go on functioning. That was better. He had just turned the corner which had seemed so far off a minute ago. Now for the next one, but how far off it looked through his exhaustion! He spat. His legs were almost giving under him. A piece of orange peel. A cab slipped past at the end of the street. He was the one who must slip away. But he could see nothing except the cab, the houses and the lights. He walked faster. There was nothing else to be done. Better. He had just turned the corner which looked so far off a few minutes ago. And now for the next, but how far off it looked through his exhaustion! He clenched his teeth and tried to force his knees to make a further effort. He was hardly making any headway now. His knees were stiff and there was an ominous irritation at the base of his spine and in his throat. His knees! He would have to drag himself back to his house on all fours, helping himself along with his hands and elbows and every instinct in him that was fighting for life. He walked more slowly. Then came street corners, where there was no shelter. What was more, they seemed to be multiplying in the wakeful darkness, like glass screens. He was behaving ridiculously in his own eyes and other people's, whether they saw him or not—an apparent contradiction due to the fact that he was a person of importance, always in the public eye even in the solitude of night time.

"Whatever happens," he muttered, "it's my duty to stay at home—all the more so if what that scoundrel Angel Face has just told me turns out to be true!"

And further on:

"Running away would be a confession of guilt!" The echo tapped out his footsteps behind him. "Running away would be a confession of guilt; it would—but I won't do it." The echo tapped out his footsteps behind him. "A confession of guilt! But I won't do it." The echo tapped out his footsteps behind him.

He put his hand to his chest as if to tear away a plaster of fear fastened there by what the favorite had told him. His medals were not there. "Running away would be a confession of guilt, but I won't do it." Angel Face's finger was pointing out the road to exile as the only possible way to safety. "You've got to save your skin, General! There's still time!" And everything that he was, everything that he stood for, and everything he loved with a child's tenderness: country, family, memories, traditions and his daughter Camila—all were revolving round that fatal forefinger, as if the disintegration of his ideas had brought the universe itself to chaos.

But after a few more steps, nothing remained of this vertiginous vision except tears of perplexity in his eyes.

" 'Generals are the Princes of the Army,' I said in one of my speeches. What a fool! I've paid dearly for that little phrase! The President will never forgive me for those 'Princes of the Army,' and as I was in his bad books, he's getting rid of me now by saddling me with the death of a colonel who always showed affectionate respect for my white hairs."

The ghost of an ironical smile appeared under his gray moustache. He was making room within himself for a new General Canales, a General Canales who walked at a snail's pace, dragging his feet like a penitent in a procession, silent, humble, sad, with the smell of burned-out rockets clinging to his clothes. The real Chamarrita, the arrogant General Canales who had left Angel Face's house at the very height of his military career, with his powerful shoulders outlined against a background of all the glorious battles waged by Alexander, Julius Caesar, Napoleon and Bolivar, now suddenly found himself supplanted by a caricature of a general, by a General Canales without any gold embroidery, plumes or braid, without boots, without spurs. Beside this somberly dressed, shaggy, deflated intruder, next to this pauper's burial, the other, authentic, true Chamarrita seemed (without any ostentation on his part) like a first-class funeral, complete with fringes, laurels, plumes and solemn salutations. The disgraced General Canales was advancing towards a defeat which would remain unknown to history, walking ahead of the real general, who remained behind like a puppet bathed in gold and blue light, his three-cornered hat pulled over his eyes, his sword broken, his hands dangling and the crosses and medals on his breast covered with rust.

Without slackening his pace, Canales removed his gaze from his likeness in full uniform; he felt himself morally defeated. He gloomily imagined himself as an exile, dressed in porter's trousers under a jacket that was too long or too short, too tight or too loose, but never the right size. He was walking among the ruins of his life, treading his gold braid underfoot.

"But I'm innocent!" And he repeated the words with the most heartfelt persuasiveness. "But I'm innocent! Why should I be afraid?"

"For that very reason!" his conscience answered, in Angel Face's own words. "For that very reason! It would be another story if you were guilty. Crime has the advantage of guaranteeing a citizen's adherence to the Government. Your country? You must escape, General; I know what I'm talking about. Neither country nor wealth can save you! The law? A fine lot of use! You must escape, General; death is lying in wait for you!"

"But I'm innocent!"

"Whether you're guilty or innocent is irrelevant, General; what matters is whether you're in favor or not with the President; it's worse to be an innocent man frowned on by the Government than a guilty one!"

He shut his ears against Angel Face's voice, and mumbled threats of vengeance; the beating of his own heart was suffocating him. Further on he began to think about his daughter. She must be waiting for him with her heart in her mouth. The clock on the tower of La Merced struck the hour. The sky was clear, studded with stars and without a cloud. When he came in sight of the corner of his house he saw lights in his windows, sending their anxious beams right into the middle of the street.

"I will leave Camila with my brother Juan until I can send for her. Angel Face offered to take her away tonight or early tomorrow morning."

He had no need of the latch-key he held in his hand, for the door opened at once.

"Papa darling!"

"Sh! Come—I'll explain everything! There's no time to lose. I'll explain. Tell my orderly to harness one of my mules—collect some money, a revolver. I'll send for my clothes later. I shan't want more than a suitcase with the barest necessities. I don't know what I'm saying, nor whether you understand! Tell them to saddle the bay mule, and you go and get my things together while I change and write a letter to my brother. You'll be staying with Juan for a few days."

Being suddenly confronted by a madman would have alarmed Camila less than to see her habitually calm father in this state of nervous agitation. His voice kept failing him. His color came and went. She had never seen him like this.

Driven by the urgency of his haste, and tormented by anxiety, unable to hear what he said nor to say anything but "Oh my God! Oh my God!," she ran to wake up the orderly and tell him to saddle the mule, a magnificent animal with eyes full of fire, and came back to pack the suitcase (towels, socks, bread—yes, with butter, but she forgot the salt); then she went to the kitchen to rouse her nurse, who was sitting on the wood basket nodding as usual in front of the dying fire beside the cat, which moved its ears at every unusual noise.

The general was writing a letter in great haste when the servant came into the room to shut and bar the windows.

Silence took possession of the house, but it was not the silken silence of sweet peaceful nights, whose nocturnal carbon-paper makes copies of happy dreams, lighter than the thoughts of flowers, less metallic than water. The silence which now took possession of the house and was broken by the general's coughing, his daughter's hurrying to and fro, the servant's sobs, and a frightened opening and shutting of cupboards, chests and commodes, was a silence as tense, constrained and uneasy as an unfamiliar garment.

A small sly-faced man, with the body of a ballet-dancer, was writing silently without lifting his pen from the paper, as if he were spinning a spider's web.

"To His Excellency the Constitutional President of the Republic.

"Your Excellency,

"In accordance with instructions received, a careful watch has been kept on the movements of General Eusebio Canales. I now have the honor to inform the President that he has been seen in the house of one of your Excellency's friends, Señor Don Miguel Angel Face. I have been informed both by the cook in that house (who was spying on her master and the housemaid) and the housemaid (who was spying on her master and the cook), that Angel Face was shut in his room with General Canales for approximately three-quarters of an hour. They add that General Canales went away in a state of great agitation. In accordance with instructions, the watch on Canales' house has been redoubled, and orders have again been given that the slightest attempt at flight must result in his death.

"The housemaid—but this the cook does not know—has supplied further details. Her master gave her to understand—so she told me on the telephone—that Canales had come to offer him his daughter in exchange for his effective intervention on his behalf with the President.

"The cook—but this the housemaid does not know—was more explicit on this subject: she said that when the general left, her master seemed very pleased and gave her orders to go out as soon as the shops opened and buy preserves, liqueurs, biscuits and sweets, because a young lady of good family was coming to live with him.

"Such is the information I have the honor to impart to the President of the Republic . . ."

He wrote the date and his signature—a scrawled flourish like a dart—and, before taking his pen from the paper to scratch his nose with it, he added as an afterthought:

"Postscript to the message sent this morning: Doctor Luis Barreño—Three people visited his clinic this afternoon, two of whom appeared to be badly off; in the evening he went for a walk in the park with his wife. Abel Carvajal, the lawyer: This afternoon he visited the American Bank, the chemist's shop opposite the Capuchin monastery and the German Club; there he talked for a long while with Mr. Romsth, who is being watched separately by the police, and he returned home at half-past seven. He has not been seen to go out again, and the watch on his house has been redoubled, according to instructions received. Signed above. Date *ut supra. Vale.*"

CHAPTER XI

The Abduction

After parting with Rodas, Lucio Vasquez went as fast as his unsteady legs would carry him to La Masacuata's bar, to see whether the time had come to lend a hand in the abduction of the girl. He hurried past the Fountain of La Merced, a region given over to terror and crime according to popular report and the lies of the women who threaded their needles of gossip with the dirty water trickling into their jugs.

"It would be a fine thing to take part in a kidnapping," said the Zany's executioner to himself without slackening his pace. "And as my business was so quickly over in the Cathedral Porch, thank God, I can treat myself to that pleasure. I've always been one for pilfering things or helping myself to a chicken, but Holy Mary! what must it be like to pinch a female?"

At last La Masacuata's bar came in sight, but he began to sweat when he saw the La Merced clock. It was nearly time unless his eyes deceived him. He greeted one or two policemen who were guarding Canales' house, and dived into the door of the bar like a rabbit into its burrow.

La Masacuata had gone to bed to await the appointed hour of two in the morning with her nerves on edge; she pressed her legs against each other, crushed her arms beneath her in uncomfortable positions and rolled her head about on the pillow sweating at every pore, but without succeeding in closing her eyes.

When Vasquez knocked she jumped out of bed and hurried to the door with a gasp of profound agitation.

"Who's there?"

"It's me, Vasquez. Open up!"

"I wasn't expecting you!"

"What time is it?" he asked as he came in.

"Quarter-past one," she replied immediately, without looking at the clock, but with the conviction born of having counted every minute, every five minutes, ten minutes, quarter-of-an-hour and twenty minutes, while waiting for two o'clock to come round.

"Well, how is it the La Merced clock says a quarter to two?"

"You don't say so! It must be fast again."

"And, tell me this, has that chap come back yet?"

"No."

Vasquez took the barkeeper in his arms, fully expecting to be rewarded with a slap. But nothing of the sort; La Masacuata had become as gentle as a dove, and let herself be embraced and kissed on the mouth, so sealing a sweet and amorous pact that that night she would refuse him nothing. The only light in the room was burning in front of an image of the Virgin of Chiquinquira, beside a bunch of paper roses. Vasquez blew out the candle and tripped up La Masacuata. The Virgin's image vanished in the darkness as their two bodies rolled on the floor trussed together like a string of garlic.

Angel Face appeared from the direction of the theater, walking fast and accompanied by a party of roughs.

"As soon as the girl is in my hands," he told them, "you can loot the house. You won't go away empty-handed, I promise you. But be careful, both now and later on, and don't blab, or I'd rather do without your help."

As they turned the corner they were stopped by a patrol. The favorite spoke to the commanding officer while the soldiers stood around.

"We're going to serenade a lady, Lieutenant."

"Will you kindly tell me where?" said the officer, tapping the ground with his sword.

"Here, in the Callejon de Jesus."

"And where are your guitars and marimbas?* A rum sort of serenade without any music!"

Angel Face discreetly slipped a hundred peso note into the officer's hand and his objections were at once overcome.

The end of the street was blocked by the bulk of the Church of La Merced—a church shaped like a tortoise with two eyes or windows in the dome. The favorite told his companions that they had better not arrive at La Masacuata's all together.

"Remember, we meet at the Two-Step Tavern," he said aloud as they separated. "The Two-Step. Don't make any mistake—The Two-Step, next to the bedding-shop."

Their footsteps faded away in different directions. The plan of escape was as follows: when the La Merced clock struck two, one or two of Angel Face's men would go up on to the roof of General Canales' house, whereupon the general's daughter would open one of the windows at the front of the house and call for help at the top of her voice against burglars, so as to attract the police keeping watch on the house. Canales would profit from the general confusion to get away by the back door.

A fool, a madman or a child would never have concocted such an absurd plan. It was quite without rhyme or reason, and if the general and the favorite

had adopted it in spite of its absurdity, it was because each of them secretly saw in it a second possibility. For Canales, the favorite's protection gave him a better chance of escape than any other—and for Angel Face success did not depend on his agreement with Canales but on the President, whom he had informed by telephone of the hour and the details of the plan as soon as the general had left his house.

April nights in the tropics are like the widows of the warm days of March —dark, cold, dishevelled and sad. From the corner between the tavern and Canales' house, Angel Face counted the shadowy dark-green figures of the police scattered here and there; then he walked slowly round the block, and afterwards stooped and slipped through the small covered doorway of the Two-Step Tavern; there was a gendarme in uniform at the door of each of the neighboring houses, not to mention innumerable agents of the Secret Police, walking nervously up and down the pavement. He felt a foreboding of evil.

"I'm taking part in a crime," he said to himself; "they'll murder this man as he leaves his house." And the more he thought about this project the blacker it seemed; the idea of kidnapping the daughter of a man doomed to die seemed to him as horrible and repugnant as it would have been congenial and pleasant to help him to escape. It was not good nature which made such a naturally unfeeling man dislike the thought of ambushing a trusting and defenseless citizen in the very heart of the town, as he escaped from his house in the belief that he was being protected by a friend of the President. Nor the fact that this protection must in the end be revealed as an exquisitely cruel device to embitter the victim's last appalling moments by making him realize that he had been played with, trapped and betrayed, as well as an

* A sort of xylophone especially popular in Guatemala and Mexico.

[44]

ingenious method of giving the crime a legal aspect by explaining it as the final resort of the authorities to prevent the escape of a presumed criminal the day before his arrest. No. Very different were the sentiments which made Angel Face bite his lips with silent disapproval of this desperate and diabolical plan. He had believed in all good faith that as the general's protector he possessed certain rights over his daughter, but he now saw them sacrificed to his accustomed role of unreasoning tool, myrmidon and executioner. A strange wind was blowing across the plain of his silence, where a wild vegetation was growing, as thirsty as tearless eyelashes, as thirsty as prickly cactuses, as thirsty as trees unrefreshed by rain. What was the meaning of this desire? Why should trees be thirsty when it rains?

The idea flashed through his brain like lightning that he might turn back, ring Canales' door-bell and warn him. (He imagined his daughter smiling gratefully at him.) But he had already crossed the threshold of the little bar, and felt his courage revived by Vasquez's brave words and the presence of the other men.

"Just try me, that's all. I'm your man. Yes, you there, I'm ready to help you in anything, d'you hear? I'm not one to back out. I'm a cat with nine lives, a true son of the brave Moor!"

Vasquez was trying to pitch his feminine voice lower in order to give his pronouncements more virility.

"If you hadn't brought me good luck," he added in a low tone, "I wouldn't be talking as I am now. No, don't you believe it. But you've put me right with La Masacuata, and now she behaves as she should to me."

"I'm very glad to find you here and so full of courage; you're a man after my own heart!" exclaimed Angel Face, effusively shaking hands with the Zany's executioner. "You've given me back the spirits the police robbed me of, friend Vasquez; there's one of them at every door."

"Come and have a drop of Dutch courage!"

"Oh, it's not for myself I'm afraid—as far as that goes it's not the first time I've been in a tight place; I'm thinking of the girl. I wouldn't like it if they nabbed us coming out of her house, you understand?"

"But, look here, who's going to nab you? As soon as they find there's something to loot in the house there won't be a single copper left in the street. Not one, I'll stake my life on that. I promise you, when they see what there is to get their claws into, they'll all be busy carrying off what they can, not the least doubt of it . . ."

"Wouldn't it be a good thing if you went and talked to them, now that you're here, and as they know you're incapable of . . . ?"

"Rubbish. No need to say anything to them. When they see the door wide open, they'll think: 'Come along, what's the harm?' Ah, but when they get wind of me! They all know what sort of a chap I am since the day Antonio Libelula and I broke into the house of that little priest, and he got the wind up so badly when he saw us drop into his room from the attic and put on the light, that he threw us the keys of the cupboard where his savings were, wrapped in a handkerchief to make no noise, and pretended to be asleep! Yes, that time I certainly got away with it! And now the boys are eager to go," finished Vasquez, pointing to the group of ill-favored, silent, verminous men, who were drinking glass after glass of brandy, tossing the liquor to the back of their throats at one gulp and spitting disgustedly as soon as the glass left their lips. "Yes, I tell you, they're ready to go."

Angel Face raised his glass and invited

Vasquez to drink to love. La Masacuata poured herself a glass of anisette. And they all three drank.

In the dim light—they had been chary of turning on the electric light, so that the only illumination in the room came from the candle in front of the Virgin of Chiquinquira—the disreputable figures of the men threw fantastic shadows, elongated like gazelles, against the yellowish walls, while the bottles on the shelves looked like colored flames. They were all watching the clock. They spat on the floor with the sound of pistol shots. Some way from the rest, Angel Face was waiting with his back against the wall beside the Virgin's image. His large black eyes moved about the room, pursuing the idea which was persistently assailing him in these decisive moments: that he needed a wife and children. He smiled inwardly as he remembered the anecdote about the political prisoner under sentence of death, who was visited by the Judge Advocate General twelve hours before the execution, to offer him a favor, even his life, on behalf of the authorities, if he would change his testimony. "Very well, the favor I shall ask is to leave a son behind me," replied the prisoner point-blank. "Granted," said the Judge Advocate, and thinking himself smart he sent for a prostitute. The condemned man sent the woman away untouched, and when the Judge Advocate General returned he said to him: "There are quite enough sons of whores already!"

Another smile twitched the corner of his lips as he said to himself: "I've been governor of a school, editor of a newspaper, diplomat, deputy and mayor, and now here I am head of a band of toughs! Such is life in the tropics!"

A double chime issued from the tower of La Merced.

"Everyone outside!" cried Angel Face, and as he went out, revolver in hand, he said to La Masacuata: "I'll be back with my prize!"

"Let's get on with it!" commanded Vasquez, climbing like a lizard up to one of the windows of the general's house, followed by two of his gang. "And no blabbing, mind!"

The double chime from the church clock was also heard in the general's house.

"Ready, Camila?"

"Yes, Papa darling!"

Canales was wearing riding breeches and a blue military tunic stripped of its gold braid, above which his hair shone spotlessly white. Camila threw herself almost fainting into his arms, without a tear or a word. The meaning of happiness or despair can only be understood by those who have spelled it out in their minds beforehand, bitten a tear-soaked handkerchief, torn it to shreds with their teeth. For Camila all this was either a game or a nightmare; it couldn't, no, it simply couldn't be true; what was happening, happening to her, happening to her father, couldn't be true. General Canales took her in his arms and said goodbye.

"This is how I embraced your mother when I went to fight for my country in the last war. The poor darling got it into her head that I wouldn't return, but it was she who didn't wait for me."

Hearing steps on the roof, the old soldier thrust Camila aside and went across the patio with its beds and pots full of flowers to the back door. The scent of every azalea, every geranium and every rose-bush said goodbye to him. The water trickling into the jug said goodbye to him, so did the light streaming from the windows. Suddenly the house became dark, as if severed at a blow from its neighbors. Flight was unworthy of a soldier. The thought of returning to liberate his country at the

head of a revolution, on the other hand
. . .

According to the plan they had agreed upon, Camila went to the window to call for help. "Burglars have broken in! Help! Burglars!"

Before her voice had faded into the immensity of the night the first gendarmes had arrived— those who had been watching the front of the house—blowing into the long hollow fingers of their whistles. There was a discordant sound of metal and wood and the street door yielded at once. Other police in plain clothes appeared at the cross-roads, ignorant of what was afoot, but for that very reason holding their well-sharpened knives ready, with their hats pulled down and their coat collars turned up. The wide open door swallowed them all—a turbulent river. Vasquez cut the electric wires as he went up to the roof; passages and rooms were all one solid shadow. Some of his companions struck matches to find their way to cupboards, dressers

and chests. And without more ado they ransacked them from top to bottom after striking off padlocks, shooting at glass doors and reducing valuable wood to splinters. Others were at large in the drawing-room, upsetting chairs, tables and corner cupboards covered with photographs, like tragic playing-cards in the shadows, or striking the keys of a small grand piano; it had been left open and groaned like an animal in pain every time they strummed on it.

Far off was heard the laugh of forks, spoons and knives as they were thrown on the ground, and then a sudden cry cut short by a blow. The old nurse, La Chabelona, had hidden Camila in the dining-room between the wall and a sideboard. The favorite threw her to the ground. The old woman's hair had caught in the handle of the silver-cupboard and its contents were scattered on the floor. Vasquez silenced her with a blow with an iron bar. He struck at her blindly. He did not even see her hands.

PART II
The 24th, 25th, 26th, and 27th of April

CHAPTER XII

Camila

She used to spend hours and hours in front of the looking-glass in her room. "If you make such faces the devil will come and look over your shoulder!" cried her old nurse. "He can't look more of a devil than me!" replied Camila. Her hair was a confusion of black flames, her dark-skinned face shone with coconut-butter cleansing-cream and her slanting

green eyes were drowning in their deep sockets. "China" Canales, as her classmates had called her when she went out with her school cloak buttoned right up to the neck, looked more grown-up now, less ugly, capricious and challenging.

"I'm fifteen," she said to the looking-glass, "but I'm still just a little donkey trailing round everywhere with a swarm of uncles, aunts and cousins."

She tugged at her hair, cried out, made faces at herself. She hated always having to be among this crowd of relations;

being the "little girl"; going everywhere with them: to the military review, to twelve o'clock Mass, to the Cerro del Carmen, for rides on the chestnut, for walks round the Teatro Colon or up and down the ravine of El Sauce.

Her uncles were moustachioed scarecrows with rings clinking on their fingers; her cousins untidy, fat, heavy as lead; her aunts repulsive. Or so they all seemed to her. She was exasperated when her cousins gave her paper cornets full of sweets with a little flap on top as if she were a child; when her uncles fondled her with hands smelling of cigar smoke, pinching her cheeks between finger and thumb and moving her face from side to side (Camila used to stiffen her neck instinctively); and when her aunts kissed her through their veils, leaving behind a feeling as if a spider's web were stuck to her skin with saliva.

On Sunday afternoons she would either go to sleep or sit bored to tears in the drawing-room looking at old photographs in the family album, or portraits hanging on the red-covered walls and ranged on the shelves of dark corner-cabinets, silver-topped tables and marble brackets, while her father looked out of the window at the empty street purring like a cat and replying to the greetings of passing neighbors and friends. Every so often someone would go by and take their hats off to him. That was General Canales. And the general would reply in a booming voice: "Good evening." "Au revoir!" "I'm delighted to see you." "Take care of yourself!"

There were photographs of her mother as a newly-married woman, with everything except her fingers and her face concealed by a fashionable dress reaching to the ankles, gloves nearly to the elbow, furs round her neck and a hat cascading ribbons and feathers under a sunshade wreathed in lace; there were photographs of her aunts, big-bosomed and stuffed like drawing-room furniture, with sculptured hair and little tiaras on their foreheads; and others of friends of past days, one in a manila shawl with combs and fans, another dressed as an Indian in sandals and embroidered tunic with a pitcher on her shoulder, others with beauty spots and jewels. They all induced in Camila a sense of crepuscular drowsiness, coupled with superstitious feelings about their inscriptions: "This portrait will follow you like my shadow." "This pale testimony of my affection will be with you always." "When these words are effaced my memory will fade." Some of the other photographs had only a few words written at the bottom between dried violets and bits of faded ribbon: "Remember 1898." "My adored one." "Until the grave and beyond." "Your incognita."

Her father's greetings were addressed to the friends who occasionally passed along the otherwise empty street, but his booming voice echoed through the drawing-room as if he were really replying to the inscriptions: "This portrait will follow you like my shadow." "I'm very glad. Good luck to you!" "This pale testimony of my affection will be with you always." "Good day, take care of yourself!" "When these words are effaced my memory will fade." "At your service! Remember me to your mother."

Sometimes a friend who had escaped from the album would stop outside the window to talk to the general. Camila would watch from behind the curtain. It was that man who had such a conquering air in his photograph, young, slim, with black eye-lashes, loud check trousers, his overcoat buttoned up and a hat that was halfway between a topper and a bowler—the very latest thing at the end of the last century.

Camila smiled and thought to herself: "You'd better have stayed as you were in the photograph. You'd have looked old-fashioned and people would laugh at your museum outfit, all the same you wouldn't have been pot-bellied and bald with your cheeks blown out as though you were sucking bulls-eyes."

From the penumbra of the dusty smelling curtains, Camila's green eyes gazed through the window at the Sunday afternoon. There was no softening of the coldness in her frozen glassy eyes as they looked out of her house to see what was happening in the street. Her father, dressed in a gleaming linen shirt and no jacket and with his elbows resting on a satin cushion, was passing the time talking to someone who seemed to be an intimate friend, across the bars of the projecting balcony. He was a bilious-looking gentleman, with a hooked nose, a small moustache and a gold-handled walking stick. What a lucky chance! He had been strolling past the house when the general stopped him with: "What a pleasure to see you here in La Merced! How splendid!" And Camila found him in the album. It wasn't easy to recognize him; she had to look hard at the photo. The poor man had once had a well-shaped nose and a round amiable face. How true it was that time dealt harshly with people. Now his face was angular, with prominent cheekbones, thin eyebrows and a jutting jaw. As he talked to her father in his slow cavernous voice, he kept raising the handle of his stick to his nose as if to smell the gold.

Immensity in motion. Herself in motion. Everything in her that was by nature still was in motion. When she saw the sea for the first time, words expressing her astonishment bubbled to her lips, but when her uncles asked her what she thought of the spectacle she said with a stupidly important air: "I knew it already by heart from photographs!"

The wind was tugging at the wide-brimmed pink hat she held in her hands. It was like a hoop. Like a big round bird.

Her cousins looked at her in wide-eyed amazement, their mouths dropping open. The deafening sound of the waves swallowed up her aunts' remarks: "How beautiful! Almost incredible! What a lot of water! How angry it seems! And look—over there—the sun is setting! We didn't leave anything in the train, did we, when we got out in such a hurry? Have you looked to see if everything's there? We must count the suitcases."

Her uncles, carrying suitcases full of thin clothes for the beach (the wrinkled clothes like dried raisins that summer visitors wear), bunches of coconuts which the ladies had bought at the stations on the way merely because they were cheap, and a collection of bundles and baskets, went off to the hotel in Indian file.

"Yes, I know what you mean," remarked the most precocious of her cousins. (A rush of blood to her skin tinged Camila's dark cheeks with faint carmine when she heard herself addressed.) "I think it's because the sea looks the same as in the moving pictures, only bigger."

Camila had heard about the moving pictures which were being shown at the Hundred Doors, close to the cathedral, but she had no idea what they were like. However, after what her cousin had said, she could easily imagine them as she stared at the sea. Everything in motion. Nothing stable. Pictures mingling with other pictures, shifting, breaking in pieces to form a new image every second, in a state that was not solid, nor liquid, nor gaseous, but which was the state of life in the sea. A luminous state. Both in the sea and in the moving pictures.

With her toes curling inside her shoes, and her eyes darting everywhere, Camila went on contemplating the scene with insatiable delight. At first she felt that her pupils had to become empty to take in the immensity, but now that immensity filled them completely. The rising tide had reached her eyes.

Followed by her cousin, she went slowly down to the beach—walking on the sand was not easy. She wanted to get closer to the waves, but instead of offering her a polite hand, the Pacific Ocean aimed a liquid slap of transparent water at her and wet her feet. She was taken by surprise and only just retreated in time, leaving behind a hostage—her pink hat—dwindling to a mere point among the waves, and yelling out a spoiled child's threat to go and complain to her papa:

"Ah—mar!"*

Neither she nor her cousin noticed that she had uttered the words "to love" for the first time as she threatened the sea. The tamarind color of the sky above the setting sun made the deep green water look colder still.

Why did she kiss her own arms there on the beach, breathing in the smell of her sun-drenched, salty skin? Why did she do the same to the fruit she was forbidden to eat, touching it with her joined lips? "Acid is bad for little girls," her aunts had sermonized at the hotel, "so are wet feet and romping." Camila had not sniffed at her father and her nurse when she kissed them. She had held her breath when she kissed the foot of the Jesus of La Merced, which was so reminiscent of a broken root. And if one did not sniff at what one kissed, the kiss had no taste. Her salty flesh, as brown as the sand, and pine kernels and quinces all tempted her to kiss them with her nostrils flaring, eager and greedy. But after speculation came reality: she did not know whether she was sniffing or biting when, at the end of the summer, she was kissed on the mouth by the same cousin who had talked about moving pictures and could whistle an Argentine tango.

---

* Ah *mar* (Oh sea!) = *Amar* (to love).

When they returned to the capital, Camila pestered her nurse to take her to the moving pictures. They were being shown at the corner of the Cathedral Porch, at the Hundred Doors. They went without her father's knowledge, biting their nails nervously and murmuring a prayer. After nearly turning away from the door when they saw how full the hall was, they took two seats close to a white curtain, on which a light as if from the sun was thrown from time to time. They were testing the apparatus, the lenses and the projector, which made a sputtering noise like the mantles of the street lamps.

Suddenly the room grew dark. Camila felt as if she were playing hide-and-seek. Everything on the screen was blurred. Figures moved about like grasshoppers. Shadowy people who seemed to be chewing as they talked, who walked in a series of jumps and whose arms moved as if they were dislocated. Camila was reminded so vividly of an occasion when she and a boy had hidden in a room with a skylight, that for a moment she forgot the moving pictures. A guttering candle had been standing in front of an almost transparent celluloid Christ in the darkest corner of the room. They hid under a bed. They had to lie flat on the ground and the bed creaked loudly and incessantly. It was an ancestral piece of furniture which could not be treated with disrespect. There was a shout of "Coming!" from the further patio. "Coming!" from the nearest patio. "Coming! Coming!" When she heard the footsteps of the "he" approaching, Camila wanted to laugh. Her companion in hiding looked at her sternly, warning her to be silent. She obeyed at first with a serious expression, but could hardly contain herself when the sickening smell coming from a half-open commode reached her nostrils, and she would have burst out laughing outright if her eyes had not begun to water from the fine dust under the bed, while at the same time something struck her on the head.

And exactly as she had left her hiding place long ago, so she now hurried away from the moving pictures with her eyes full of tears, among a crowd who were leaving their seats and hastening through the darkness to the exits. They did not stop till they reached the Portal del Comercio. And there Camila learned that the audience had left so as to avoid excommunication: a woman in a tight-fitting dress had been shown on the screen dancing the Argentine tango with a long-haired, moustachioed man wearing a flowing artist's tie.

Vasquez went out into the street still holding the massive iron bar with which he had silenced La Chabelona; he gave a signal with his hand and Angel Face followed carrying the general's daughter in his arms. They disappeared inside the Two-Step Tavern just as the police were beginning to make off with their loot. Those who had not helped themselves to a saddle were carrying off on their backs a clock, a large mirror, a statue, a table, a crucifix, a tortoise, hens, ducks, doves or any other of God's creations. Men's clothes, women's shoes, Chinese knick-knacks, flowers, images of saints, basins, trivets, lamps, a chandelier, bottles of medicine, portraits, books, umbrellas for water from the sky and chamber-pots for human water.

The innkeeper was waiting in the Two-Step Tavern with a bar in her hand, ready to barricade the door behind them.

Camila had never dreamed of the existence of this hovel smelling of musty bedding, only a few yards from the house where she had lived so contentedly, spoiled by the old soldier (impossible to believe that he had been happy yesterday!), and looked after by her nurse (impossible to believe that she was now

lying seriously injured). The flowers in the patio, untrodden yesterday, were now laid flat; her cat had fled, her canary was dead—crushed, cage and all. When the favorite removed the black scarf from her eyes, Camila had the impression that she was very far away from home. She passed her hand over her face two or three times, looking about her to see where she was. Her fingers stopped moving to stifle a cry of dismay when she realized her desperate plight. It was not a dream.

"Señorita"—the voice of the man who had broken the disastrous news to her that afternoon came floating towards her heavy numbed body, "at least you're in no danger here. What can we give you to quiet your fears?"

"Water and fire!" said the innkeeper as she hurriedly raked a few embers to the top of the earthenware pot which served her as an oven, while Lucio Vasquez seized the opportunity to attack a bottle of strong brandy, swallowing it without tasting it, as if he were drinking rat poison.

The innkeeper revived the fire by blowing at it, muttering all the time: "Burn up quickly! Burn up quickly!" Behind her, against the wall of the back room, now glowing red in the light from the embers, Vasquez's shadow slipped past on his way to the patio.

La Masacuata dropped a live ember into a bowl full of water, making it bubble and hiss like a terrified person, with the dead charcoal floating in it like the black kernel of some infernal fruit; then she removed it with the tongs. After a few sips Camila found her voice again.

"And my father?" was the first thing she said.

"Keep calm, don't worry, drink some more charcoal water; the general's all right," replied Angel Face.

"Are you sure?"

"I think so."

"But some misfortune—"

"Sh! Don't tempt fate!"

Camila turned and looked at Angel Face. The expression of a face is often more revealing than words. But her eyes lost themselves in the favorite's blank, dark pupils.

"You must sit down, my dear," remarked La Masacuata.

She was dragging the bench on which Vasquez had been sitting when the stranger who paid for his beer with a large note first came into the bar.

Had that afternoon been years ago, or only a few hours? The favorite gazed first at the general's daughter, then at the candle flame alight in front of the Virgin of Chiquinquira darkened by the thought of putting out the light and having his will of the girl. One puff . . . and she would be his either willingly or by force. But his eyes moved from the Virgin's image to look at Camila; she had sunk on to the bench, and when he saw her pale face sprinkled with tears, her disheveled hair and her body like an immature angel's, his expression changed and he took the cup from her hand with a fatherly air, saying: "Poor little girl!"

The innkeeper's discreet coughs to signify that she was going to leave them alone, and her foul language when she found Vasquez lying completely drunk in the tiny patio smelling of potted roses which lay behind the back room, brought a fresh outburst of tears from Camila.

"You've sozzled yourself pretty quick, you wretch," La Masacuata scolded him; "the only thing you know how to do is drive me crazy! It's true enough what they say; one can't close an eye without your swiping something! All very fine to say you love me! Oh yes—no doubt you do! Hardly turned my head and you've pinched the bottle! It doesn't cost you a thing, does it? Just because I trusted you!

Get out of here, you thief, before I throw you out!"

The drunken man answered in a complaining tone; his head struck the ground as the woman began hauling him along by the legs. The door into the patio was blown to by the wind. Then silence.

"It's over now, it's all over," Angel Face was repeating into the ear of the weeping Camila. "Your father's not in danger, and you're quite safe in this hiding-place; I'm here to protect you. It's all over, don't cry; you'll only upset yourself more. Stop crying and look at me and I'll explain everything."

Camila's sobs gradually died away. Angel Face was stroking her hair, and he took her handkerchief from her hand to dry her eyes. Like whitewash mixed with pink paint the light of dawn colored the horizon and shone between the objects in the room and under the doors. Human beings sensed each other's presence before they could see each other. Trees were driven demented by the first trilling of the birds and were unable to scratch themselves. Yawn after yawn from the fountains. And the sky flung aside the dark tresses of night, the tresses of death, and put on a golden wig.

"But you must keep calm—otherwise all will be lost. You'll endanger yourself, you'll endanger your father, you'll endanger me. I'll come back this evening and take you to your uncle's house. The chief thing is to gain time. We must be patient. One can't arrange everything all at once—some things are trickier than others."

"It's not myself I'm thinking of; I feel safer after what you've told me, and I'm grateful. I do understand that I must stay here. It's my father I'm worried about. I do so want to be sure that nothing's happened to my father."

"I promise to bring you news of him."

"Today?"

"Today."

Before he went out, Angel Face turned and gave her an affectionate little pat on the cheek.

"Feeling calmer?"

General Canales' daughter looked up at him with eyes that were again full of tears and answered:

"Bring me news . . ."

CHAPTER XIII

Arrests

Genaro Rodas' wife did not even wait for the bread to arrive before she hurried out of the house. God only knew whether the baskets of loaves would be delivered. She left her husband stretched on the bed fully clothed, limp as a rag, and her infant asleep in the basket which served for its cradle. Six o'clock in the morning.

The La Merced clock was striking just as she tapped on the door of Canales' house. "I hope they'll forgive me waking them so early," she thought, holding the knocker in her hand ready to let it fall again. "But are they coming to open the door or not? The General must know as soon as possible what Lucio Vasquez told my crazy husband in that bar called The Lion's Awakening."

She stopped knocking and waited for the door to open. "The beggars have laid the blame for the murder in the Cathedral Porch on him," she reflected. "They're going to come and arrest him this morning; worst of all they mean to kidnap the young lady. What an outrage! What an outrage!" she repeated inwardly as she went on knocking.

Her heart seemed to turn over again. "If they arrest the general—well, after all he's a man and he can go to prison. But if they kidnap the young lady! God help us! There'd be no getting over the disgrace. I'd bet anything there's one of those miserable ladinos at the bottom of

all this—bringing his sly tricks to the city from the mountains."

She knocked again. The house, the street, the air echoed the sound like a drum. It drove her frantic that no one came. To pass the time she spelled out the name of the tavern on the corner: The Two-Step. There were only a few letters to decipher, but then she noticed two painted figures one on each side of the door: a man on one side, a woman on the other. From the woman's mouth came the legend: "Come and dance a little Two-Step!," and from behind the man, who was holding a bottle in his hand, came the reply: "No thanks! I prefer the bottle dance!"

Tired of knocking—either they weren't there or they were not going to open up—she pushed the door. It gave to her hand. Had it only been on the latch? Wrapping her fringed shawl round her shoulders, she entered the hall with a sense of deep foreboding, and went through into the passage hardly knowing what she was doing; the sight that met her eyes pierced her as a bird is pierced by a shot, leaving her drained of blood, short of breath, her eyes blank, her limbs paralyzed: there were flower vases and quetzal plumes lying on the ground; screens, windows and mirrors broken; cupboards forced open; locks violated; papers, clothes, furniture and carpets all destroyed, all grown old in a single night, all converted into a worthless confusion of lifeless dirty rubbish, unfamiliar and soulless.

The old nurse, La Chabelona, was wandering about like a ghost in search of her young lady, with her head cracked open.

"Ha-ha-ha!" she laughed. "Tee-hee-hee! Where are you hiding, Camila my girl? I'm coming! Why don't you answer? Coming! Coming! COMING!"

She imagined she was playing at hide-and-seek with Camila, and looked for her over and over again in the same corners, among the flower pots, under beds, behind doors, turning everything upside-down like a whirlwind.

"Ha-ha-ha! Tee-hee-hee! Oh-ho-ho! Coming! Coming! Come out, Camila my girl, I can't find you! Come out, little Camila; I'm tired of looking for you! Ha-ha-ha! Come out! I'm coming! Tee-hee-hee! Oh-ho-ho!"

In the course of her search she happened to go up to the fountain and when she saw her own reflection in its still waters, she screamed like a wounded monkey, and with her laugh turning into a terrified chattering, her hair over her face and her hands over her hair she sank gradually to the ground to escape from this extraordinary vision. She whispered broken excuses as if to ask forgiveness from herself for being so ugly, so old, so small and so dishevelled. Suddenly she screamed again. Through the ragged cascade of her hair and between the bars of her fingers she had seen the sun leap upon her from the roof, and throw her shadow on to the floor of the patio. Frantic with rage, she stood up and attacked her own shadow and reflection, striking the water with her hands and the ground with her feet. She wanted to destroy them. Her shadow twisted and turned like an animal under the lash, but in spite of her furious kicking and stamping it was still there. Her reflection was shivered to pieces in the turbulence of the beaten water, but reappeared as soon as it was still again. She yelled like a wild beast with rage at her inability to destroy this sooty deposit sprinkled on the stones, which fled from her kicking feet as if it really felt the blows, or to batter to pieces this other luminous dust floating on the water, like a fish with a suggestion of her own image about it.

Her feet were beginning to bleed, her hands were dropping to her sides with fatigue, but her shadow and her reflection remained indestructible.

Convulsed with rage, she made a last desperate effort and threw herself head first against the fountain . . .

Two roses fell into the water . . .

The thorny branch of a rose tree had torn out her eyes . . .

After writhing on the ground like her own shadow, she lay at last still and apparently lifeless at the foot of an orange tree.

A military band was passing down the street. What vigorous martial music! What an eager vision of triumphal arches it summoned up! However, in spite of the trumpeters' efforts to blow hard and in time, the townspeople did not open their eyes impatiently that morning, like heroes tired of seeing the sword rust in the golden peace of cornfields, but rather to the pleasant prospect of a holiday, humbly resolving to pray that God should deliver them from evil thoughts, words or deeds directed against the President of the Republic.

After a brief spell of unconsciousness La Chabelona became aware of the band. She was in darkness. Her young lady must have crept up on tiptoe and covered her eyes from behind.

"Camila, my dear, I know it's you. Let me look at you!" she stammered, putting her hands to her face to take away the girl's hands which were hurting her horribly.

The wind blew the music away down the street in gusts. The music and the darkness with which blindness had bandaged her eyes as if in a child's game, brought back the memory of the school where she had learned her letters, down in the Old Town. Then with a leap through the years she saw herself grown-up, sitting in the shade of two mango trees, and then, gradually, little by little, another leap and she was in an ox-cart, rumbling along a flat road smelling of hay. The creaking of the wheels was like a double crown of thorns drawing blood from the silence of the beardless carter who made a woman of her: chewing as they went, the patient oxen dragged along the nuptial couch. Rapture of the sky above the springy fields . . . But her memories suddenly dissolved, and she saw a crowd of men pouring into the general's house with the force of a torrent, panting like black animals; heard their fiendish cries, blows, blasphemies, coarse laughter, and the piano screaming as if they were wrenching its teeth out by main force. Her young lady vanished like a perfume, and she felt a violent blow in the middle of her forehead accompanied by a strange cry and all-pervading darkness.

Genaro Rodas' wife, Niña Fedina, found the old servant lying in the patio with her cheeks bathed in blood, her hair dishevelled, her clothes torn to pieces, fighting to keep off the flies which invisible hands were throwing at her face—and fled in terror through the house like someone who has seen a ghost.

"Poor thing! Poor thing!" she kept muttering to herself.

Beneath one of the windows she found the letter the general had written to his brother Juan. He asked him to look after Camila. But Niña Fedina did not read it all, partly because she was distracted by La Chabelona's cries—they seemed to come from the broken mirrors, the splintered window-panes, the damaged chairs, the forced cupboards and the fallen pictures—and partly because of her urgent need to escape from the house. She wiped the sweat from her face with a handkerchief folded in four, nervously crushed in a hand ornamented with cheap rings, slipped the letter into her bodice and hurried out into the street.

Too late. A rough-looking officer stopped her at the door. The house was surrounded by soldiers. From the patio came the tortured cries of the nurse.

Lucio Vasquez, who had been egged on by La Masacuata and Camila to watch from the door of the Two-Step Tavern, held his breath when he saw them arrest the wife of his friend Genaro Rodas, to whom he had revealed the plan for the general's arrest in his cups last night at the Lion's Awakening.

A soldier came up to the tavern. "They're looking for the general's daughter!" thought the innkeeper with her heart in her boots. The same thought made Vasquez's hair stand on end. But the soldier had come to tell them to close the bar. They shut the doors and stood watching what went on in the street through the cracks.

In the darkness Vasquez rallied a little and began fondling La Masacuata on the pretext of being afraid, but she stopped him out of force of habit. She would have boxed his ears for two pins.

"Don't be so stuck-up!"

"So that's what you think? Well you're wrong! And I'd like to know why I should let you mess me about. Didn't I tell you last night that that fool of a woman said the general's daughter . . ."

"Look out! They'll hear you!" interrupted Vasquez. They were stooping to look out into the street through the cracks in the door as they talked.

"Don't be a fool, I'm talking quietly enough! If I hadn't told you that woman was going to get the general's daughter to be godmother to her brat, you'd have brought Genaro into it and then the fat would have been in the fire."

"I dare say," answered the other, hawking to get rid of some immovable substance stuck between his gullet and the back of his nose.

"Don't be so disgusting, you uneducated brute!"

"Very dainty all of a sudden!"

"Sh!"

At that moment the Judge Advocate General was seen getting out of a ramshackle cab.

"It's the ˙ Judge Advocate," said Vasquez.

"What's he come for?" asked La Masacuata.

"To arrest the general."

"And he's dressed himself up like a peacock for that? I ask you! Just look at him! Why don't you pinch one of those feathers he's got on his head?"

"No thanks. What a one for questions you are. He's dressed like that because he's on his way to see the President."

"Lucky fellow! If they didn't arrest the general last night I'm a whore!"

"Why don't you shut up?"

When the Judge Advocate General got out of his carriage, orders were given in a low tone and a captain went into the house at the head of a squad of soldiers, carrying his naked sword in one hand and a revolver in the other, like the officers in the color prints of the Russo-Japanese war.

And a few minutes later—they were centuries to Vasquez, who was watching everything that happened with his heart in his mouth—the officer returned looking pale and extremely agitated, to tell the Judge Advocate what had happened.

"What's that?" shouted the Judge Advocate. "What's that?" The words came bursting out between explosions of air.

"What? What? What? You say he's escaped?" he roared, with the veins on his forehead swelling up like black question marks. "And that—that—that—the house has been looted?"

Without a moment's hesitation he disappeared through the front door, followed by the officer; after a rapid survey he was back in the street, his fat hand angrily grasping the hilt of his sword, and so pale that his lips were indistin-

guishable from his blanched moustache.

"How did he get away? That's what I want to know!" he exclaimed as he came out of the house. "What was the telephone invented for? To see that orders were carried out! To arrest the enemies of the Government! The old fox! I'll hang him if I catch him! I wouldn't care to be in his shoes!"

The Judge Advocate General's gaze suddenly fell on Niña Fedina. An officer and a sergeant were dragging her by main force towards him as he stood there shouting.

"The bitch!" he cried, and without taking his eyes off her he added: "We'll make her talk! Lieutenant, take ten men and convey her as quickly as possible where she belongs! And solitary confinement, you understand?"

A petrified cry filled the air, a sharp, lacerating, inhuman cry.

"Oh my God, what are they doing to that poor crucified Christ?" groaned Vasquez. La Chabelona's increasingly piercing shrieks made his blood run cold.

"Christ?" the bartender corrected him sarcastically. "Can't you hear it's a woman? I suppose you think all men whistle like female blackbirds!"

"Shut your trap . . ."

The Judge Advocate gave orders for the neighboring houses to be searched. Parties of soldiers dispersed in all directions under corporals or sergeants. They ransacked patios, bedrooms, private offices, attics, fountains. They went on to the roofs and rummaged among linen cupboards, beds, carpets, sideboards, casks, dressers and chests. If anyone was slow to open his door they felled him with their rifle butts. Dogs barked frenziedly beside their white-faced masters. The sound of barking spouted from each house as from a watering-can.

"Suppose they come here?" said Vasquez, who was almost speechless with terror. "We've got ourselves into a fine mess! If we'd got something out of it it might be different, but for less than nothing . . ."

La Masacuata hurried off to warn Camila.

"If you want to know what I think," said Vasquez, following her, "she ought to cover her face and get away from here." And he backed to the door again without waiting for an answer.

"Wait! Wait!" he said with his eye to the crack. "The Judge Advocate has countermanded the order; they've stopped searching. We're saved!"

The barkeeper took two steps to the door to see with her own eyes what Lucio had announced so jubilantly.

"Just look at your crucified Christ!" whispered the woman.

"Who is she?"

"The nurse—can't you see?" and she withdrew her body out of range of Vasquez's lustful hand: "Will you be quiet! Be quiet! Be quiet, blast you!"

"Poor thing, look at the way they're dragging her along!"

"She looks as if a tram had run over her!"

"Why do people squint when they're dying?"

"Ugh! I don't want to see!"

The unfortunate nurse, La Chabelona, had been dragged out of the general's house by a squad of men led by a captain with a drawn sword. It was impossible for the Judge Advocate to interrogate her. Twenty-four hours earlier this relic of a human being, who was now breathing her last, had been the mainstay of a house in which the only political activity had been the canary's schemes to get bird seed, the concentric circles spreading beneath the jet of the fountain, the general's interminable games of patience and Camila's whims.

The Judge Advocate jumped into his carriage, followed by an officer. They were held up at the first corner. Four ragged, filthy men had arrived with a stretcher to take La Chabelona's corpse to the dissecting room. The soldiers filed off to their barracks and La Masacuata opened up her bar. Sitting on his usual seat, Vasquez made little attempt to disguise the agitation caused in him by the arrest of Genaro Rodas' wife; his head was as hot as a brick kiln; he was full of wind from the alcohol he had drunk, and waves of intoxication kept returning to him, along with fears about the general's escape.

Meanwhile Niña Fedina was hustled away to prison by her guard, who pushed her off the pavement every few minutes into the middle of the street. She let herself be manhandled in silence, but suddenly lost patience as they went along and struck one of them full in the face. A blow with a rifle butt was the unexpected reply, while another soldier hit her from behind so violently that she staggered, her teeth rattled in her head and she saw stars.

"So that's what your weapons are for, is it, you cowardly blackguards? You ought to be ashamed of yourselves!" intervened a woman returning from market with a basket full of vegetables and fruit.

"You shut up!" shouted one of the soldiers.

"None of your cheek, you bully!"

"Now then, Señora, get along, will you? Hurry on wherever you were going. Or have you got nothing to do?" shouted a sergeant.

"What about you, you fat swine!"

"Be quiet!" interrupted an officer, "or we'll bash your face in for you!"

"Bash my face in indeed! That's enough of that, you dirty Indians with your sleeves out at elbows and no seats to your trousers! Better have a look at yourselves and keep your traps shut, you lousy lot—insulting people just for the fun of it!"

And the unknown defender of Genaro

Rodas' wife was left behind among the startled passers-by, while the captive herself went on her way to prison, a tragic figure, her drawn face covered in sweat, and with the fringe of her bombazine shawl sweeping the ground.

The Judge Advocate General's carriage arrived at the house of Abel Carvajal the lawyer just as he was leaving for the palace in his top hat and morning coat. The Judge Advocate leaped from the step on to the pavement, setting the carriage rocking behind him. Carvajal had shut the door and was meticulously pulling on one of his gloves when his colleague arrested him. Dressed in his ceremonial clothes, he was escorted by a picket of soldiers along the middle of the street to the Second Police Station, the outside of which was decorated with flags and paper chains. They took him straight to the cell where the student and the sacristan were imprisoned.

CHAPTER XIV

Let the Whole World Sing!

The streets were gradually being revealed to view in the fugitive light of dawn; around them lay roofs and fields redolent of the freshness of April. The milk mules could be seen arriving at a gallop with the lids of their cans jangling, urged along by grunts and blows from their muleteers. The morning light shone on the cows drawn up outside the porticos of the richer houses or at the street corners in the poorer quarters, while their patrons—some on the way to convalescence, others to extinction—with their eyes still sunk and glazed with sleep, waited on their chosen cow and came up in turn to receive their milk, skillfully tilting the jug so as to get more liquid than froth. The bread delivery women went by with their heads sunk on their chests, backs bowed, straining legs and bare feet, threading their way with short, unsteady steps under the weight of their huge baskets. Baskets were piled on baskets in pagodas, leaving in the air an aroma of pastry covered in sugar and toasted sesame seeds. And the alarm clocks announced the beginning of a national holiday, setting in motion phantoms of metal and air, a symphony of smells and an explosion of colors; while between darkness and dawn there sounded from the churches the timid yet daring bell announcing early Mass— timid and daring, because if on ordinary holidays its chime suggested chocolate cake and canonical biscuits, on a national holiday it savored of forbidden fruit.

A national holiday . . .

Up from the streets along with the smell of the good earth, rose the jubilation of the inhabitants as they emptied basins of water out of their windows to settle the dust raised by the troops carrying the flag to the Palace (it smelled like a new handkerchief), or by the carriages of important people dressed in full regalia, doctors in frock coats, generals in brilliant uniforms smelling of mothballs—the former in shining toppers, the latter in three-cornered hats with plumes; or by the trotting horses of lesser officials, the value of whose services was measured by the sum the State would one day pay for their funerals.

Señor! Señor! Heaven and earth are full of your glory! Pleased at the response his efforts for their welfare met with from the people, the President allowed himself to be seen, a long way off, among a group of his intimate friends.

Señor! Señor! Heaven and earth are full of your glory! The women felt the divine power of their Beloved Deity. The more important priests paid him homage. The lawyers imagined they were

attending one of Alfonso el Sabio's tournaments. The diplomats, excellencies from Tiflis perhaps, put on grand airs as if they were at the court of the Sun King at Versailles. Native and foreign journalists congratulated themselves on being in the presence of a second Pericles. Señor! Señor! Heaven and earth are full of your glory! The poets felt they were in Athens, so they announced to the world at large. A sculptor of saintly figures imagined he was Phidias, smiled, rubbed his hands and turned his eyes to heaven when he heard the cheering in the streets in honor of their eminent ruler. Señor! Señor! Heaven and earth are full of your glory! A composer of funeral marches, a devotee of Bacchus and also of religion, craned his tomato-colored face from a window to see what was happening in the street.

But if the artists believed they were in Athens, the Jewish bankers imagined they were in Carthage as they passed through the rooms of the statesman who had given them his confidence and entrusted the nation's savings to their bottomless coffers at an interest of zero and nothing per cent—by which transaction they had managed to get rich and replace the gold and silver currency with the foreskins of the circumcised. Señor! Señor! Heaven and earth are full of your glory!

Angel Face made his way among the guests. (He was as beautiful and as wicked as Satan.)

"The people want you to come out on to the balcony, Mr. President."

"The people?"

The leader put a germ of interrogation into these two words. There was silence all round him. Weighed down by a deep sadness which he angrily suppressed as soon as he became aware of it, he got up from his chair and went out on to the balcony.

He appeared before the crowd surrounded by a group of his intimates.

Some women had come to congratulate him on the happy anniversary of his escape from death, and one of them, who had been given the task of making a speech, began as soon as she saw the President:

"Son of the people . . . !"

The leader swallowed a bitter mouthful of saliva, perhaps remembering his student years, when he lived in poverty with his mother in a town paved with bad intentions; but the favorite interposed in a sycophantic undertone:

"So was Jesus a son of the people."

"Son of the pe-eople!" repeated the speechifier, "of the people, I say. On this radiantly beautiful day the sun is shining in the sky, shedding its light on your eyes and on your life, and exemplifying by the blessed succession of day and night in the dome of heaven, the blackness of that unforgivable night when criminal hands —instead of sowing the seed as you, Señor, had taught them—laid a bomb at your feet, which in spite of every European scientific device left you scatheless."

A burst of organized applause drowned the voice of the "Talking Cow," as the female orator was unkindly nicknamed, and a succession of acclamations fanned the air around the hero of the day and his suite.

"Long live the President!"

"Long live the President of the Republic!"

"Long live the Constitutional President of the Republic!"

"Let our applause go on echoing throughout the world forever: Long live the Constitutional President of the Republic, Benefactor of his Country, Head of the great Liberal Party, and Liberal-hearted Protector of Studious Youth!"

The "Talking Cow" went on:

"There would have been a hundred stains on our flag had the plans of these wicked sons of our Fatherland succeeded, supported as they were in their criminal attempt by the President's enemies. They never paused to reflect that God's hand was protecting your precious life, with the support of all those who recognize that you are worthy to be First Citizen of the Nation and who therefore surrounded you at that terrible moment, and who surround you now and will continue to do so as long as it is necessary!

"Yes, gentlemen—ladies and gentlemen; today we realize more fully than ever that if those dreadful plans had been successful on that day of tragic memory for our nation—now marching at the head of civilized peoples—our Fatherland would have been bereft of its father and protector, and at the mercy of those who sharpen their daggers in darkness to plunge them into the breast of Democracy, as that great statesman Juan Montalvo said!

"Thanks to your escape, our flag still flutters above us unstained. And that is why we are here today, gentlemen, to honor the illustrious protector of the poorer classes, who watches over us with a father's love and has brought our nation, as I have already said, into the vanguard of that progress to which Fulton gave the first impulse with his discovery of steam, and which Juan Santa Maria defended from piracy by setting fire to the fatal powder in Lempira. Long live our Fatherland! Long live the Constitutional President of the Republic, Head of the Liberal Party, Benefactor of the Nation, Protector of defenseless women and children, and of education!"

The "Talking Cow's" vivats were lost in a conflagration of cheering which was extinguished by a sea of clapping.

The President said a few words in reply, with his right hand grasping the marble balcony; he turned slightly sideways so as not to expose his breast and moved his head from left to right to embrace the crowd, his brows drawn together, his eyes watchful. Men and women alike wiped away a few tears.

"Won't you come indoors again, Mr. President?" put in Angel Face, hearing him sniff, "as you find the crowd so affecting . . ."

As the President returned from the balcony followed by one or two friends, the Judge Advocate hurried forward to inform him of General Canales' flight and also in order to be the first to congratulate him on his speech; but like everyone else who approached with this intention he stopped dead, suddenly inhibited by a strange feeling of fear, as of some supernatural agency, and rather than remain with his hand outstretched, he offered it to Angel Face.

The favorite turned his back, and it was with his hand still in mid-air that the Judge Advocate General heard the first of a series of explosions, following each other rapidly like a discharge of artillery. Already screams could be heard; already people were jumping, running, kicking over chairs, and women were fainting; already there was the tramp of soldiers, as they scattered among the crowd like grains of rice, their hands on the stiff fastenings of their cartridge-pouches, their rifles loaded, accompanied by machine-guns, red mirrors, officers, guns . . .

A colonel disappeared upstairs, revolver in hand. Another ran down a spiral staircase, revolver in hand. It was nothing. A captain went past a window, revolver in hand. Another stood at a door, revolver in hand. It was nothing. It was nothing! But the air felt cold. The news spread through the agitated crowd. It was nothing. Gradually the guests formed into groups; some had made water in their terror, others had lost their gloves; those whose color returned to them had not regained the power of speech, and those who had recovered the power of speech had lost their color. The one question nobody could answer was where and when the President had disappeared.

On the floor at the foot of a little staircase lay the leading drummer of the military band. He had rolled down from the first floor, drum and all, and thus provoked the panic!

CHAPTER XV

Uncles and Aunts

The favorite left the Palace between the Lord Chief Justice—a little old man in a top hat and frock coat looking like a child's drawing of a rat—and a member of parliament, as cadaverous as some ancient statue of a saint. They were arguing in the most mouth-watering way as to whether the Grand Hotel or an inn near by would most effectively drive away the fright they had all been given by that ridiculous drummer, whom they consigned without a twinge of remorse to prison, Hell, or worse. When the member of parliament put the case for the Grand Hotel he seemed to be laying down obligatory rules as to the most aristocratic setting in which to lift the elbow, an activity which had favorable repercussions on the exchequer. When the judge spoke it was with the emphasis of someone pronouncing sentence: "intrinsic excellence is always to be found where there is lack of outer display, and that is the reason, my friend, why I prefer the humble inn, where one is at ease and among friends, to the luxurious hotel where all is not gold that glitters."

Angel Face left them still arguing at the corner of the Palace—it was better to wash one's hands of a dispute between two such authorities—and set off for the El Incienso quarter, in search of Juan Canales' house. It was of urgent importance that this gentleman should fetch or

send for his niece from the Two-Step Tavern. "What does it matter whether he goes himself or sends for her?" he said to himself, "so long as she ceases to be my responsibility, so long as she ceases to exist for me any more than she did yesterday, when she was nothing to me." Two or three passers-by made way for him respectfully, stepping off the pavement into the road. He thanked them without noticing who they were.

Don Juan, the general's brother, lived at El Incienso in a house close to "The Coin," as the Mint was called, a building, it must be said, of patibulary gloom. The peeling walls were reinforced with flaking beams of wood, and through the iron bars of the windows one could glimpse rooms like the cages of wild beasts. Here the devil's millions were kept safe.

When the favorite knocked a dog answered. It was clear from the frenzied way this Cerberus barked that he was tied up.

Hat in hand, Angel Face entered the door—he was as beautiful and as wicked as Satan; he was pleased to be in the house where the general's daughter was to be taken, but distracted by the dog's barking, and repeated invitations to "Come in" from a florid-complexioned, smiling, pot-bellied man who was none other than Don Juan Canales.

"Do come in, I beg you; come in! This way, if you'll be so kind! And to what do I owe the pleasure of this visit?" Don Juan said all this like an automaton, in a tone of voice which was far from expressing the agitation he felt in the presence of this exquisite satellite of the President.

Angel Face glanced round the room. With what a chorus of barking that bad-tempered dog greeted visitors to the house! He noticed a collection of portraits of the Canales brothers, and that the general's had been removed. A looking-glass at the other end of the room reflected the place where the picture had hung and a section of the room papered in yellow—the color of a telegram.

While Don Juan went on exhausting his stock-in-trade of formally polite remarks, Angel Face reflected that the dog was still the guardian of the house as in primitive times. The defender of the tribe. Even the President himself owned a kennel of foreign dogs.

The master of the house could be seen in the mirror gesticulating distractedly. Don Juan Canales, having used up every phrase in his repertory, felt like a swimmer who has plunged into deep water.

"Here, in my house," he was saying, "we (my wife and your humble servant) have felt genuine indignation at my brother Eusebio's behavior! What a story it is! Crime is always a detestable thing, and more so in this case, when the victim was in every way estimable, a man who was a credit to our Army, and above all—I ask you!—a friend of the President!"

Angel Face maintained the terrible silence of someone watching a man drown because he has no means of saving him—a silence only comparable to that of visitors who are too timid either to confirm or contradict what is said.

Finding that his words fell on deaf ears, Don Juan lost his nerve completely and began to beat the air with his hands and search for solid ground with his feet. His brain was in a ferment. He believed himself implicated in the murder in the Cathedral Porch and all its far-reaching political ramifications. The fact that he was innocent made no difference. How complicated it all was. How complicated! "It's a lottery, my friend, it's a lottery! It's a lottery, my friend, a lottery!" This phrase, describing the typical state of affairs in the country, used to be shouted by Old Fulgencio, a good old man who

sold lottery tickets in the street, and was a devout Catholic with a sharp eye for business. Instead of Angel Face, Canales saw the skeleton silhouette of Old Fulgencio, whose bony limbs, jaws and fingers all seemed to be jerking on wires. Old Fulgencio used to grip his black leather portfolio under his angular arm, smooth out the wrinkles in his face, slap at the pendulous seat of his trousers, stretch out his neck and say in a voice which emerged simultaneously from his nose and his toothless mouth: "The lottery is the only law on this earth, my friend! The lottery can send you to prison, have you shot, make you a deputy, a diplomat, President of the Republic, a general or a minister! What's the good of work, when all this can be got by the lottery? It's a lottery, my friend—so come on and buy a lottery ticket!" And the whole of that knotted skeleton, that twisted vine-stem, was shaken by laughter, which spouted from his mouth like a list of winning lottery numbers.

Angel Face gazed at Canales in silence, asking himself quite a different question: how could this cowardly and repellent man have anything to do with Camila?

"It's being said—anyway my wife was told so—that they want to implicate me in the murder of Colonel Parrales Sonriente!" went on Canales, pulling a handkerchief out of his pocket with great difficulty and mopping the large drops of sweat that rolled down his forehead.

"I know nothing about that," the other man said shortly.

"It would be unjust! As I told you just now, my wife and I have disapproved of Eusebio's behavior from the very first. Besides, I don't know if you're aware of it, but my brother and I have seen very little of each other lately. Almost nothing. In fact nothing. We used to meet like strangers: good morning, good morning; good evening, good evening; that was all. Goodbye, goodbye, but that was all."

Don Juan's voice was full of uncertainty. His wife, who had been following the interview from behind a screen, thought it was time to come to her husband's help.

"Introduce me, Juan," she exclaimed as she came in, with a nod and a polite smile to Angel Face.

"Oh yes, of course!" answered her distraught husband, as he and the favorite got up from their chairs. "Let me introduce my wife!"

"Judith de Canales."

Angel Face heard the name of Don Juan's wife, but he had no recollection of mentioning his own.

This visit was prolonging itself unnecessarily, because of the inexplicable influence which had begun to trouble his heart and disturb his entire life, and any remarks which had nothing to do with Camila failed to penetrate his ears.

"But why don't these people talk about their niece?" he wondered. "If they talked of her I should be all attention; if they talked of her I should tell them they needn't worry, that Don Juan couldn't be mixed up in any murder; if only they'd talk of her! But what a fool I am! It's she and they, not I; I'm out of it, out of it, miles away, nothing to do with her . . ."

Doña Judith sat down on the sofa and wiped her nose with a little lace handkerchief to keep herself in countenance.

"You were saying? I'm afraid I interrupted you. I'm so sorry . . ."

"Of . . .!"

"If . . .!"

"Have . . .!"

All three of them started speaking at once, and after several polite "do go on"s, Don Juan was left in possession of the floor, he didn't quite know why. ("Idiot!" his wife's eyes shouted at him.)

"I was just telling our friend here that you and I were outraged when we were told, in the most confidential way, that my brother Eusebio had been one of Colonel Parrales Sonriente's assassins."

"Oh, yes, yes, indeed!" agreed Doña Judith, thrusting forward her prominent breasts. "Juan and I said that my brother-in-law the general should never have degraded his uniform with such a barbarous action; and the worst of it is, the very last straw, that now they tell us people are trying to implicate my husband!"

"I've also been explaining to Don Miguel that my brother and I had drifted apart a long time ago, that we were enemies . . . yes, deadly enemies; he couldn't bear the sight of me, nor I of him!"

"Not quite so bad as that, but family matters always lead to anger and quarreling," added Doña Judith, allowing a sigh to float away on the air.

"I know," put in Angel Face; "but Don Juan mustn't forget that there's always an indestructible bond between brothers . . ."

"What do you mean, Don Miguel? That I was his accomplice?"

"Excuse me!"

"You mustn't believe that," put in Doña Judith hurriedly, with lowered eyes. "All bonds are destroyed when money matters come up; it's sad that it should be so, but one sees it happen every day. Money is no respecter of blood ties!"

"Excuse me! I said just now that there is an indestructible bond between brothers, because in spite of the deep differences of opinion between Don Juan and the general, when the general saw that he was ruined and must leave the country, he told me . . ."

"If he tried to mix me up in his crime, he's a villain! Oh, what a slander!"

"But he did nothing of the sort!"

"Juan, Juan, do let our visitor speak!"

"He told me that he counted on you both to see that his daughter should not be left destitute, and he asked me to come and talk to you about having her here in this house . . ."

This time it was Angel Face who felt that his words were falling on deaf ears. He seemed to be talking to people who didn't understand Spanish. His words rebounded as from a mirror, unheeded either by the portly clean-shaven Don Juan or by Doña Judith, encased in her breasts as if in a wheelbarrow.

"And it's for you to consider what can best be done for the girl."

"Yes, of course!" As soon as Don Juan realized that Angel Face had not come to arrest him, he recovered his normal presence of mind. "I don't really know what to say to you; the truth is you've quite taken me by surprise! Of course it's out of the question to have her here. One can't play with fire, you know! I'm sure the poor girl would have been happy here, but my wife and I can't risk losing our friends; they would hold it against us if we opened the doors of our respectable home to the daughter of one of the President's enemies. Besides, it's common knowledge that my fine brother offered—how shall I say?—well, he offered his daughter to an intimate friend of the Chief of State, so that . . ."

"Simply to avoid being put in prison!" interrupted Doña Judith, letting her prominent bosom subside in yet another sigh. "But, as Juan says, he offered his daughter to a friend of the President's, who was to offer her in his turn to the President himself, who (it's natural and logical to suppose) rejected the disgraceful suggestion. And then, the Prince of the Army (as they nicknamed the general after his famous speech) saw that there was no way out for him, and decided to escape and leave his daughter

to us. That was it! What can one expect from a man who has infected his relations with suspicion like the plague, and dishonored the family name! Don't imagine we haven't suffered as a result of this affair. It's quite turned our hair white, as God and the Virgin are my witness!"

A flash of anger shot through the black depths of Angel Face's eyes.

"Then there's nothing more to be said . . ."

"We're sorry you should have had the bother of coming to see us. If you had sent a message . . ."

"And if it hadn't been utterly impossible for us," added Doña Judith, "we should have accepted with pleasure for your sake."

Angel Face went out without another word or glance in their direction.

The dog barked frenziedly, dragging its chain across the ground from side to side as far as it would go.

"I shall go and see your brothers," were his final words at the front door.

"You'll be wasting your time," Don Juan hastened to say. "I have the reputation of being a conservative as I live in this district, yet I won't take her into my house; but they are liberals . . . Oh well, they'll just think you're mad, or simply joking . . ."

He was standing on the door-step as he said these words; he shut the door slowly, rubbed his fat hands together, hesitated for a moment, then walked away. He felt an irresistible desire to caress someone, but not his wife; and he went to get the dog which was still barking.

"Leave the dog if you're going out," shouted his wife from the patio, where she was pruning her rose trees now that the sun was off them.

"Yes, I'm going out now."

"Well, hurry, because I'm going to church for my Hour of Prayer, and I'd rather not be out in the streets after six."

CHAPTER XVI

In the Casa Nueva

Towards eight o'clock in the morning (how fortunate people were in the days of the clepsydra, when there were no grasshopper clocks reckoning the time by leaps and bounds!) Niña Fedina was shut into a tomb-like cell the shape of a guitar, after the usual formalities and an exhaustive examination of everything she had on. They searched her from head to foot, her fingernails, her arm-pits, every-where—a most offensive process—and they became even more thorough after they found a letter written by General Canales in her bodice, the letter she had picked up from the floor of his house.

Tired with standing, and having no room to take even two steps, she sat down—after all it was better to sit. But after a little she got up again. The cold from the floor had penetrated her but-tocks, her shins, her hands, her ears—human flesh is very susceptible to cold—and she remained standing for a while, then sat down again, stood up, sat down, and stood up by turns . . .

She could hear the prisoners who had been let out of their cells for an airing in the yard, singing songs as fresh as raw vegetables, in spite of the misery in their hearts. At times they hummed these airs sleepily; then their cruel monotony, the sense of doomed oppression they con-veyed, would suddenly be broken by cries of desperation. The singers blasphemed, they hurled insults, they swore . . .

From the very first, Niña Fedina was frightened by a discordant voice which repeated over and over again like some-one intoning a psalm:

> From the Casa Nueva
> to the houses of ill-fame,
> O pretty little sky,
> is only a step,

and now that we are alone,
> O pretty little sky,
> Give me a kiss.
> Ay, ay, ay, ay!
> give me a kiss,
> for from here to
> the houses of ill-fame,
> O pretty little sky,
> is only a step.

The two first lines did not go with the rest of the song; however, this trifling cir-cumstance seemed to emphasize the close relationship of the houses of ill-fame and the Casa Nueva. The break in the rhythm, though a sacrifice to realism, underlined the tormenting truth which filled Niña Fedina with fear of being afraid, making her tremble before she had experienced to the full that obscure and horrifying terror she was to feel later, when the voice on the worn gramo-phone record, pregnant with a more than criminal secrecy, had penetrated to her very bones. It was unfair that she had only this bitter song to feed upon. If she had been flayed alive she would not have suffered more torment than she did in her dungeon, listening to something which to the other prisoners, who forgot that a prostitute's bed is colder than prison, was the fulfillment of all their hopes of free-dom and warmth.

She found some comfort in thinking of her child. She thought of him as if she still carried him in her womb. Mothers never reach a state of feeling completely empty of their children. The first thing she would do when she got out of prison was get him baptized. Everything had been arranged. The dress and bonnet Señorita Camila had given him were very pretty. And she planned to celebrate the occasion with tamal and chocolate for breakfast, Valencian rice and stew for midday, cinnamon water, almond syrup, ices and wafers in the evening. She had ordered the little invitation cards for her friends from the printer with the glass eye. And she wanted to hire two carriages from Shumann's, drawn by those big horses like locomotives, with tinkling silver-plated harness and drivers in tall hats and frock coats. Then she tried to drive these thoughts from her brain, so as to avoid sharing the fate of the man who said to himself on the eve of his wedding: "This time tomorrow you'll be mine, my little sweetheart!" and who had the misfortune to be knocked on the head by a brick in the street on his way to the church next day.

And she began thinking of her child again, with such happy absorption that without realizing it she found herself gazing at a network of obscene drawings traced on the wall, which were a fresh source of agitation to her. Crosses, texts, men's names, dates, cabalistic figures, were jumbled up among sexual organs of all sizes. There was the word of God beside a phallus, the number thirteen on top of an enormous testicle, devils with their bodies twisted like candelabra, little flowers with fingers instead of petals, caricatures of judges and magistrates, small boats, anchors, suns, cradles, bottles, interlaced hands, eyes, hearts pierced by daggers, suns with policemen's moustaches, moons with faces like old maids, three or five-pointed stars, watches, sirens, guitars with wings, arrows . . .

Panic-stricken, she tried to escape from this world of madness and perversion, only to bump into the obscenities covering the other walls. She closed her eyes, mute with terror; she was like a woman beginning to slide down a slippery slope, with chasms opening around her instead of windows, and the sky displaying its stars as a wolf displays its teeth.

On the ground a party of ants were carrying off a dead cockroach. Still under the influence of the obscene drawings, Niña Fedina thought she was looking at female genitals being dragged by their own hair towards the beds of vice.

From the Casa Nueva
to the houses of ill-fame,
O pretty little sky . . .

And the song again began rubbing at her living flesh gently with little splinters of glass, as if to wear away her feminine modesty.

In the town the celebrations in honor of the President of the Republic were still going on. In the evenings a cinema screen was erected like a gallows in the Plaza Central, and blurred fragments of films were exhibited to the crowd, who watched as enthusiastically as if they were witnessing an auto-da-fé. The flood-lit public buildings stood out against the dark sky. A stream of passers-by rolled themselves like a turban around the sharp-pointed railings of the circular public garden. The flower of society used to gather there and stroll round the gardens in the evenings, while the populace watched the cinema in religious silence under the stars. Packed together like sardines, old men and old women, bachelors and married couples were already yawning with undisguised boredom and watching the passers-by from their chairs and benches in the square, with a compliment for every girl and a greeting for their friends. From time to time, rich and poor alike looked up at the sky: a colored rocket exploded and let fall its threads of rainbow silks.

The first night in a prison cell is a terrible thing. The prisoner feels that he is cut off from life in a nightmare world, there in the darkness. The walls vanish, the ceiling fades, the ground is lost to view, but this brings no feeling of freedom—rather of death.

Niña Fedina began a hurried prayer: "Oh most merciful Virgin Mary, it is said that you never abandon anyone who has sought your aid, implored your help and claimed your protection! So it is with confidence I turn to you, oh Virgin of Virgins, and throw myself at your feet, weeping for my sins. Do not reject my prayers, oh Virgin Mary, but listen with a favorable and receptive ear. Amen." The darkness was choking her. She could not pray any more. She slipped to the floor, stretching out her arms—they seemed very long, very long—to embrace the cold floor, all the cold floors of all the prisoners who were being persecuted in the name of justice, the dying and the homeless . . .

She repeated the litany:

> *Ora pro nobis*
> *Ora pro nobis*
> *Ora pro nobis*
> *Ora pro nobis*
> *Ora pro nobis*
> *Ora pro nobis*
> *Ora pro nobis*
> *Ora pro nobis*

She sat up slowly. She was hungry. Who would suckle her child? She went to the door on all fours and beat on it in vain.

> *Ora pro nobis*
> *Ora pro nobis*
> *Ora pro nobis*

In the distance she heard a clock strike twelve.

> *Ora pro nobis*
> *Ora pro nobis*

In the outside world where her child was . . .

> *Ora pro nobis*

She had counted twelve strokes—rallying her forces, she made an effort to imagine she was free, and succeeded. She pictured herself at home among her be-longings and friends, saying to Juanita: "Goodbye, it was lovely to see you!," going out and clapping her hands to call Gabrielita, seeing to the stove, bowing to Don Timoteo. She seemed to see her shop as if it were alive, some part of herself and others . . .

Outside the celebrations went on, with the cinema screen standing like a scaffold and people walking round the garden like slaves round a water-wheel.

The door of the cell opened when she was least expecting it. The noise of the lock unfastening made her start back as if from the brink of a precipice. Two men had come to find her in the darkness; they pushed her in silence along a narrow corridor swept by the night breeze and through two darkened rooms into another where lights were burning. When she came in, the Judge Advocate General was talking to his clerk in a low voice.

"That's the gentleman who plays the harmonium at the Virgin of Carmel!" thought Niña Fedina. "It seemed to me I recognized him when I was arrested; I've seen him in church. He can't be a bad man!"

The Judge Advocate gave her a long look, then he asked her some general questions: her name, age, state, profession, address. Rodas' wife answered in a firm voice, adding a question of her own when the clerk had written down a final answer—a question which went unheard because just then the telephone rang and a harsh woman's voice was clearly heard in the silence of the adjoining room, saying: "Yes! How's it going? I'm so glad! I sent to Canducha to inquire this morning. The dress? The dress is all right, yes, it's well cut. What? No, no, it isn't stained . . . I said it wasn't stained . . . Yes, without fail. Yes, yes . . . yes, come without fail. Goodbye. Sleep well. Goodbye."

Meanwhile the Judge Advocate was

answering Niña Fedina's question in a familiar, cruelly mocking and ironical tone:

"Don't worry; that's what we're here for, to tell people like you, who don't know, why they've been arrested."

Then in a different voice, with his toad-like eyes bulging from their sockets, he added slowly:

"But first you must tell me what you were doing in General Eusebio Canales' house this morning."

"I'd gone—I'd gone to see the general on business."

"What was the business, may I ask?"

"Only a little matter, Señor! An errand I'd undertaken! To—look here, I'll tell you everything: I went to tell him that he was going to be arrested for the murder of that colonel (I forget his name) who was assassinated in the Cathedral Porch."

"And you've got the nerve to ask me why you're in prison? Does that seem a little thing, a little thing, you slut? Does that seem a little thing, a little thing?"

Each time he said "little" the Judge Advocate's rage increased.

"Wait a moment, Señor, let me explain! Wait a moment, Señor, it's not what you think! Wait! Listen! For heaven's sake! When I got to the general's house the general wasn't there; I didn't see him, I didn't see anyone, they had all gone, the house was empty, except for the servant who was running around!"

"And that seems a little thing? A little thing? And what time did you get there?"

"The clock of La Merced was just striking six in the morning, Señor!"

"You've got a good memory! And how did you know that the general was going to be arrested?"

"Me?"

"Yes, you!"

"I heard it from my husband."

"And what's your husband's name?"

"Genaro Rodas."

"Who did he hear it from? How did he know? Who told him?"

"A friend of his, Señor, called Lucio Vasquez, a member of the Secret Police. He told my husband and my husband . . ."

"And you told the general!" interrupted the Judge Advocate.

Niña Fedina shook her head as much as to say: "It's not true! NO!"

"And which way did the general go?"

"But, good heavens, how can I say when I never saw the general? Don't you understand, I never saw him, I never saw him! Why should I lie about it? Especially as this gentleman's writing everything I say down."

She pointed to the clerk, who stared back at her with his pale freckled face, like white blotting-paper which has blotted a great many dots.

"It's nothing to do with you what he's writing. Answer my question! Which way did the general go?"

There was a long silence. Then the Judge Advocate's voice rapped out, more sternly: "Which way did the general go?"

"I don't know! How can I possibly tell? I don't know, I never saw him—I never spoke to him!"

"You're making a mistake in denying it, because the authorities know everything—including the fact that you talked to the general."

"You make me laugh!"

"Listen to me; it's no laughing matter. The authorities know everything—everything, everything!" At each "everything" he made the table shake. "If you didn't see the general how did you come by this letter? I suppose it jumped into your bodice of its own account?"

"That's the letter I found lying in his house; I swiped it off the ground when I went out. But it's no good saying anything, since you don't believe me any more than if I was a liar!"

"Swiped it! She can't even talk properly!" grumbled the clerk.

"Look here, stop telling stories, Señora, and confess the truth, because all you'll get with your lies is a punishment that'll make you remember me for the rest of your life!"

"But I've told you the truth, and if you won't believe me I can't beat it into you with a stick as if you were my son!"

"You're going to pay for this, you just mark my words! And another thing: what had you to do with the general anyway? What were you, what are you, to him? His sister or what? What did you get out of him?"

"Me? Out of the general? Nothing. I only saw him twice, but you see it just happened that his daughter had promised to be godmother to my son."

"That's not a reason!"

The clerk put in from behind:

"All stupid lying!"

"And if I was upset, and lost my head, and ran off where you know I went, that was because Lucio told my husband that a man was going to carry off the general's daughter."

"Stop lying! You'd much better make a clean breast of it and tell me where the general is hiding; because I know you know, and that you're the only person who does know, and that you're going to tell us here and now—to tell us—to tell me. Stop crying and talk! I'm listening!"

And in a softer voice, almost in the tone of a confessor, he added:

"If you tell me where the general is—look here, listen to me: I know you know and are going to tell me—if you tell me where the general is hiding I'll let you off; I'll have you set free and you can go straight home to your house in peace. Think of that. Just think of that!"

"Oh dear, Señor, I'd tell you if I knew! But I don't know, unfortunately I don't know. Holy Mother of God, what shall I do?"

"Why do you deny it? Can't you see that you're ruining your own chances?"

In the intervals between the Judge Advocate's remarks, the clerk went on sucking his teeth.

"Well, if it's no use treating you kindly, if you're such scum as all that . . ." (the Judge Advocate said these words more quickly and with the increasing fury of a volcano about to erupt) ". . . then we'll make you talk by other means. You realize you've committed a grave crime against the security of the State, and that the law holds you responsible for the flight of a seditious traitor, rebel, assassin and enemy of the President? And that's saying quite a lot, quite a lot, quite a lot!"

Señora Rodas did not know what to do. This diabolical man's words concealed an urgent and terrible threat, perhaps even of death. Her teeth chattered, her fingers and legs trembled. When the hands tremble it seems as if they had no bones and were being shaken like gloves. When the teeth chatter and one cannot speak, one seems to be telegraphing one's anxiety. And when the legs tremble it seems as if one were standing in a carriage dragged along by two runaway horses, like a soul carried off by the devil.

"Señor!" she implored.

"I'm not joking! Come on, quickly now! Where is the general?"

A door opened some way off and a baby's crying was heard. Passionate, despairing crying.

"Do it for your child!"

Even before the Judge Advocate had spoken, Niña Fedina had thrown back her head and was looking in every direction to see where the crying came from.

"He's been crying for the last two hours, and it's no use your trying to find him. He's crying from hunger and he'll die of hunger if you don't tell me where the general is."

She rushed to the door, but was stopped by three men, three sinister-looking brutes who had very little trouble in overcoming her poor female strength. Her hair came down in the course of the futile struggle, her blouse came out of her skirt and her petticoats fell to the ground. Little she cared. Almost naked, she crawled back to the Judge Advocate General and begged him on her knees to let her suckle her baby.

"Anything you please, but first tell me where the general is!"

"I implore you by the Virgin of Carmel, Señor," she entreated, embracing his shoe. "Yes, by the Virgin of Carmel, let me feed my little boy. Listen, he hardly has the strength to cry any more; listen, he's dying! Afterwards you can kill me if you want to!"

"No Virgin of Carmel will do you any good here! If you don't tell me where the general is hiding, here we stay, and your son too till he cries himself to death!"

Like a madwoman she threw herself on her knees in front of the men guarding the door. Then she struggled with them. Then she came back and knelt to the Judge Advocate again, trying to kiss his shoes.

"Señor, for my child's sake!"

"Well, for your child's sake, where is the general? It's useless to kneel and play the actress like this, because if you don't answer my question you have no hope at all of suckling your baby!"

As he said this, the Judge Advocate stood up. The clerk was still sucking his teeth and holding his pen ready to write down the statement which would not come from the lips of the unfortunate mother.

"Where is the general?"

Just as water weeps in the gutters on winter nights, the baby went on crying, blubbering and whimpering.

"Where is the general?"

Niña Fedina was as silent as a wounded animal, biting her lips and not knowing what to do.

"Where is the general?"

Five, ten, fifteen minutes passed in this way. At last the Judge Advocate wiped his mouth on a black-edged handkerchief and added a threat to his questions:

"Well if you won't answer we'll make you crush some quicklime and see if that reminds you which way the general went!"

"I'll do whatever you like; only first let me—let me feed my little boy. Don't be so unjust, Señor, the poor little thing has done nothing! You can punish me as much as you like!"

One of the men guarding the door pushed her roughly to the ground; another gave her a kick which laid her flat. Her tears and indignation blurred the bricks in the wall, the objects in the room. She could take in nothing but her child's cries.

At one o'clock in the morning she began pounding quicklime to stop them hitting her about. Her little boy was still crying . . .

From time to time the Judge Advocate repeated:

"Where is the general? Where is the general?"

One o'clock.

Two.

And at last three. Her little boy was crying.

Three o'clock; it seemed like five.

Would four o'clock never come? And her child went on crying.

And four o'clock. Her child was still crying.

"Where is the general? Where is the general?"

With her hands covered all over in innumerable deep cracks, which opened wider with every movement she made, with the tips of her fingers raw, wounds between them, and bleeding nails, Niña

Fedina groaned with pain as she lifted and rolled the stone on the quicklime. When she stopped, to beg pity for her child rather than for her own sufferings, they beat her.

"Where is the general? Where is the general?"

She wasn't listening to the Judge Advocate's voice. Her baby's wailings, growing feebler every moment, filled her ears.

At twenty to five they left her lying unconscious on the ground. A viscous stream was coming from her lips, and milk whiter than the lime itself was flowing from her breasts, which were lacerated with almost invisible fistulas. Now and again a few furtive tears escaped from her inflamed eyes.

Later on, when the first light of dawn was appearing, they took her back to her cell. There she watched over her frozen, dying baby, lying as limp as a rag doll in his mother's lap. The child revived a little and seized avidly upon her breast, but when he took the nipple in his mouth and tasted the sharpness of the lime, he dropped it and began crying again, and nothing would induce him to return to it.

She shouted and beat on the door with the baby in her arms. He was growing cold. He was growing cold. They couldn't possibly let an innocent creature die like this; and she began banging on the door and shouting again.

"Oh my son is dying! Oh my son is dying! Oh my life, my little one, my life! For God's sake come! Open up, for God's sake, open the door! My son is dying! Holy Virgin! Blessed Saint Anthony! Jesus of Saint Catherine!"

Outside the celebrations went on. The second day was just like the first, with the cinema screen like a scaffold, and people walking round the garden like slaves round a water-wheel.

CHAPTER XVII

Love's Stratagems

"Will he come or not?"

"He'll turn up any minute, you'll see."

"He's already late, but if only he comes it doesn't matter, does it?"

"You can count on it, as sure as it's night now; I'll eat my boots if he doesn't come. Don't you worry."

"And you think he'll bring me news of Papa? He suggested it himself . . ."

"Of course. All the more reason."

"Oh, I hope to God it's not bad news! I don't know what I'm doing. I feel I'm going mad. I want him to come quickly to relieve my fears, yet I don't want him to come at all if he brings bad news."

From the corner of her little improvised kitchen, La Masacuata was listening to Camila, who lay on the bed, talking in a tremulous voice. A lighted candle had been stuck to the floor in front of the Virgin of Chiquinquira.

"With you in such a fix I'm sure he'll come, and with news which'll please you, you'll see. How can I tell, d'you say? . . . Because that's my line and there's nothing I don't know about affairs of the heart. One swallow may not make a summer but men are all the same . . . like bees round a honey-pot . . ."

The sound of the bellows interrupted the barkeeper's remarks. Camila watched her absent-mindedly as she blew up the fire.

"Love is like an iced drink, my dear. If you drink it as soon as it's made there's plenty of good syrup, but it runs out everywhere, and you must drink it up quick or it'll spill over; and then afterwards—afterwards there's nothing left but a lump of ice with no color and no taste."

Footsteps were heard in the street. Camila's heart beat so violently that she had to press her two hands over it. They passed the door and went quickly away.

"I thought it was him."

"He won't be long now . . ."

"It must be because he went to my uncle's house before coming here; very likely he'll bring my Uncle Juan with him."

"Pst! The cat! The cat's drinking your milk; scare it away!"

Camila turned to look at the animal; it had been frightened by the barwoman's shout and was licking its milky whiskers beside her forgotten cup on a chair.

"What's the cat's name?"

"Benjie."

"I had one called Dewdrop. It was a female."

Again footsteps were heard, and perhaps . . .

Yes, it was Angel Face.

While La Masacuata unbarred the door, Camila tried to smooth her hair back a little with her hands. Her heart was pounding in her breast. At the end of this eternal, interminable day, as it had sometimes seemed, she felt numb, weak, lifeless and haggard, like a sick person who hears whispered preparations for her operation.

"Good news, Señorita, it's all right!" said Angel Face from the door, removing the troubled expression from his face.

She was waiting for him beside the bed, standing with one hand on the headboard, her eyes full of tears and her expression cold. The favorite took her hands.

"First the news about your father; that's the most important thing to you." After saying this he looked at La Masacuata, and changed his mind without altering his tone of voice. "But your father doesn't know that you're hiding here . . ."

"And where is he?"

"You must keep calm!"

"If only I knew nothing had happened to him, I could bear anything!"

"Sit down," interrupted the barkeeper to Angel Face, pointing to the bench.

"Thanks."

"And as you've got plenty to talk about, if there's nothing you want perhaps you'll let me go off for a little while. I want to go and see what's happened to Lucio. He went out this morning and hasn't been back since."

The favorite was on the point of asking the woman not to leave him alone with Camila. But she had already disappeared into the dark little patio to change her skirt, and Camila was saying:

"God will reward you for everything, Señora! Poor thing, she's so kind. And everything she says is amusing. She says you are very good, very rich and charming, and that's she's known you a long time."

"Yes she's a good sort. However we couldn't talk openly in front of her and it's better she should go. The only thing that's known about your father is that he's on the run, and until he's crossed the frontier we can have no definite news. But tell me, did you say anything about your father to this woman?"

"No, because I thought she knew all about it."

"Well it's better not to breathe a word to her."

"And my uncle and aunt—what did they say?"

"I've not been able to go and see them because of trying to get news of your father; but I've told them I'll visit them tomorrow."

"I'm sorry to be such a nuisance, but I'm sure you understand I should feel happier there with them; especially with my Uncle Juan; he's my godfather and has always been like a second father to me."

"Did you see each other often?"

"Almost every day. Almost—yes. Yes, because if we didn't go to his house he came to ours, either with his wife or alone. He was the brother my father loved the best. He always said to me: 'When I go I shall leave you with Juan; you must go to his house and obey him as if he was your father.' And last Sunday we all dined together."

"Anyway, you must realize that I only hid you here to prevent your being bothered by the police, and because it's nearer."

The tired flame of the untrimmed candle fluttered like the gaze of a shortsighted person. Angel Face felt himself enfeebled and diminished in stature in its light. Camila looked paler, more alone, and more seductive than ever in her little lemon-yellow frock.

"What are you thinking about?"

His voice was intimate and relaxed.

"About what my poor father must be suffering, on the run through unknown dark places—I'm not explaining myself properly—hungry, tired, thirsty and with no one to help him. May the Virgin go with him! I've kept her candle burning all day."

"You mustn't think of that sort of thing, don't go to meet misfortune; things will happen as it's written they will. You never guessed you would get to know me, nor I that I could be of use to your father!" He took one of her hands in his and she allowed him to stroke it as they both gazed at the Virgin's picture.

The favorite was thinking:

In the keyhole of heaven
You would fit neatly, for the locksmith
Printed your outline in snow
On a star, when you were born!

These lines were running through his head at the moment, just as if they embodied the rhythm now uniting their two hearts.

"You tell me that my father is going a long way away. When shall we know more?"

"I really haven't an idea, but it must be a matter of days."

"Many days?"

"No."

"Perhaps my Uncle Juan has had news of him."

"Very likely."

"You seem embarrassed when I talk about my uncle and aunt."

"What on earth can you mean? Not in the least. Quite the reverse. I realize if it wasn't for them my own responsibility would be greater. Where should I take you if not to them?"

Angel Face's tone of voice changed when he talked of her uncle, and could stop drawing imaginary pictures of the general's flight while all the time expecting to see him return handcuffed and under escort, or as cold as marble on a bloodstained hurdle.

Suddenly the door opened. It was La Masacuata in a state of great agitation. The bars of the door clattered to the floor. A gust of air nearly blew the candle out.

"You must excuse me for interrupting you and coming in so suddenly. They've arrested Lucio! I'd just heard the news from a friend when this paper arrived. He's in prison. It's that Genaro Rodas' doing! What a man! I've been worrying my head off the whole blessed evening! Every few moments my heart was going pom-pom, pom-pom, pom-pom. That fellow went and told them it was you and Lucio who carried off the young lady from her house."

The favorite could do nothing to prevent the catastrophe. A handful of words had been enough to cause the explosion. He and Camila and their unlucky love affair had been sent sky-high in a second, in less than a second. When Angel Face began taking stock of the situation, Camila was lying face downwards on the bed, weeping inconsolably; the innkeeper was still describing the abduction in detail, without the smallest idea that she was precipitating a whole little world into the abyss; and as for him, he felt as if he were being buried alive with his eyes open.

After crying for some time, Camila got up like a sleep-walker and asked the barkeeper for a wrap so that she could go out.

"And if you're really a gentleman," she said, turning to Angel Face, when the woman had handed her a shawl, "please take me to my Uncle Juan's house."

The favorite wanted to say what could not be said: words inexpressible by the lips, but which dance in the eyes of those whose dearest hopes have been frustrated by fate.

"Where's my hat?" he asked, his voice hoarse with anxious swallowing.

And before leaving he turned, hat in hand, for a last look at the inn room which had just seen the shipwreck of his dreams.

"But I'm afraid," he objected as he was just going out, "I'm afraid it may be too late."

"If we were going to a strange house it would be, but we're going to my house; any of my uncles' houses are home to me."

Angel Face held her back gently by the arm, and, as if wrenching the words from himself by force, told her the brutal truth:

"You mustn't think of your Uncle Juan's house any more; he doesn't want to hear anything about you, or the general, he disowns him as a brother. He told me so today."

"But you said just now that you hadn't seen them, that you'd only made an appointment to go! What am I to think? You forget what you told me a moment ago and say dreadful things about my uncle, so as to keep me a prisoner here in this inn and prevent my escaping! You say my uncle and aunt didn't want to hear anything about us, that they wouldn't take me into their house? Well, you must be mad. Come there with me and I'll prove the contrary to you!"

"I'm not mad. You must believe me. I'd give my life to prevent exposing you to humiliation, and if I lied it was because—I don't know. I think I lied out of tenderness to you, to spare you the pain you're feeling now as long as I could. I meant to go back tomorrow and renew my entreaties, pull some other string, beg them not to abandon you in the street; but that's impossible now that you're going away. That's impossible now."

The brightly lit streets seemed lonelier than ever. The innkeeper followed them outside holding the candle that had been burning in front of the Virgin, to light their first steps. The wind blew it out; the little flame seemed to cross itself as it died.

CHAPTER XVIII

Knocking

Rat-tat-tat! Rat-tat-tat!

The sound of knocking ran through the house like an exploding squib, waking the dog, which instantly began to bark in the direction of the street. The noise had burned into its dreams. Camila turned to look at Angel Face—she felt safe here in the doorway of her Uncle Juan's house—and said to him proudly:

"He's barking because he doesn't recognize me! Ruby! Ruby!" she cried to the dog, but it went on barking. "Ruby! Ruby! It's me! Don't you know me, Ruby? Run and get them to come and open the door."

And turning to Angel Face again:

"We must just wait a moment!"

"Yes, yes, don't worry about me. We'll wait."

He spoke disconnectedly, like someone who has lost everything and is indifferent to everything.

"Perhaps they haven't heard; we must knock louder."

And she raised and let fall the knocker a good many times; it was a brass knocker in the shape of a hand.

"The servants must be asleep; they've had plenty of time to come to the door! My father used to sleep badly and he was quite right when he said, after a bad night, 'Oh, if I could only sleep like a servant!'"

Ruby gave the only sign of life in the whole house. His barking came sometimes from the hall, sometimes from the patio. He rushed tirelessly to and fro as the blows from the knocker fell like stones into the silence, tightening Camila's throat with anxiety.

"It's very odd!" she remarked, without leaving the door. "They really must be asleep. I'll knock harder still and see if that'll bring them."

Rat-tat-tat-tat! Rat-tat-tat-tat!

"Now they'll come. They can't have heard before."

"The neighbors are going to be the first to come!" said Angel Face, for although they could see nothing in the mist, they heard the sound of doors opening.

"There can't be anything wrong, can there?"

"Oh no! Knock, knock, don't worry!"

"Let's wait a moment and see if they're coming now."

And Camila began to count in her head to pass the time: "One, two, three, four, five, six, seven, eight, nine, ten, eleven, twelve, thirteen, fourteen, fifteen, sixteen, seventeen, eighteen, nineteen, twenty, twenty-one, twenty-two, twenty-three, twenty-three, twenty-three . . . twe-nty-four . . . twe-nty-five . . ."

"They're not coming!"

"Twenty-six, twenty-seven, twenty-eight, twenty-nine, thir-ty, thirty-one, thirty-two, thirty-three, thirty-four, thirty-five," she was terrified of reaching fifty, "thirty-six . . . thirty-seven . . . thirty-seven, thirty-eight."

Suddenly, without knowing why, she realized that what Angel Face had told her about her Uncle Juan was true, and seized with anguish and alarm she knocked again and again. Rat-tat-tat! She wouldn't let go of the knocker. Rat-tat-tat-tat! It's impossible! Rat-tat-tattattattat tattattattattattattat.

She got the same reply as before: the dog's ceaseless barking. What could she have done, unknown to herself, to prevent them opening the door to her? She knocked again. She put fresh hope into every blow of the knocker. What would become of her if they left her in the street? The mere thought made her strength fail her. She knocked and knocked. She knocked furiously, as if she were hammering away at an enemy's head. Her feet felt heavy, her mouth had a bitter taste, her tongue was rough as a dish-cloth and her teeth tingled with fear.

There was the creak of an opening window and she thought she heard voices. Her whole body came to life. They were coming at last, thank God! She was glad to be leaving this man whose black eyes sparkled with diabolical fire like a cat's—this individual who repelled her in spite of his angelic beauty. During this brief instant, the world of the house and the world of the street, separated from one another by the door, brushed against one another like two extinct stars.

A house makes it possible to eat one's bread in privacy—and bread eaten in privacy is sweet, it teaches one wisdom—a house enjoys the safety of permanence and of being socially approved. It is like a family portrait with the father wearing his best tie, the mother displaying her finest jewels and the children's hair brushed with real eau de Cologne. The street, on the other hand, is an unstable, dangerous, adventurous world, false as a looking-glass— the public laundry of all the dirty linen in the neighborhood.

How often she had played in that doorway as a child! How many times too, while her father and Uncle Juan talked business just before they parted, she had amused herself staring up at the eaves of the neighboring houses, silhouetted like scaly backbones against the blue sky.

"Didn't you hear them come to that window? Surely you did? But they don't open the door. Or—can we have mistaken the house? That would be funny!"

And letting go the knocker she stepped down from the pavement to look at the front of the house. She had made no mistake. It was indeed her Uncle Juan's house. "Juan Canales, Engineer," said a metal plate on the door. She screwed up her face like a child's and burst into tears. Her tears ran down like galloping horses, bringing with them from the innermost recesses of her brain the somber thought that Angel Face had spoken the truth as they left the Two-Step Tavern. She didn't want to believe it even though it was true.

The streets were swathed in mist, a mist which smelled of verdure and stuccoed the houses in pale greenish cream.

"Please come with me to see my other uncles. We'll go and see my Uncle Luis first, shall we?"

"Wherever you say."

"Then come along." The tears were falling from her eyes like rain. "They don't want to let me in here."

They set off. At every step she turned her head—she couldn't give up hope that they would open the door at the last moment. Angel Face walked in gloomy silence. He would go and see Don Juan Canales again; such outrageous behavior could not be left unavenged. The dog's barks were still heard, growing more distant with every step. Soon this last comfort vanished. Even the dog was now inaudible. Opposite the Mint they met a drunken postman, throwing his letters into the street as he went along like a sleepwalker. He could hardly stand. Every now and then he raised his arms in the air and burst into a cackle like a farmyard fowl, as he struggled to disentangle the buttons of his uniform from the streams of his saliva. Camila and Angel Face, moved by an identical impulse, began to pick up the letters and put them in his bag, at the same time advising him not to throw them away again.

"Tha-ank you; tha-ank you ve-ry much!" he enunciated carefully, leaning against the wall of the Mint. Then, when the letters were all back in his bag and they had left him, he moved on again, singing:

> To get up to heaven
> You must have
> a tall ladder and
> also a little one!

And half-singing, half-talking, he began on another tune:

> Ascend, ascend
> Oh Virgin to heaven,
> ascend, ascend,
> you will ascend to your kingdom.

"When Saint John gives the signal, I, Gup-Gup-Gumercindo Solares, will stop being a postman, will stop being a postman, will stop being a postman . . ."

And then, singing again:

> When I die
> Who will bury me?
> Only the Sisters
> Of Charity!

"Oh, you're no good, you're no good, you're no good!"

He staggered away into the mist. He was a little man with a big head. His uniform was too big for him, and his cap too small.

Meanwhile Don Juan Canales had been doing his utmost to get in touch with his brother José Antonio. The telephone exchange wouldn't answer and he began to be sick of the noise of the handle as he wound it. At last a sepulchral voice answered. He asked for Don José Antonio Canales' house, and contrary to his expectations at once heard the voice of his eldest brother come over the line.

"Yes, yes, it's Juan speaking . . . I thought you didn't recognize me . . . Well, look here . . . the girl and that fellow, yes, of course, of course . . . certainly . . . yes, yes, . . . what d'you say? No! We didn't let them in! The very idea! And no doubt they went straight to you from here . . . What? What's that? Just as I thought. We were trembling in our shoes by the time they left. The same with you? And it's not good for your wife to be alarmed; my wife wanted to go to the door, but I wouldn't let her. Naturally! Naturally! That's obvious! Yes, and have all the neighborhood up in arms! Yes, indeed. And even worse here. They must have been furious. And I suppose they went to Luis after you? No? No? Oh well, they will . . ."

Beginning as a faint pallor, rapidly brightening to a subdued lemon color, then to orange, and then to the red of a newly-lit fire mixed with the dull gold of the first flames, the dawn surprised them in the street as they came away from knocking in vain on Don José Antonio's front door.

At every step Camila kept repeating: "I'll manage somehow!"

Her teeth were chattering with cold.

Her large tearful eyes gazed at the dawn with unconscious bitterness. She walked uncertainly like someone pursued by fate and unaware of what she was doing.

The birds were greeting the dawn in the public parks and in the little patio gardens. A celestial concert of musical trills arose into the heavenly blue morning sky, while the roses unfolded and the chiming bells wishing God good morning alternated with the soft thuds of meat being chopped up in the butchers' shops; the rising notes of the cocks, as they beat time with their wings, with the muted report of bread falling into the bakers' trays; and the voices and footsteps of all-night revelers with the noise of a door opening, as some little old woman set off to Communion or a servant hurried out to get bread for a traveler with a train to catch.

Day was dawning . . .

The turkey-buzzards were quarreling and pecking one another over the corpse of a cat. The dogs were running panting after the bitches, with burning eyes and tongues hanging out. A mongrel limped by with its tail between its legs, turning to cast a sad, frightened look behind it, with teeth bared. The dogs left Niagara-like patterns along all the walls and doors.

Day was dawning . . .

The parties of Indians who swept the central streets of the town at nights were returning home, one after another, like phantoms dressed in serge, laughing and talking in a language which sounded like a cicada's song in the morning silence. They carried their brooms under their arms like umbrellas. Teeth as white as almond paste in copper faces. Bare feet. Rags. Sometimes one of them would stop at the edge of the pavement and blow his nose by squeezing it between thumb and forefinger and leaning forward. They all took their hats off as they passed a church door.

Day was dawning . . .

Inaccessible monkey-puzzle trees, like green spiders-webs thrown out to catch the disappearing stars. Crowds going to Communion. Whistle of railway engines from afar.

La Masacuata was delighted to see them come back together. She hadn't been able to sleep a wink all night for worrying, and she was on the point of setting off for the prison with Lucio Vasquez's breakfast.

Angel Face said goodbye to Camila, who was weeping over the unbelievable misfortune that had befallen her.

"I'll see you soon," he said without knowing why; there was nothing more for him to do here.

And as he went out he felt his eyes fill with tears for the first time since his mother's death.

CHAPTER XIX

Accounts and Chocolate

The Judge Advocate General finished drinking his chocolate with rice, tipping the cup up twice so as to drain it to the dregs; then he wiped his grayish moustache on the sleeve of his shirt, and moving closer to the lamp, peered into the bowl to see if it was really empty.

It was impossible to say, when he had taken off his collar, whether this Bachelor of Law was a man or a woman as he sat there among his official papers and his grimy law books, silent and ugly, short-sighted and greedy, like a tree made of official stamped paper—a tree whose roots drew their nourishment from all social classes down to the most humble and poverty-stricken.

When he looked up from the chocolate bowl which he had been exploring with his fingers to see if there was any left, he saw the servant come in at the only door

of his study—a spectral figure dragging her feet slowly one after the other, one after the other, as if her shoes were too large for her.

"You don't mean to say you've drunk your chocolate already?"

"Yes, and God bless you for it, it was delicious! I always love feeling the last of it slip down my gullet."

"Where did you put the cup?" asked the servant, hunting about among the books which cast a shadow on the table.

"Over there! Can't you see it?"

"And while I remember it, just look at those drawers full of official stamped paper! Tomorrow if you like I'll go out and see if I can sell it."

"Well be careful not to let anyone know. People are so malicious."

"I wasn't born yesterday! There must be more than four hundred sheets at twenty-five centavos there, and two hundred at fifty. I was counting them while my iron was heating up only this afternoon."

A loud knock on the street door made her break off.

"What a way to knock! The fools!" grumbled the Judge Advocate.

"Yes they always knock like that. Who can it be this time? I often hear them right over in the kitchen."

She was on her way to see who was at the door as she said these last words. The poor creature looked like an umbrella, with her small head and long faded skirts.

"I'm not at home!" shouted the Judge Advocate General. "Wait a moment. Better go to the window . . ."

After a few moments the old woman returned, still with dragging feet, and handed him a letter.

"They're waiting for an answer."

The Judge Advocate tore open the envelope crossly, glanced at the little card inside it, and said in a milder tone:

"Say I've received the note!"

She went off, with dragging feet, to give the message to the boy who had brought it, afterwards shutting and fastening the window.

It was some time before she returned; she was seeing that the doors were locked. She had not yet taken away the dirty chocolate cup.

Meanwhile, her master was lolling in an armchair, carefully re-reading the little card he had just received, down to the last full-stop and comma. It was from a colleague who was making him a proposition.

"Concepcion Gold-Tooth," wrote the lawyer Vidalitas, "a friend of the President's and proprietress of a well-known brothel, came to see me this morning at my office to tell me that she had seen a pretty young woman in the Casa Nueva prison who would do for her establishment. She offers 10,000 pesos for her. As I know the prisoner is held on your orders, I'm writing to ask if it would be inconvenient for you to accept this small sum and hand over the woman to my client."

"If there's nothing more you want, I'll go to bed."

"No, nothing, goodnight."

"Goodnight. May the souls in Purgatory rest in peace!"

As the servant went away with dragging feet, the Judge Advocate was running over the sum he would get from the proposed transaction, figure by figure—one, nought, nought, nought—ten thousand pesos!

The old woman reappeared:

"I forgot to tell you that the priest sent to say he'll be saying Mass earlier than usual tomorrow."

"Ah yes! Tomorrow's Saturday. Call me when the bells start ringing, will you? Because I got no sleep last night and I may not wake."

"Very well, I'll wake you."

So saying she went slowly away with dragging feet. But she was soon back again. She had forgotten to carry away the dirty cup to the sink. She was already undressed when she remembered. "How lucky I remembered," she muttered to herself. "Just supposing I hadn't!" She struggled into her shoes. "Just supposing I hadn't." And she ended up with: "Well, thank God I did!" muffled by a sigh. If she hadn't been incapable of leaving a piece of crockery unwashed she would have been in bed by now.

The Judge Advocate was unaware of the old woman's final entry and exit; he was too deeply absorbed in reading his latest masterpiece: the indictment concerning General Eusebio Canales' escape. There were four accused: Fedina de Rodas, Genaro Rodas, Lucio Vasquez, and—he passed his tongue over his lips, for he had a score to settle with the last of the four—Miguel Angel Face.

The abduction of the general's daughter was like the black cloud expelled by a cuttlefish when attacked—merely a ruse to deceive the watchful authorities, he reflected. Fedina Rodas' statement proved this conclusively. The house was empty when she arrived there in search of the general at six in the morning. Her statement had made an impression of truth on him from the first, and if he put on the screw a little it was just to make quite certain: what she said convicted Angel Face irrefutably. The house was already empty by six o'clock, and since it appeared from the information given by the police that the general arrived home exactly at midnight, it followed that the wanted man must have escaped at two in the morning while the other was making a pretense of carrying off his daughter.

What a disillusionment for the President when he discovered that his most trusted confidant had arranged and supervised the flight of one of his bitterest enemies! What would he do when he learned that the intimate friend of Colonel Parrales Sonriente was concerned in the flight of one of his assassins?

Although he knew them by memory, he read and re-read all the articles relating to accomplices in the military statute-book, and his basilisk eyes shone with pleasure to find in every other line of this legal volume the following little phrase: "pain of death" or else its variant "capital punishment."

"Ah, Don Miguelin Miguelito, at last I have you in my power and for just as long as I want! When you insulted me yesterday at the Palace I never thought we should meet again so soon! And there will be endless turns of the screw of my vengeance I promise you!"

With his thoughts inflamed by the idea of revenge, and his heart a ball of cold steel, he went up the steps of the Palace at eleven o'clock next morning. He was carrying his indictment and a warrant for the arrest of Angel Face.

"Look here, Mr. Judge Advocate," said the President after the facts had been set before him, "I must ask you to drop this case and listen to me: neither the Señora de Rodas nor Miguel is guilty; you must set the woman free and countermand the arrest. It is you who are the guilty ones, you fools! Government servants indeed! You are servants in no sense of the word! What use are you? None whatever! At the first sign of an attempt at flight the police should have riddled General Canales with bullets. Those were their orders! But the police can't see an open house without their fingers itching to loot it! It's your contention that Angel Face played a part in Canales' escape? He was not planning his escape but his death. But the police are such a lot of officious fools . . . you can go. And as to the other two accused men, Vasquez and Rodas, they can take what's coming to them. They're a pair of ruffians, especially Vasquez, who knows more about the affair than he has any right to. You can go."

CHAPTER XX

Wolves of the Same Pack

All Genaro Rodas' tears had not been enough to wash away his recollection of the expression in the dying Zany's eyes, and he now stood before the Judge Advocate General with hanging head, his last spark of courage destroyed by his family misfortunes and the despondency into which loss of liberty casts even the most hardened. The Judge Advocate gave orders for his handcuffs to be removed, and told him to come closer in the tone of voice used to servants.

"My boy," he said, after a silence so long that it amounted to an accusation, "I know everything, and I'm only questioning you because I want to hear from your own lips how this beggar died in the Cathedral Porch."

"What happened . . ." began Genaro precipitately, and then stopped, as if afraid of what he was about to say.

"Yes, what happened . . . ?"

"Oh, Señor, for the love of God don't do anything to me! Oh no, Señor, I'll tell you the truth but don't do anything to me, for mercy's sake, Señor!"

"Don't be afraid, my boy. The law may treat hardened criminals severely, but not a good chap like you. Stop worrying and tell me the truth."

"Oh I'm so afraid you'll do something to me!"

He writhed in a supplicating manner as he spoke, as if to defend himself from some threat floating in the air around him.

"No, no, come along now!"

"What happened? It was that night —you know the one—the night I'd arranged to meet Lucio Vasquez by the Cathedral and I went up through the native quarter. You see, Señor, I wanted a job and this Lucio had told me he could get me one in the Secret Police. We met, as I say, and it was 'How goes it?' and this and that; then this fellow asked me to have a drink in the bar a little way beyond the Plaza de Armas, called The Lion's Awakening. But one drink turned into two, three, four, five drinks, and to make a long story short . . ."

"Yes, yes," agreed the Judge Advocate, turning to look at the freckled clerk who was taking down the accused man's statement.

"Well then, you see, it turned out he hadn't managed to get me the job in the Secret Police. Then I said it didn't matter. Then—oh yes, I remember, he paid for the drinks. And then the two of us went out again to the Cathedral Porch, where Lucio had to go on duty, so he told me, and keep an eye open for a dumb chap with rabies, who had to be shot. So I said to him: 'I'm off!' When I got to the Porch, I was a bit behind him. He crossed the road slowly, but when he reached the entrance to the Porch he came running out again. I ran after him, thinking someone was chasing us. Vasquez caught hold of something which was up against the wall—it was this dumb chap, who began yelling as if the wall had fallen on top of him when he felt himself caught. Then Vasquez pulled out his revolver and never said a word but let him have it, and then again. Oh no, Señor, I wasn't the guilty one; don't do anything to me, I didn't kill him! Just from looking for a job, Señor—you see what happened? I'd better have stayed a carpenter. Whatever got into me to want to be a policeman?"

Once again the Judge Advocate's cold gaze seemed to meet Rodas full in the eye. Without changing his expression, the Judge Advocate silently pressed a bell.

Footsteps were heard and several jailers preceded by a chief warder appeared at the door.

"Warder, see that this man gets two hundred lashes, will you?"

The Judge Advocate's voice did not change in the very smallest degree as he gave the order; it was as if a bank manager had given instructions for two hundred pesos to be paid to one of his clients.

Rodas did not understand. He raised his head and looked at the barefooted myrmidons who were waiting for him. And he understood still less when he saw their calm impassive faces devoid of any trace of surprise. The clerk turned his freckled countenance and expressionless eyes towards him. The warder said something to the Judge Advocate. The Judge Advocate said something to the warder. Rodas was deaf. Rodas understood nothing. But he felt as if he was going to shit in his trousers when the warder shouted to him to go into the next room, a long hall with a vaulted roof, and gave him a brutal shove as he came within reach.

When the other prisoner, Lucio Vasquez, came into the room, the Judge Advocate was still fulminating against Rodas.

"It's no use treating that sort well! What they need is the stick and then some more of the stick!"

Although Vasquez felt he was among his own sort, he didn't trust them an inch, especially when he heard this remark. It was too serious a matter to have had a hand in General Canales' flight, even against his will—and what a fool he had been!

"Your name?"

"Lucio Vasquez."

"You were born where?"

"Here."

"In prison?"

"No, of course not: in the capital."

"Married? Single?"

"Single all my life!"

"Answer the questions properly! Profession or occupation?"

"Employed in Government service."

"You were arrested?"

"Yes."

"For what offense?"

"Murder when on patrol."

"Age?"

"I have no age."

"What d'you mean you have no age?"

"I don't know how old I am; but put me down as thirty-five, if I must have an age!"

"What do you know about the murder of the Zany?"

The Judge Advocate General hurled this question at the prisoner point-blank, staring him full in the eye, but contrary to his expectations his words produced no effect on Vasquez's assurance, and he answered quite naturally and almost with satisfaction:

"What I know about the murder of the Zany is that I killed him myself"; and with his hand on his breast he repeated so that there should be no mistake: "I did!"

"Do you take this for some sort of a joke?" roared the Judge Advocate. "Or can you be so ignorant that you don't realize it may cost you your life?"

"Perhaps."

"What d'you mean 'perhaps'?"

For a moment the lawyer didn't know what attitude to take. He was disconcerted by Vasquez's placidity, his high guitar-like voice, his sharp eyes. To gain time he turned to the clerk.

"Write . . ."

And in a tremulous voice he added:

"Write down that Lucio Vasquez states that he murdered the Zany, with Genaro Rodas as accomplice."

"I've written that already," muttered the clerk between his teeth.

"It's clear to me," put in Lucio calmly, and in a slightly bantering tone which made the lawyer bite his lips, "that the Judge Advocate doesn't know much about this affair. What does that statement amount to? Anyone could see that I wouldn't have dirtied my hands for a slobbering idiot like that . . ."

"Show respect for the tribunal, or you'll suffer for it!"

"What I was saying was altogether to the point. I'm saying that I wouldn't have been so daft as to kill that fellow just for the pleasure of killing him, and that I did it because I was obeying the President's explicit orders . . ."

"Silence, you liar! Ah, our task would be easy if . . ."

He left the sentence unfinished, because at this moment the jailers came in dragging Rodas, with dangling arms, and legs trailing along the floor like a rag doll or Saint Veronica's veil.

"How many did you give him?" the Judge Advocate asked the warder, who was smiling at the clerk, with his whiplash rolled round his neck like a monkey's tail.

"Two hundred!"

"Well—"

The clerk came to the Judge Advocate's rescue:

"I should give him another two hundred," he muttered, running the words together so that the others shouldn't hear.

The Judge Advocate took his advice:

"Yes, Chief, see that he gets another two hundred while I attend to this fellow."

"What a nerve! That's just what one would expect from someone with a face like an old bicycle seat!" thought Vasquez.

The jailers retraced their steps dragging their wretched burden and followed by the chief warder. They threw him down on a mattress in the corner where punishment was administered. Four of them held his hands and feet, while the others beat him. The warder kept the count. Rodas shrank before the first strokes, but he was at the end of his tether now and could not struggle and howl with pain as he had done when they began beating him a few minutes ago. Beneath the blows of the wet, flexible, greenish-yellow quince twigs the clotted blood oozed out of the wounds left by the first session, which had already begun to dry up. Strangled cries as of an animal dying without being clearly conscious of its pain were his final protest. He buried his face in the mattress, his expression contorted, his hair in confusion. His piercing cries were mingled with the panting of the jailers, whom the warder punished with his whip for not hitting hard enough.

"Our task would be easy, Lucio Vasquez, if we allowed every citizen who committed a crime to go free if he simply asserted it had been done on the President's orders! What proof have you? The President isn't a madman, to give such an order. Where is the paper showing that he instructed you to treat this poor wretch in such a wicked and cowardly manner?"

Vasquez turned pale and put his trembling hands in his trouser pockets while he searched for an answer.

"When you're before a tribunal you must support your statements with documents, you know; otherwise where should we be? Where is the order you received?"

"Well, you see, I haven't got the order. I gave it back. The President must know that."

"How did that happen? And why did you give it back?"

"Because it said at the bottom that it must be given back after the order was carried out! I wasn't to keep it, you see? I think—you understand—"

"Not a word, not one word more! Trying to humbug me with your big talk about the President! I'm not a schoolboy to believe that kind of foolishness, you blackguard! A person's statement is no proof, except in cases specified in the Legal Code, when a police statement can function as full proof. But I'm not going to give you a lecture on Criminal Law. And that's enough—enough; I've said quite enough . . ."

"Well, if you don't want to believe me, go and ask him; perhaps you'll believe what he tells you. Perhaps I wasn't with you when the beggars accused—"

"Silence! Or I'll have you beaten till you shut up! I can just see myself going to ask the President! I tell you, Vasquez, that you know a great deal more about the matter than you have any right to, and your head is in danger!"

Lucio bent his head as if guillotined by the Judge Advocate General's words. The wind was roaring angrily against the windows.

CHAPTER XXI

Vicious Circle

Angel Face tore off his collar and tie in a fury. Nothing could be stupider, he thought, than the little explanations people invented for the behavior of others. The behavior of others . . . of others! Sometimes their criticism would amount to no more than an acrimonious muttering. Anything in one's favor was suppressed, the rest exaggerated. What a lot of filth! It was as painful as a brush on a sore place. And a veiled reproach, disguised as ordinary friendly or even charitable comment, could wound one more deeply still, like a brush with extra fine hairs. Even the servants! To hell with all tittle-tattlers!

A tug, and all the buttons flew off his shirt. He had ripped it down the front. It was as if he had torn open his breast. His servants had been telling him in great detail what people were saying about his love affair. Men who are reluctant to marry for fear of sharing their house with a woman who repeats what everyone says about them except the good things, like a schoolgirl on prize day, end by hearing it all from the lips of their servants, as Angel Face had done.

He drew the curtains of his room before finally taking off his shirt. He badly needed sleep or (at least) that his room should appear to exclude the coming day—a day, as he told himself bitterly, which could not fail to be as bad as the last.

"Sleep!" he repeated as he sat on the edge of his bed, unbuttoning his trousers, with no shoes or socks on and his shirt open. "Oh, but what an idiot! I've not taken off my jacket!"

Walking on his heels with his toes curled up so as to keep the soles of his feet away from the cold concrete floor, he succeeded in hanging his coat on the back of a chair, and then returned to his bed by means of a series of rapid, chilly little hops on one foot like a heron. Then bang! down he came, defeated by this brute of a floor. The legs of his trousers revolved in the air like the hands of an enormous clock. The floor seemed to be made of ice rather than concrete. How horrible! Ice with salt on it. Ice made of tears. He jumped into bed as if from an iceberg on to a lifeboat. He wanted to escape from everything that had happened, and as he fell on the bed he imagined that it was an island, a white island surrounded by semi-darkness, and by motionless pulverized events. He was going to forget, to sleep, to cease to exist. He was tired of arguments that could be assembled and taken to pieces like the parts of a machine. To the devil with the tortuosities of common sense! Better far unreasoning sleep, that gentle stupor, at first blue in color, then green and

afterwards black, which distills itself from the eyes throughout the organism and annihilates the personality. Oh, desire! The desired object is at once possessed and not possessed. It is like a gold nightingale, caged by our ten joined fingers. Integral, restorative sleep, free from intrusions, entering through the mirrors of the eyes and leaving by the windows of the nose—that was what he longed for, sleep as relaxed as that of the old days. Soon he became aware that sleep was high above him, above the roof of his house, in the clear light of day—that unforgettable day. He turned on his face. No use. On his left side, to quiet the beating of his heart. On his right side. It was all the same. A hundred hours separated him from the perfect sleep of the days when he went to bed free from sentimental preoccupations. His instinct accused him of suffering these torments because he had not taken Camila by force.

The dark side of life looms so close at times that suicide seems the only means of escaping it. "I shall cease to exist!" he thought. And trembled inwardly. He touched one foot with the other. He was troubled by the absence of nails on the cross from which he was hanging. "There's something about drunkards walking that reminds one of hanged men," he thought, "and hanged men remind one of drunkards when they kick their legs or swing in the wind." His instinct accused him. A drunkard's sex. A hanged man's sex. And you, Angel Face, are no better! . . .

"An animal makes no mistake in its sexual reckonings," he thought. "We piss children into the graveyard. The trumpets of Judgment Day—very well, it won't be a trumpet. Golden scissors will cut through the continuous stream of children. We men are like pigs' tripes stuffed with mincemeat by a demon butcher to make sausages. And when I mastered my own nature so as to save

Camila from my desire, I left a part of myself unstuffed; that's why I feel empty, uneasy, angry, ill, caught in a trap. Woman is the mincemeat into which man stuffs himself like a pig's tripes for his own gratification. What vulgarity!"

The sheets clung to him like skirts. Skirts unendurably soaked with sweat.

The Tree of Dreadful Night must feel pain in its leaves. "Oh my poor head!" The liquid sound of the carillon. Bruges, the city of the dead. Corkscrews of silk round his neck. "Never . . ." But there's a phonograph somewhere in the neighborhood. I've never heard it. I didn't know it existed. First news of it. They've got a dog in the house at the back. There must be two. But here they have a phonograph. Only one. "Between the phonograph's trumpet here, and the dogs in the house at the back listening to their master's voice, is my house, my head, myself. To be close and to be far away is to be neighbors. That's the worst of being someone's neighbor. But as for them they've got work to do. They play the phonograph, and speak ill of everyone. I can imagine what they say about me. What a couple of dried-up aniseeds! They can say what they like about me, what do I care? but about her—! If I can prove that they've said as much as a single word against her I'll make them members of the Young Liberals. I've often threatened to do it but today I think I will. That'll embitter their lives! But perhaps I won't; they're not worth it. I can hear them saying everywhere: 'He kidnapped the poor girl after midnight, he took her to an inn belonging to a procuress and violated her; the secret police guarded the door so that no one should come in!' They'll imagine the scene with me undressing her, tearing her clothes, and Camila like a bird caught in a trap with trembling flesh and feathers. 'And he took her by force,' they'll say, 'without caressing her, and with his eyes shut as if he were committing a crime or swallowing a purge.' If they only knew that it wasn't like that at all, and that here I am half repenting of my chivalrous behavior! If they realized that everything they say is false. It's the girl they'd really like to be imagining. Imagining her with me, with me and with themselves. Themselves undressing her, themselves doing what they think I did. The young Liberals are too good for such a pair of angels. I must think of something worse. The ideal punishment, since they are both bachelors—yes they really are old bachelors—would be to saddle them with two of those women who hang round the President. That would do fine! But one of them is pregnant. That doesn't matter. Better still. When the President arranges a marriage it doesn't do to look at the bride's belly. So let them marry out of fear, let them marry . . ."

He curled himself up in bed with his arms between his legs, and buried his head in his pillows, seeking for some respite from the agonizing lightning-flashes of his ideas. There were physical shocks in store for him in the cold corners of the bed, giving him temporary relief from the reckless flight of his thoughts. In the end he pursued these welcome if painful sensations even further by stretching his legs outside the sheet till they touched the brass bar at the foot of the bed. Then he gradually opened his eyes. As he did so he seemed to be breaking a fine seam between his lashes. He was suspended from his eyes; they were fixed to the ceiling like cupping-glasses; he was weightless as the shadows, his bones flaccid, his ribs reduced to cartilage and his head to putty. A cotton-wool hand was going through the motions of knocking in the semi-darkness. A sleep-walker's cotton-wool hand . . . The houses are made of knockers. The towns are forests of trees made of knockers . . .

[85]

Leaves of sound fell to the ground as she knocked. The tree-trunk of the door stood intact after the leaves of intact sound had fallen. There was nothing for her to do but knock . . . there was nothing for them to do but open the door . . . But they didn't open. She might have knocked down the door. Blow after blow, she might have knocked down the door; blow after blow, and then nothing; she might have knocked down the house . . .

"Who is it? What?"

"They have just brought the notification of a death."

"Yes, but don't take it to him, because he must be asleep. Put it here on his desk."

" 'Señor Joaquin Ceron died last night, fortified by the last Sacraments. His wife, children and other relatives have the sad duty of informing you of this fact, and beg you to commend his soul to God and attend the obsequies at the General Cemetery today at 4 P.M. The mourners will meet at the door of the cemetery. House of the deceased: Callejon del Carrocero.' "

He had involuntarily listened to one of his servants reading aloud the announcement of Don Joaquin Ceron's death.

He disengaged one of his arms from the sheets and folded it under his head. Don Juan Canales was marching through his brain dressed in feathers. He had snatched up four hearts made of wood and four Sacred Hearts, and was playing on them like castanets. And in his occiput he could feel Doña Judith, with her cyclopean breasts imprisoned in her creaking corsets made of metal thread and sand, and her hair dressed in the Pompeian style with a magnificent comb in it which made her look like a dragon. He was seized with cramp in the arm which was pillowing his head, and he stretched it cautiously, like a garment with a scorpion on it . . .

Cautiously . . .

A lift full of ants was ascending towards his shoulder. A lift full of magnetic ants was descending towards his elbow. The cramp went through the tube of his forearm and vanished among the shadows. His hand was a jet of water—a jet of double fingers. He felt ten thousand finger-nails gush to the floor.

"Poor little girl, knocking and knocking and then nothing . . . they are brutes, obstinate mules; if they open the door I'll spit in their faces. As sure as three and two make five . . . and five ten . . . and nine, nineteen, I'll spit in their faces. At first she knocked cheerfully, but in the end she seemed to be hitting the ground with a pick. She wasn't knocking, she was digging her own grave. What a desolate awakening! I'll go and see her tomorrow if I can. On the pretext of bringing her some news of her father. Oh, if only I could get news of him today. I could—although she may not believe what I say . . ."

"I do believe what you say! I'm convinced, I'm absolutely convinced that my uncles have disowned my father and told you that they never want to set eyes on me in their houses again." So Camila was thinking as she lay in bed with a pain in her side in La Masacuata's house, while in the tavern itself, separated from the bedroom by a partition made of old planks, sailcloth and bundles, the customers were discussing the events of the day between glasses: the general's flight, the abduction of his daughter, the favorite's activities. The barkeeper pretended not to hear anything they said but did not miss a word of it.

A sudden violent wave of faintness carried Camila far away from this pestilent crew. A sensation of falling vertically and in silence. After hesitating whether to cry out—which would be rash—or not cry out, and perhaps lose consciousness completely, she decided to cry out. Then a feeling of cold, as from the feathers of dead birds, enveloped her. La Masacuata ran to her at once—what had happened?—and so soon as she saw her lying there as green as bottle-glass, with her arms as stiff as broom-sticks, her jaws clenched and her eyes closed, she hurriedly took a mouthful of brandy from the nearest bottle and sprayed her face with it. She was so worried that she didn't hear her customers leave. She implored the Virgin of Chichinquira and all the saints not to let the girl die here in her house.

"When we parted this morning, what I said made her cry. What else could she do? When something that seems impossible comes true, one cries either from joy or sorrow . . ."

So thought Angel Face as he lay in bed, half asleep, half awake, aware of an angelic bluish conflagration, and gradually floating, asleep now, with the drift of his own thoughts, disembodied, without shape, like a warm current of air moved by his own breath . . .

As his body sank into nothingness, Camila alone remained—tall, sweet and cruel as a cross in a graveyard.

The god of Sleep, who sails the dark seas of reality, took Miguel on board one of his many boats. Invisible hands dragged him away from the gaping jaws of events—the hungry waves quarreling fiercely over morsels of their victims.

"Who is it?" asked Sleep.

"Miguel Angel Face," replied his invisible henchmen. Their impalpable hands emerged from the blackness like white shadows.

"Take him to the boat of . . ." Sleep hesitated. ". . . of lovers who have given up hope of loving and resigned themselves to being loved."

And Sleep's men were obediently conveying him to this boat, moving across

the blanket of unreality which covers life's daily happenings with a fine dust, when a sudden noise wrenched him from their grasp like a clutching hand . . .

The bed . . .

The servants . . .

No; the note, no. A child!

Angel Face rubbed his eyes and raised his head in terror. Two yards from his bed stood a child, so short of breath that he couldn't speak. At last he said:

"The innkeeper . . . sent me . . . to tell you . . . to go there . . . because . . . the young lady . . . is very ill."

If he had heard these words from the President himself the favorite could not have dressed himself so quickly. He rushed out into the street wearing the first hat he could seize from the rack, with his shoes unlaced and his tie untidily knotted.

"Who is it?" asked Sleep. His men had just fished up a fading rose from the dirty waters of life.

"Camila Canales," they replied.

"Very well, put her in the boat for unhappy lovers, if there's room . . ."

"What do you think, doctor?" Angel Face's voice had softened to a paternal tone. Camila was very seriously ill.

"I think the fever is likely to increase. She is developing pneumonia . . ."

CHAPTER XXII

The Living Tomb

Her son had ceased to exist. With the automaton-like movements of those who are losing their sanity in the chaos of their collapsing lives, Niña Fedina lifted the corpse to her fevered face. It weighed no more than a dried husk. She kissed it. She stroked it. Suddenly she went down on her knees—a pale yellow gleam was filtering in under the door—and bent down close to the crack through which this bright streak of dawn light was coming at ground level, to get a better view of all that was left of her little one.

With his little face puckered like the surface of a scar, two black circles round his eyes and clay-colored lips, he looked more like a swaddled fetus than a child of several months old. She took him hastily away from the light, pressing him against her swollen breasts. She reproached God in an inarticulate language made up of words and tears mixed; at moments her heart stopped beating and she would stammer out her grief in lament upon lament, like the hiccup of a dying person. "My son . . . son . . . son!"

The tears rolled down her expressionless face. She wept until she almost lost consciousness, forgetting her husband who had been threatened with death by starvation in prison if she didn't confess; ignoring her own physical pain, her ulcerated hands and breasts, her burning eyes, her bruised back; setting aside all worries about her neglected business; completely stunned and stupefied. And when her tears dried up and she could weep no more, she felt that she had become her son's tomb, that he was again enclosed in her womb, that his last endless sleep was hers. For an instant a sharp joy cut into the eternity of her suffering. The idea of being her son's tomb was like soothing balm to her heart. She felt the joy of Eastern women who are buried with their lovers. And a greater joy still, for she was not being buried with her son; she was his living tomb, his last cradle, the maternal lap, and they would wait together, closely united, until they were summoned to their God. Without drying her tears she tidied her hair as if she were getting ready for a party, and crouched in a corner of the cellar with the corpse pressed against her breasts and between her arms and legs.

Tombs do not embrace the dead, therefore she must not kiss him; but they press heavily, heavily upon them, as she was doing. They are stiff corselets of strength and tenderness, forcing the dead to suffer the irritation of worms and the heat of decomposition in silence and without moving. The wavering gleam from the crack under the door would only grow brighter every thousand years. The shadows, pursued by the rising light, clambered slowly up the walls like scorpions. They were walls of bones . . . bones tattooed with obscene drawings. Niña Fedina shut her eyes—tombs are dark inside—and did not utter a word nor a moan—tombs are silent.

It was the middle of the afternoon. A smell of cypresses washed by water from the sky. Swallows. A half moon. The streets were still bathed in sunlight and full of boisterous children. The schools were emptying a river of new lives into the town. Some were playing tag as they came out, zigzagging to and fro like flies. Others made a ring round two of their schoolmates who were attacking each other like fighting-cocks. Bloody noses, sniveling, tears. Some ran along knocking on doors. Others raided the confectioners' shops for treacle toffees, coconut cakes, almond tarts, and meringues, or fell like pirates on baskets of fruits, leaving them like empty dismantled boats. Behind came those who were busy swopping stamps or trying to cut a dash by smoking.

A cab stopped in front of the Casa Nueva and set down three young women and a very stout old one. There was no mistaking what they were from their appearance. The young women were dressed in bright-colored cotton stuffs, red stockings, yellow shoes with exaggeratedly high heels, skirts above the knee exposing knickers with long, dirty lace flounces, and blouses opening to the navel. Their hair was done in the Louis

[88]

XV style, as it was called, consisting of a large quantity of greasy curls tied on either side with a green or yellow ribbon; and the color of their cheeks was reminiscent of the red electric lamps over the doors of brothels. The old woman, who was dressed in black with a purple shawl, descended unsteadily from the carriage, clutching at the door with a fat hand thickly covered in diamonds.

"The cab is to wait, isn't it, Niña Chonita?" asked the youngest of the three Graces, raising her shrill voice so that even the stones in the deserted street could hear her.

"Yes, of course, it can wait here," answered the old woman.

And all four went into the Casa Nueva, where the concierge received them warmly.

Some other people were waiting in that inhospitable hall.

"Tell me, Chinta, is the secretary in?" the old woman asked the concierge.

"Yes, Doña Chon, he's just arrived."

"Then tell him, for heaven's sake, that if he'll see me I've brought him a little written order, which is very important to me."

The old woman remained silent while the concierge was away. For persons over a certain age the building still retained the atmosphere of a convent, for before becoming a prison for delinquents it had been a prison of love. Nothing but women. The sweet voices of the Teresian nuns floated down from its great walls like a flight of doves. There were no lilies to be seen, but the light was white, caressing and cheerful, and fasting and sackcloth had been replaced by the thorns of all the tortures that had flourished under the spiders-webs and the sign of the cross.

When the concierge returned, Doña Chon went in to explain her business to the secretary. She had already spoken to the Prison Governor. The Judge Advo-cate General had given orders that in exchange for ten thousand pesos—but that he did not mention—they should hand over to her the prisoner Fedina de Rodas, who from that moment would become an inmate of The Sweet Enchantment, as Doña Chon Gold-Tooth's brothel was called.

Two knocks echoed like thunder through the cell where the unhappy woman still sat crouched with her child, motionless, her eyes closed, almost without breathing. With a great effort she pretended not to hear. Then the bolts groaned. A prolonged squealing of disused hinges sounded in the silence like a lament. They opened the door and seized her roughly. She shut her eyes tightly so as not to see the light—tombs are dark inside. And so they dragged her away like a blind woman, with her little treasured corpse pressed to her breast. She had been bought like an animal for the basest of trades.

"She's acting dumb!"

"She's shutting her eyes so as not to see us!"

"She's ashamed, that's what it is!"

"Perhaps she doesn't want them to wake her baby!"

Such were the comments of Chon Gold-Tooth and the three Graces during the journey. The cab rumbled along the unsurfaced road, making an infernal noise. The driver, a Spaniard of Quixotic appearance, heaped insults on his horses; they were destined for the bull-ring, for he was a picador. Sitting beside him, Niña Fedina made the short journey from the Casa Nueva to the houses of ill-fame (as in the song) in total ignorance of her surroundings, without moving her eyelids or her lips, but clutching her child to her with all her strength.

While Doña Chon paid off the cab the others helped Fedina to get down and pushed her with friendly hands inside The Sweet Enchantment.

One or two clients, nearly all soldiers, were spending the night in the saloon of the brothel.

"What time is it, you there, eh?" Doña Chon called to the barman as she came in.

One of the soldiers answered:

"Twenty past six, Doña Chompipa."

"So you're here, you old troublemaker, are you? I didn't notice you!"

"And it's twenty five past by this clock," put in the barman.

They were all interested in the new girl. They all wanted to spend the night with her. Fedina still obstinately maintained a tomblike silence, with her child's body clasped in her arms; she kept her eyes shut, she felt cold and heavy as stone.

"Go along," Gold-Tooth said to the three Graces, "take her to the kitchen and get Manuela to give her a bite to eat, and make her tidy herself up a bit."

An artillery captain with pale blue eyes went up to the new girl to feel her legs. But one of the three Graces defended her. Then another soldier put his arms around her as if she had been a palm-tree trunk, rolling his eyes and showing his splendid Indian's teeth, like a dog with a bitch in heat. And afterwards he kissed her, rubbing her icy cheek, salt with dried tears, with his brandy-flavored lips.

These were good times for both barracks and brothel! The warmth of the whores was a compensation for the cold of the shooting-range.

"Now then, you old trouble-maker, you womanizer, be quiet, will you?" interrupted Doña Chon, putting an end to this indecent behavior. "Ah well, we'll have to tie you up!"

Fedina didn't defend herself from this lustful manhandling, but contented herself with pressing together her eyelids and lips to protect her tomblike blindness and silence from assault, while she clutched her dead child to her and rocked him in her arms as if he were asleep.

They led her to a little patio, where the afternoon was gradually drowning in a fountain. There was the sound of women moaning, weak voices, whispering of invalids, schoolgirls, prisoners or nuns, affected laughter, harsh little cries and the tread of stockinged feet. Someone threw a pack of cards out of the door of a room, and it fell in a fan on the floor. No one knew who had done it. A woman with dishevelled hair put her head out through a hatch, stared at the cards as if they represented Fate itself, and wiped a tear from her pale cheek.

A red lantern hung over the street door of The Sweet Enchantment. It looked like the inflamed eye of an animal. Men and stones took on a sinister hue. The mystery of the developing-room. Men came to bathe themselves in this red light like victims of smallpox hoping to cure their scars. They exposed their faces to the light shamefacedly, as if they were drinking blood, and afterwards returned to the street lights, to the white light of the municipal lamps and the clear light of their homes, with the uneasy feeling that they had fogged a photograph.

Fedina still took in nothing that was happening around her, but was possessed with the idea that she had no existence except for her child. She kept her eyes and lips more tightly shut than ever, and the little corpse still clutched to her overfull breasts. Her companions did everything they could think of to shake her out of this state on the way to the kitchen.

Manuela Calvario, the cook, had for many years reigned over the region between the coal-bin and the rubbish heap at The Sweet Enchantment; she looked like God the Father without a beard and wearing starched skirts. The flabby jowls

of this respectable and gigantic cook were filled with an airy substance which found vent in words as soon as she caught sight of Fedina.

"Another shameless hussy! Well, where did this one come from? And what's that she's holding so tightly?"

The three Graces, not daring to speak though they didn't know why, made the cook understand by signs, such as putting one hand above another to represent bars, that she had come from the prison.

"Dirty bitch!" was the woman's next remark. And after the others had gone she added: "I ought to give you poison instead of food! Here's your snack! Here . . . take that . . . and that!"

And she dealt her several blows on the back with the spit.

Fedina sat down on the ground holding her little corpse, without answering or opening her eyes. She had carried him so long in the same position that she no longer felt his weight. Manuela walked up and down, gesticulating and crossing herself.

In the course of her comings and goings she noticed a bad smell in the kitchen. She returned from the sink carrying a dish. Without more ado she began kicking Fedina and shouting:

"You've got something rotten there and it stinks. Take it away from here! Get rid of it! I won't have it here!"

Her noisy shouts brought Doña Chon to the kitchen, and between them, by main force as if they were breaking the branches of a tree, they succeeded in opening the wretched woman's arms; but when she realized that they were taking away her child she opened her eyes, let out a yell and fell senseless.

"It's the child that stinks! It's dead! How horrible!" exclaimed Doña Manuela. Gold-tooth was speechless, and while the prostitutes poured into the kitchen she ran to the telephone to in-

form the authorities. Everyone wanted to see and kiss the child; they covered it in kisses and snatched it from each other's hands and lips. The little wrinkled face of the corpse was masked by the saliva of vice, and it was now beginning to give out a bad smell. There was loud weeping and talk of arrangements for a wake. Major Farfan went to get the authorization of the police. The largest of the private bedrooms was cleared; they burned incense to remove the smell of stale semen from the hangings; Manuela burned tar in the kitchen, and the child was laid on a black enamel tray, among flowers and linen, where it lay curled up, dry and yellow, like a sarsaparilla seed . . .

It was as if each of them had lost a son that night. Four wax candles were burning. A smell of maize-cakes and brandy, of ailing flesh, of cigarette-ends and wine. A half-drunk woman, with one of her breasts bare, was chewing rather than smoking a cigar, and kept repeating, amid floods of tears:

Sleep, my little boy,
My pumpkin-head,
for if not, the wolf
will kill you dead!

Sleep, my life,
for I must go
to wash your linen
and sit down to sew!

CHAPTER XXIII

The President's Mail-Bag

(1) The widow Alexandra Bran, domiciled in this town, proprietress of the bedding shop called La Ballena Franca, states that as her business adjoins the Two-Step Tavern she has been in a position to observe several persons who frequent the aforesaid tavern, especially at night, on the Christian pretext of visiting

a sick woman. She is bringing these circumstances to the notice of the President because, from the conversations she has heard through the wall, it seems to her that General Eusebio Canales may be hiding in the Tavern, and that the persons who go there are conspiring against the safety of the State and the President's invaluable life.

(2) Soledad Belmares, resident in this town, states: that she now has nothing to eat because she has come to the end of her resources, and since she is a stranger and unknown here no one will lend her money, that in these circumstances she begs the President to set her son Manuel Belmares H. and her brother-in-law Federico Horneros P. at liberty; the Minister of her country can certify that they are not involved in politics, but only came here to earn their living by honest work, their sole offense having been that they accepted a recommendation from General Eusebio Canales to assist them to get work at the railway station.

(3) Colonel Prudencio Perfecto Paz states: that his recent journey to the frontier was undertaken with the object of seeing what was the condition of the land, roads and foot-paths, in order to decide what places should be occupied. He gives a detailed description of a plan of campaign which could be developed at favorable strategic points in case of a revolutionary rising; he confirms the report that men are being enlisted at the frontiers for that purpose and that Juan Leon Parada and others are so engaged, and that they possess by way of arms: hand grenades, machine-guns, small-bore rifles, dynamite and everything else necessary for mine-laying; and that the revolutionaries have from 25 to 30 armed men who could attack the forces of the Supreme Government at any moment. He has not been able to confirm the re-

port that Canales is their leader, but if that should be the case, they will certainly invade our territory unless diplomatic steps are taken to intern the revolutionaries. He is ready to carry through the invasion announced for the beginning of next month, but he lacks arms for his brigade of riflemen, having nothing else but what is in ammunition dump Cal. 43; and with the exception of a few sick, who are requiring proper treatment, the troops are in good shape and are receiving instruction from six to eight every morning; a head of cattle is provided for their provisions each week, and the signatory has already asked for sacks of sand from the port to build block-houses.

(4) Juan Antonia Mares thanks the President for the interest he was so kind as to show him, in getting his doctors to look after him. He is now ready again for service and begs permission to come to the capital to attend to various matters arising from his special knowledge of the political activities of Abel Carvajal, the lawyer.

(5) Luis Raveles M. states that in view of his illness and lack of means to regain his health he wishes to return to the United States, where he begs for some employment in one of the Consulates of the Republic, not at New Orleans, nor under the same conditions as before, but as a sincere friend of the President's. At the end of last January he was so extremely fortunate as to have his name on the audience list, but when he was in the anteroom and about to enter he noticed a certain air of suspicion on the part of the General Staff, who altered the position of his name on the list, and when his turn arrived an officer took him into a separate room, searched him as if he was an anarchist and told him he was doing so because of information that he had been

paid by Abel Carvajal, the lawyer, to assassinate the President. On his return he found his audience had been cancelled, and though he has since done everything possible to speak to the President, in order to tell him certain things which could not be entrusted to paper, he has met with no success.

(6) Nicomedes Aceituno writes stating that on his way back to the capital after one of his frequent journeys on business, he noticed that the poster fastened to the reservoir, on which the President's name appears, had been almost completely destroyed; six letters having been torn away and others damaged.

(7) Lucio Vasquez, detained in the Central Prison by order of the Judge Advocate General, begs for an audience.

(8) Catarino Regisio states: that he is manager of the property "La Tierra" belonging to General Eusebio Canales, and that one day last August the gentleman in question was visited by four friends, to whom he declared (being drunk at the time) that if the revolution should take place he had two battalions at his disposal: one was under the orders of one of themselves, Major Farfan, and the other of a Lieutenant-Colonel whose name was not mentioned. Since the rumors of revolution continue, the signatory is writing to inform the President of this, as he has been unable to do so in person in spite of several requests for an audience.

(9) General Megadeo Rayon forwards a letter received by him from the priest, Antonio Blas Custodio, who states therein that Father Urquijo has been slandering him (on account of his replacing the Father in the parish of San Lucas by order of the Archbishop), and stirring up the Catholic population with his lies, assisted by Doña Arcadia de Ayuso. Since the presence of Father Urquijo, a friend of Abel Carvajal the lawyer, might have serious consequences, the signatory is communicating the facts to the President.

(10) Alfredo Toledano, of this town, states that as he suffers from insomnia and never goes to sleep till late, he surprised one of the President's friends, Miguel Angel Face, knocking violently on the door of the house of Don Juan Canales, brother of the general of the same name who is always criticizing the government. He is informing the President in case it may be of interest.

(11) Nicomedes Aceituno, commercial traveler, states that the man who defaced the President's name on the reservoir was Guillermo Lizazo, the accountant, in a state of intoxication.

(12) Casimiro Rebeco Luna states: that he will shortly have completed two and a half years' detention in the Second Police Station; that as he is poor and has no relatives to intercede on his behalf he begs the President to be so good as to order him to be set at liberty; that the offense of which he is accused is that of having removed the announcement of the President's mother's anniversary from the door of the church where he is sacristan, on the instigation of enemies of the Government; that it is not certain that he did so, and that if he did, it was because he mistook it for another notice, since he cannot read.

(13) Doctor Luis Barreño begs the President's permission to travel abroad for the purpose of study, accompanied by his wife.

(14) Adelaida Peñal, inmate of the brothel called The Sweet Enchantment in

this town, wishes to inform the President that Major Modesto Farfan told her when drunk that General Eusebio Canales was the only general worth his salt he had known in the army, and that his disgrace· was due to the President's fear of able leaders, but that the revolution would be triumphant in spite of all.

(15) Monica Perdomino, patient in the General Hospital, in bed No. 14 in San Rafael ward, states that her bed being next to that of the patient Fedina Rodas, she has heard the aforesaid patient talking about General Canales in her delirium; that as she was not fully in her right mind she did not understand what the woman said, but that it might be advisable for someone to keep watch and take notes. The signatory sends the President this information out of her humble admiration for his Government.

(16) Tomas Javeli announces his marriage to Señorita Arquelina Suarez, and desires to dedicate it to the President of the Republic.

April 28th.

CHAPTER XXIV

The Whore-House

"Be quiet, will you? Be quiet! What a way to go on! Ever since God's dawn we've had nothing but chatter and jabber; anyone would think you were senseless animals!" cried Gold-Tooth.

Dressed in a black blouse and purple skirt, Her Excellency was digesting her dinner in a leather chair behind the bar counter.

A little while later she said to a copper-skinned servant with smooth, shining hair:

"Pancha, go and tell the women to come here; this'll never do—the clients will be arriving any moment and they ought to be here ready and waiting! God only knows one has to keep on hurrying these girls all the time!"

Two girls came running in on stockinged feet.

"Not so much noise, Consuelo! Oh what pretty little dears! Jesus Maria, just look what games they get up to! And look here, Adelaida—Adelaida, I'm talking to you!—if the Major comes it would be a good idea to take his sword away as security for what he owes us. What does he owe the house, you great ape?"

"Exactly nine hundred, plus the thirty-six I lent him last night," replied the barman.

"A sword isn't worth as much as that; no, not even if it's made of gold; still it's better than a poke in the eye! Adelaida! Am I talking to the wall or to you?"

"I heard you, Doña Chon, I heard," said Adelaida Peñal between bursts of laughter, and went on frolicking with her companion, whom she had hold of by the hair.

The assortment of women provided by The Sweet Enchantment were sitting about on the old divans in silence. Tall, short, fat, thin, old, young, adolescent, meek, farouche; blondes, redheads, brunettes, with small eyes or large eyes, white-skinned, dark-skinned, and mulattos. Though they were all different they seemed alike; they smelled alike—they smelled of men, all of them smelled of men, the acrid smell of stale shellfish. Inside their cheap little cotton chemises their breasts swung to and fro as if they were almost liquid. As they sat lolling with thighs apart, they displayed legs as thin as drain-pipes, bright-colored garters, and knickers that were either red trimmed with white lace, or pale salmon-pink trimmed with black.

Waiting for the clients made them irritable. They waited like emigrants with animal expressions in their eyes, sitting in huddled groups in front of the mirrors. To avoid getting too fidgety, some slept, some smoked, some ate peppermints, and others counted the spots of fly-dirt on the blue and white paper-chains decorating the ceiling; enemies were quarreling, friends slowly and immodestly caressing each other.

Nearly all of them had nicknames. A girl with large eyes would be called Codfish; if she was short Little Codfish, and if she was getting on in years and buxom, Big Codfish. A girl with a turn-up nose was Snubby; a brunette, Blackie; a mulatto, Darkie; a girl with slanting eyes, China; a blonde, Sugar; a stammerer, Stutter.

Besides these general appellations there was the Convalescent, the Sow, Big Feet, Honey-tongue, the Monkey, the Tapeworm, the Dove, the Bombshell, No-guts, Deaf-ears.

During the early hours of the night, a few men would come in to amuse themselves for a little by amorous talk, and by kissing and pestering any of the girls who were free. They all had plenty of assurance. Doña Chon would have liked to box their ears for them, for they had committed the crime in her eyes of being poor, but she put up with them in her house instead of sending them packing for the sake of the "queens." Poor queens! They got involved with these men, who exploited them as ponces and cheated them as lovers, out of their craving for affection and to have someone of their own.

Some inexperienced boys would also turn up during the early part of the night. They used to come in trembling all over, hardly able to speak, moving awkwardly like dazzled butterflies, and did not recover until they were out in the street again. Fair game. Docile and up to no tricks. Fifteen years old. "Good night." "Don't forget me." Instead of the guilt and bravado with which they had

entered, they left the brothel with a bad taste in their mouths, and that pleasant fatigue that comes from much laughing and repeated tumbles with a woman.

Ah, how good it was to be outside that stinking house! They munched the air as if it was new-mown hay and gazed at the stars as though they reflected their own strength.

Afterwards the serious clients began to arrive in relays. A respectable businessman, ardent and pot-bellied, with an astronomical amount of flesh surrounding his thoracic cavity. A shop assistant, who embraced the girls as if measuring cloth by the yard, in contrast to the doctor, who looked as if he were auscultating them. A journalist who always left something behind in pawn, even if it was only his hat. A lawyer who suggested both a cat and a geranium with his air of vulgar and uneasy domesticity. A countryman with milk-white teeth. A round-shouldered civil servant, unattractive to women. A portly tradesman. A workman smelling of sheepskin. A rich man who was always slyly touching his pocket-book or his watch or his rings. A chemist, more taciturn than the hairdresser but less polite than the dentist.

By midnight the room was in a ferment. Men and women were using their mouths to inflame each other's passions. Kisses—lascivious contacts of flesh and saliva—alternated with bites, confidences with blows, smiles with bursts of coarse laughter, and the popping of champagne corks with the popping of bullets, when some blustering individual was present who wanted to cut a dash.

"This is the life!" said an old man with his elbows on a table, his eyes roving here and there, his feet moving restlessly and a network of veins standing out from his burning forehead.

And with mounting excitement he inquired of one of his companions in debauchery:

"Can I go with that woman over there?"

"Why yes, old man, that's what they're here for."

"And that one next her? I like her even better!"

"Well, you can have her too."

A dark girl with provocatively bare feet was crossing the room.

"And that one walking over there?"

"Which? The very dark mulatto?"

"What's she called?"

"Adelaida; they call her the Sow. But I shouldn't pick her because she's with Major Farfan. I think he keeps her."

"Look how the Sow's making up to him," remarked the old man in a low voice.

The girl was using all her most serpentine arts to make the Major lose his head—she gazed at him from close range with the bewitching love-philters of her eyes, made more beautiful than ever by belladonna; she exhausted him by pressing kisses on him with her fleshy lips and tongue as if sticking on stamps, and leaned against him with all the weight of her warm breasts and protruding stomach.

"Take off this beastly thing," whispered the Sow into Farfan's ear. And without waiting for an answer—it was too late for that—she unfastened the sword from his belt and handed it to the barman.

A railway-train of cries went by at full speed, passed through the tunnels of every ear in the room, and speeded on its way . . .

Couples were dancing, in time and out of time to the music, with the movements of two-headed animals. A man with his face daubed to look like a woman was playing the piano. Both his mouth and the piano had a few ivories missing. "Because I'm a flirt, a dreadful flirt, and terribly refined!" he replied to people who asked him why he painted his face,

adding ingratiatingly: "My friends call me Pepe and the boys call me Violeta. I wear a low-cut vest (although I don't play tennis) to show off my dove's breasts; a monocle for smartness and a frock-coat out of absentmindedness. I use powder (oh how spiteful people are!) and rouge to hide the smallpox scars I have on my face—there they are and there they'll stay. The beastly disease scattered them all over me like confetti. Oh well—what does it matter! It's just my little way!"

A railway-train of cries went by at full speed. Crushed between the wheels and the pistons, a drunk woman lay writhing limply, her face the color of bran. She was pressing her hands against her groins, while the tears washed away the paint from her cheeks and lips.

"Oh my ovaaAAries! Oh my ovAAAries! Oh my ovaaAAAAAAries! My ovaries! Oh . . . my ovaries! Oh!"

Everyone but those too drunk to move joined the group that had collected to see what was happening. In the general confusion the married men tried to find out if someone had attacked her, thinking to make their escape before the police arrived; while the rest took a less serious view of the matter and ran to and fro for the pleasure of being jostled by the crowd.

More and more kept joining the group round the woman, who lay twisting and shivering, with rolling eyes and protruding tongue. At the height of the crisis her false teeth became loose. There was frenzied excitement among the spectators. A loud laugh went up when her teeth slipped suddenly to the concrete floor.

Doña Chon brought this disgraceful scene to an end. She had been somewhere behind the scenes and came running to the rescue like a fat hen, cackling after her chicks; she took the unfortunate shrieking girl by one arm and swept the floor with her as far as the kitchen, where with Manuela's help she shut her in the coal-shed, after the cook had dealt her several blows with the spit.

The old man who had become enamored of the Sow took advantage of the confusion to snatch her from the Major, who was too drunk to see anything.

"What a filthy bitch, eh, Major Farfan?" exclaimed Gold-Tooth when she returned from the kitchen. "Her ovaries didn't hurt her enough to stop her gorging herself and sleeping all day; it's just as if, when the battle began, a soldier got a pain in his . . . !"

A burst of loud drunken laughter drowned her voice. They laughed as if they were spitting out toffee. Meanwhile Doña Chon turned to the barman and said:

"I wanted to have the big girl I fetched from the Casa Nueva yesterday, instead of that obstinate brute; what a pity she was taken bad!"

"Ah yes, she was a fine girl!"

"I told the lawyer he must fix it that the Judge Advocate pays back my money. The son of a whore isn't going to hold on to my ten thousand pesos. Not he—the fool!"

"You're quite right! As for that lawyer, I happen to know he's a bad lot!"

"Dirty swindlers all of them!"

"And lecherous into the bargain, you know!"

"Anything you like, but I promise you one thing: he won't catch me twice! If he thinks he can sit there on his fat arse . . . !"

She left the sentence unfinished and went to the window to see who was knocking.

"Holy Jesus Maria and all the angels! Talk of the devil and here he comes!" she said aloud to the man who was standing at the door, bathed in the purplish light from the lantern, with his scarf pulled up

to his eyes; and without answering his "Good evenings," she went off to tell the concierge to open the door at once.

"Come along quick and open the door, Pancha! Hurry! Open up quick, it's Don Miguelito!"

Doña Chon had recognized him from pure intuition and also from his satanic eyes.

"Well! What a miracle!"

Angel Face glanced round the room as he greeted her, and was reassured by the sight of a recumbent form which must be that of Major Farfan; a long stream of saliva was coming from his open mouth.

"A great miracle, because it isn't often the likes of you visit us poor folk!"

"No, Doña Chon, true enough!"

"You've come in the nick! I was just calling on the Saints to help me because of some trouble I'm in, and they've sent you to me!"

"Well, I'm always at your service, you know."

"Thank you. I'll tell you about my trouble but first you must have a drink."

"Don't bother . . ."

"It's no bother! Just a little something, a little of what you like, whatever you have a fancy for! To show there's no ill-feeling! How would a whisky be? But I'll have it served in my room. Come this way."

Gold-Tooth's private apartments were completely separate from the rest of the house and seemed to be a world apart. Tables, chests of drawers and sideboards were crowded with engravings, sculptures and religious images and relics. A Holy Family caught the eye by its great size and the skill with which it was executed. The Infant Christ was as tall as a lily; the only thing he lacked was speech. A brilliantly painted Saint Joseph, with the Virgin in a star-spangled dress, were on either side. The Virgin was decked in jewels, and Saint Joseph was holding a cup ornamented with two stones, each worth a fortune. Under a large glass case was a dark-skinned dying Christ, covered in blood, and in a wide glass case framed in shells a Virgin was ascending to heaven—an imitation in sculpture of Murillo's picture. The most valuable thing about it was the serpent made of emeralds coiled at her feet. Between the sacred images were portraits of Doña Chon (the diminutive of Concepcion, which was her real name) at the age of twenty, when she had a President of the Republic at her feet offering to take her to "Paris, France," as well as two magistrates of the Supreme Court and three butchers who fought each other with knives for her sake at a fair. And over in a corner, out of sight of the visitors, was a portrait of the survivor, a hairy individual who had in the end become her husband.

"Sit down here on the sofa, Don Miguelito, you'll be better off here."

"You do yourself well, Doña Chon."

"I do my best . . ."

"It's like a church!"

"Now you mustn't tease me! Don't make fun of my saints!"

"And what can I do for you?"

"Drink up your whisky first."

"Very well. Cheers!"

"Cheers, Don Miguelito! And please forgive me for not joining you, but I'm a little upset in my stomach. Put your glass here—put it on this little table. Here give it to me."

"Thank you."

"Well as I was saying, Don Miguelito, I'm in great trouble and I'd be glad of your advice—the sort only people like you can give. One of the women I've got here suddenly became no good to me, so I set about looking for another; then a friend of mine told me there was a prisoner in the Casa Nueva, shut up by order of the Judge Advocate, a fine girl and just what I wanted. Well, I know

what's what, so I went straight to my lawyer, Don Juan Vidalitas, who has got hold of women for me before, and made him write a proper letter to the Judge Advocate General—offering ten thousand pesos for her."

"Ten thousand pesos?"

"That's right. I didn't have to say it twice. He answered on the spot that that would be all right, and as soon as he got the cash (which I counted out myself in 500 peso notes on his desk) he gave me a written order to the Casa Nueva to hand over the woman to me. They told me she was there for political reasons. It seems they nabbed her in General Canales' house . . ."

"What did you say?"

Angel Face had been following Gold-Tooth's story inattentively with his ears pricked towards the door to make sure that Major Farfan did not leave (he had been looking for him for many hours) but when he heard Canales' name it was as if a network of fine wires had suddenly spread before him. This unhappy woman must be the servant Chabela, about whom Camila had talked in her feverish delirium.

"Excuse my interrupting . . . where is this woman?"

"You shall hear, but let me go on with my story. I took the Judge Advocate's order and went myself with three of my girls to fetch her from the Casa Nueva. I wasn't going to be given a pig in a poke. We went in a cab to be more comfortable. So there we are arriving; I hand in the order, they examine it and read it carefully, they fetch the girl, they hand her over, and, to make a long story short, we bring her back here where they're all waiting for her and they all like her. Nothing wrong so far, eh, Don Miguelito?"

"And where have you put her?"

Angel Face would have liked to take

her away that same night. The minutes seemed like years while this horrible old woman was telling her story.

"You're all the same, you young nobs, no holding you! But just let me tell you. After we'd left the Casa Nueva, I noticed that this woman refused to open her eyes or say one word. You might as well have talked to the wall! I thought she was up to some game or other. And what's more I noticed that she was hugging a bundle about the size of a baby in her arms."

The image of Camila in the favorite's mind lengthened out until it split in half like a figure of eight, with the rapidity of a soap-bubble that is burst by a shot.

"A baby?"

"That's right. My cook, Manuela Calvario Cristales, found out that what the wretched woman was rocking in her arms was a little dead baby, already beginning to stink. She called me, I ran to the kitchen, and between the two of us we took it away by main force; but we'd hardly got her arms apart—Manuela almost broke them to do it—and taken the brat away from her, when she opened her eyes as wide as the dead on Judgment Day, and let out a yell that must have been heard as far away as the market, and fell flat on the floor."

"Dead?"

"We thought so for a moment. They came and fetched her away, wrapped in a sheet, to San Juan de Dios. I didn't want to look. It quite upset me. They say the tears came running from her shut eyes like the water which is no use to any of us."

Doña Chon paused for breath, then she muttered:

"The girls who were visiting the hospital this morning asked after her and it seems she's very bad. Now here's what worries me. As you can imagine I won't dream of letting the Judge Advocate keep my ten thousand pesos, and I'm trying to

think how I can get him to pay them back, because why in heaven's name should he keep what's mine? Why in heaven's name? I'd a thousand times rather make a present of them to the poorhouse!"

"Your lawyer must get them back for you, and as for this poor woman . . ."

"Exactly! And he's been twice today—sorry to interrupt—my lawyer Vidalitas went twice to see him; once to his house and once to his office, and each time he said the same thing—that he wasn't going to give me back a thing. You see what a dirty swindler that man is! He says if a cow dies after it's been bought it's not the seller's but the buyer's loss. Talking about people as if they were animals! That's what he said. Oh really, I'd like to . . . !"

Angel face was silent. Who was this woman who had been sold? Who was the dead child?

Doña Chon displayed her gold teeth as she said menacingly:

"Ah, but what I'm going to do is give him such a basting as he never had before, even from his mother. If they put me in prison it'll be for something. It's hard enough to earn one's living, God knows, without people robbing one like this! Damn the old ruffian! Already this morning I told them to throw earth from the graveyard on to his doorstep. We'll see if that brings him bad luck . . ."

"And did they bury the child?"

"We held a wake for it here in this house; the girls are very sentimental. There were maize cakes . . ."

"A regular party?"

"That's right!"

"And the police? What are they doing?"

"We paid them to give us a death certificate. Next day we buried the brat on the island in a beautiful coffin lined with white satin."

"And aren't you afraid that there may be relatives who'll claim the body, or at least want to be notified?"

"That would be the last straw! But who's going to claim it? The father, Rodas, is in prison, and the mother's in hospital as you know."

Angel Face smiled inwardly; an enormous weight had been lifted from his mind. This was no relation of Camila's.

"Do advise me, Don Miguelito—you're so clever—how can I prevent that old miser hanging on to my money? It was ten thousand pesos—remember? Not a flea-bite exactly!"

"My advice is to go and see the President and complain to him. Ask for an audience, and tell him the story. He'll put it right. He has it in his power."

"That's what I thought, and I'll do it too. Tomorrow I'll send him an urgent telegram asking for an audience. Luckily we're old friends. When he was only a Minister he had a passion for me. It's a long time ago now. I was young and pretty then; slim as a reed, just like that photograph over there. I remember we lived at El Cielito with my mother—may she rest in peace! And a parrot gave her a peck in the eye and blinded her—did you ever hear of such bad luck! I must admit I roasted that parrot—I would gladly have roasted two of them—and gave it to my dog and the stupid brute ate it and got rabies. The most cheerful thing that I remember about those days is that all the funerals used to go past the house. Corpses were always going by. It was because of that that we broke for good with the President. He was afraid of funerals; what did I care? They weren't my fault. He was just like a child; his head full of stories. He believed every little thing anyone told him, whether it was bad or good. At first I was very struck on him and I used to keep kissing him when that endless procession of corpses went by in different colored

coffins. Afterwards I got fed up with that and dropped it. What he liked best was for someone to lick his ear, though it sometimes tasted like death. I can see him now, sitting there where you're sitting, with his white silk handkerchief tightly knotted round his neck, his wide hat, his spats with pink tabs and his blue suit."

"And afterwards—I suppose he must have been President already when he was a witness at your wedding?"

"Not a bit of it. My late husband—may he rest in peace—didn't care for such things. 'Only dogs need witnesses and people staring at them when they get married,' he used to say, 'and then off they go with a string of other dogs behind them, all slobbering with their tongues hanging out . . .' "

CHAPTER XXV

Death's Halting-Place

The priest arrived at a cassock-splitting speed. "Some people would be willing to hurry for much less than this," he reflected. "What can be more precious in the whole world than a human soul?" And some people would get up from the dinner-table with a rumbling belly for much less. Bel-ly! I bel-ieve in the three separate persons of the Trinity, and one true God. The belly-rumbling is not there, but here with me, me, me, in my own stomach, stomach, stomach . . . From your belly, Jesus . . . there is the table already laid, with a white cloth, clean china, and a dried-up old servant.

When the priest came in, followed by some female neighbors addicted to witnessing death agonies, Angel Face tore himself from the head of Camila's bed, his footsteps sounding like the tearing-up of roots. The barkeeper brought a chair for the priest, and then they all withdrew.

"I, a miserable sinner, confess to God," they were saying.

"In Nomine Patris et Filii et . . . my daughter, how long is it since your last confession?"

"Two months."

"Have you made your act of contrition?"

"Yes, Father . . ."

"Tell me your sins."

"Father, I confess to having lied—"

"Over a serious matter?"

"No, and I disobeyed my father, and . . ."

(*Tick-tock, tick-tock, tick-tock*)

". . . and Father, I confess to . . ."

(*Tick-tock*)

". . . failing to go to Mass."

The sick girl and her confessor seemed to be talking in a crypt. The Devil, the Guardian Angel and Death were present at the confession. Death emptied his vacant stare into Camila's eyes; the Devil sat at the head of the bed spitting out spiders, and the Angel wept in a corner, with long-drawn-out sobs.

"Father, I confess to not saying my prayers night and morning, and . . ."

(*Tick-tock, tick-tock*)

". . . to quarreling with my girl-friends!"

"Over some matter affecting your reputation?"

"No . . ."

"My daughter, you have committed very grave offenses against God."

"Father, I confess to riding astride like a man."

"Were there other people present, and did it create a scandal?"

"No, there were only a few Indians."

"So you felt you could do anything a man could do? That also is a grave sin, for Our Lord God created a woman to be a woman, and she should not try to be otherwise and imitate a man; that would be following the example of the Devil, who wanted to be equal with God."

In the other part of the room, in front of the bar-counter, covered like an altar with bottles of every color, Angel Face, La Masacuata and the neighbors were waiting, not uttering a word but exchanging glances full of fear and hope, and breathing out a symphony of sighs, heavy with the oppressive idea of death. The half-shut door gave a glimpse of the brightly lit street, the porch of the Church of La Merced, some houses and a few passers-by. It enraged Angel Face to see these people coming and going, indifferent to the fact that Camila was dying—large grains of sand in a sieve of sun; shadows possessed of common sense; walking factories of excrement . . .

The confessor's voice dragged little chains of words through the silence. The sick girl coughed. The air tore at the drums of her lungs.

"Father, I confess to all those venial and mortal sins that I have committed but forgotten."

The Latin words of the absolution, the hurried disappearance of the Devil, and the Angel's return like a light to spread his warm white wings over Camila, put an end to the favorite's anger against the passers-by, his childish hatred tinged with tenderness, and gave him the idea—grace comes by devious paths—of saving a man who was in grave danger of death. Perhaps God would grant him Camila's life in exchange, although this seemed impossible according to medical science.

The priest went noiselessly away; he stopped in the doorway to light a maize-leaf cigarette and gather up his cassock, for according to the law he had to keep it hidden under his cloak while he was in the street. He seemed harmless and gentle, a burned-out ash of a man. The news went around that he had been summoned to confess a dying woman. The neighbors left the house behind him, and Angel Face went off to carry out his plan.

The Callejon de Jesus, the White House, and the Cavalry Barracks. Here he inquired of the corporal on guard for Major Farfan. He was told to wait a moment and the soldier went inside calling out:

"Major Farfan! Major Farfan!"

His voice died away in the huge courtyard, and the only response was a tremulous echo from the eaves of distant houses: "Jor fan fan! Jor fan fan!"

The favorite stood waiting a few steps from the door, taking no part in what was happening around him. Dogs and turkey-buzzards were quarreling over the dead body of a cat in the middle of the road, directly opposite a window from which an officer was amusedly watching the ferocious battle and twirling the ends of his moustaches. Two ladies were drinking fruit-juice in a little shop swarming with flies. From the front door of the next house emerged five little boys in sailor suits, followed by a gentleman as pale as a turnip and a pregnant lady (papa and mamma). A butcher pushed his way between the boys, lighting a cigarette; his clothes were covered in bloodstains, his sleeves were rolled up, and he carried his sharp butcher's cleaver close to his heart. Soldiers came in and out, and a serpentine trail of the wet prints of bare feet wound over the tiles of the entrance hall to be lost in the courtyard. The barrack keys jingled against the sentinel's rifle as he stood at attention beside the officer on guard, who was sitting on an iron chair in the middle of a ring of gobbets of spittle.

Walking softly like a little deer, a white-haired woman, whose skin was burnt copper-color by the sun and wrinkled with age, went up to the officer and respectfully covering her head with her cotton shawl said imploringly:

"Excuse me, Señor, but I beg you for mercy's sake to let me talk to my son. The Virgin will reward you."

Before replying the officer expelled a jet of saliva smelling of tobacco and dental decay.

"What is your son's name, Señora?"

"Ismael, Señor."

"Ismael what?"

"Ismael Mijo, Señor."

The officer spat again.

"But what's his surname?"

"It's Mijo, Señor."

"Look, here, you'd better come back another day, we're busy."

The old woman withdrew without lowering her shawl, slowly, counting out her steps as if measuring her misfortune; she paused briefly at the edge of the pavement and then turned back again and approached the officer who was still sitting on his chair.

"Excuse me, Señor, but I can't stay here any longer; I come from very far away, more than twenty leagues, and so if I don't see him today I don't know when I can come back. Please won't you send for him?"

"I've told you already, we're busy. Go away and don't bother me!"

Angel Face had witnessed this scene and, impelled by the desire to do good so that God should reward him by saving Camila, he said to the officer in a low voice:

"Send for the boy, Lieutenant, and here's something for cigarettes."

The soldier took the money without glancing at the stranger and gave orders for Ismael Mijo to be sent for. The little old woman stood gazing at her benefactor as if he were an angel.

Major Farfan was not in the barracks. A secretary appeared at one of the balconies with his pen behind his ear, and told the favorite that at this hour of the night he could usually be found at The Sweet Enchantment, because the noble son of Mars divided his time between duty and love. However, it wouldn't do any harm to go to his house. Angel Face took a cab. Farfan rented furnished rooms in a remote suburb; through the cracks made by the damp in the unpainted door Angel Face could see into the darkened interior. He knocked twice, three times. There was no one there. He left at once, and went to see how Camila was, before going on to The Sweet Enchantment. The cab made a surprisingly loud noise on the paved road after leaving the unsurfaced lanes—horses' hooves, and wheels, wheels and horses' hooves.

When Gold-Tooth had finished her story of her love affair with the President, Angel Face went back to the saloon. It was vital not to lose sight of Major Farfan, and also to find out rather more about the woman who had been arrested in General Canales' house and sold by that swine the Judge Advocate General for ten thousand pesos.

Dancing was in full swing. Couples were revolving to the strains of a waltz, accompanied in a quavering voice by Farfan, who was as drunk as a lord:

Why do the whores
all love me so?
Because I sing them
the "Flor del Café"

All of a sudden he sat up, and realizing that the Sow was no longer with him, he stopped singing and exclaimed between hiccups:

"So the Sow's gone away, has she, you bastards? She's busy, is she, you bastards? . . . well I'm off . . . I tell you I'm off, I t-ell you I'm off . . . I'm off . . . well, why don't I go? . . . I'm off, I do believe . . ."

He got up with difficulty, supporting himself on the table, to which he had been anchored, and on chairs and walls, and staggered towards the door. The servant ran to open it.

"I t-ell you I'm o-off! The whore will come back, won't she, Ña Chon? But I'm off! There's nothing left for us regular soldiers to do but drink ourselves to death, and afterwards they can distill us instead of cremating us! Hurrah for pork stew and the working man!"

Angel Face caught up with him at once. He was walking along the tightrope of the road like an acrobat; now he would stop with his right foot in the air, now with the left, now again with the right, now with both . . . On the point of falling, he saved himself and remarked: "That's the way, as the mule said to the bridle."

The open windows of another brothel shed their light into the street. A longhaired pianist was playing Beethoven's Moonlight Sonata. There was no one to listen to him in the empty room, except the chairs arranged like guests around a small grand piano, no larger than Jonah's whale. The favorite stood still, pierced by the music. He propped the Major against the wall—poor tractable puppet that he was—and went closer so as to subject the fragments of his broken heart to the notes: he was returning to life among the dead—a dead man with burning eyes, suspended far above the earth—while the eyes of the street lamps were extinguished one by one, and the night dew dripped from the roofs like nails for crucifying drunkards or fastening down coffin lids. Each little hammer inside the magnetic box of the piano joined together the fine sand of musical sounds, and, after holding them together for a while, let them go again in the fingers of arpeggios, doubled to knock on the permanently shut door of love; always the same fingers; always the same hand. The moon was drifting through a paved sky towards the sleeping fields, leaving dark groves behind her, full of terror for the birds, and for those who find the world as supernaturally vast when love is born as it is small and empty when love dies.

Farfan awoke to find himself lying on the bar counter of a small tavern, and being shaken by a stranger as a tree is shaken to bring down the ripe fruit.

"Don't you recognize me, Major?"

"Yes—no—for the moment—in a moment—"

"You remember?"

"Ah—oOOh!" yawned Farfan, getting off the counter where he had been lying, as damp with sweat as a pack-mule.

"Miguel Angel Face, at your service." The Major saluted.

"Excuse me; I didn't recognize you, you see. But yes, of course it's you one sees about always with the President."

"Good! Don't be surprised at my waking you up like this, Major—so suddenly—"

"Don't worry about that."

"But you have to get back to barracks, and it's important I talk to you privately; it happens that the proprietress of this—café, shall we say?—is out. I hunted for you everywhere, like a needle in a haystack, yesterday afternoon—in the barracks, at your rooms. You must promise not to repeat to a single soul what I'm now going to tell you."

"Word of honor."

The favorite shook the Major's hand warmly, and with his eyes on the door said in a low voice:

"I'm in a position to know that orders have been issued to do away with you. Instructions have been sent to the Military Hospital that when next you're confined to bed after a drinking-bout you shall be given a fatal dose of sedative. The harlot you've been going with at The Sweet Enchantment has informed the President of your revolutionary outbursts."

Farfan had been rooted to the spot by the favorite's words. He raised his clenched fists:

"Oh the bitch!"

And after going through the motions of hitting her, he bowed his head as if crushed.

"My God, what am I to do?"

"For the moment don't get drunk; that's the way to stave off the immediate danger, and don't—"

"Yes, that's what I was thinking; but I may not be able to do it; it'll be difficult. What were you going to say?"

"I was also going to say that you shouldn't eat in barracks."

"I don't know how to thank you."

"With silence—"

"Naturally, but that's not enough. However, some chance will turn up, and from now on here's a man you can count on—who owes you his life."

"I'll give you another piece of good advice as a friend. Try and find a way of getting on the right side of the President."

"Yes, that's the thing, isn't it?"

"It'll cost you nothing."

Both were silently adding to these words: "To commit a crime for example," the most effective means of gaining the leader's good will; or "to commit a public outrage on defenseless people"; or "to demonstrate the superiority of force to public opinion," or "to get rich at the expense of the nation"; or . . .

A murderous crime would be best; the annihilation of one of his fellows was the clearest proof of a citizen's complete adherence to the President. Two months in prison for appearance's sake, and immediately afterwards a public position of trust, such as was only given to those with a law suit pending, so that they could be conveniently sent back to prison if they didn't behave well.

"It'll cost you nothing."

"You're extremely kind."

"No, Major, don't thank me; my decision to save you is my offering to God for the health of someone who is very, very seriously ill. Your life for hers."

"Your beloved perhaps?"

The most beautiful word in the Song of Songs floated for a moment, like some charming embroidery, among trees full of cherubs and orange blossom.

After the Major had left, Angel Face pinched himself to find out if it were really he—the man who had driven so many to their deaths—who was now pushing a man towards life, and the inviolable blue of the morning.

CHAPTER XXVI

Whirlwind

Dismissing the portly figure of the Major from his mind, Angel Face shut the door and went on tiptoe into the darkened back room. He felt as if he were dreaming. The difference between reality and dreams is purely artificial. Asleep, awake, which was he? In the half-darkness he seemed to feel the earth moving beneath him. The clock and the flies kept Camila company as she lay close to death. The clock let drop the little rice grains of its pulsations to mark out the path of return when she had ceased to exist. The flies ran over the walls, cleaning the cold of death off their little wings. Others buzzed about tirelessly and swiftly. He stepped quietly up to the bed. The sick girl was still delirious . . .

The ingenuity of dreams . . . pools of camphorated oil . . . the slow dialogue of the stars . . . the invisible, salty, naked contact of empty space . . . the double hinge of the hands . . . the uselessness of hands within hands . . . scented soap . . . the garden in the reading-book . . . in the tiger's den . . . in the great beyond of parakeets . . . in God's cage . . .

In God's cage, midnight Mass for a cock—a cock with a drop of moonlight on its comb . . . it pecks at the host . . . it is lit and extinguished, lit and ex-tinguished, lit and extinguished. The Mass is sung . . . it isn't a cock; it's a flash of celluloid lightning in the neck of a large bottle surrounded by little soldiers . . . lightning from the White Rose pastry-shop, made by Saint Rose . . . Beer-froth of the cock for the chicken . . . for chicken . . .

Lay her now upon her bier
Matatero, tero, la!
For she is not happy here
Matatero, tero, la!

No one is blowing his nose; it is the sound of a drum; a drum tracing down-strokes in the school of the wind . . . Stop! it's not a drum; it's a door echoing to a blow from a knocker shaped like a brass hand! The knocks penetrate into every corner of the intestinal silence of the house, like augers. Rat-tat-tat . . . The drum of the house. Every house has its door-drum to summon the people who are its life, and when it is shut it is as if they lived death . . . Rat-tat of the house . . . door . . . rat-tat of the house . . . the water in the fountain is all eyes when it hears the sound of the door-drum, and people say crossly to the servants: "Oh they're knocking!" and the walls send back an echo which repeats over and over again: "Oh they're knock-ing, go and open the door-r-r-r!" "Oh they're knocking, go and open the door-r-r-r!" and the ashes stir restlessly but can do nothing (while the cat sits like a watchful sentinel) except send a gentle shiver through the bars of the grate; and the roses take fright, innocent victims of the intransigence of their thorns; and the mirrors speak with the living voices of rapt mediums through the spirits of the dead furniture: "Oh they're knocking, come and open!"

The whole house, trembling as if in an earthquake, wants to go and see who is knocking, knocking, knocking at the drum-door: casseroles dance about, flower-pots move softly, wash-basins go rataplan! rataplan!, plates give a china cough, cups and cutlery scatter like silver laughter, empty bottles follow the bottle decorated with candle-grease tears which is used and not used for a candlestick in the back room; prayer-books, Easter palm-branches try to defend the house against the storm of knocking, scissors, shells, portraits, old locks of hair, cruets, cardboard boxes, matches, nails . . .

Only her uncles pretend to be asleep among these wakeful inanimate objects, in the islands of their double beds, under the protective covering of quilts smelling of gastric juices. In vain does the door-drum take bites out of the spacious silence. "They're still knocking!" murmurs the wife of one of her uncles, the most double-faced of her aunts. "Yes, but it would be risky to open the door," her husband answers in the darkness. "What time is it? Oh, my dear, I was so fast asleep! . . . They're still knocking!" "Yes, but it would be risky to open the door!" "What will the neighbors think?" "Yes, but it would be risky to open the door! If we only had ourselves to consider of course we'd open the door, but just think what people would say about us! . . . They're still knocking!" "Yes, but it would be risky to open the door!" "It's outrageous, did you ever hear of anything like it? So inconsiderate, so rude!" "Yes, but it would be risky to open the door!"

Her uncle's harsh voice grew softer, and came now from the throats of the servants. Chattering phantoms smelling of veal have arrived in their master's bedroom: "Sir! Madam! Listen how they're knocking! . . ." and they go back to their pallet beds, their fleas and their dreams, repeating over and over again: "Oh dear! but it would be risky to open the door! Oh dear! . . . but it would be risky to open the door!"

Rat-tat-tat on the drum of the house

. . . darkness of the street . . . the dogs cover the sky with the tiles of their barking, making a roof for the stars, for black reptiles and clay washer-women who plunge their arms deep in foam of silver lightning . . .

"Papa . . . papa darling . . . papa!" She called out to her father in her delirium, to her old nurse lying dead in the hospital, to her uncles, who would not let her into their houses even when she was dying.

Angel Face laid his hand on her forehead. "Every recovery is a miracle!" he thought as he caressed her. "If only I could drive away the disease with the warmth of my hand!" He was suffering the inarticulate grief of those who watch a young creature die, a tremulous tenderness which sent anguish creeping under his skin and through his flesh. What could he do? His mind began mechanically introducing prayers among his thoughts: "If only I could get beneath her eyelids and remove the tears of pity and loneliness from her eyes—from those pupils colored like the wings of hope. May God preserve you! We exiles pray to you, oh Lord!"

"It's a crime to go on living every day . . . when one loves. Grant us to-day, oh Lord!"

When he thought of his own house it was as if it were a stranger's. His home was here—with Camila; it was not his house, but Camila was here. And supposing Camila were not here? A vague, wandering pain pierced his body. Supposing Camila were not here?

A lorry went by, shaking the house. There was a clinking of bottles on the shelves in the bar; a knocker rattled, the neighboring houses shook. Angel Face was so startled that he felt he must have been falling asleep where he stood. Better sit down. There was a chair beside the medicine table. A moment later it was supporting his body. The tiny sound of the clock, the smell of camphor, the light from the candles offered up to the all-powerful Jesus of La Merced and Jesus of la Candelaria, the table, the towels, the medicines, Saint Francis' rope belt (lent by a neighbor to keep the devil at bay), were all gently disintegrating to a slow rhythm, a descending scale of somnolence, a momentary dissolution, a pleasurable discomfort full of more holes than a sponge, invisible, semi-liquid, hidden, traversed by the shadows of disconnected dreams:

Who is playing the guitar? . . . Little bones are breaking in the dark cellar, whence rises the song of the agricultural engineer . . . It is bitterly cold among the leaves . . . From all the pores of the earth rises an interminable, demoniac laugh, like a four-cornered wing . . . Are they laughing, are they spitting, what are they doing? It isn't night, but he is separated from Camila by darkness, the darkness of the skulls laughing in the confusion of the mortuary . . . The laughter comes from teeth that are blackened and horrible, but when it reaches the air it mingles with water vapor and rises up to form clouds. Fences made out of human intestines divide up the earth. Perspectives made by human eyes divide up the sky . . . A horse's ribs serve as a violin for the raging hurricane. He sees Camila's funeral passing by. Her eyes are swimming in foam from the bridles of the river of black carriages . . . the Dead Sea must have eyes!

Her green eyes! . . . why are the drivers waving their white gloves in the darkness? . . . Behind the funeral procession an ossuary full of children's thighbones is singing; "Moon, moon, take your prune and throw the stone in the lagoon!" Each tender little bone is singing this song: "Moon, moon, take your prune and throw the stone in the lagoon!" Hip-bones with eyes like buttonholes: "Moon, moon, take your prune

and throw the stone in the lagoon!" . . . Why does daily life have to go on? . . . Why does the tram go on running? . . . Why doesn't everyone die? . . . After Camila's funeral nothing can be the same, everything is superfluous, artificial, does not exist . . . It would be better if he could laugh . . . The tower leans over with laughing . . . they search her pockets for souvenirs . . . The dust left by Camila's days . . . Trivial rubbish . . . A thread . . . Camila should be here now . . . A thread . . . A dirty card . . . Oh the cheek of that diplomat who brings in wine and tinned goods without paying the duty and then sells them in a shop kept by a Tyrolese! . . . Letthewholeworldsing . . . Shipwreck . . . Lifebelts, like white crowns . . . Letthewholeworldsing . . . Camila, motionless in his arms . . . Meeting . . . The bellringer's hand . . . They are turning the corners of the street . . . Pale with emotion . . . Livid, silent, disembodied . . . Why don't they offer her an arm? . . . She is letting herself down with the spiders-web of her sense of touch, and leaning on the arm she needs; she only holds on to the sleeve . . . In the telegraph wires . . . he has wasted time looking at the telegraph wires, and out of a big house in the Callejon del Judio come five men made of opaque glass, who bar his way, each with a trickle of blood coming from his temple . . . He fights desperately to get to the place where Camila is waiting for him, smelling of postage-stamp gum . . . Far off he sees Mount Carmel . . .

In his dream Angel Face tries to fight his way out. He is blind . . . He is weeping . . . He tries to bite through the thin thread of darkness which separates him from the human anthill which is being installed under straw awnings on the little mound, to sell toys, fruit and toffee . . . He puts out his claws . . .

his hair bristles . . . He succeeds in crossing a little bridge and runs to find Camila, but the five men made of opaque glass bar his way again. "They're dividing her into little bits for Corpus Christi!" He shouts at them: "Let me pass! before they destroy her completely. She can't defend herself because she's dead!" "Don't you see?" "Look! Look! Every shadow has a fruit and a little piece of Camila is threaded into every fruit!" "How can one believe one's eyes? I saw her buried and I was sure it wasn't her, she's here at the feast of Corpus Christi, at this cemetery, smelling of quinces, mangoes, pears and peaches; and they have made little white doves out of her body, dozens, hundreds of little white cotton doves fastened to colored ribbons embroidered with legends such as 'Remember Me,' 'Eternal Love,' 'I am thinking of You,' 'Love me for Ever,' 'Do not Forget Me.' " His voice is drowned in the strident sound of toy trumpets, and drums made out of the guts of the bad years and stale bread; in the crowd of people (fathers climbing with dragging footsteps, children running after each other); in the clanging of bells in the steeples, in the heat of the sun, in the warmth of blind candles at noon, in the glittering monstrance . . . The five opaque men are joining together into a single man, a shape made of sleeping smoke . . . From a distance they no longer look solid . . . they are drinking soda-water . . . A flag of soda-water held in hands waving like cries . . . Skaters . . . Camila is gliding among invisible skaters, across a public mirror which reflects good and bad impartially. The cosmetic quality of her perfumed voice cloys as she tries to defend herself by saying: "No, no, not here!" "But why not here?" "Because I'm dead." "And what of that?" "It's just that . . ." "What, tell me, what?" Between the two

of them there passed a current of cold air from the vast sky and a column of men in red trousers. Camila walks off behind them. On the impulse of the moment he walks off behind her . . . At the last rat-tat of the drum, the column suddenly comes to a half . . . The President is approaching . . . a gilded figure . . . Tantarara! . . . The crowd retreats, trembling . . . The men in red trousers are having a game with their heads . . . Bravo! Bravo! Done it again! Have another go, well done! The men in red trousers do not obey orders. They obey the voice of the public and go on playing with their heads . . . Three times . . . One! off with his head . . . Two! throw it up high to be combed among the stars . . . Three! Catch it in your hands and put it back . . . Bravo! Bravo! Again! Have another go! That's it! Have another go! . . . It makes the flesh creep . . . gradually the voices die away . . . the drum is heard . . . Everyone sees something they don't want to see. The men in red trousers take off their heads and throw them in the air, but do not catch them when they fall. The skulls smash on the ground in front of the two rows of motionless figures with their arms tied behind their backs.

Angel Face was woken by two loud knocks on the door. What a horrible nightmare! Thank heaven reality was quite different. Returning from a nightmare produces the same feeling of well-being as returning from a funeral. He ran to see who was knocking. Was it news of the general or an urgent summons from the President?

"Good morning."

"Good morning," replied the favorite to an individual taller than himself, with a rather pink face, who bent his head and peered at him through his thick spectacles.

"Excuse me. Perhaps you can tell me

if the lady who cooks for the musicians lives here. She is a lady dressed in black . . ."

Angel Face shut the door in his face. The short-sighted man was still peering about looking for him. Seeing that he wasn't there he asked at the next house.

"Goodbye, Niña Tomasita. Good luck!"

"I'm going to the little market place."

The two voices had spoken at once. La Masacuata was already at the door when Angel Face went to open it.

"How did it go?" he asked La Masacuata, who had just returned from the prison.

"Same as usual."

"What did they say?"

"Nothing."

"Did you see Vasquez?"

"Did I see him? Not likely. They took in his breakfast basket and brought it back again, and that was that!"

"Then he's not in the prison?"

"You could have knocked me down with a feather when they brought out the basket untouched, but a gentleman there told me he'd been sent out to work."

"The governor?"

"No. I gave the brute a piece of my mind. He tried to mess me about."

"How do you think Camila is?"

"It's taking its course. Yes, poor girl, it's taking its course!"

"She's very very bad, isn't she?"

"She's lucky. What could be better than to go before ever you know what life is about! You're the one I'm sorry for. You ought to go and pray to Jesus of La Merced. Who knows, he might perform a miracle for you. This morning before I went to the prison I left a candle there and I said to him: 'Look here, my little Negro, here I am coming to you, because you're not our papa for nothing, and you must listen to me: you can save that girl's life; I asked the Virgin to save

her before I got up and now I'm bothering you for the same reason; I'll leave you this candle and I'm going away trusting in your power, but I'll be back again soon to remind you of my prayer!' "

Half asleep, Angel Face remembered his dream. Among the men in red trousers, the Judge Advocate General—with the face of an owl—was fencing with an unknown man, kissing him, licking him, eating him, excreting him, eating him again . . .

CHAPTER XXVII

The Road to Exile

General Canales' mount stumbled on in the dim light of dusk, drunk with fatigue under the dead weight of the rider clinging to the pommel. The birds flew over the woods, and the clouds passed over the mountains, climbing here, descending there, descending here, climbing there, just as (before sleep and exhaustion had overcome him) the rider himself had climbed and descended—over pathless hills, through wide and stony rivers whose rushing waters refreshed his mule, across slopes laced with mud down which stones slid to shatter themselves over precipices, through inextricable thickets full of angry brambles, and along goat-tracks evocative of witches and highwaymen.

The night's tongue was hanging out. A league of marshy land. Then a shadowy form appeared, lifted the rider from his mount, led him to a deserted hut and went silently away. But he returned at once. He must have gone outside among the cicadas singing: cricricri, cricricri, cricricri! He stayed in the cabin for a short while and then vanished like smoke. Now he was back again. He came in and out, in and out. It was as if he went away to report his find and returned to make sure he was still there. The starlit landscape seemed to follow his lizard-like comings and goings, like a faithful dog wagging a tail of sounds (cricricri, cricricri, cricricri) in the silence of the night.

In the end he returned to the hut for good. The wind was leaping through the branches of the trees. Day was dawning in the night-school where the frogs had been learning to read the stars. An atmosphere of happy digestion. The five senses of light. Objects began to take shape to the eyes of the man squatting by the door, a timid good man who was silenced by the impressiveness of dawn and the innocent breathing of the sleeping horseman. Last night he had been a mere shape, today he was a man; it was he who had taken the rider from his horse. When it grew light he made a fire, placing the rough-hewn smoky hearth-stones crosswise, scraping the old ashes with a piece of candlewood, and putting together dry twigs and green wood. Green wood does not burn quietly; it talks like a parrot, sweats, contracts, laughs and cries. The horseman awoke frozen with terror at what he saw, and not yet fully himself; he took one jump to the door, pistol in hand, determined to sell his life dearly. Undisturbed by the barrel of the weapon pointing at him, the other man silently pointed to the coffee-pot simmering beside the fire. But the rider paid no attention. He advanced slowly towards the door—the hut was sure to be surrounded by soldiers—and saw before him nothing but a wide plain bathed in rosy mist. Distance. Like a blue lather. Trees. Clouds. A titillation of bird-trills. His mule was dozing under a fig-tree. He stood listening unwinkingly to test the evidence of his eyes, and heard nothing at all except the harmonious concert of the birds and the slow gliding of a stream, whose copious waters left an al-

most imperceptible ssss on the youthful air, like castor sugar falling into a bowl of hot coffee.

"You're not from the Government?" murmured the man who had unhorsed him, carefully stowing away forty or fifty corn-cobs behind him.

The horseman raised his eyes and looked at his companion. He shook his head from side to side without moving his mouth from his mug of coffee.

"Tatita!"* murmured the other with a sly expression, letting his eyes wander round the room like those of a lost dog.

"I'm on the run . . ."

The man stopped hiding his corn-cobs and went to pour out more coffee for his visitor. Canales could not speak of his misfortunes.

"Same as me, Señor! I'm running away because of the corn-cobs I took. But I'm not a thief; it was my land until they took it away from me; and my mules too . . ."

General Canales was interested in what the Indian was saying, and wanted to hear his explanation of how one could steal without being a thief.

"I'll tell you, Tatita, how it is I steal although I'm not a thief by trade; before this I was the owner of a little bit of land close by, and eight mules. I had my house, my wife and children, and I was as honest as you are . . ."

"Yes, and then?"

"Three years ago the Political Commissioner came here and told me to take a load of pinewood on the mules' backs for the President's fête-day. I took them, Señor, what else could I do? When he arrived and saw my mules, he put me in prison in a cell by myself, and he and the mayor, a ladino, divided my animals between them, and when I asked for the money they owed me for my work, the

---

* Little father. Term of respect used by the Indians to the Whites.

Commissioner told me I was a brute and if I didn't hold my jaw as once he'd put me in irons. 'Very well, Señor Commissioner,' I said to him, 'do what you like to me, but the mules belong to me.' I couldn't say anything more, Tatita, because he hit me such a whack on the head with his belt that it was nearly the death of me . . ."

A bitter smile came and went under the gray moustache of the old soldier in disgrace. The Indian went on in the same tone without raising his voice:

"When I left hospital they came and told me they had put my children in prison but they'd set them free if I gave them three thousand pesos. As my children were young and tender, I hurried off to the Governor and asked him to keep them in prison and not send them to the barracks, and I would mortgage my land and raise the three thousand pesos. I went to the capital and the lawyer there arranged with a foreign gentleman to sign a paper saying they would give me three thousand pesos on a mortgage. That's what they read out to me, but it wasn't what they wrote. Soon afterwards they sent a man from the law-courts to tell me I was to leave my land because it wasn't mine any longer, because I'd sold it to the foreigner for three thousand pesos. I swore to God that this wasn't true, but they believed the lawyer and not me, and I had to leave my land, and in spite of their taking the three thousand pesos from me my sons went to the barracks: one died guarding the frontier; the other was so badly wounded he'd have been better dead, and their mamma, my wife, died of malaria. And that's why I came to steal, although I'm not a thief, Tata, even if they beat me to death or throw me in jail."

"And that's what we soldiers are defending!"

"What did you say, Tata?"

A storm of feelings was raging in old Canales' breast, such feelings as are always aroused in the heart of a good man when confronted with injustice. He suffered on behalf of his country, as though its very blood was corrupt. He suffered in his skin, in the marrow of his bones and the roots of his hair, under his nails, between his teeth. Which was the truth? Had he never thought with his head hitherto, but always with his kepi? It is a more despicable and therefore a sadder thing to be a solider simply in order to keep a gang of ruffians, exploiters and self-important betrayers of their country in power, than it is to die of hunger in exile. By what right are soldiers forced to be loyal to régimes which are themselves disloyal to ideas, to the world and to their nation?

The Indian was gazing at the general as if he were some strange fetish, but without understanding the few words which he had uttered.

"You must go, Tatita, before the mounted police get here!"

Canales asked the Indian to go with him into the neighboring state, and the Indian agreed; for he was like a rootless tree without his land. And the pay was good.

They left the cabin without putting out the fire. They cut their way through the forest with their machetes. The tracks of a jaguar wound away ahead of them. Darkness. Light. Darkness. Light. Patchwork of leaves. They saw the hut shining behind them like a meteor. Noon. Motionless clouds. Motionless trees. Dejection. Blinding whiteness. Stones and more stones. Insects. Skeletons, bare of flesh and warm like newly ironed underclothes. Decomposition. Flustered birds, circling overhead. Water and thirst. The tropics. Timeless change, and always, always the same heat.

The general was wearing a handkerchief to keep the sun off the nape of his neck. The Indian walked beside him, keeping pace with the mule.

"I think if we walk all night we may reach the frontier tomorrow morning, and it wouldn't be a bad idea to risk taking to the main road, because I have to stop at the house of some friends at Las Aldeas."

"The main road, Tata! What are you thinking of? You'll run into the mounted police!"

"Come along! Follow me! Nothing venture, nothing have, and these friends of mine may be very useful to us!"

"Oh no, Tata!"

And the Indian gave a sudden start and said:

"Don't you hear? Don't you hear, Tata?"

A troop of horses could be heard approaching, but soon afterwards the wind dropped. The sound seemed to be left behind, as if they were going away.

"Quiet!"

"It's the mounted police, Tata, I know what I'm talking about, and now we'll have to take this path, even though it's a longer way round to Las Aldeas!"

The general plunged down a side track after the Indian. He had to dismount and lead the mule. As the gully swallowed them up they had the feeling of being inside a snail-shell, sheltered from the danger threatening them. It grew suddenly dark. The shadows were gathering in the depths of the sleeping ravine. Trees and birds seemed like mysterious portents in the gentle, continuously fluctuating breeze. A cloud of reddish dust between them and the stars was all they saw of the mounted police as they galloped past the place they had just left.

They had been traveling all night.

"When we get to the top of the hill we'll see Las Aldeas, Tata."

The Indian went on ahead with the mule to announce their arrival to Ca-

nales' friends, three unmarried sisters who divided their lives between hymns and quinsy, novenas and ear-ache, pains in the face and pains in back and side. They breakfasted on the news. They nearly fainted. They received the general in their bedroom. The drawing-room did not inspire them with confidence.

In country villages visitors enter a house unannounced and go right into the kitchen calling out: "Ave Maria! Ave Maria!"

The soldier told them the story of his misfortunes in a slow, dispassionate tone, shedding a few tears when he mentioned his daughter.

His friends wept with grief; so great was their grief that for the moment they forgot their own sorrow, the death of their mother, for whom they were wearing deepest mourning.

"But we'll arrange for your escape—the crossing of the frontier at any rate. I'll go and ask the neighbors. This is the moment to remember which of them are smugglers. And I know nearly all the possible crossing-places are guarded by the authorities."

It was the eldest sister speaking and she looked questioningly at the others.

"Yes, we'll take care of your escape as my sister says, General; and as I don't think some provisions would come amiss I'll go and get them ready," said the second sister, whose toothache had yielded to the shock of Canales' arrival. The youngest added:

"Since you're going to spend the day with us I'll stay and talk to you and cheer you up a bit."

The general looked gratefully at the three sisters—the service they were doing him was beyond price—and begged them in a low voice to forgive him for being such a nuisance.

"Not another word, General!"

"No, General, you mustn't talk like that!"

"I realize how good and kind you are, my dears, but I know I'm compromising you by being in your house."

"But we're you're friends after all—you can imagine that since Mamma died . . ."

"And tell me, what did your dear Mamma die of?"

"My sister will tell you, we'll go and get things ready."

So said the eldest. Then she sighed. She was carrying her stays rolled up in her shawl and she went off to put them on in the kitchen, where the second sister was preparing some provisions for the general, surrounded by pigs and poultry.

"It wasn't possible to take her to the capital and they didn't understand her illness here; you know how it is, General. She got worse and worse. Poor darling! She died weeping because she was leaving us alone in the world. It couldn't be helped. But just imagine, we hadn't anything to pay the doctor, who sent in a bill for fifteen visits amounting to something like the entire value of this house—all that our father left us. Excuse me a moment, I must go and see what your servant wants."

When the younger sister went out, Canales fell asleep. Eyes closed. Feather-light body.

"What do you want, boy?"

"For the love of heaven tell me where I can go and relieve myself . . ."

"Over there—in the pigsty!"

The peace of the countryside wove itself into the sleeping soldier's dreams. The gratefulness of the cornfields, the tenderness of the pastures with their simple little flowers. The morning was soon over, what with the terror of some partridges spattered with shot by sportsmen, the black terror of a burial spattered with holy water by the priest, and the troublesome behavior of an active young bullock. Several important events took place in the dove-cote in the spinsters' patio:

the death of a seducer, a courtship and thirty marriages in the sunshine. Nothing at all, as you might say!

Nothing at all, as you might say! said the pigeons, looking out of the little windows of their houses. Nothing at all, as you might say!

At twelve o'clock they woke the general for lunch. Rice with herbs. Beef broth. Stew. Chicken. Beans. Bananas. Coffee.

"Ave Maria!"

The voice of the Political Commissioner broke in upon their lunch. The spinsters turned pale and did not know what to do. The general slipped behind a door.

"Don't be alarmed, my dears; I'm not the Devil with Eleven Thousand Horns! Good gracious, how frightened you are, and after I've been so kind to you too!"

The poor things had quite lost the power of speech.

"And aren't you going to ask me to come in and sit down—even if it's on the floor?"

The youngest brought up a chair for the most important official in the village.

"Thanks very much. But who was having lunch with you? I see there's a fourth place laid."

All three stared at the general's plate.

"It was—you know—" stammered the elder, twisting her fingers in her misery.

The second sister came to the rescue:

"It's rather difficult to explain, but although Mamma is dead, we always lay a place for her, so as not to feel too lonely."

"Why, it looks as if you're turning into spiritualists."

"Won't you have something, Commissioner?"

"That's kind of you but I've already eaten. My wife has just given me lunch, and I couldn't take my siesta because I received a telegram from the Minister of the Interior instructing me to take proceedings against you if you don't pay the doctor."

"But, Commissioner, that's not fair, you know it isn't . . ."

"That may be so, but needs must when the devil drives."

"Of course," exclaimed the three sisters, with tears in their eyes.

"I'm very sorry to have to come and upset you like this, but that's how it is, as you know already; nine thousand pesos, the house or . . ."

The doctor's odious stubbornness was plainly expressed in the way the Commissioner turned on his heel, and presented them with his back—a back which looked like a tree-trunk.

The general heard them weeping. They locked and barred the street-door, in terror lest the Commissioner should return. Their tears splashed on to the plate of chicken.

"How cruel life is, General! You're lucky to be leaving this country for ever."

"What did he threaten you with?" asked Canales, addressing the eldest of the three who said to her sisters without drying her tears:

"One of you tell him."

"With taking Mamma out of her grave," stammered the youngest.

Canales stared at all three sisters, and stopped eating.

"What do you say?"

"Exactly that, General; with taking Mamma out of her grave."

"But that's iniquitous!"

"Tell him."

"All right. But you must understand, General, that our village doctor is a scoundrel of the deepest dye; we were told so before, but one can only learn from experience. What were we to do? It's difficult to believe people can be so wicked."

"A few radishes, General?"

The second sister handed the dish, and while Canales helped himself to radishes the youngest went on with her story:

"We fell into his trap. This is his game: when one of his patients falls seriously ill, and the last thing the relatives are thinking about is a funeral, he has a burial vault built. Then, when the moment comes—this was what happened to us—rather than let Mamma lie in the bare earth we accepted one of the recesses in his vault without realizing what we were letting ourselves in for."

"And he knew we were unprotected women," remarked the eldest sister between sobs.

"I can tell you, General, the day he sent in the bill we were all three thunderstruck: nine thousand pesos for fifteen visits; nine thousand pesos or this house, because it appears he wants to get married, or . . ."

"Or if we didn't pay—he told my sister —oh it's too abominable—'you can take your rubbish out of my vault!' "

Canales struck the table with his fist.

"Dirty little quack!"

He thumped on the table again, making the plates, cutlery and glasses rattle, and opening and shutting his fingers as if he wanted to strangle this particular scoundrel and also destroy the whole social system which produced one shameful abuse after another.

"Have simple people been promised a Kingdom of Heaven on earth—what sanctimonious rubbish!—merely so that they should put up with such rogues?" he reflected. "No! We've had quite enough of this Reign of Camels! I swear I will work for total revolution; everything must be turned upside down! The people must rise against these parasites, exploiters of official positions and idlers who would be better off cultivating the soil. Everyone must take his share in destruction! destruction! destruction! Not a single puppet among them shall keep his head."

His departure was fixed for ten o'clock that night, according to an arrangement with a smuggler who was a friend of the family. The general wrote several letters, including an urgent one to his daughter. The Indian was going to pass himself off as a carrier and return by the main road. There were no goodbyes. The horses moved off with their hooves wrapped in rags, while the sisters stood against the wall in a dark alley, weeping bitterly. When he reached the wider road the general felt a hand seize the bridle of his horse. He heard dragging footsteps.

"What a fright they gave me," whispered the smuggler. "I almost stopped breathing! But don't worry—they're only some men going with the doctor to serenade his sweetheart."

A candlewood torch was burning at the end of the street, sending out tongues of flame to join and separate the shapes of the houses and trees, and of five or six men standing together under a window.

"Which of them is the doctor?" asked the general, with his pistol in his hand.

The smuggler reined in his horse, raised his arm and pointed to a man holding a guitar. A shot tore through the air, and a man fell to the ground, as a banana falls from the bunch.

"Jesus Maria! Look what you've done! We must get away, quick—or they'll get us! Come on, spur your horse!"

"It's what . . . everyone must . . . do to . . . free the . . . people!" The words were jerked out of Canales between the strides of his galloping horse.

The noise of the horses' hooves woke the dogs, the dogs woke the hens, the hens woke the cocks, the cocks woke the villagers, who came reluctantly back to life, yawning, stretching and afraid.

The party of serenaders lifted up the doctor's dead body. People came out with lanterns from the surrounding houses. The lady who had been the object of the serenade could not weep, but stood stunned with shock and half undressed, holding a Chinese lantern in her white hand, her gaze lost in the murderous darkness.

"We're alongside the river now, General, but it needs a brave man to get across where we mean to cross, I don't mind telling you. Oh life, if only you lasted for ever!"

"Who's afraid?" answered Canales, who was riding behind on a black horse.

"Bravo! A man feels as strong as a lion when someone's after him! Hold on to me, tight, tight, or you'll lose the way!"

Everything was indistinct around them, the air was warm but with icy currents in it. They could hear the river rushing through the reeds.

They dismounted and plunged into a gully. The smuggler tethered the horses in a place he knew of, where he could collect them on his return. Between the shadows, patches of river reflected the starlit sky and a strange floating vegetation of mottled green trees with eyes the color of talc, and white teeth. The water gurgled past the sleepy, greasy banks, smelling of frogs.

The smuggler and the general leaped from islet to islet in silence, each with his pistol in his hand. Their shadows followed them like alligators; the alligators followed them like shadows. Clouds of insects stung them, there was a winged poison in the air. There was the smell of the sea, of the sea caught in the net of the forest, with all its fish, its stars, corals and madrepores, its profundities and currents. The moss dangled overhead like the slimy tentacles of moribund octopuses. Even the wind beasts dared not go where they were going. Canales kept turning his head in every direction, lost in this ominous, inaccessible region, as destructive by nature as its fauna. An alligator which had obviously tasted human flesh attacked the smuggler, but he had time to jump out of the way. It was not so with the general, who turned round to defend himself and stopped dead to find another alligator waiting for him with open jaws. It was a crucial moment. A deathly shiver ran down his spine. His hair stood on end. He was speechless with horror. He clenched his fists. There were three successive shots and the echo repeated them, before he took advantage of the wounded beast's flight to leap to safety. The smuggler

fired again. Recovering from his terror the general ran forward and shook him by the hand, burning his fingers on his pistol barrel.

The sun was rising when they parted at the frontier. Over the emerald fields, over the mountains with their dense clump of trees like musical boxes for the birds, and over the forest, alligator-shaped clouds floated by, carrying treasures of light on their backs.

PART III
Weeks, Months, Years . . .

CHAPTER XXVIII

Conversation in the Darkness

The first voice:
"What day is it?"
The second voice:
"Why yes, what day can it be?"
The third voice:
"Wait a moment. I was arrested on a Friday. Friday, Saturday, Sunday, Monday . . . Monday. But how long have I been here? So what day is it?"
The first voice:
"I feel as if we were very far away, don't you? very far away."
Third voice:
"Don't talk like that!"
The first two voices:
"We mustn't . . ."
". . . talk like that!"
The third voice:
"But don't stop talking. I'm terrified of the silence; I'm afraid. I keep imagining a hand stretching out through the darkness, to seize me by the neck and strangle me."
The second voice:
"Talk for God's sake! Tell us what's happening in the town; you were the last

to see it. What people are doing; how everything's going . . . Sometimes I imagine the whole city buried in shadows as we are, shut in between very high walls, and the streets deep in the dead mud of winter. I don't know if it's the same with you, but at the end of the winter I couldn't bear to think that the mud was drying up. When I talk about the town it gives me a damnable craving to eat; I long for some Californian apples . . ."
The first voice:
"Or oranges perhaps! As for me I'd rather have a cup of hot tea."
The second voice:
"And to think that everything must be going on as usual in the town, as if nothing had happened, as if we weren't buried alive here! The trams must all be running. What time is it, for that matter?"
The first voice:
"It must be about . . ."
The second voice.
"I haven't the faintest idea."
The first voice:
"It must be about . . ."
The third voice:
"Talk! Go on talking. For heaven's sake don't stop talking! I'm terrified of

the silence; I'm afraid, I keep imagining a hand stretching out through the darkness, to seize me by the neck and strangle me!"

And he added in a voice of anguish:

"I didn't want to tell you, but I'm afraid we may be flogged . . ."

The first voice:

"Don't talk about it. It must be terrible to be beaten!"

The second voice:

"Even the grandchildren of men who have been flogged feel the shame of it!"

The first voice:

"You're talking wickedly! Much better keep quiet!"

The second voice:

"Everything's wicked to a sacristan."

The first voice:

"Nothing of the sort! What stories have they been stuffing you with?"

The second voice:

"I tell you that everything that other people do is wicked to a sacristan!"

The third voice:

"Talk! Go on talking! Don't stop, for the sake of whatever you love most in the world! The silence terrifies me; I'm afraid. I keep imagining a hand stretching out through the darkness to seize me by the neck and strangle me!"

The student and the sacristan were still imprisoned in the jail where the beggars had spent one night, but they now had the lawyer Carvajal for company.

"My arrest happened in a very terrible way," said Carvajal. "The servant who went out to buy bread in the morning came back with the news that the house was surrounded by soldiers. She told my wife and my wife told me, but I thought nothing of it, and imagined that they were after some brandy-smuggler or other. I finished shaving, had my bath and my breakfast and dressed myself to go and congratulate the President—up to the nines in fact! 'Hallo, my friend, what a surprise,' I said to the Judge Advocate General when I found him on my doorstep in full uniform. 'I've come for you,' he replied, 'and be quick because I'm late already!' I went with him a little way and when he asked me if I had no idea why the soldiers were surrounding the house, I said no I hadn't. 'Well then I'll tell you, you little rat,' he said. 'They've come to arrest you.' I looked at his face and saw he wasn't joking. Just then an officer took hold of me by the arm, and they escorted me away, dressed as I was in my morning coat and top hat, and threw my carcass into this jail."

And after a pause he added:

"Now you two talk! I'm terrified of the darkness. I'm afraid!"

"Oh dear! Oh dear! What's happening?" exclaimed the student. "The sacristan's head is as cold as a millstone!"

"What d'you mean?"

"I've been touching him, and he can't feel anything any more and . . ."

"It wasn't me, take care what you say!"

"Who was it then? You, Carvajal?"

"No."

"Then . . . is there a dead man among us?"

"No, it's not a dead man. It's me . . ."

"But who are you?" put in the student. "You seem very cold!"

An extremely weak voice replied:

"I'm one of you."

The first three voices:

"Ohhh!"

The sacristan told Carvajal the story of his own misfortunes.

"I left the sacristy"—and he pictured himself coming out of the tidy sacristy with its smell of extinguished censers, old woodwork, gold ornaments and locks of dead people's hair. "I crossed the church"—and he saw himself traversing the church, overawed by the proximity of the Blessed Sacrament, the immobility of the candles and the mobility of the flies

—"and I went to take down the notice of the Virgin of La O's novena, because one of the brothers had told me to, now that it was over. But the trouble was that as I can't read, I removed a paper announcing the anniversary of the President's mother instead by mistake. It was by the President's orders that the Blessed Sacrament had been exposed. I couldn't have done anything worse. They arrested me and put me in this prison as a revolutionary!"

The student was the only one who kept silent about the reason for his arrest. Talking about his diseased lungs caused him less pain than speaking ill of his country. He dwelt on his physical infirmities in order to forget that he had seen the light during a shipwreck, that he had seen the light among corpses, that he had opened his eyes in a school with no windows, where they had extinguished the small light of faith in him as soon as he arrived, without putting anything in its place except darkness, chaos, confusion and the astronomical melancholy of a eunuch. And in a low voice he began reciting this poem to lost generations:

We anchor in the ports of nothingness,
With no lights on the masts of our arms;
We are wet with tears, brine-soaked
As sailors returned from the sea.

Your mouth is my delight—kiss me!
and your hand in my hand lay yesterday.
Ah! how useless does life flow again
through the cold river-bed of the heart!

The knapsack torn and the honey spilt,
the bees flew away through space
like meteors. Not yet,
The rose of the winds had lost its petals;
the heart bounded over the graves.

Ah, ri-ri-ri, rumbling, rumbling cart!
Through the moonless night go the horses

Filled with roses to the hooves,
As if returning from the stars
And not from the cemetery.

Ah ri-ri-ri, rumbling, rumbling cart,
funicular of tears, ri-ri-ri,
between feathered brows, ri-ri-ri.

Riddle of dawn in the stars
illusion of bends in the road,
and how far from the world and how
    early!

Waves of tears strive in the ocean
to reach the strand of the eyelids.

"Talk, go on talking!" said Carvajal after a long silence. "Go on talking!"

"Let's talk about liberty!" murmured the student.

"What an idea!" interrupted the sacristan. "Fancy talking about liberty in prison!"

"And don't you suppose sick people talk about health in hospital?"

The fourth voice murmured faintly: "There's no hope of freedom for us, my friends; we must put up with this as long as God wills. The men of this town who desired their country's good are far away now: some of them begging outside houses in a foreign land, others rotting in a common grave. A day will come when no one dares walk the streets of this town. Already the trees don't bear fruit as they used to. Maize is less nourishing than it was. Sleep is less restful; water is less refreshing. The air is becoming impossible to breathe. Plagues follow epidemics, epidemics follow plagues, and soon an earthquake will put an end to us all. My eyes tell me that our race is doomed! When it thunders, it is a voice from heaven crying: 'You are evil and corrupt, you are accomplices in wickedness!' Hundreds of men have had their brains blown out against our prison walls by murderous bullets. Our marble palaces are wet with innocent blood. Where can one turn one's eyes in search of freedom?"

The sacristan:

"To God, who is omnipotent!"

The student:

"What's the use, if He doesn't answer?"

The sacristan:

"Because it is His Blessed Will."

The student:

"What a pity!"

The third voice:

"Talk! Go on talking, for heaven's sake! Don't stop! I'm terrified of the silence; I'm afraid. I keep imagining a hand stretching out through the darkness to seize us by the neck and strangle us!"

"Better to pray."

The sacristan's voice spread Christian resignation throughout the prison cell. Carvajal, who had passed as a liberal and a priest-hater among his neighbors, murmured:

"Let us pray . . ."

But the student broke in:

"What's the good of praying! We ought not to pray! We ought to try and break this door down and go to meet the revolution!"

Two arms belonging to someone he could not see embraced him warmly, and he felt against his cheek the bristles of a small beard wet with tears:

"You can die in peace, ex-master of the Infant School of San José. There's hope yet in a country where youth can talk like that!"

The third voice:

"Talk, go on talking, go on talking!"

CHAPTER XXIX

Council of War

The indictment charging Canales and Carvajal with sedition, rebellion and trea-son, with all possible aggravating circumstances, ran to so many pages that it was impossible to read it right through at a sitting. Fourteen witnesses stated unanimously on oath that on the night of April 21st they had been in the Cathedral Porch, in which they habitually spent the night owing to their extreme poverty; and that they saw General Eusebio Canales and Abel Carvajal, the lawyer, fall upon a soldier who had been identified as Colonel José Parrales Sonriente and strangle him, in spite of the resistance he put up; he fought hand to hand like a lion, but was unable to use his weapons to defend himself against superior strength. They stated also that as soon as the murder had been committed, Carvajal addressed the following or similar words to Canales: "Now that we have killed 'the man with the little mule' the military leaders will have to hand over their weapons and recognize you, General, as the Supreme Head of the Army. It will soon be dawn; let's hurry off with the news to those who are collected in my house, so that they may proceed with the arrest and execution of the President of the Republic, and the organization of a new government."

Carvajal was astounded. Every page of the indictment had a surprise in store for him. It would have been laughable except that the accusation was much too serious. And he went on reading. He was reading by the light of a window giving onto a shut-in patio, in the little unfurnished room reserved for those condemned to death. The Council of War which was to try the case was meeting that night, and they had left him alone with the indictment to prepare his defense. But they had left it till the last moment. He was trembling all over. He read without understanding or pausing, tormented by the fact that the darkness was devouring the manuscript, which seemed to be dissolving gradually into damp ashes in his hands. He did not succeed in reading much of it. The sun was setting. Its light was growing dim and his eyes were clouded with anguish at its loss. A last line, two words, the stroke of a pen, a date, a page . . . He tried in vain to read the number of the page; darkness was flooding over the paper like a black ink stain, yet he still hung impatiently over the dossier as if, instead of his having to read it, it was to be tied round his neck like a stone before he was hurled into the abyss. The rattling of the non-political prisoners' chains could be heard all along the invisible courtyards, and from further off still came the muted sounds of the traffic in the city streets.

"Oh God! My poor frozen body needs warmth and my eyes need light more desperately than do those of all the inhabitants of the hemisphere the sun is now shining on put together. If they knew of my sufferings they would be more merciful than you, oh God, and give me back the sun so that I could finish reading . . ."

Again and again he counted the pages he had not read, by touch alone. Ninety-one. Again and again he passed his fingertips over the surface of the rough-grained sheets, trying to read as the blind do in his desperation.

Last night, in the small hours, they had moved him in a locked van with a great display of force from the Second Police Station to the Central Prison; however, so great was his pleasure at seeing and hearing and feeling the street around him that for a moment he thought they were taking him to his own house: the words died on his lips in bitter tears and longing.

The myrmidons of the law found him with the indictment in his arms and the sweet taste of the wet streets in his mouth; they snatched the documents from him and pushed him without a word into the room where the Council of War was sitting.

"But, Mr. President," Carvajal plucked up courage to say to the general who was presiding over the council, "how can I defend myself when you don't even give me time to read the indictment?"

"That is nothing to do with us," answered the President; "the intervals between sessions are short, time is passing, and this matter is urgent. We have been summoned here to pronounce sentence."

What followed was like a dream to Carvajal, half ritual, half farce. He was the principal actor and faced them all from his position on the see-saw of death, in the middle of a hostile void. But he did not feel afraid; he felt nothing; his anxieties lay dormant under his numbed skin. He made an impression of great courage. The table round which the tribunal sat was covered by a flag, as prescribed by the regulations. Military uniforms. Reading of the documents. Of numerous documents. Taking of oaths. The military statute-book lay like a stone on the table, on top of the flag. The beggars were sitting in the witnesses' seats. Flatfoot sat stiffly erect, with his cheerful toothless drunkard's face, his hair neatly brushed, not missing a word of what was read out, nor an expression on the President's face. Salvador the Tiger followed the proceedings with the dignity of a gorilla, picking his flattened nose or the few teeth scattered in his huge mouth, stretching from ear to ear. The tall, bony, sinister-looking Widower twisted his face into a corpselike rictus to smile at the members of the tribunal. Plump, wrinkled, dwarfish Lulo gave way to sudden outbursts of laughter or anger, amiability or hatred, and then shut his eyes and stopped his ears to show that he wanted to hear and see nothing that was going on. Don Juan, a small, moody-looking figure, was dressed in his inevitable frock-coat and other shabby garments exhaling a bourgeois and family atmosphere (a broad tie stained with tomato-juice, down-at-heel patent leather shoes, false cuffs, a removable dickey) and was given an air of gentlemanly elegance by his straw hat and stone deafness. Don Juan, who could not hear a thing, was counting the soldiers posted all round the walls of the room at intervals of two yards. Close to him was Ricardo the Musician, with his head and part of his face swathed in a colored bandanna, a scarlet nose and his bristly beard greasy with food. Ricardo the Musician was talking to himself, with his eyes fixed on the swollen belly of the deaf-mute, who was dribbling over the seat and scratching the lice in her left armpit. After the deaf-mute came Pereque, a Negro with only one ear the shape of a small chamber-pot. After Pereque, Little Miona, who was exceedingly thin, blind in one eye, moustachioed and stank of old mattresses.

After reading the indictment, the Prosecutor, a soldier with his hair *en brosse* and his small head emerging from a military tunic with a collar twice too big for it, got to his feet to ask for a sentence of death. Carvajal turned and looked at the members of the tribunal, searching for signs of wisdom and judgment. The first one his eyes encountered was as drunk as it was possible to be. His brown hands were outlined against the flag; they were like the hands of a peasant acting in a play about a trial at a village fête. Next to him was a dark-skinned officer, also drunk. And the President, who was giving the most finished performance of them all as an alcoholic, seemed on the point of passing out.

He could not say anything in his defense. He tried to utter a few words, but at once received the painful impression that no one was listening—and in fact no one was listening. His words crumbled in his mouth like damp bread.

The sentence had been drawn up and written out in advance; there was something portentous about it, in contrast to the simplicity of those who were putting it into effect and would sign it (puppets made of gold and dried beef, bathed from head to foot in the diarrhetic light of the oil lamp) or in contrast to the beggars with their toads' eyes and their snakelike shadows lying like black moons on the orange floor—or to the little soldiers sucking their chin-straps, or to the furniture, as silent as if it stood in a house where a crime had been committed.

"I appeal against the sentence!"

Carvajal's voice was in his boots.

"Let's keep to the point," grumbled the President, "there's no question of an appeal or peal, or any other such rubbish here!"

A glass of water as large as the immensity he was holding in his hands helped him to swallow what he was trying to expel from his body: the idea of suffering, of the mechanism of death, of the impact of bullets on bones, blood on the living skin, glazed eyes, warm linen, the earth. Terrified he gave back the glass and kept his hand outstretched until he could summon up the courage to withdraw it. He refused the cigarette he was offered. He fingered his neck with trembling hands, while his unfocused gaze, unrelated to the pale cement of his face, wandered round the whitewashed walls of the room.

More dead than alive, he was pushed along a drafty passage; there was a sharp taste in his mouth, his legs were giving under him, and he had a tear in each eye.

"Here, have a drink," said a lieutenant with eyes like a heron's.

He raised the bottle to his mouth—it seemed enormous—and drank.

"Lieutenant," said a voice from the shadows, "you will join the batteries to-

morrow. We have orders that no indul-
gences of any description are to be
granted to political offenders."

A few steps further on they entombed
him in an underground dungeon three
yards long by two and a half wide, in
which twelve prisoners condemned to
death were already standing packed together like sardines, motionless for lack
of space, satisfying their physical needs
where they stood and trampling on their
own excrement. Carvajal was Number
13. When the soldiers left them, the painful breathing of the mass of doomed men
filled the silence of the cell, already disturbed by the distant cries of a walled-up
prisoner.

Two or three times Carvajal caught
himself mechanically counting the cries
of this poor wretch, who had been condemned to die of thirst: Seventy-two!
Seventy-three! Seventy-four!

The stench of the trampled excrement
and the lack of fresh air made him feel
faint, and carried him away from this
group of human beings to wander along
the brink of infernal precipices of despair, counting the prisoner's cries.

Lucio Vasquez was pacing to and fro
in a neighboring cell, completely yellow
with jaundice, with his nails and eyeballs
the color of the underside of an ilex leaf.
The only thing that sustained him in his
misery was the idea that he would one
day have his revenge on Genaro Rodas,
whom he believed to be responsible for
his troubles. He was kept alive by this
remote hope, as black and sweet as molasses. He would wait there in the
shadows for all eternity if only he could
avenge himself. Such pitch-black night
inhabited his ignoble breast, that nothing
but the image of the knife cutting into
Rodas' entrail and leaving a wound like
an open mouth could let any light in
upon his malevolent thoughts. With his
hands cramped by the cold, Vasquez
spent hour after hour motionless as a

worm made of yellow mud, savoring his
revenge. Kill him! Kill him! And as if his
enemy were already at hand, he would
stretch out in the darkness, feel the ice-
cold handle of his knife, and hurl himself
on Rodas in his imagination, like a ghost
going through its accustomed movements.

He was jolted back to reality by the
cries of the walled-up prisoner:

"*Per Dio, per favori* . . . water!
Water! Water! Water! Tineti, water,
water! *Per Dio, per favori,* waaater,
waaater . . . water!"

The walled-up man threw himself
against the door of his cell, which had
been completely obliterated on the outside by a layer of bricks cemented to the
floor, cemented to the walls.

"Water, Tineti! Water, Tineti! Water,
per Dio, water, *per favori,* Tineti!"

Devoid of tears, devoid of saliva, devoid of anything that was wet or cool,
with his throat a burning thorn-bush,
revolving in a world of lights and patches
of darkness, he hammered out his inces-
sant cry:

"Water, Tineti! Water, Tineti! Water,
Tineti!"

A Chinaman with his face scarred with
smallpox looked after the prisoners.
Every few centuries he would come by
like a last breath of life. Did this strange
semi-divine being really exist, or was he a
fiction of all their imaginations? The
trampled excrement and the cries of the
walled-up prisoners were making their
heads swim and it was possible, yes possible, that this benevolent angel was only
a fantastic vision.

"Water, Tineti! Water, Tineti! *Per Dio,
per favori,* water, water, water, water!"

Soldiers came in and went out again,
tramping across the tiled floor in their
leather sandals, and among them there
were some who used to roar with laughter and shout back at the walled-up
prisoner:

"Tyrolese, Tyrolese! What did you do to the green parrot who talks like a man?"

"Water, *per Dio,* water, Signori, water *per favori!"*. .

Vasquez was brooding over his revenge, and the cries of the Italian left the air as dry and thirsty as a husk of sugar cane. The sound of a shot made him catch his breath. The executions had begun. It must be three in the morning.

CHAPTER XXX

Marriage in Extremis

"There's someone dangerously ill in our neighborhood!"

A spinster came out of the door of every house.

"Someone dangerously ill in our neighborhood!"

A woman called Petronila, with a face like a conscript's and the manner of a diplomat, who (for lack of other attractions) would at least have preferred to be called Berta, came out of the House of the Two Hundred. Next came a friend of the Two Hundred called Silvia, with a face like a chick-pea and clothes of Merovingian cut.

Then Silvia's friend Engracia, with her stays—or rather her armor—eating into her flesh, and her tight shoes into her corns, and a watch-chain hanging round her neck like a halter. Then Engracia's cousin, with a heart-shaped head like a viper's; she was harsh-voiced, dumpy and masculine-looking, hardly bigger than one of Engracia's legs, and had a habit of forecasting disasters out of the almanac and prophesying the coming of comets, anti-Christ, or an age when men would climb up trees to escape from the ardent pursuit of women, and women would go up and fetch them down again.

Someone seriously ill in our neighbor-

hood! What a godsend! They were not aware of entertaining such a thought, yet it was almost explicit in the way their soft voices tried to conceal their gratification over an event which might give many of them work for their scissors, and leave plenty of material over for all of them to cut a dress-length for themselves.

La Masacuata was waiting for them.

"My sisters are ready," declared Petronila from the Two Hundred, without saying what they were ready for.

"If you're short of linen of course you can count on me," remarked Silvia.

And Engracia, little Engracia, who smelled of beef broth when she didn't smell of hair-lotion, added, only half-enunciating the words because her stays were suffocating her:

"I thought of her and said a prayer for the souls of the dying after I had finished my Hour of Prayer."

They were gathered in the room behind the shop, speaking in undertones and trying not to disturb the silence which hung round the invalid's bed like some pharmaceutical product, nor to worry the gentleman who sat with her night and day. A real gentleman, yes indeed. They went up to the bed on tiptoe, more from desire to get a look at his face than at Camila lying there, a ghostly figure with her long eyelashes, her thin, thin neck, her hair in confusion; and, scenting a mystery of some sort—isn't there always a mystery where there is love?—they refused to rest till they had extracted the key to it from the barkeeper. He was her sweetheart! Her sweetheart! Her sweetheart! Her sweetheart! Of course that was it. He was her sweetheart! They all repeated the golden word—all except Silvia, who went discreetly away as soon as she found out that Camila was General Canales' daughter, and did not return. Better not get mixed up with enemies of the Government. He may very well be her sweet-heart, she said to herself, and on the President's side as well, but I'm my brother's sister, and my brother is a deputy, and I might compromise him. "We must trust in God!"

"We must trust in God," she repeated, out in the street by now.

Angel Face was hardly aware of the old maids, although they were anxious to complete their errand of mercy to the sick girl by consoling her lover. He thanked them without hearing what they said—mere words—with his whole soul involved in Camila's involuntary but agonizing moans, nor did he respond to their demonstrations of emotion when they shook his hand. Crushed by his own misery, he felt his body growing cold. He had the impression that it was raining, that his limbs were numb, that he was entangled with invisible phantoms in a space larger than life, a space in which air, light, shadows and objects were iso-lated and alone.

The doctor broke in on the vicious circle of his thoughts.

"Then, doctor . . . ?"

"Only a miracle can save her!"

"You'll come back, won't you?"

The barkeeper never sat down for a moment; yet nothing seemed to exhaust her. She was laundress to the neighbor-hood, and used to put the linen to soak very early in the morning before taking Vasquez's breakfast to the prison; she had had no news of him lately. When she got back she would soap, rub and hang out the washing, and while it dried she would hurry home to do her housework and other chores, see to the invalid, light candles in front of the saints, try and make Angel Face take a little food, wait for the doctor, go to the chemist, put up with the "she-priests," as she called the spinsters, and quarrel with the propri-etress of the mattress-shop. "Mattresses for lazy pigs!" she shouted from her doorway, pretending to whisk away the flies with a rag. "Mattresses for lazy pigs!"

"Nothing but a miracle can save her!"

Angel Face repeated the doctor's words. A miracle, the arbitrary persis-tence of what is perishable, the triumph of a fragment of humanity over the sterile Absolute. He felt a craving to cry out to God to perform the miracle; yet all the while the world was revolving out of reach—useless, hostile, uncertain and purposeless.

They were all expecting the crisis from one moment to the next. The howling of a dog, a loud knock on a door, the chiming of the La Merced clock would make the neighbors cross themselves and exclaim between sighs: "She's at peace at last! Yes, her hour has struck! Poor young man! But it had to be! It was God's will! We shall all come to it!"

Petronila was reporting on the state of affairs to a friend of hers: one of those men who go on looking like little boys even when they are old; he taught Eng-lish and other more unusual subjects and was familiarly known as the Teacher. She wanted to know whether it was pos-sible to save Camila's life by supernatural means, and the Teacher ought to know, because as well as giving English lessons he devoted his spare time to the study of theosophy, spiritualism, magic, astrology, hypnotism, and the occult sciences, and was even the inventor of a method which he called: "A repository of witchcraft useful for finding hidden treasure in haunted houses." The Teacher had never been able to account for his addiction to the unknown. As a young man he had been attracted to the Church, but a mar-ried woman more experienced and domi-neering than himself intervened when he was going to sing the Epistles, and he hung up his cassock and other priestly garments and was left looking rather foolish and lonely. He left the theological college for a commercial school, and would have successfully finished his training had he not been obliged to fly from his professor of accountancy who fell madly in love with him. Mechanics, in the strenuous shape of the iron-works, now opened its grimy arms to him, and he was taken on by a work-shop near his house to blow the bellows, but as he was neither used to hard work nor sufficiently strong for it, he soon gave up the job. Why should he work, when he was the only nephew of a very rich lady who had intended him for the priesthood, a purpose which she had still not abandoned? "Go back to the Church," she used to say, "instead of yawning your head off here; go back to the Church. Can't you see that you're sick of the world, and that you're a bit crazy anyway and as weak as water; that you've tried everything and nothing satisfies you—soldier, musician, bullfighter! Or if you don't want to be a priest why don't you take up teaching— give English lessons for instance? If you're not one of the Lord's chosen, why don't you choose children? English is easier than Latin and more useful, and if you give English lessons your pupils will suppose you're speaking English although they can't understand—and if they don't understand, all the better."

Petronila lowered her voice, as she always did when she was wearing her heart on her sleeve.

"A lover who adores her, who worships her, Teacher; although he kidnapped her, he has treated her with respect and hopes the Church will bless their lifelong union. One doesn't see that sort of thing every day . . ."

"Less often than ever nowadays, my child," put in the tallest member of the Two Hundred, a woman who seemed to have climbed a few rungs of the ladder of her own body, as she came into the room carrying a bunch of roses.

"And this lover of hers has over- whelmed her with kindness, Teacher, and certainly won't survive her—oh dear!"

"Did you say, Petronila," said the Teacher slowly, "that the medical faculty declare they can't do a thing to snatch her out of the hands of the Fates?"

"Yes indeed; they've given her up three times."

"And did you say, Nila, that nothing but a miracle could save her?"

"Just think of it! My heart bleeds for that poor young man . . ."

"Well I've got the key; we'll bring about that miracle. The only thing that can fight death is love, because they are equally strong, as the Song of Songs tells us. And if, as you say, this girl's sweetheart adores her—loves her deeply, I mean, with all his heart and soul and intends to marry her, we can save her life by means of the sacrament of marriage. According to my theory of grafting, that is what should be done in this case."

Petronila very nearly fainted into the Teacher's arms. She aroused the whole household, went back to her friends' house, and sent La Masacuata to speak to the priest, and that same day Camila and Angel Face were married on the very threshold of the next world. The favorite grasped a long, delicate hand, as cold as an ivory paper-knife, in his own feverish right hand, while the priest read the Latin words of the sacrament. The members of the Two Hundred were present— Engracia and the Teacher dressed in black. When the ceremony was over the Teacher exclaimed:

"Make thee another self, for love of me!"

CHAPTER XXXI

Sentinels Made of Ice

In the entrance to the prison two rows of gleaming bayonets could be seen; the soldiers on guard were sitting opposite one another like travelers in a dark railway-carriage. Suddenly one of the passing vehicles stopped at the door. The driver leaned back to get more purchase on the reins, rocking from side to side like a dirty rag doll and spitting out an oath. He had nearly lost his balance! Punished by the brakes, the wheels screeched their way along the smooth high walls of the sinister building, and a pot-bellied man whose legs could hardly reach the ground slowly alighted. Feeling his cab relieved of the weight of the Judge Advocate General, the driver gripped his unlit cigarette between his dry lips—what a relief to be left alone with the horses!—loosened the reins and drove off to wait opposite, beside a garden as stony as a traitor's heart, just at the moment that a woman threw herself on her knees at the Judge Advocate's feet, begging him loudly to listen to her.

"Get up, Señora; I can't listen to you like that! No, no, get up please; I haven't the honor of your acquaintance . . ."

"I'm the wife of Carvajal the lawyer . . ."

"Get up . . ."

But she burst out again:

"I've been looking for you all day and night, Señor, at all hours, everywhere; in your house, in your mother's house, in your office, but without success. You are the only person who knows what has become of my husband; only you know, only you can tell me. Where is he? What has happened to him? Tell me if he is alive, Señor? Tell me that he is alive, Señor?"

"As it happens, Señora, the Council of War which is to hear my colleague's case has received an urgent summons for to-night."

"Aaaaah!"

The intensity of her relief kept her trembling lips apart. Alive! There was

hope in the news. Alive! And as he was innocent—free . . .

But the Judge Advocate's cold expression did not change as he added:

"The political situation of our country does not permit of the Government showing any pity whatsoever to its enemies, Señora. That is all I can say to you. Go and see the President and beg for your husband's life, or he may be sentenced to death and shot within twenty-four hours, by the law of the land . . ."

"La . . . la . . . la . . ."

"The law comes before individuals, Señora, and unless the President reprieves him . . ."

"La-La-La . . ."

She could not speak. She stood there white as the handkerchief she was tearing to pieces with her teeth, otherwise motionless, abstracted, twisting her fingers together.

The Judge Advocate General disappeared between the two rows of bayonets. After a moment of animation, while carriages full of smart ladies and gentlemen came by on their way home from the most fashionable promenade in the town, the street was left exhausted and alone. A tiny tram came sparking and whistling out of a side road, and went off heeling over on its rails.

"La-La-La . . ."

She could not speak. A pair of ice-cold pincers had her by the neck in a tenacious grip, and her body was gradually slipping downwards from her shoulders to the ground. She was nothing but an empty dress, with a head, hands and feet. The sound of a cab approaching along the street resounded in her ears. She stopped it. The horses seemed to swell like tears as they arched their necks, drew back on their haunches and came to a halt. She told the driver to take her to the President's country house as fast as possible, but she was in such a hurry

—such a desperate hurry—that although the horses set off at full speed she never stopped insisting that the driver must make them go faster . . . Surely they ought to be there by now? . . . Faster . . . she must save her husband . . . Faster, faster, faster . . . she snatched the whip from the driver . . . she must save her husband . . . the horses increased their speed under her cruel lashing . . . The whip scorched their flanks . . . save her husband . . . They ought to be there by now . . . But the carriage wouldn't move . . . she could feel that it wasn't moving, the wheels were revolving round the sleeping axles without advancing at all; they were standing still in the same place . . . yet she must save her husband . . . yes, yes, yes, yes, yes . . . her hair had come down—save him—her blouse came unfastened—save him. But the carriage wouldn't move . . . she could feel that it wasn't moving, only the front wheels were turning, she could feel the back wheels lagging behind so that the carriage was lengthening out like the bellows of a camera, and she could see the horses getting smaller and smaller in the distance . . . The driver had taken his whip away from her . . . they couldn't go on like this . . . yes, yes, yes, yes they could . . . No, they couldn't . . . yes . . . no, yes . . . no . . . But why not? . . . Why not? . . . yes . . . no . . . yes . . . no . . She tore off her rings, her brooch, her earrings, her bracelet, put them in her jacket pocket and threw them to the driver, begging him not to stop. She must save her husband. But still they hadn't got there . . . She must get there, get there, get there, but still they hadn't arrived . . . She must get there, beg for her husband's life and save him . . . but still they hadn't arrived. Stones, ruts, dust, dried mud, grass, but still they hadn't arrived . . . They were stuck fast like telegraph wires, or rather they were going backwards like the telegraph wires, like the plantations of trees, like the fallow fields, like the clouds gilded by the setting sun, the lonely crossroads and the motionless oxen.

At last they turned aside towards the President's house, along a narrow ribbon of road disappearing between streambeds and trees. Her heart was beating suffocatingly. The road wound its way between the little houses of a clean deserted village. Here they began to meet vehicles returning from the President's estate—landaus, sulkies, buggies—in which sat people whose faces and clothes all seemed alike. The noise of the wheels and of the horses' hoofs advanced along the paved road; but they still hadn't arrived; they still hadn't arrived . . . Among those returning in the carriages—bureaucrats out of a job, and corpulent, smartly dressed officers—they met others on foot: farm-owners who had been urgently summoned by the President months and months ago; countrymen in boots like leather bags; schoolmistresses, stopping every few minutes to get their breath, their eyes blinded with dust, their shoes falling to bits, their skirts turned up to their knees; and parties of Indian policemen who understood little of what was going on around them. She must save him . . . yes, yes, but would they ever get there? The first thing was to get there, to get there before the audience was over, to get there, to beg for his life, to save him, but would they ever get there? There was not much further to go, only just beyond the village. They should be there by now, but there was no end to the village. This was the road along which the figures of Jesus and the Virgin of Sorrows had been carried on Maundy Thursday. The hounds had howled at the melancholy music of the trumpets as the procession passed in front of the balcony where the President stood under a canopy of purple stuff and bougainvilleas. Jesus passed in front of Caesar, bowed under the weight of the wooden cross, but it was to Caesar that men and women turned their admiring gaze. Suffering was not enough, it was not enough to weep for hours on end, it was not enough for families and towns to be aged by despair; the culminating outrage must take place—the image of Christ in his agony must pass before the President with his eyes shadowed by an infamous golden canopy, between two rows of grotesque puppets and to the rattle of pagan music.

The carriage stopped at the gate of the magnificent house. Carvajal's wife hurried up an avenue of pollarded trees. An officer came out and barred the way.

"Señora, Señora . . ."

"I've come to see the President . . ."

"The President cannot see anyone, Señora; you must go away . . ."

"Yes, yes, yes, he can. He will see me. I am Carvajal's wife." And she pushed forward, escaping from the soldiers who hurried after her, protesting loudly, and came to a little house with its lights shining dimly through the shadows of dusk. "They are going to shoot my husband, General!"

Walking up and down the passage of this doll's-house, with his hands behind his back, was a tall, swarthy man, tattooed all over with gold braid. She went up to him bravely:

"They are going to shoot my husband, General!"

The officer who had followed her from the door kept repeating that it was impossible for her to see the President.

In spite of his natural good manners the general answered bluntly:

"The President can see no one, Señora. You must go away . . ."

"Oh General! Oh General! What will become of me without my husband? What will become of me without my husband? No, no, General! He will see me! Let me pass, let me pass! Tell him I'm here! They are going to shoot my husband!"

The beating of her heart was audible through her dress. They would not let her go down on her knees. Her ear-drums were buzzing in the silence with which they greeted her requests.

Dead leaves crackled in the dusk, as if afraid of the wind blowing them along the ground. She sank on to a bench. The soldiers were made of black ice. Her sobs rose to her lips with a sound like the rustle of starched flounces, almost with the sound of knives. The saliva was bubbling from the corners of her mouth with each moan. She sank on to a bench and watered it with her tears as though it had been a whetstone. They had hustled her away from the place where the President probably was to be found. The sound of a passing patrol made her shiver with cold. They smelled of garlic sausage, molasses and peeled pinewood. The seat vanished into the darkness like a plank into the sea. She moved from place to place so as not to be shipwrecked on her seat in the darkness, so as to stay alive. Twice, thrice, many times she was stopped by the sentinels posted among the trees. In harsh voices they refused to let her pass, and threatened her with the butts or barrels of their rifles when she insisted. Frustrated on the right, she ran to the left. She stumbled over stones and hurt herself on thorny bushes. Her way was barred by more sentinels made of ice. She entreated, she fought, she stretched out her hand like a beggar, and when none of them would listen to her she started running in the opposite direction.

The trees swept her shadowy figure towards the cab, but no sooner had she put her foot on the step then she turned and rushed back like a lunatic to try one last entreaty. The driver woke up suddenly, nearly throwing away the trinkets lying warm in his pocket as he pulled his hand out to take the reins. The time passed very slowly for him; he was impatient to make an impression on La Minga. Ear-rings, rings, bracelet . . . they should stand him in good stead! He scratched one foot with the other, pulled his hat over his eyes and spat. What had been going on here in the darkness? Carvajal's wife returned to the cab like a sleepwalker. She took her seat in the cab and told the driver to wait a little, perhaps they would open the door . . . Half an hour . . . an hour . . .

The cab made no noise; or was it that she could not hear very well, or was it still motionless? The road dipped sharply down a very steep hill into a ravine. Afterwards it rocketed up again towards the town. The first dark walls. The first white house. An advertisement for Onofroff in the hollow of a wall.

Everything seemed to be welded together with her grief . . . the air . . . everything. A solar system in every tear . . . Centipedes of dew were falling from the roofs on to the narrow pavements . . . Her blood was hardly circulating in her veins . . . How are you? . . . I'm ill, very ill indeed . . . And how will you be tomorrow? . . . Just the same, and the day after as well . . . She was answering her own questions . . . and the day after tomorrow too . . .

The weight of the dead makes the earth turn by night, and by day it is the weight of the living . . . When there are more dead than living there will be eternal night, night without end, for the living will not be heavy enough to bring the dawn . . .

The cab stopped, the road went on further, but not for her, for she was at the door of the prison where almost certainly . . . she walked slowly along,

step by step, leaning against the wall. She was not wearing mourning. She had acquired a bat's sense of touch in the darkness . . . Fear, cold, disgust, she overcame them all in order to press herself against the wall which would echo the sound of the shots . . . After all, while she stood there how could they possibly shoot her husband, just like that, with a fusillade, with bullets, with weapons? How could men like him, people like him, with eyes, with a mouth, with hands, with hair on their heads, with nails on their fingers, with teeth in their mouths, with a tongue, with a throat . . . It was impossible that they should shoot men thus, men with the same colored skin, with the same tone of voice, with the same way of seeing, hearing, going to bed, getting up, loving, washing their faces, eating, laughing, walking, with the same beliefs and the same doubts . . .

CHAPTER XXXII

The President

Urgently summoned to the Presidential house, Angel Face brooded anxiously over Camila's state, with a new resilience in his worried gaze, a new humanity mirrored in his eyes. He turned and twisted among his doubts, like a snake in its own coils: should he go or not; the President or Camila, Camila or the President?

He could still feel the barkeeper pushing him gently on the shoulder, and hear the thread of entreaty running through her voice. He would have a chance to put in a word for Vasquez. "You go, I'll stay here and look after her." Once in the street he drew a deep breath. He was on his way to the President's house in a cab. Clatter of horses' hoofs on the stones, liquid flow of the wheels. "The Red Padlock" . . . "The Bee-Hive" . . . "The

Vol-can-o" . . . He carefully spelled out the names of the shops he passed; they were more visible at night than by day. "The Rail-way" . . . "The Hen and Chickens" . . . Sometimes his eye fell on a Chinese name: "Lon Ley Lon and Co" . . . "Quan See Chan" . . . "Fu Quan Yen" . . . "Chon Chan Lou" . . . "Sey Yon Sey" . . . He went on thinking about General Canales. They must have sent for him to tell him the latest news . . . Impossible! . . . Why impossible? . . . They had caught him and killed him . . . or else they hadn't killed him but brought him back a prisoner. A cloud of dust blew up suddenly. The wind played at bullfights with the cab. Anything was possible! When they reached the country the cab traveled more smoothly, like a solid body that had suddenly become liquid. Angel Face gripped his knees with his hands and sighed. The noise of the cab was lost among the thousand sounds of the slowly moving, advancing, numismatic night. He thought he heard the wings of a bird. They passed a few scattered houses. Some half-dead dogs barked at them . . .

The Under-secretary for War was waiting for him at the door of his office, and after barely as much time as it took to shake hands and lay his cigar on the edge of a bowl he led him straight to the President's apartments.

"General," said Angel Face, taking the Under-secretary by the arm, "you don't happen to know what the boss wants me for?"

"No, Don Miguelito, I am 'not aware' of the reason."

He knew now what it was. A short laugh, repeated two or three times, confirmed the truth of what the Under-secretary's evasive reply had led him to suppose. When he reached the door he saw a forest of bottles standing on a round table beside a plate of cold meat with avocado and pimento salad. The picture was completed by several chairs lying on the floor. The windows with their panes of opaque white glass each surmounted by a red crest fought to keep out the light coming from the lamps in the gardens. The officers and soldiers on guard were fully armed, there was an officer at the door and a soldier in the tree outside. The President advanced from the far end of the room; the ground seemed to advance under his feet and the house over his head.

"Mr. President," the favorite began, but was interrupted before he could go on:

"Ni-ni-mierva!"

"Are you referring to the goddess, Mr. President?"

His Excellency went up to the table with a springy gait, and ignoring the favorite's eulogy of Minerva, he exclaimed:

"Do you know, Miguel, that the man who discovered alcohol was looking for an elixir to produce long life?"

"No, Mr. President, I didn't know that," the favorite hastened to reply.

"That's odd."

"It would be odd, certainly, for a man of such wide knowledge as you, Mr. President, who have every right to consider himself as one of the foremost statesmen of modern times, but not for me."

His Excellency dropped his lids over his eyes, to shut out the chaotic vision of his surroundings that his alcoholic state was presenting him with at the moment.

"H'm, yes, I do know a lot!"

So saying he let his hand drop among the black forest of whisky bottles, and poured out a glass for Angel Face.

"Drink, Miguel." He choked on the words. Something had caught in his throat; he struck himself on the chest to get rid of it, while the muscles of his thin neck tightened and the veins in his forehead swelled. The favorite made him swallow some soda-water and after a few belches he regained the power of speech.

"Ha ha! Ha ha!" He burst out laughing and pointed at Angel Face. "Ha ha! Ha ha! At the point of death . . ." Explosion after explosion of laughter. "At the point of death. Ha ha! Ha ha!"

The favorite turned pale. The glass of whisky, from which he had just drunk the President's health, trembled in his hand.

"The Pres—"

"—IDENT knows everything," interrupted His Excellency. "Ha ha! Ha ha! At the point of death. And on the advice of a half-wit—all spiritualists are that! Ha ha! Ha ha! Ha ha!"

Angel Face stopped his mouth with his tumbler and drank his whisky so as to stifle his own indignant outburst; he had just seen red, he had just been on the point of hurling himself at his master and ramming his miserable laughter down his throat. It was the flame from his alcohol-saturated blood. If a train had gone over his body it would have caused him less pain. He felt sick with disgust, yet he still went on behaving like a well-trained, intelligent dog, content with its portion of filth and full of the instinct of self-preservation. He smiled to conceal his animosity, but there was death in his velvety eyes; he was like a poisoned man who feels his face beginning to swell.

His Excellency was pursuing a fly.

"Do you know the fly game, Miguel?"

"No, Mr. President."

"Oh, it's true youUUU . . . at the point of death! Ha ha! Ha ha! Tee hee, tee hee! Ho ho! Ho ho! Hoo hoo! Hoo hoo!"

And still roaring with laughter he went on pursuing the fly as it flew from place to place, with his shirt-tails coming out of his belt, his fly buttons undone, his shoes untied, dribbling at the mouth and with his eyes exuding a bright yellow rheum.

"Miguel," he said, stopping from shortage of breath without having caught his prey. "The fly game is the most amusing and the easiest game to learn in the world; the only thing you need is patience. We used to play the fly game for *reals* in my village when I was a boy."

When he mentioned his native village he frowned, and a shadow darkened his face; he turned to look at a map of the Republic which was hanging behind him, and directed a blow at the name of his village.

He had a vision of the streets where he had walked as a poor boy, an unjustly poor boy, where he had walked as a young man, obliged to earn his living while the well-born ladinos spent their time going from one spree to the next. He saw himself as an insignificant figure, isolated in his local rut, sitting under the lamp by which he used to study at night, while his mother slept in a camp bed and the wind buffeted the deserted streets with gusts impregnated with the smell of mutton. And he saw himself later on in his third-rate lawyer's office, among prostitutes, gamblers, offal-sellers, horse-thieves, despised by his colleagues who had important law-suits on their hands.

He swallowed a great many drinks, one after another. His puffy eyes were shining in his green face and his nails with their black edges outlined his small hands.

"Ungrateful beasts!"

The favorite supported him by the arm. The President's eyes seemed to be seeing corpses as they traveled about the disorderly room, and he said again:

"Ungrateful beasts!" Then he added under his breath: "I loved and shall al-

[131]

ways love Parrales Sonriente; I was going to have made him a general, because he trampled on my countrymen and humiliated them, and if it hadn't been for my mother he would have finished them off altogether and avenged me for all the grudges I bear against them, things I alone know about. Ungrateful beasts! And it's intolerable that they should have assassinated him, now that people are plotting against my life on all sides, my friends are deserting me, my enemies increasing and—no, no! Not a stone shall be left standing in the Cathedral Porch."

Words slithered from his lips like vehicles on a slippery road. He leaned on the favorite's shoulder, with his other hand pressed to his stomach, his head spinning, his eyes discolored, his breath ice-cold, and soon threw up a jet of orange-colored fluid. The Under-secretary came running in with an enamel basin with the arms of the Republic on the bottom—and when the deluge was over—most of it went over the favorite— the two of them half-carried, half-dragged him onto a bed.

He was crying and repeating over and over again:

"Ungrateful brutes! Ungrateful brutes!"

"I congratulate you, Don Miguelito, I congratulate you," murmured the Under-secretary as they went out. "The President gave orders that the announcement of your marriage should be published in all the papers, with his own name at the head of the sponsors."

They went into the passage. The Under-secretary raised his voice:

"And that in spite of the fact that he wasn't best pleased with you at first. 'No friend of Parrales Sonriente should have done what Miguel did,' he said to me. 'He should have at least asked my permission before marrying the daughter of one of my enemies.' There are some people who would like to do you an injury, Don Miguelito; yes, they would like to do you an injury. Of course I tried to make him understand that love is an obstinate, over-confident, unscrupulous, deceitful emotion."

"Thank you very much, General."

"Well then, come and look at this!" went on the Under-secretary in a jovial tone, and giving Miguel a series of friendly little pushes towards his office, laughing all the time, he went on: "Come and look at the newspaper! We got the lady's photograph from her Uncle Juan. Splendid, my dear fellow! Splendid!"

The favorite dug his nails into the low rag of a newspaper. Beside the portrait of the Chief Witness, was that of Don Juan Canales, the engineer, and his brother Don José Antonio.

"Wedding in the fashionable world. Last night a marriage was celebrated between the beautiful Señorita Camila Canales and Señor Don Miguel Angel Face. Both parties . . ." From here his eyes moved on to the list of witnesses. ". . . the witnesses to the wedding were His Excellency the Constitutional President of the Republic, in whose house the ceremony was performed, and the Ministers of State, Generals . . ." he skipped the list of their names ". . . and the esteemed uncles of the bride, Don Juan Canales the engineer and Don José Antonio of the same name. A portrait of Señorita Canales will be found in the social columns of today's issue of *El Nacional*," the paragraph concluded, "and we have pleasure in congratulating the contracting parties and wishing them every happiness in their new home."

Angel Face did not know where to look. "The Battle of Verdun still continues. The Germans are expected to launch a desperate offensive tonight."

His eyes left the page of telegrams and he re-read the paragraph under Camila's portrait. The only person he loved had already been drawn into this grotesque farce in which they were all taking part.

The Under-secretary took the paper from him.

"You can hardly believe your eyes, eh, you lucky man!"

Angel Face smiled.

"But you need a change of clothes, my friend. Take my carriage."

"Thank you very much, General."

"Look—it's out there. Tell the driver to take you home as fast as possible and then come back for me. Good night and my congratulations . . . Oh and by the way, do take the paper for your wife to see, and congratulate her from your humble servant . . . !"

"I'm very grateful for everything. Good night."

The carriage moved off with the favorite inside, as soundlessly as a black shadow pulled by two horses made of smoke. The song of the crickets formed a roof over the solitude of the mignonette-scented fields, the warm solitude of the fields of early maize, the dew-soaked pastures and the garden hedges thick with jasmine.

"Yes, if he goes on making fun of me I'll strangle him," he thought, hiding his face in the seat behind him, lest the driver should read in his eyes what they were picturing: a lump of frozen meat with the presidential scarf across the chest, the flat face stiff and still, the hands covered by cuffs so that only the fingers were visible, the patent-leather shoes covered in blood.

His bellicose mood did not adapt itself easily to the jolting of the carriage. He would have liked to sit quite still, as motionless as a murderer reconstructing his crime in prison—in an apparent and external immobility which was the necessary compensation for the tempest raging in his thoughts. His blood tingled in his veins. He thrust his face out into the cool night, while he wiped himself clean of the President's vomit with a handkerchief

damp with sweat and tears. He was cursing and weeping with rage. "Oh if only I could clean away the laughter that he vomited over my soul!"

A carriage with an officer in it overtook and brushed past them. The sky was blinking over its eternal game of chess. The horses were galloping wildly towards the town in a cloud of dust. "Check to the Queen!" said Angel Face to himself, looking at the dust cloud in which the officer was hurrying off to fetch one of the President's concubines. He seemed like a Messenger of the gods.

In the central railway station goods were being unloaded with a shattering noise, among the snorts of the steaming locomotives. The street was dominated by the figure of a Negro leaning on the green balcony of an upper window. Some drunks were reeling by and a stupid-looking man was pulling along a barrel-organ like a gun after a military defeat.

CHAPTER XXXIII

Dotting the I's

Carvajal's widow wandered from house to house, but was received coldly in them all; few of them dared show the grief they felt over her husband's death for fear of being taken for enemies of the Government, and in some cases the servants came to the window and shouted disagreeably:

"Who is it you want to see? Oh they're not at home."

The ice she had collected from these visits melted as soon as she got home. She returned to shed floods of tears in front of her husband's portrait, with no other companion but her little son, a deaf servant who kept on telling the child at the top of her voice: "A father's love is the best thing in the world!," and a parrot which repeated again and again: "A royal parrot from Portugal, dressed in green and without a *real!* Shake hands, Polly! Good morning, lawyer! Polly, shake hands! The turkey-buzzards are in the laundry. It smells of burned rags. Blessed be the Holy Sacraments on the altar, the Queen of all the angels, and the Virgin conceived without sin! Ay! Ay!"

She had gone out to ask for signatures to a petition begging the President to let her have her husband's body, but she had not dared mention the subject in any of the houses she visited; they had received her so ungraciously, so reluctantly, with little coughs and ominous silences. And now she had brought the paper home under her black shawl and it still had no other signature but her own.

They had turned their heads aside, pretending not to see her; they had received her at the door without the usual: "Do come in"; she began to feel as if she had some invisible infectious disease, something worse than poverty, worse than cholera, worse than yellow fever, yet she was flooded with "anonymous letters," as the deaf servant described the notes she found pushed under the little door between the kitchen and a dark unfrequented alley. Left there under cover of darkness and written in a trembling hand, they spoke of her as a saint, martyr and innocent victim, elevated her unfortunate husband to the skies and described the crimes of Colonel Parrales Sonriente in horrifying detail.

Early next morning there were two anonymous letters under the door. The servant brought them wrapped in her apron, because her hands were wet. The first said:

"Señora, this is not the most suitable means of conveying to you and your afflicted family the deep respect I feel for the character of your husband, our esteemed fellow citizen Don Abel Carvajal, but please allow me to make use of it out of caution, since there are certain truths which cannot be trusted to paper. Some day I will tell you my real name. My father was one of the victims of the man for whom all the torments of Hell are waiting—Colonel Parrales Sonriente —that hired assassin whose deeds will some day figure in history, if there is anyone prepared to dip his pen in snake-poison to write it. My father was murdered by this cowardly man on a lonely road many years ago. Nothing was proved, naturally enough, and the crime would have remained a mystery except for a perfect stranger who wrote anonymously to my family describing the horrible murder in detail. I do not know whether that exemplary man, your husband, a hero who already has a monument erected to him in the hearts of his fellow-townsmen, was in fact the avenger of Parrales Sonriente's victims, for there are many different stories circulating about this; but in any case I believe it to be my duty to express my sympathy, and to assure you, Señora, that we all weep with you for the loss of a man who delivered his country from one of the numerous bandits in gold braid who have used North American gold to subject it to a reign of blood and squalor.

I kiss your hands,

Cruz de Calatrava."

Drained and empty, paralyzed by a deep-seated inertia which kept her lying on her bed for hours on end like a corpse, or sometimes more motionless even than a corpse, she reduced her activities to the sphere of her bed-table (which was covered with objects in immediate use so as to avoid getting up) or to attacks of hysteria if anyone opened the door, used a broom or made a noise anywhere near her. The darkness, the silence, the dirt gave tangible shape to her desolation, to her desire to be alone with her grief, with that part of her which had died with her husband and was slowly gaining the mastery of her body and soul.

"Most respected and esteemed Señora" —she began reading the other anonymous letter aloud—"I heard from some friends that you had your ear to the prison wall the night your husband was shot. Even if you heard and counted nine detonations, you will not know which among them snatched the lawyer Carvajal, God rest his soul, from among the living.

"After much hesitation for fear of causing you pain, I have decided to write under an assumed name—it is not safe to trust to paper these days—and communicate everything I know about the matter, for I witnessed the execution. A thin, dark-skinned man with almost white hair falling over his broad forehead was walking in front of your husband. I have not been able to find out his name. In spite of the suffering shown by his tears, there was great human kindness in his deep-sunk eyes, and one could read in them that their owner was a noble and generous man. The lawyer stumbled after him without raising his eyes from the ground—perhaps he couldn't even see it—his forehead damp with sweat and one hand on his breast as if to keep his heart from bursting. When he came out into the courtyard and found himself surrounded by soldiers, he rubbed his eyes with the back of his hand as if he couldn't believe what he saw. He was wearing a faded suit too small for him, the sleeves of the coat only reaching to his elbows and the trousers to his knees —old, crumpled, dirty, tattered clothes, such as all condemned prisoners wear, having given their own to the friends they leave behind entombed in underground prison cells, or to the warders in exchange for some special indulgence. His threadbare shirt was kept together by one little bone button. He wore no tie and no shoes. The presence of his companions in misfortune, half naked like himself, revived his courage. When they had finished reading the death sentence, he raised his head, looked sadly at the row of bayonets and said something inaudible. The old man next to him also tried to speak, but the officers silenced him by threatening him with their swords. Their hands were trembling from drink, and the swords looked like the blue flames of burning alcohol in the pale dawn light. Meanwhile a voice clashed with its own echo rebounding from the walls as it pronounced the words: 'For the Nation!' One, two, three, four, five, six, seven, eight, nine rounds of firing followed. Without knowing what I was doing I was counting them on my fingers, and so I got the strange impression that I had one finger too many. The victims shut their eyes and twisted their bodies as if to grope their way out of range of death. A veil of smoke hung between us and this handful of men, who tried in vain to catch hold of each other as they fell, rather than roll into the void alone. The final shots rang out like a burst of damp rockets, exploding late and badly. Your husband was fortunate enough to be killed by the first round of firing. Above, in the blue, inaccessible sky, we heard the almost imperceptible sound of bells, birds, rivers. I was told that the Judge Advocate had undertaken to bury the bod—"

She turned the page anxiously. "Bod—" But the rest of the word was not there, nor on any of the other pages; the letter had broken off suddenly, and the rest was missing. She re-read the letter, but in vain; she searched inside her envelope, unmade the bed, looked inside the pillows, on the floor and the table, turned everything upside down in her eagerness to know where her husband was buried.

In the patio the parrot was chattering: "Royal parrot from Portugal, dressed in green, and without a *real!* Ah, here comes the lawyer! Hurrah, royal parrot! The liar told me! I don't cry, but I don't forget!"

The Judge Advocate General's servant left Carvajal's widow standing on the doorstep while she attended to two women talking at the tops of their voices in the entrance hall.

"Listen, just listen to me," one of them was saying; "you just go and tell him I'm not waiting for him any longer. I'm not an Indian, damn him, to be left freezing my arse on this stone seat! It reminds me of his pretty face! Tell him I've come to see if he's at last going to give me back the ten thousand pesos he swindled me out of for a woman from the Casa Nueva, who was no use to me, because the day I brought her home with me she fell down in a fit. And look here! tell him it's the last time I shall bother him; what I'm going to do now is go and complain to the President."

"Don't work yourself up so, Doña Chon, take that miserable old expression off your face," said the other woman.

"Señorita," the servant was beginning, but the Señorita interrupted:

"Shut up, will you?"

"Tell him what I said, and don't let him say I didn't give him fair warning: tell him Doña Chon and one of the girls came to see him, that they waited for him, and when they saw he wasn't coming, they went away saying he'd soon see what stuff they were made of . . ."

Absorbed in her own thoughts, Carvajal's widow did not take in what was happening. In her black clothes, with nothing showing but her face, she looked like a corpse in a coffin with a window in it. The servant tapped her on the shoulder—the old woman's fingers felt as though they were covered in spiders-webs—and told her to come in. They entered

the house. The widow could not speak distinctly, but muttered like someone tired out by reading aloud for a long time.

"Yes, Señora, leave your letter with me. When he comes in—and he can't be long now, he ought to be here already—I'll give it to him, and tell him what you want."

"For the love of God . . ."

An individual wearing a coffee-colored cotton suit, followed by a soldier with his Remington rifle over his shoulder, a knife in his belt and a well-filled cartridge-belt round his hips, came in just as Carvajal's widow was leaving.

"Excuse me," he said to the servant, "is the Judge Advocate in?"

"No, he's not."

"And where can I wait for him?"

"Sit down there, and the soldier too."

The prisoner and his guard sat down in silence on the stone bench ungraciously indicated by the servant.

The patio was full of the scent of verbena and begonias. A cat was walking on the roof. A mocking-bird was trying to fly inside its wicker cage. From far off came the sound of the water sleepily running into the fountain, as if dazed with falling.

The Judge Advocate locked the door with a rattle of keys, put them in his pocket and went up to the prisoner and the soldier. Both stood up.

"Genaro Rodas?" he inquired, sniffing. Whenever he came in from the street his house seemed to smell of cat-shit.

"Yes, Señor, at your service."

"Does your guard understand Spanish?"

"Not very well," replied Rodas, and turning to the soldier he added: "What d'you say? Do you understand Castillian?"

"Half understand."

"Very well," put in the Advocate General. "You'd better stay here. I'll talk to him. Stay here till he comes back. He's going to talk to me."

Rodas stopped at the door of the study. The Judge Advocate told him to go in, and laid the weapons he was carrying on a table covered with books and papers—a revolver, a knife, a knuckle-duster and a truncheon.

"I expect you've been notified of the sentence."

"Yes, Señor, I have."

"Six years and eight months, if I remember right."

"But, Señor, I wasn't Lucio Vasquez's accomplice; whatever he did he did without my help; by the time I got there the Zany was already rolling down the steps of the Porch covered in blood and as good as dead. What could I do? It was an order. It was aɴ order, so he said."

"Well, God has already judged him . . ."

Rodas turned to look at the Judge Advocate General, as if unable to credit what the sinister expression of his face confirmed, and remained silent.

"And he wasn't a bad chap," sighed Rodas, dropping his voice as he let fall these last few words to his friend's memory; he had taken in the news between two heart-beats and already he felt it in his blood. "Well, it can't be helped now! We used to call him Velvet, because he never missed a chance and knew how to cadge special favors."

"According to the verdict he was sentenced as perpetrator of the crime, and you as his accomplice."

"But I had a defense."

"It was the advocate for your defense, in point of fact, who, knowing the President's views, asked for a death sentence for Vasquez and the maximum penalty for you."

"Poor chap. At least I'm alive to tell the tale."

"And you can go free at once if you want to; because the President needs someone like you, someone who has been inside for a bit for political reasons. It's a question of keeping an eye on one of his friends, whom he has reason to suspect of betraying him . . ."

"You mean . . ."

"Do you know Don Miguel Angel Face?"

"Only by name; he was the one who went off with General Canales' daughter, wasn't he?"

"That's the man. You'll recognize him easily because he's very handsome: a tall man, well built, with black eyes, a pale face, and silky hair, and moves gracefully. A dangerous customer. The Government wants to know everything he does, the people he goes to see, or talks to in the street, the places he frequents in the morning, afternoon and night, and the same for his wife; I'll give you full instructions and money for this."

The prisoner followed the Judge Advocate's movements stupidly, as with these words he took a pen from the table, dipped it in a large inkpot with a figure of the goddess Themis standing between two wells of black ink, and handed it to Rodas, saying:

"Sign here; tomorrow I'll give orders for you to be set free. Get your things ready to leave tomorrow."

Rodas signed. Joy was dancing through his body like a playful little bull.

"I'm very grateful, you know," he said as he went out; he almost embraced the soldier who was waiting for him, and went off to the prison like a man going to heaven.

But the Judge Advocate General was even more delighted with the paper Rodas had just signed, and which read as follows:

"I have received from Doña Concepcion Gamucino, known as 'Gold-Tooth,' proprietress of the brothel known as The Sweet Enchantment, the sum of ten thousand pesos in the national currency, a sum which she gave me as partial compensation for the damage she had done me in corrupting my wife, Señora Fedina de Rodas, by taking advantage of her good faith and that of the authorities to offer her employment as a servant, and then enrolling her, without any authorization, among the girls of her establishment.

Genaro Rodas."

He heard the servant's voice calling through the door:

"Can I come in?"

"Yes, come in."

"I came to see if there was anything you wanted. I'm going to the shop to buy candles and I must tell you there were two women from one of the brothels here, who told me to tell you that if you don't pay back the ten thousand pesos you robbed them of they'll go and complain to the President."

"And what else?" grumbled the Judge Advocate, looking annoyed and stooping to pick up a postage stamp from the floor.

"And a lady dressed in mourning came to see you; I think she's the wife of the man who was shot . . ."

"Which one of them?"

"Señor Carvajal."

"Well, what did she want?"

"The poor thing gave me this letter. I think she wants to know where her husband is buried."

While the Judge Advocate was reluctantly glancing over the black-edged pages the servant went on:

"I must tell you I promised to do what I could for her, because I felt sorry for her, and the poor thing went away full of hope."

"I've told you often enough that I don't like your sympathizing with people. You mustn't encourage them to hope. When will you understand that you mustn't encourage people to hope? In my house the first thing everyone, down to the cat, has to learn is that there are never grounds for hope of any description for anyone. It's only possible to go on holding a position like mine if you obey orders; the President's rule of conduct is never to give grounds for hope, and everyone must be kicked and beaten until they realize the fact. When this lady comes back you must return her her letter, neatly folded, and tell her there is no way of finding out where her husband is buried."

"Don't be so angry, you'll make yourself ill; I'll tell her. God will take care of you and your affairs."

And she went out carrying the letter and dragging her feet, one after the other, one after the other, under her rustling skirts.

When she got to the kitchen she crumpled up the letter and threw it among the coals. The paper curled up in the flames like a living thing, and then suddenly turned into a mass of tiny worms made of gold wire. Along the shelves where pots of spices were arranged, like boats against a bridge, came a black cat; it jumped on to the stone seat beside the old woman, rubbed itself against her barren belly, purring like a four-legged embodiment of sound, and fixed its golden eyes with satanic curiosity on the heart of the fire where the letter was now burned to ashes.

CHAPTER XXXIV

Light for the Blind

Camila was standing in the middle of the room, supported on her husband's arm and a walking-stick. The main door gave onto a patio smelling of cats and poppies. The window looked onto the town where she had been brought as a convalescent in a wheelchair, and a small door led into another room. In spite of the sun setting alight the green fires of her eyes, and the air filling her lungs like a heavy chain, Camila wondered if it could really be she who was walking. Her feet felt too large, her legs like stilts. She seemed to be walking in another world, with her eyes wide open; she was new-born, disembodied. She was surrounded by phantoms, walking among a foam of cobwebs. It was as if she had died in a dream, without ceasing to exist, and had come back to life to find she could not distinguish dreams from reality. Her father, her home, her old nurse Chabela, all belonged to her previous existence. Her husband, the house where they were temporarily living, the servants, all belonged to her new existence. It was she, yet it was not she, who was walking about in this room. She felt as if she had returned to life in a new world. When she spoke of herself, it was of someone leaning on the walking-stick of her past life; she had an understanding with things that were invisible, and if she was left alone she got lost in this other world, sitting with her mind far away, with frozen hair, her hands lying in the lap of her long skirt and noises echoing in her ears.

She soon began to move about, but she remained an invalid none-the-less, or rather she remained absorbed in the evaluation of all the overwhelming things that had happened to her since her husband first pressed his lips to her cheek. It was all too much for her to take in, but she clung to it as the only thing that was really hers in an alien world. She looked with pleasure at the moonlight shining on the earth, at the moon itself opposite the cloud-capped volcanoes, and at the stars like golden lice in an empty pigeon-loft.

Angel Face was aware that his wife was shivering inside her white flannel garments, not from cold, not as people normally shiver, but as angels shiver—and he led her step by step back to her bedroom. The grotesque head over the fountain . . . the motionless hammock; the water as motionless as the hammock . . . damp flower-pots . . . wax flowers . . . passages patched with moonlight . . .

They went to bed, talking to each other through the wall. There was a communicating door between their bedrooms. Buttons came sleepily out of buttonholes with a gentle sound like that of cutting a flower-stalk; shoes fell to the ground with the noise of dropping anchors, and stockings were peeled from skin as smoke is peeled from a chimney.

Angel Face talked to her about the objects of his personal toilet ranged on a table beside his towel-rail, so as to create a foolish but intimate family atmosphere in this huge, apparently uninhabited house, and to remove his thoughts from that narrow little door, like the gateway to heaven, which led from one bedroom to the other.

Then he fell onto his bed with all his weight and lay there for a long time without moving, lapped around by the mysterious tide of the relationship that was continuously being created and destroyed between the two of them. He kidnaps her with the intention of making her his own by force; then out of blind instinct love develops. Abandoning his plan, he tries to take her to her uncle's house; the door is shut against them. So she is in his power again, and surely there is now no risk in making her his, since this is what the world believes. But knowing this, she tries to shun him. Her illness stands in the way. In a very few hours she gets much worse. She is dying. Death will come and cut the knot. He knows this, and at times he is resigned, although more often he is in revolt against these blind forces. Death's summons frustrates his dearest hope, and fate is waiting till the last moment to unite them.

Childlike before she could walk, she becomes an adolescent when she gets up and takes her first steps. In the space of a single night the blood has returned to her lips, her bodice has filled out with its fruit, and she is troubled and damp with sweat at the approach of the man she has never really thought of as her husband.

Angel Face jumped up from the bed. He felt that he was separated from Camila by something that was neither his fault nor hers; by a marriage to which neither of them had given their consent. Camila closed her eyes. His footsteps moved away towards the window.

The moon went in and out of floating niches in the clouds. The road flowed like a river of white bones under bridges of shadow. Now and again everything grew indistinct, with the patina of some old religious relic, only to reappear brightened with gold thread. A vast black eyelid intervened, and cut off this vision seen through flickering eyelids. Its enormous lashes seemed to come from the highest of the volcanoes and spread like a huge spider over the skeleton of the town, plunging it in mourning shadow. The dogs shook their ears like door-knockers, night birds flew through the sky, a moan passed from cypress to cypress and there was a sound of clocks being wound and set. The moon disappeared completely behind the tall summit of a crater and a mist like a bride's veil came to rest among the houses. Angel Face shut the window. In her bedroom Camila was drawing slow, difficult breaths, as if she had fallen asleep with her head under the clothes, or a phantom presence were sitting on her breast.

Sometimes they went bathing. The shadows of the trees dappled the white shirts of the traveling vendors of earthenware jars, brooms, mocking-birds in wicker cages, pine-cones, wood and maize. They had covered long distances walking on tip-toe without ever resting their heels on the ground. The sun was sweating with them. They panted and waved their arms about and then vanished like a flock of birds.

Camila stopped in the shadow of a hut to watch the coffee being picked. The pickers' hands moved among the metallic foliage like hungry animals; up and down they went, joining together as if crazily tickling the tree, then separating again as if unbuttoning its shirt.

Angel Face put his arm around her waist and led her along a path lying stricken under the slumberous heat of the trees. They were conscious of their heads and their torsos; the rest of their bodies, legs and hands floated along among orchids and bright-colored lizards in a half-light which gradually changed to a honeyed darkness as they penetrated further into the wood. He could feel Camila's body through her thin blouse as one feels the smooth, silky, moist grains of maize through the young leaf. The wind ruffled their hair. As they went down to the bathing-place the sun was asleep in the water. Invisible presences were floating among shady tufts of ferns. The keeper of the baths came out of a zinc-roofed house, munching beans; he greeted them with a nod, swallowed the mouthful with which his cheeks were bulging, and looked them up and down with a self-important air. They asked for two bathing-boxes. He went to fetch the keys, and opened two little cabins separated by a partition. They kissed each other quickly before parting to go into their cabins. The bathing-box proprietor had a bad eye and he covered his face to protect it.

They felt strange, separated from each other, and with the forest noises all round them. A broken looking-glass saw Angel Face strip with youthful haste. Why must he be a man—when it would be so much better to be a tree, a cloud, a dragon-fly, a bubble or a humming-bird? Standing on the highest step of the swimming-bath, Camila shrieked to feel the cold water on her feet; she screamed again on the second step, more piercingly on the third, and more piercingly still on the fourth then—splash! Her Indian chemise swelled out like a crinoline, like a balloon, but almost at the same moment the water saturated it, molding her body in the garish blues, yellows and greens of the material: firm breasts and stomach, the gentle curve of the hips, smooth back, and rather thin shoulders. Her plunge over, Camila came out again, somewhat agitated by the watery silence of the reeds. But she heard her husband's voice at her door, asking if he could come in, and she felt safe.

The water frisked around them like a happy animal. Among the shining cobwebs of its reflection on the walls of the baths, they saw the reflections of their own bodies like monstrous spiders. The air was pervaded by a smell of water plants, by the presence of the distant volcanoes, the dampness of frogs' bellies, the breath of calves as they sucked in the white liquid into which the pasture had been transformed, the coolness of the waterfalls laughing as they fell, the restless flight of green flies. An impalpable veil of silent aitches enveloped them, together with the sound of someone singing in the ravine and the fluttering of a shara-bird.

The bathing-box keeper looked in to ask if the horses from La Quebraditas were for them. It was time to dress and leave the baths. Camila felt a worm wriggling in the towel she had thrown over her shoulders to protect her clothes from her wet hair. For her to feel it, to scream, for Angel Face to come and deal with the worm was a matter of only a few seconds. But she was not enjoying herself any more; the forest had begun to frighten her; it seemed to be sunk in a damp, sleepless torpor, exuding worms.

The horses were flicking away flies with their tails under a fig-tree. The groom who had brought them came up to Angel Face, hat in hand.

"Oh, so it's you! Good morning! And what are you doing here?"

"Working! I've been coming here ever since you did me the service of getting me out of the barracks, nearly a year ago."

"How fast time goes!"

"It seems like it. The sun'll be gone soon now, boss, and we've some way to go."

Angel Face asked Camila if they should leave; he had stopped to pay the attendant.

"Whenever you like."

"But aren't you hungry? Don't you want to eat something? Perhaps we can buy something from the attendant."

"Some eggs?" suggested the groom, and from the pocket of his jacket (which had more buttons than buttonholes) he extracted a handkerchief with three eggs wrapped in it.

"Thank you very much," said Camila, "they look very fresh."

"Don't thank me, young lady, and as for the eggs they're goodness itself. The hens laid them this very morning and I said to my wife: 'Put them aside for me. I think I'll take them to Don Angel!'"

They took leave of the attendant, who was still wiping his bad eye and eating beans.

"And I've been thinking," the groom went on, "that it would be a good thing for the Señora to swallow those eggs raw, because it's quite a stretch from here and she might get hungry."

"No, I don't like raw eggs and they might make me ill," replied Camila.

"I thought the Señora looked as if she needed taking care of!"

"That's because I've only just got out of bed."

"Yes," said Angel Face, "she's been very ill."

"But now you're going to get better," said the man while he tightened the girths of the saddles. "Women are like flowers, they need watering; marriage'll soon put you to rights!"

Camila lowered her eyelids, blushing and confused, like a plant that finds eyes growing everywhere instead of leaves; she exchanged a glance with her husband—a glance full of mutual desire, silently sealing a compact that had been lacking between them hitherto.

CHAPTER XXXV

The Song of Songs

"Suppose fate had not brought us together!" they used to say. And the thought of the risk they had run filled them with such terror that if they happened to be apart they would seek each other out, if they were together they embraced, if they were in each other's arms they held each other tighter, and not content with holding each other tighter they kissed each other and gazed into each other's eyes, and found them so alight with happiness that they passed into a transparent state of amnesia, in blissful accord with the trees, newly swollen with sap, and with the little morsels of flesh covered in bright-colored feathers that flew about more swiftly than the echo.

But the serpents considered the ques-

tion. If fate had not brought them together, would they have been happy? The right to destroy this useless and charming Paradise was put to auction among the infernal shadows; the evil spirits began to keep watch, and the uncertain voice of doubt sprouted from the damp vaccine of guilt, while the calendar spun cobwebs in the corners of time.

Neither he nor she could afford to stay away from the party the President of the Republic was giving in his country residence that night.

Their house suddenly seemed alien to them; they were at a loss what to do, and sat sadly surrounded by a sofa, a looking-glass and other furniture, instead of by the marvelous world of the first months of their marriage. They felt sorry for each other, and ashamed of being themselves.

The dining-room clock struck the hours, but it seemed such a long way away that they had the feeling that they would need either a boat or a balloon to reach it. And there they sat . . .

They ate in silence with their eyes on the pendulum which was bringing them closer to the party with each oscillation. Angel Face got up to put on his dress-coat, and felt cold as he thrust his arms into the sleeves, like someone wrapping himself in banana leaves. Camila tried to fold up her napkin, but it was the napkin which folded up her hands, and she sat between the table and her chair without the strength to take the first step. She drew back her foot. Now she had taken the first step. Angel Face returned to see what the time was and then went back to his room for his gloves. She heard his footsteps far away, as if in a tunnel. He said something. Something. His voice sounded indistinct. A moment later he reappeared in the dining-room carrying his wife's fan. He could not remember what he had gone to fetch from his room and had been hunting about vaguely everywhere. At last he remembered, but his gloves were already on his hands.

"Be sure and see that the lights aren't left on; put them out and shut the doors carefully; then go to bed," Camila told the servants who were watching their departure from the door into the passage.

They set off in a carriage drawn by well-fed horses, trotting in the river of clinking coins made by the harness. Camila buried herself in her corner; she could not shake off the torpor oppressing her, and the dead light from the street lamps shone in her eyes. Every now and then a sudden movement of the carriage jolted her off her seat, interrupting her smooth progress in rhythm with the vehicle. Angel Face's enemies had been saying he was no longer in favor, and it was hinted in the Club of the Friends of the President that he ought now to be called Miguel Canales instead of his own name. Rocked by the bounding wheels, he was savoring in advance the surprise that would be caused by his appearance at the party.

The carriage left the paved streets and glided down a sandy hill, the wheels making a hollow sound. Camila was afraid; she could see nothing at all in the darkness of the surrounding countryside, only the stars; nor could she hear anything from the dew-soaked fields except the song of the crickets; she was afraid, and she shrank back as if she were being dragged to her death along a path (or semblance of a path) with a yawning abyss on one side and, on the other, Lucifer's wing stretched out like a rock in the darkness.

"What's the matter?" said Angel Face, gently taking her by the shoulders and moving her away from the door.

"I'm scared!"

"Sh! Be quiet!"

"This man's going to turn us over at this rate. Tell him not to go so fast. Do tell him! Oh dear, didn't you hear what I said? Tell him! You're so silent!"

"These carriages . . ." Angel Face began, but stopped short because his wife clutched him and there was an unexpected bump on the springs. They felt as if they were rolling down the slope.

"It's all right," he said, pulling himself together, "it's all right—the wheels must have caught in a rut."

The wind was blowing over the rocks with a screech like tearing linen. Angel Face put his head out of the window and shouted to the driver to be more careful. The man turned his dark pock-marked face to look at him and slowed the horses to a funereal pace.

The carriage stopped at the far end of a little village. An officer in a cloak advanced towards them clicking his spurs, recognized them and told the driver to go on. The wind sighed through the dry and broken corn-stalks. The silhouette of a cow was barely visible in a yard. The trees were asleep. Two hundred yards further on two officers approached to see who they were, but the carriage hardly paused. And now that they were about to alight in front of the Presidential Residence, three colonels came forward to search the carriage.

Angel Face greeted the staff officers. (He was as beautiful and wicked as Satan.) A nostalgia for the warmth of home was floating in the inexplicable vastness of night. A light on the horizon marked the site of an artillery fort guarding the safety of the President of the Republic.

Camila lowered her eyes when confronted by a man with a Mephistophelian scowl, stooping shoulders, slit-like eyes, and long thin legs. As they came in, this man slowly stretched out his arm and opened his hand as if he were going to set free a dove instead of speak to them.

[143]

"Parthenius of Bethany," he began, "was taken prisoner in Mithridates' wars and carried off to Rome, where he taught the Alexandrian language. Propertius, Ovid, Virgil, Horace and I got it from him . . ."

Two elderly ladies were talking together at the door of the room where the President was receiving his guests.

"Yes, yes," one was saying, patting her hair. "I've told him they must re-elect him."

"And what did he say? I'm really interested . . ."

"He only smiled, but I know he will be re-elected. He's the best President we've ever had, Candidita. Do you know that ever since he was in office, Moncho, my husband, has always had a good job?"

Behind these ladies the Teacher was pontificating to a group of friends.

"The President wants to see you," the Judge Advocate was saying, turning to right and left, as he walked through the crowd. "The President wants to see you, the President wants to see you . . ."

"Thank you!" replied the Teacher.

"Thank you!" said a Negro jockey with bow legs and gold teeth, assuming the remark was meant for him.

Camila would have liked to have passed unnoticed. But that was impossible. Her exotic beauty, her clear impassive green eyes, her exquisite figure sheathed in her white silk dress, her small breasts, her graceful movements, and above all the fact that she was General Canales' daughter, singled her out.

One of a group of ladies remarked:

"I don't think much of her. A woman who doesn't wear stays—anyone can see how common she is!"

"And she's had her wedding-gown altered into an evening dress," whispered another.

"People who don't know how to behave always make themselves conspicuous, you know," a lady with thin hair took the opportunity of adding.

"Oh, how unkind we're being! I said that about the dress because obviously they're hard up!"

"Of course they're hard up, and we all know why!" remarked the thin-haired one, adding in a low voice: "They say the President hasn't given him a thing since his marriage to that girl!"

"But Angel Face is completely loyal . . ."

"He was, rather. Because you know people are saying—for what it's worth—that Angel Face only ran off with his present wife so as to throw dust in the eyes of the police while his father-in-law, the general, escaped; and that he wouldn't have got away otherwise!"

Camila and Angel Face advanced among the guests towards the far end of the room where the President was. His Excellency was talking to Canon Irrefragable, among a group of ladies who had forgotten what they meant to say as soon as they found themselves in the Leader's proximity, and looked as though they had swallowed lighted candles and did not dare to breathe or open their lips. There were bankers out on bail, with lawsuits pending against them; secretaries with revolutionary sympathies, who never took their eyes from the President, but dared not greet him when he looked at them nor absent themselves when he turned away; village notables, whose political enthusiasms had lost their fire, but who showed a trace of outraged human dignity at being treated as mice when they were really lions.

Camila and Angel Face went up to shake hands with the President. Angel Face introduced his wife. The President gave Camila his cold little right hand and let his eyes rest on her as he uttered her name, as if to say: "You see what sort of a man I am!" Meanwhile the Canon was paying homage to a beauty with the same name and unique character as Albanio's beloved, by quoting some lines by Garcilaso:

Nature desired but once to make
A face so fair as this—
And then the mold did break!

The servants were handing round champagne, little cakes, salted almonds, sweets and cigarettes. The champagne set a match to the as yet unlit fire of this official entertainment, gradually spreading an animation which looked more genuine when reflected in the quiet mirrors than in the drawing-rooms themselves.

"General," the President's voice was heard to say, "take the gentlemen away; I wish to have supper alone with the ladies."

The men hurried towards the doors opening on to the brilliant night in a compact group, without a word, some eager to carry out their master's orders, others trying to conceal their anger by their haste. The women looked at each other, not daring even to hide their feet under their chairs.

"The poet can stay," suggested the President.

The officers shut all the doors. The poet was embarrassed to find himself among so many ladies.

"Recite something, poet," ordered the President; "something good—the Song of Songs":

The song of songs which is Solomon's,
Let him kiss me with the kiss of his
   mouth!
I am black but beautiful, O ye daughters
   of Jerusalem,
As the curtains of Solomon.
Do not consider me that I am brown
Because the sun hath altered my color.

A bundle of myrrh is my beloved to me:
He shall abide between my breasts . . .

I sat down under his shadow whom I
   desired
And his fruit was sweet to my palate,
He brought me into the cellar of wine,
He set in order charity in me.

I adjure you oh daughters of Jerusalem
That you stir not up, nor make the be-
   loved awake
Till she please
Till she please . . .

How beautiful art thou, my love;
Thy eyes are dove's eyes;
Thy hair is as flocks of goats
Thy teeth as flocks of sheep,
Which come up from the washing,
All with twins;
And there is none barren among them.

There are threescore queens and four-
   score concubines.

The President stood up with a baleful expression on his face. His footsteps echoed like those of a jaguar in flight on the stones of a dry river-bed; and he vanished through a door, pulling aside the curtains and brushing between them.

The poet and his audience were left astounded, shrunk to insignificance and empty, in an atmosphere of uneasiness such as is felt after the sun has set. An usher announced that supper was ready. The doors were opened and, while the men who had been waiting in the passage came shivering back into the drawing-room, the poet came up to Camila and asked her to have supper with him. She stood up and was just going to take his arm when a hand from behind stopped her. She almost cried out. Angel Face had been hidden all the time behind a curtain close to his wife; everyone saw him come out of his hiding-place.

The wooden bars of the marimba had begun to vibrate and so had the resonators hanging like little coffins beneath them.

CHAPTER XXXVI

The Revolution

Nothing was visible ahead. Behind them crept the track like a long silent snake unrolling its fluid, smooth, frozen coils. The ribs of the earth could be counted in the meager dried-up marshlands, untouched by winter. The trees raised themselves to the full height of their thick, sappy branches in order to breathe. The bonfires dazzled the eyes of the tired horses. A man turned his back to urinate. His legs were invisible. The time had come for his companions to take stock of their situation, but they were too busy cleaning their rifles with grease and bits of cotton which still smelled of woman. Death had been carrying them off one by one, withering them as they lay in their beds, with no advantage to their children or anyone else. It was better to risk their lives and see what would come of that. Bullets feel nothing when they pierce a man's body; to them flesh is like sweet warm air—air with a certain substance. And they whistle like birds. The time had come to take stock, but they were too busy sharpening the machetes the leaders of the revolution had bought from an iron-monger whose shop had been burned down. The sharpened edge was like the smile on a Negro's face.

"Sing, comrade," said a voice. "I heard you singing a little while ago!"

"Why did you court me, hard-hearted
With a mistress of your own?
Better if you had left me
Like a dead tree alone."

"Go on, comrade, sing!"

"We went to the lagoon
We hurried to the fair;
This year there shone no moon
And there was no one there."

"Sing, comrade, sing!"

The quinine light of the moon was spreading over the countryside and the leaves were shivering on the trees. They waited in vain for the order to advance. A distant sound of barking showed where a village must be hidden. The sun was rising. The troops, waiting in motionless readiness to attack the first garrison that same night, felt as if some strange subterranean force was robbing them of their mobility and turning them to stone. The rain turned the sunless morning to soup; it ran down the faces and backs of the soldiers. Sounds echoed more loudly through God's falling tears. The first news they got was brief and contradictory, as if spoken by small voices, afraid to tell all they knew. Deep in the soldiers' hearts something like an iron ball or a splinter of bone was consolidating. The whole camp was bleeding as from a single wound. General Canales was dead. The news took shape in syllables and sentences, syllables out of a spelling-book. Sentences from the funeral service. The taste of cigarettes and brandy was tainted with anger and exclamations of grief. It was impossible to believe what was being said—yet it must be true. The older men were silent, waiting impatiently to hear the bare truth, some standing, others stretched or squatting on the ground; they took off their straw hats, threw them down beside them and scratched their heads furiously. The young men had hurried down into the ravine in search of more news. They were stupefied by the reverberating heat of the sun. A flock of birds was circling in the distance. From time to time there was the sound of a shot. Evening began to close in. A raw sky beneath a torn cloak of clouds. The camp fires were put out and there was nothing but a gray shapeless darkness, a black solitude composed of sky, earth, animals and men. Then a galloping horse broke the silence with the rataplan! rataplan! of its hoofs, repeated by the echoes all through the multiplication table. It came closer and closer, from sentinel to sentinel, and soon it was here in their midst, and they thought they must be dreaming when they heard what the rider had to tell. General Canales had died suddenly, just after eating a meal, when he was about to lead his troops into action. And now their orders were to wait.

"They must have given him something, some chiltepe root perhaps—it's a deadly poison which leaves no trace—for him to die just now," said a voice.

"He ought to have been more on his guard!" murmured another.

"Ahhhh!" They were all silent, all deeply stirred, down to their bare heels, buried in the ground. "His daughter?"

After a long and unpleasant pause, another voice added: "If you like I'll call down a curse on her; I was taught one by a witch-doctor down on the coast; he told it to me when maize was short in the mountains and I went down there to buy some. What do you say?"

"Well," came the other voice out of the shadows, "I'm for it myself, because she killed her father."

Once more a horse was heard galloping along the track—rataplan, rataplan, rataplan; once more the sentinels' shouts were heard and once more silence reigned. The howl of coyotes rose like a double staircase towards the newly risen moon with its broad halo. The echo repeated it.

And each time anyone described what had happened, General Canales came out

of his grave and died all over again: he sat down to eat by lamplight at a table without a cloth, they heard the rattle of cutlery and plates, the footsteps of the orderly, a glass of water being poured out and a newspaper unfolded, and then— nothing more, not even a groan. They found him lying across the table dead, his cheek resting on *El Nacional,* his eyes half closed, glassy, staring at something that was not there.

The men went back reluctantly to their daily tasks; they were tired of living like domestic animals, and they had joined Chamarrita's revolution—this was their affectionate nickname for General Canales—to make a change in their way of life, and because Chamarrita had promised to give them back the vineyards that had been taken away from them on the pretext of abolishing communities; to make fair distribution of water supplies; to suppress the pillory; to form agricultural cooperatives to import machinery, the best seed, pure-bred stock, fertilizers and technicians; to make transport easier and cheaper and so facilitate export and sale of products; to confine power to those elected by the people and responsible to the people themselves; to abolish private schools, institute proportional taxation, make medicine cheaper and doctors and lawyers available to all; to grant freedom in religion, so that the Indians should be able to worship their gods and rebuild their temples, safe from persecution.

Camila heard of her father's death many days later. An unknown voice told her the news over the telephone.

"Your father died of reading in the newspaper that the President of the Republic was a witness at your wedding."

"It's not true!" she cried.

"What isn't true?" said the voice, laughing disagreeably.

"It isn't true; he wasn't a witness!

Hullo! Hullo!" But the unknown person had already put the receiver down very slowly like someone slipping away by stealth. "Hullo! Hullo!"

She sank into a wicker chair. She felt stunned. After a little while it seemed to her that the room had lost its old appearance and become different, with a different color, a different atmosphere. Dead! Dead! Dead! Camila twisted her hands as though to break something, and broke into a laugh with set jaws and her eyes full of unshed tears.

A water-cart was going along the street; its taps were weeping and its metal tanks laughing.

CHAPTER XXXVII

Tohil's* Dance

"What would you like, gentlemen?"

"A beer."

"Not for me: I'll have a whisky."

"And a brandy for me."

"Then that's . . . ?"

"One beer, one whisky, one brandy."

"And some cocktail snacks!"

"Then that's one beer, one whisky, one brandy and some cocktail snacks."

"Hullo there!" Angel Face's voice was heard saying as he came back, buttoning his fly-buttons rather hastily.

"What'll you have?"

"Anything. Bring me some mineral water."

"Ah! then it's one beer, one whisky, one brandy and one mineral water."

Angel Face pulled up his chair and sat down beside a man six feet tall, who had the appearance and gestures of a Negro although he was white-skinned, a back as straight as a poker, a pair of anvils for hands and a scar between his blond brows.

---

* The God of rain in Maya-Guatemalan mythology.

"Make room for me, Mr. Gengis," he said, "I want to sit beside you."

"With pleasure, Señor."

"I'll have my drink and then go, because the boss is expecting me."

"Oh," said Mr. Gengis, "if you're going to see the President, you must stop being a damn fool and tell him the things they say about you aren't true—not true at all."

"That goes without saying," said another of the four, the one who had asked for brandy.

"I should know that," put in Angel Face to Mr. Gengis.

"So does everyone," exclaimed the American, hitting the marble-topped table with the flat of his hands. "Of course! But I was there that night and heard with my own ears the Judge Advocate say you were against the re-election, and friendly to the revolution like the late General Canales."

Angel Face made a poor show of concealing his anxiety. Under the circumstances it was foolhardy to go and see the President.

The waiter came up with their drinks. He was wearing a white jacket with the word "Gambrinus" embroidered on it in red chain-stitch.

"That's one whisky—one beer . . ."

Mr. Gengis swallowed the whisky at a gulp without blinking, like someone taking a purge; then he took out his pipe and filled it with tobacco.

"Yes, my friend, these things have a way of getting to the President's ears just when one least expects it, and it's not very amusing for you, I'm afraid. Now's your moment to tell him straight out what's what. It's a tricky situation."

"Thanks for the advice, Mr. Gengis. I'll see you later. I'm going to try and get a cab now, so as to get there quicker. Thanks again, eh? And I'll be seeing you all later."

Mr. Gengis lit his pipe.

"How many whiskies have you drunk, Mr. Gengis?" asked one of the men at the table.

"Eighteen!" replied the American, his pipe in his mouth, one eye half shut and the other—very blue—staring at the little yellow match-flame.

"And you're quite right! Whisky's splendid stuff, isn't it?"

"God knows. I couldn't say. You must ask people who don't drink it out of sheer desperation, like me."

"You mustn't say that, Mr. Gengis!"

"Why not say it if it's what I think? In my country everyone says exactly what he thinks. Exactly."

"That's an admirable quality."

"Oh no—I like it better as you do here: you say what you don't think, so long as it's pleasant!"

"So in your country, you don't tell stories?"

"Oh no, absolutely not; except what are in the Bible!"

"Another whisky, Mr. Gengis?"

"Yes I think I'll have another whisky!"

"Bravo, I like that, you're a man who's ready to die for his beliefs!"

"Comment?"

"My friend said you were a man who would die . . ."

"Yes, I understood about dying for one's beliefs. No, I'm a man who lives for his beliefs. I'm very much alive. Dying is not important; I shall die when God wills."

"Mr. Gengis would like it to rain whisky!"

"No, no, why? Then they wouldn't sell umbrellas as umbrellas but for funnels," and he added, after a pause filled with pipesmoke and a soft sound of breathing, while the others laughed: "Angel Face is a good chap; but if he doesn't do what I say he'll never be forgiven, but be sent packing instead!"

A party of silent men suddenly came into the bar; there were a lot of them— too many to come through the door at the same time. Most of them remained standing by the door, between the tables, or close to the bar-counter. They would not be there long, it wasn't worth sitting down. "Silence!" called a rather short, rather old, rather bald, rather healthy, rather mad, rather harsh-voiced, rather dirty man; he spread out a large printed notice, and two other men helped him fix it to one of the looking-glasses with black wax.

"CITIZENS:

"Merely by uttering the name of the President of the Republic we shed light from the torch of Peace upon those sacred interests of a Nation which, under his wise rule, has conquered and will go on conquering the inestimable benefits of Progress in every sphere, and of Order in every form of Progress!!!! As free citizens, conscious of our obligation to watch over our own destiny (which is also that of the Nation) and as men of goodwill and enemies of Anarchy, we hereby proclaim!!! That the welfare of the Republic depends upon the RE-ELEC-TION OF OUR ILLUSTRIOUS MANDATORY AND ON NOTHING ELSE BUT HIS RE-ELEC-TION! Why hazard the ship of State in unknown waters, when we have at its head at present the most accomplished Statesman of our day, whom History will salute as a Great Man among Great men, a Wise Man among the Wise, a Liberal, a Thinker and a Democrat??? Even to imagine any other than Him in this high office amounts to an attempt upon the Destiny of the Nation (which is our own destiny); and whoever dares to do so—if any such there be—deserves to be shut up as a dangerous lunatic, or if he is not mad, tried as a traitor to his Country according to the law!!! FELLOW CITIZENS, THE BALLOT-BOXES ARE WAITING!!! VOTE!!! FOR!!! OUR!!! CANDIDATE!!! WHO!!! WILL!!! BE!!!

RE-ELECTED!!!! BY!!! THE!!! PEO-
PLE!!!"

The reading aloud of this notice
aroused universal enthusiasm in the bar;
there were shouts and applause; and in
answer to a general demand, a carelessly
dressed man with long black hair and
steely eyes got up to speak:

"Patriots, I think as a Poet, but I speak
as a patriotic citizen! A Poet means a
man who invented the sky; you must
listen therefore to a disorganized ha-
rangue from the inventor of this useless,
beautiful thing we call the sky. When
that German whom the Germans did not
understand—no, I do not mean Goethe,
Kant or Schopenhauer—wrote of a Superman, he was undoubtedly foretelling
the birth in America, to Father Cosmos
and Mother Nature, of the first truly
superior man who has ever existed. I am
speaking, gentlemen, of him who excels
the dawn in brightness, whom his country has called 'the Well-deserving,' of the
Chief of the Party and Protector of Studious Youth. It is the Constitutional
President of the Republic, gentlemen—as
no doubt you have all realized—whom I
refer to as Nietzsche's Superman, the
Super-unique . . . I say it and I repeat
it from this platform." As he said this he
banged on the bar-counter with his hand.
"And so, compatriots, although I am not
one of those who has made politics his
livelihood, it is my disinterested, whole-
hearted and honest belief that since there
does not exist among us another hyper-
superman and super-citizen, we should
be mad or blind, criminally blind or mad,
if we allowed the reins of government to
pass from the hands of this super-unique
charioteer who now and forever guides
our beloved country, to those of another
citizen, some ordinary citizen—a citizen,
fellow citizens, who even if he possessed
all the good qualities on earth must still
remain a mere man. In the old, exhausted continent of Europe, Democracy
has done away with Emperors and
Kings; but we must realize—and we *do*
realize—that now that it has been trans-
planted to America, it has been injected
with the almost divine graft of the Superman, and is building a new form of government: Super-democracy. And now,
gentlemen, I shall have much pleasure in
reciting . . ."

"Recite, poet," cried a voice, "but not
the ode."

". . . my Nocturne in C Major to the
Super-Unique!"

The poet's magnificent oration was
succeeded by others even more impas-
sioned, aimed at the "infamous" party
supporting the San Juan alphabet, the
abracadabra system and other theological
suppositories. The nose of one of those
taking part began to bleed, and he
shouted loudly between speeches, for
someone to bring him a new brick soaked
in water, so that he could stop the
hemorrhage by sniffing it.

"By now," said Mr. Gengis, "Angel
Face is between the wall and the President. I like the way this poet speaks, but
I think it must be very sad to be a poet;
and to be a lawyer must be the saddest
thing in the world. And now I'm going to
have another whisky! Another whisky,"
he shouted, "for this super-hyper-ferro-
quasi-carrilero!"

As Angel Face was leaving "Gambrinus," he met the Secretary of State for
War.

"Where are you off to, General?"

"To see the boss . . ."

"Then let's go together."

"Are you going there too? Let's wait
for my carriage, it won't be long. Between ourselves, I've just been visiting a
widow."

"I know you're fond of merry widows,
General."

"Now then, none of your musical
talk!"

"I wasn't talking music, but Clicquot!"

"Clicquot nothing! A dish fit for a king!"

"Really?"

The carriage rolled silently along as if its wheels were made of blotting-paper. Gendarmes were posted at the corners of the roads and they heard them passing the signal along: "The Secretary of State for War. The Secretary of State for War."

The President was pacing his study with short steps; he was wearing a hat pulled down over his forehead, his coat collar turned up over a scarf, and his waistcoat buttons undone. Black suit, black hat, black boots.

"What's the weather like, General?"

"Cold, Mr. President."

"And here's Miguel without an over-coat!"

"Mr. President . . ."

"Rubbish. You're trembling, and you're going to tell me you're not cold. You're very unwise. General, send someone to Miguel's house for his overcoat at once."

The Secretary of State went out saluting—he nearly tripped over his sword—while the President sat down on a wicker sofa and offered Angel Face the chair next to it.

"You see, Miguel, I have to do everything myself and supervise everything, because I rule over a nation of 'intenders,'" he said as he sat down. "And when I can't see to things myself I have to rely on my friends." He paused for a moment. "I mean by 'intenders' people with every intention of doing or undoing, but who from lack of will power do neither. They are neither fish, fowl nor good red herring. For instance, our industrialists spend their lives repeating over and over again: I intend to build a factory, I intend to set up new machinery, I intend this, I intend that, and so on *ad infinitum*. The agriculturalist says: I intend to try out new methods, I intend to export my products; the writer: I intend to write a book; the professor: I intend to found a school; the business-man: I intend to carry out such and such transactions, and the journalists—those swine with lumps of lard where their souls ought to be—I intend to improve the country. But, as I told you, nobody ever does a thing, and so naturally it is I, the President of the Republic, who has to do everything, and take all the blame as well. You might almost say that if it weren't for me Fortune wouldn't exist, as I have even to take the part of the blind goddess in the lottery . . ."

He stroked his moustache with his transparent, delicate reed-brown finger-tips, and went on in a different tone:

"This is all leading up to the fact that circumstances oblige me to make use of the services of men like you, who are useful to have close at hand but even more useful outside the Republic, where my enemies' schemes, intrigues and malicious writings are endangering my re-election . . ."

He let his eyes drop, like two mosquitoes gorged with blood, and went on:

"I'm not talking about Canales and his followers: death has always been my most trusty ally, Miguel! I'm talking of the people who are trying to influence North American opinion, in the hope of discrediting me in Washington. When a caged wild animal begins to molt, it doesn't mean that it wants to have the rest of its hair pulled out by force, does it? Very well, then. Am I an old man with a pickled brain and a heart as hard as ebony, as they say? Let the blackguards say what they like! But that the people themselves should, for political reasons, take advantage of what I've done to save my country from the onslaughts of these sons of bitches—that is a bit too much! My re-election hangs in the balance, and that is why I've sent for

[151]

you. You must go to Washington and bring me back a detailed report on those dark clouds of hate, and those funeral ceremonies where the only respectable rôle—as in all funerals—is that of the corpse."

"Mr. President," stammered Angel Face, divided between his desire to follow Mr. Gengis' advice to put his cards on the table and the fear of losing, by some indiscretion, the chance of making a journey which he had realized from the first might be his salvation. "The President knows that I am unconditionally at his service for any purpose whatever; however, if I may say two words, since I have always wanted to be the last, but also the most loyal and devoted of his servants, before undertaking such a delicate mission I would like to ask the President to be so kind, if he sees no objection, as to give orders for an investigation into the truth of the unfounded charges of my being an enemy of the President's, made against me, by the Judge Advocate General for one . . ."

"But who is paying any attention to such tarradiddles?"

"The President cannot doubt my unconditional loyalty to his person and his Government; but I do not want him to give me his complete confidence before discovering whether the Judge Advocate's accusations are true or false."

"I am not asking your advice as to what I should do, Miguel! That's enough! I know all about it, and I'll go further and tell you that this desk contains the charge that the Judge Advocate General drew up against you at the time of General Canales' flight; and more still: I can tell you that the Judge Advocate's hatred of you derives from a circumstance of which you are perhaps ignorant. The Judge Advocate, in agreement with the police, had formed a plan of kidnapping the lady who is now your wife and selling her to the proprietress of a brothel, from

whom, as you know, he had received ten thousand pesos in advance. The woman who had to suffer in her stead was a poor creature who has gone half mad as a result."

Angel Face sat quite still, careful not to show his master the slightest change of expression, and burying his feelings deep in his heart behind the guard of his black velvet eyes. He was pale and cold as his wicker chair.

"If the President will allow me, I would rather stay beside him, and defend him with my own blood."

"Do you mean you won't accept?"

"Absolutely not, Mr. President."

"Very well then. All this is quite superfluous—mere words; tomorrow's newspapers will publish the news of your impending departure, and you cannot let me down; the War Office has orders to let you have the money you'll need for the journey today; I will send it to the station with my instructions."

Angel Face began to be aware of the pulsation of an underground clock marking the fatal passage of time. Through a wide-open window, his eyes looked out under their black brows and saw a bonfire burning beside a greenish-black cypress grove and walls of white smoke, in the middle of a patio half-effaced by the darkness. Groups of sentinels were standing about under the seedling stars. Four priestly figures stood at the corners of the patio, all four dressed in moss as water-diviners; all four with their hands covered in yellowish-green frog-skin; all four with the eye on the bright side of their faces shut, and the eye on the dark side open. All at once there was a sound of native drums: tom-tom, tom-tom, tom-tom, and a great many men disguised as animals came leaping in, in Indian file. Down the blood-stained, vibrant drumsticks came crabs of falling air and worms of fire. The men danced rather than be rooted to the ground or to the wind by the sound of the tom-tom; they fed the bonfire with turpentine from their foreheads. From the dung-colored semi-darkness emerged a little man with a face like a dried fruit; his tongue protruded between his cheeks, there were thorns on his forehead, he had no ears, and wore round his navel a woollen cord from which hung warriors' heads and calabash leaves. He went up to blow on the clustered flames, and to the blind delight of the men-animals he took some of the fire in his mouth and chewed it as if it was copal without burning himself. A cry came from the darkness enveloping the trees, and from near and far came the mournful voices of the tribes who had been fighting blindly since birth: with their entrails—for they were animals of hunger, with their throats—for they were birds of thirst, and with their fear, their nausea and their physical needs, crying upon Tohil, the Giver of Fire, to give them back the lighted torch of fire. Tohil arrived riding on a river of pigeons' breasts which flowed like milk. The deer came running so that the water should not stop flowing; their horns were as slender as rain, and their little hoofs fell on the cheerful sand as light as air. The birds came hurrying so that their reflections should swim on the water—birds with bones more delicate than their feathers. Rataplan! Rataplan! echoed from under the earth.

Tohil demanded human sacrifices. The tribes led their best hunters before him—with their blow-pipes held ready and their slings charged.

"And do these men hunt other men?" asked Tohil.

Rataplan! Rataplan! echoed from under the earth.

"We'll do as you ask," replied the tribes, "on condition that you, the Giver of Fire, will return fire to us, so that neither our flesh, nor the air, nor our nails, nor our tongues, nor our hair shall freeze any more! On condition that you do not go on destroying our lives, and subjecting us to a living death!" "I am content," said Tohil. Rataplan! Rataplan! echoed from under the earth. "I am content! I can prevail over men who are hunters of men. Henceforth there will be neither true death nor true life. Now dance the jicara in my honor!"

And each hunter-warrior blew on their gourds without pausing for breath, to the rhythm of the tom-tom, and the echo and the drumming which set Tohil's eyes dancing.

After this inexplicable vision, Angel Face said goodbye to the President. As he was leaving, the Secretary of State for War called him and gave him a wad of notes and his overcoat.

"Are you coming, General?" He could scarcely find words.

"I wish I could. But perhaps I shall join you there, or else we shall meet again some time; I have to stay here for the present, you see," and he twisted his head over his right shoulder, "listening to my master's voice."

CHAPTER XXXVIII

The Journey

The river that was flowing over the roof while she packed the trunks did not debouch inside the house, but very far away, in the wide expanse leading to the open country or perhaps to the sea. A strong gust of wind forced open the window; the rain came pouring in as if the glass had been broken to smithereens, the curtains and papers blew about, doors banged, but Camila went on with her task, isolated among the trunks she was filling; and although she felt the lightning right to the roots of her hair, nothing seemed to her either complete or different —everything was alike empty, disconnected, weightless, without body, without soul, as she was herself.

"Is it better to live here, or where one is out of range of that monster—what do you think?" said Angel Face, shutting the window. "It was just what I wanted. Perhaps I'm running away though!"

"But after what you told me about those wild witch-doctors dancing in his house . . ."

"That's not worth worrying about!" His voice was drowned by a thunderclap. "And anyway what could they possibly find out by their divinations? After all, he's the one who is sending me to Washington; he is the one who's paying for my journey. And, good lord! everything may well look quite different when I'm far away. Anything's possible. You'll join me, with the excuse that you're ill, or else that I am, and after that he could look for us as hard as he likes!"

"But supposing he won't let me go?"

"Well then I shall come back and keep my mouth shut, and we shall be no worse off than before, shall we? Nothing venture . . ."

"You always think everything's so easy!"

"We've got enough to live on anywhere; and I mean live, really live, not just go on repeating all day long: 'I think with the President's mind therefore I exist, I think with the President's mind therefore I exist.'"

Camila gazed at him with eyes full of tears; her mouth seemed to be full of hair and her ears of rain.

"What are you crying about? Don't cry."

"Well what else can I do?"

"Women are all the same."

"Leave me alone!"

"You'll make yourself ill if you go on crying like that—for heaven's sake!"

"No, leave me alone!"

"Anyone would think I was dying or else about to be buried alive!"

"Leave me alone!"

Angel Face held her close. His hard, masculine cheeks were unused to tears, but two burning drops twisted their way down them, like reluctantly extracted nails.

"But you will write to me?" murmured Camila.

"Of course I will."

"Very often, please! You see we've never been separated before. Don't leave me without letters; it'll be agony for me if days go by without news of you. And take care of yourself! Don't trust anyone, d'you hear? Don't pay attention to what anyone says, least of all your compatriots —they're a bad lot. But above all, I beg you," her husband's kisses interrupted her, "I—beg—you—to—I beg you—to write—to me!"

Angel Face shut the trunks without removing his gaze from his wife's adoring eyes. It was raining in torrents. The water poured through the gutters like heavy chains. They were both choking with misery at the thought of the following day—now so close—and when everything was ready, they undressed in silence and got into bed, where they were kept awake by the sound of the clock clipping pieces off their last hours together—clippety-clack, clippety-clack— and the droning of mosquitoes.

"It's just flashed through my mind that I forgot to tell them to shut up the rooms to keep out the mosquitoes. Good heavens, what a fool!"

Angel Face's only reply was to hold her more tightly to him; she was like a little sheep, too weak to bleat.

He did not dare put out the light, nor shut his eyes, nor utter a word. They were so much closer in the light; the human voice creates such a distance between speakers, the closed eyelids are so great a barrier. And to be in darkness is a form of separation; and there was so much they wanted to say to each other

this last night, that the longest of conversations would have seemed like a telegram.

The noise of the servants chasing a hen among the seedbeds filled the patio. The rain had stopped and the water was dripping into the gutters like a clepsydra. The hen ran, crouched and fluttered, trying to escape from death.

"My little mill-stone," whispered Angel Face in her ear, smoothing her rounded stomach with his hand.

"My love!" she said, pressing her body against his. Her legs moved under the sheet like oars resting on the rippling water of a bottomless river.

The servants were still running about and shouting. Palpitating and terrified, the hen escaped from their hands, its eyes starting from its head, its beak wide open, its wings spread out like a cross, its breathing reduced to a thread.

Tightly enlaced, they caressed each other with trembling fingers—fingers that were half-dead and half-asleep, insubstantial. "My love!" she said to him. "My heaven," he said to her. "My heaven!" she said to him.

The hen ran against a wall, or the wall fell on top of it. It felt the two things happen simultaneously. They twisted its neck. It flapped its wings as if it could fly even now it was dead. "The wretched bird has gone and made a mess!" cried the cook, shaking the feathers which had soiled her apron, and went off to wash her hands in the rain-water in the fountain.

Camila shut her eyes . . . Her husband's weight . . . A flapping of wings . . . A stain . . .

And, more slowly now, the clock went clippety clack! clippety clack! clippety clack! clippety clack!

Angel Face hastily looked through the papers that had been handed him at the station by an officer. As he left the town behind him, it seemed to claw at the sky with the grimy nails of its roofs. The documents had a calming effect on him. What luck to be traveling away from that man in a first-class carriage, surrounded with attentions, with no spy at his heels and his pocket full of checks! He half shut his eyes, the better to preserve his thoughts. The fields came alive as the train passed through them, and began running after each other like children, one behind the other, one behind the other, one behind the other: trees, houses, bridges.

"What luck to be sitting in a first-class carriage, traveling away from that man!"

One behind the other, one behind the other, one behind the other. The house chased the tree, the tree chased the fence, the fence the bridge, the bridge the road, the road the river, the river the mountain, the mountain the cloud, the cloud the cornfield, the cornfield the laborer, the laborer the animal . . .

Surrounded with attentions and with no spy at his heels . . .

The animal chased the house, the house the tree, the tree the fence, the fence the bridge, the bridge the road, the road the river, the river the mountain, the mountain the cloud . . .

The reflection of a village ran along the transparent surface of a stream as dark as the depths of a pitcher.

The cloud chased the cornfield, the cornfield the laborer, the laborer the animal . . .

With no spy at his heels and checks in his pocket.

The animal chased the house, the house the tree, the tree the fence, the fence . . .

With a lot of checks in his pocket!

A bridge like a billiard-rest flashed past the window . . . Light and shade, ladders, steel fringe, swallows' wings . . .

The fence chased the bridge, the bridge the road, the road the river, the river the mountain, the mountain . . .

Angel Face let his head fall against the back of his seat. His sleepy eyes followed the low, flat, hot, monotonous coast-line, with a confused feeling of being in the train, of not being in the train, of lagging behind the train, further behind the train, further behind, still further behind, still further behind, further, further, further, further . . .

Suddenly he opened his eyes. He had been asleep with the unrelaxed sleep of a fugitive, the restlessness of someone who knows that danger may be filtering through the very air he breathes; and it seemed to him that he had just jumped into his seat in the train through an invisible hole. His neck hurt him, his face was sweating and there was a cloud of flies on his forehead.

Above the passing greenery, motionless clouds were gathering, swollen from the water they had sucked up from the sea, and with beams of light emerging like claws from behind their gray plush centers.

A village came and went—an apparently uninhabited village, a collection of toffee houses and dried maize leaves, grouped between the church and the cemetery. "How I wish I had the faith which built that church," thought Angel Face. "The church and the cemetery! Nothing is left alive now but faith and the dead!" His eyes were misted with the pleasure of escape. Yet this country with its slow-moving springtime was his country, his tenderness, his mother; and however much it might put new life into him to leave these villages behind, when he was among men of other countries he would always be a dead man among the living, eclipsed by the invisible presence of these trees and tombstones.

Station followed station. The train ran on without stopping, rattling over the badly laid rails. Here a whistle, there a grinding of brakes, further on still a hill crowned with a ring of dirty smoke. The passengers fanned themselves with hats, newspapers and handkerchiefs; they were suspended in hot air watered by a thousand drops of their own sweat; they were exasperated by the discomfort of their seats, by the noise, by the way their clothes pricked them as if insects' feet were hopping all over their skin, and their heads itched as if their hair was alive; they were as thirsty as if they had taken a purge, and as sad as death.

Dusk followed the harsh daylight, a shower of rain was wrung from the clouds, and now the horizon began to disintegrate, and far, very far away in the distance there shone a tin of sardines surrounded by blue oil.

One of the railway officials came along to light the lamps in the compartments. Angel Face straightened his collar and tie and looked at his watch. They were due at the port in twenty minutes—it seemed a century to him in his impatience to be safe and sound on the boat. He put his face close to the window trying to distinguish something in the darkness. There was a vegetable smell. He heard a river running by. And again further on, perhaps the same river.

The train slowed down among the streets of a small village, slung like hammocks in the darkness; it stopped very gradually, and after the second-class passengers had got out carrying bundles, it went on at a still slower rate towards the quays. Now he could hear the breaking of the waves and make out the indistinct pale shape of the Customs office with its smell of tar; he could hear the somnolent breathing of millions of gentle, salt-soaked creatures.

Angel Face waved a greeting from a distance to the man waiting in the station —it was Major Farfan. He was delighted to find a friend whose life he had saved

at this crucial moment in his own.
"Major Farfan!"

Farfan saluted him from a distance,
and coming up to the window told him
not to worry about his luggage—some
soldiers were coming to take it to the
boat. When the train stopped he got in
and shook hands warmly with Angel
Face. The other passengers got out in a
great hurry.

"Well and how have things been going
with you?"

"And you, my dear Major? But there's
no need to ask—one can see from your
face . . ."

"The President wired to me to look
after you and see you had everything you
want."

"Most kind of you, Major!"

It had taken only a few minutes for
the compartment to empty itself. Farfan
put his head out of one of the windows
and shouted:

"Are they coming for the luggage,
Lieutenant? What's the meaning of this
delay?"

At his words a group of armed soldiers
appeared at the door. Angel Face saw the
trap too late.

"I arrest you by order of the President," said Farfan, revolver in hand.

"But, Major . . . if the President
. . . it's impossible! Come with me,
please come with me, and let me send a
wire!"

"My orders are explicit, Don Miguel,
and you'd better come quietly!"

"As you like; but I mustn't miss my
ship. I'm on a mission, I can't . . ."

"Silence, please, and hand over everything you have on you immediately!"

"Farfan!"

"Hand it over, I tell you!"

"No. Listen to me, Major!"

"Come along, do what you're told, do
what you're told!"

"It would be better if you'd listen to
me, Major!"

"Let's have no more threats!"

"I have confidential instructions from
the President in my possession—and
you'll be responsible!"

"Search him, sergeant! We'll soon see
who's master!"

An individual with a handkerchief tied
over his face appeared out of the darkness. He was as tall as Angel Face, as
pale as Angel Face and with hair of the
same light brown as Angel Face; he took
possession of everything the sergeant was
abstracting from the real Angel Face
(passport, checks, wedding-ring engraved
with his wife's name—this he slipped off
his finger with the aid of a large dollop of
spit—cuff-links, handkerchiefs) and disappeared immediately.

Much later the ship's siren sounded.
The prisoner put his hands over his ears.
His eyes were blinded with tears. He
would have liked to break down the
door, escape, run, fly, cross the sea, cease
to be the man he was—what a restless
river ran beneath his skin, what a scar
had burnt into his flesh!—and become
that other man, who was traveling to
New York with his luggage and his name
in cabin No. 17.

CHAPTER XXXIX

The Port

Everything was quiet in the hush that
precedes a change of tide, except the
crickets (damp with sea-spray and with
stars glowing in their wing-cases), the
reflection of the lighthouse, like a safety-
pin in the darkness, and the prisoner,
pacing up and down with his hair over
his forehead and his clothes in disorder,
as if he had just taken part in a riot. He
was incapable of sitting down, and kept
making the tentative gestures of a sleeper
who defends himself with groans and
muttered words from being dragged by
God's hand toward his inevitable doom

—wounds, disembowelment or sudden death.

"Farfan is my only hope!" he kept repeating. "Lucky it wasn't the Colonel! For all my wife knows, I may have been shot and buried already. Nothing to report."

There was a pounding noise on the floor as if two feet were thudding along the railway carriage, which stood motionless on the rails, guarded by pickets of sentinels; but Angel Face was far away among the little villages he had just passed through, sunk in the slime of darkness or the blinding dust of sunny days, eaten up with fear of the church and the cemetery, the church and the cemetery, the church and the cemetery. Nothing was left alive but faith and the dead!

The clock at Garrison Headquarters struck one. The chandelier shook. The large hand had rounded the cape of midnight.

Major Farfan lazily thrust first his right arm, and then the left, into his tunic, and with equal slowness began to fasten it, starting with the button over his navel; he saw none of the things that lay in front of him: a map of the Republic shaped like a yawn, a towel covered in dried mucus and sleepy flies, a saddle, a rifle, knapsacks. Button by button, he reached the collar. When he got to the collar he threw back his head, so that his eyes fell on something that he could not look at without saluting: the President's portrait.

He finished fastening his buttons, broke wind, lit a cigarette from the lamp, took up his riding-whip and went out. The soldiers did not hear him go; they were asleep on the floor, wrapped in their ponchos like mummies; the sentinels presented arms and the officer on duty got up with the object of spitting out a worm of ash, all that was left of the cigarette between his sleeping lips, and only just

had time to wipe it away with the back of his hand as he saluted: "Nothing to report, sir."

The rivers were flowing into the sea like cats' whiskers in a saucer of milk. The liquid shadow of the trees, the heavy shapes of rutting crocodiles, the water in the malaria-haunted marshes, weary tears —all were moving towards the sea.

A man with a lantern joined Farfan as he entered the railway-coach. They were followed by two smiling soldiers who were busily undoing the knots in the rope with which the prisoner was to be bound. Farfan ordered them to tie him up, and they went off with him towards the village, followed by the sentinels who had been guarding the coach. Angel Face made no attempt to resist. In the major's manner and voice and the rigorousness he exacted from the soldiers, who would have treated him brutally enough without any incitement, he thought he divined a stratagem by which his friend could help him later on when they got to Headquarters without compromising himself beforehand. But he was not taken to Headquarters. When they left the station they turned off towards the farthest stretch of the railway line, where they forced him with blows to get into a goods-wagon with its floor covered in manure. They hit him without provocation, as if they had been given orders to do so.

"But why are they hitting me, Farfan?" Angel Face demanded of the major, who was following behind, in conversation with the man with a lantern.

The only reply he got was a blow with the stock of a rifle; but instead of striking him on the back they hit him on the head, making one of his ears bleed and sending him face downwards in the manure.

He took a breath, and spat out the dung; blood was dripping onto his clothes and he tried to protest.

"Will you shut up! Will you shut up!" cried Farfan, raising his riding-whip.

"Major Farfan!" cried Angel Face, holding his ground but almost frantic; there was a smell of blood in the air.

Farfan was afraid of what Angel Face might say, and struck him with the whip. It left its mark on the unfortunate man's cheek; with one knee on the ground he struggled to free his hands from their bonds.

"I understand," he said in a voice trembling with uncontrollable bitterness; "I understand. This exploit may earn you another star . . ."

"Shut up, unless you want . . ." interrupted Farfan, raising the whip again.

The man with the lantern held him back by the arm.

"Go on, hit me, don't stop, don't be afraid; I'm a man, and only eunuchs use whips!"

Two, three, four, five times the lash fell on the victim's face in less than a minute.

"Easy now, Major, easy now!" interposed the man with the lantern.

"No, no! I'm going to make this son of a bitch bite the dust. He can't get away with insulting the army like that. The swine! The shit!" He had broken his whip, but he was belaboring the prisoner violently with his pistol barrel, tearing off chunks of hair and leaving his face and head in ribbons, and with every blow he dealt he repeated in a stifled voice: "the army . . . orders . . . filthy . . . swine . . . take that!"

They dragged their victim's almost inanimate body from the manure in which he had fallen, and carried him from one end to the other of the railway line, where the goods-train was making ready to return to the capital.

The man with the lantern got into one of the trucks, accompanied by Farfan. They had been talking and drinking at Headquarters until it was time to start.

"The first time I tried to join the Secret Police," the man with the lantern was saying, "a great pal of mine called Lucio Vasquez—known as Velvet—was one of them . . ."

"I think I've heard of him," said the major.

"They didn't get me that time. He was a pretty tough chap—that's why they called him Velvet—and instead I got a stretch in clink and lost what my wife and I—I was married then—had put into a little business as well. And they even took my wife to The Sweet Enchantment, poor thing . . ."

Farfan woke up at the mention of The Sweet Enchantment, but the recollection of the Sow, that putrescent specimen of her sex, stinking of the latrine, who had once aroused his enthusiasm, now left him cold. He was like a man swimming under water, battling all the time with an imaginary Angel Face, who kept on saying over and over again: "another star! another star!"

"And what was your wife's name? I knew almost all the girls at The Sweet Enchantment."

"You'd be none the wiser if I told you, for she left as soon as she got there. We had a little nipper and he died there and it nearly sent her off her rocker. It was no place for her, you know! Now she's in the hospital laundry with the nuns. She'd never have made a whore!"

"But I think I did know her. Because I was the one who got permission from the police for the wake Doña Chon held for the baby; but I had no idea it was your little boy!"

"And as for me, I was fed up in clink, without a *real*. No thanks! If you start looking back at what you've been through, you feel like taking to your heels and running for your life!"

"And as for me, I didn't know a thing until a tart tried to get me into trouble with the President."

"This chap Angel Face was mixed up with General Canales; he was fast and loose with the daughter—he married her later on—and didn't carry out the President's orders, so they say. I know all this because Vasquez—Velvet—met him in a tavern called the Two-Step, a few hours before the general escaped."

"The Two-Step?" repeated the Major, searching his memory.

"It was an inn right on the corner. And, believe it or not, there were a man and a woman painted on the wall, one on each side of the door; the woman was saying—I remember the words still: 'Come and dance the two-step!' And the chap had a bottle in his hand and was saying: 'No thanks! I prefer the bottle dance!' "

The train slowly got under way. A small patch of dawn light was floating in the blue sea. Gradually, out of the shadows, came the straw huts of the village, the distant mountains, the wretched little cargo-boats and Garrison Headquarters—like a box of matches full of crickets in uniform.

CHAPTER XL

Blind Man's Buff

"He went away so many hours ago!"

On the day of departure, the person left behind starts counting each hour until there are enough to say: "He went away so many days ago!" But after two weeks the days are lost count of, and then it is: "He went away so many weeks ago!" A whole month. Then the months are lost count of. A whole year. Then the years are lost count of . . .

Camila was watching for the postman at one of the drawing-room windows, hidden behind the curtain so as not to be seen from the street; she was pregnant and was sewing baby-clothes.

The postman heralded his arrival by knocking like a lunatic on all the front doors. Knock by knock, he came level with the window. Camila left her sewing to listen and look, her heart leaping in her breast with agitation and pleasure. "At last I shall get the letter I long for! 'My beloved Camila,' in large letters . . ."

But the postman did not knock. Perhaps it was because . . . Perhaps later . . . And she took up her sewing again, humming a song to drive away her sad thoughts.

The postman came by again in the afternoon. It would have been impossible to sew a single stitch in the space of time it took her to get from the window to the door. Cold, breathless, all ears, she stood waiting for his knock; and, realizing at last that the silence of the house was unbroken, she shut her eyes in terror, and was shaken by sobs, sudden retching and sighs. Why not go out on the doorstep? Perhaps . . . the postman may have forgotten—he's a fine postman!—and he'll bring it tomorrow as if nothing had happened.

Next day she almost wrenched the door off its hinges, she opened it so wide. She ran to wait for the postman, partly so that he shouldn't forget her, but also just for luck. But he was already going by as usual, evading her questions, dressed in pea-green (the color of hope), with his little frog's eyes and his teeth bared like those of a skeleton in the anatomy-school.

A month, two months, three, four . . .

She no longer frequented the rooms looking onto the street; the weight of her grief drew her to the back of the house. She thought of herself as a kitchen utensil, a piece of coal or wood, an earthenware jar, mere rubbish.

"They're not just whims, but pregnant cravings," explained a neighbor with some knowledge of midwifery when the servants consulted her, more for the pleasure of talking than in search of a cure; as for remedies they had plenty of their own: they put candles in front of the saints, or relieved their own poverty and the burden on the house by removing small objects of value.

But one fine day the invalid went out of doors. Corpses float. Sitting huddled in a cab, avoiding the eyes of anyone she knew—nearly all of them turned away rather than greet her—she set off, determined to see the President at all costs. She breakfasted, lunched and dined off a tear-soaked handkerchief. She was still biting it as she sat in the waiting-room. What a lot of misery there was, to judge by the waiting crowd! Peasants sitting on the edges of their gold chairs; townspeople sitting in the middle and leaning against the backs. Ladies were directed to armchairs in low voices. Someone was talking in a door-way. The President! The mere thought made all her muscles stiffen. Her child kicked her in the stomach as if to say: "Let's get out of here!" There was the noise of people changing their positions. Yawns. Muttered remarks. The footsteps of staff officers. The movements of a soldier as he cleaned one of the windows. Flies. The little kicks of the child in her womb. "Don't be so rough! Why are you so cross? We're going to see the President to ask him what has happened to someone who doesn't know you exist, but will love you very much when he comes home! Oh, so you're impatient to come out and take part in what people call life! It's not that I'm against it, but you're better off and safer where you are!"

The President would not see her. Someone told her she had better apply for an audience. Telegrams, letters, official forms—everything was useless. He did not answer.

Night fell and dawn came, and her

eyelids were hollowed by lack of sleep or floated in lakes of tears. A large patio. She was lying in a hammock, playing with a caramel out of the Thousand and One Nights and a little black rubber ball. The caramel was in her mouth, the ball in her hands. Moving the caramel from one cheek to another, she dropped the little ball, which bounced on the floor of the passage under the hammock and rolled away into the patio a long way off, getting smaller and smaller until it vanished altogether, while the caramel in her mouth grew larger. She was not fully asleep. Her body trembled at the touch of the sheets. It was a dream lit both by dream lights and electric-light. The soap slipped out of her hands several times like the rubber ball, and her breakfast roll—she was eating it out of pure hunger—seemed to swell in her mouth like the caramel.

Everyone was at Mass and the streets were deserted when she went to several Government offices by turns, to watch for the Ministers to arrive; she did not know how to win over the grumpy little old porters—bundles of deformed flesh, who refused to answer her questions and threw her out when she became insistent.

But her husband had run to pick up the little ball. Now she remembered the rest of her dream. The big patio. The little black ball. Her husband getting smaller all the time, further away all the time as if seen through the wrong end of a telescope, till he disappeared out of the patio after the ball, while the caramel swelled inside her mouth—and she was not thinking about her child.

She wrote to the Consul at New York, to the Minister at Washington, to a friend of a woman friend and to the brother-in-law of a man friend, asking for news of her husband, and she might as well have thrown her letters in the dustbin. She heard through a Jewish grocer that the distinguished secretary of the American Legation, who was a detective as well as a diplomat, had definite news of Angel Face's arrival in New York. Not only were there official records of his disembarkation to be found in the port and hotel registers and the police files, but his arrival had also been reported by the newspapers and by people who had recently returned from the city.

"And now they're looking for him," the Jew told her, "and they must find him, dead or alive, although it seems as if he'd taken another boat from New York to Singapore."

"And where's that?" she asked.

"Where do you suppose? Why in Indochina," replied the Jew, with a click of his false teeth.

"And how long would it take a letter to get here from there?" she persisted.

"I don't know exactly, but not more than three months." She counted on her fingers. Angel Face had been gone for four.

In New York or Singapore. What a weight was lifted from her mind! What an immense comfort to think of him far away, to know that he hadn't been murdered at the port as some people said, that he was far away from her in New York or Singapore but thinking of her all the time!

She held on to the counter in the Jew's shop to prevent herself from fainting. Her joy made her feel ill. She walked away as if on air, as if on her husband's arm in a new country, leaving behind the hams wrapped in silver paper, the bottles in Italian straw, the tinned jams, chocolates, apples, herrings, olives, dried cod and muscat grapes. "What a fool, I was, tormenting myself like that! Now I understand why he hasn't written; but I must go on playing the part of a deserted woman, blind with jealousy, trying to find the man who has left her—or else of

a wife who wants her husband beside her during the difficult ordeal of childbirth."

She reserved a cabin and packed her bags; everything was ready for her departure when she was refused a passport. A hole full of nicotine-stained teeth surrounded by a rim of swollen flesh moved up and down, down and up, to tell her that orders had been issued that she should not be given a passport. She moved her own lips up and down, down and up, in an attempt to repeat the words as if she must have heard them wrong.

And she spent a fortune on telegrams to the President. No answer came. She got no help from Government officials. The Under-secretary for War, a man who was naturally indulgent to women, advised her not to go on insisting, for no amount of effort would get her a passport; her husband had tried to trifle with the President and the position was hopeless.

They advised her to go and see a certain influential little priest, or else one of the mistresses of the man who provided the President with horses; and as a rumor that Angel Face had died of yellow fever in Panama was running round at the time, there were plenty who were ready to take her to the spiritualists to settle her doubts.

They did not wait for her to ask them twice. But the medium seemed a little reluctant. "I don't like the idea of the spirit of someone who was the President's enemy materializing in me," she said, her withered shanks shaking under her frozen clothes. But prayers and money together will move mountains, and by much greasing of her palm they induced her to agree. The lights were put out. Camila was terrified when she heard them summon Angel Face's spirit, and they had to drag her out practically unconscious; she was told that she had heard the voice of her husband, who had died on the high seas and was now in an inaccessible sphere of universal Being, lying in the most comfortable bed, on a mattress of water, with fishes for springs and the most delicious of pillows—non-existence.

Thin and wrinkled as an old cat, and with nothing left of her face but eyes— green eyes with dark rings round them as big as her transparent ears—she was barely twenty years old when she gave birth to a little boy. On the advice of her doctor she went to stay in the country for a while as soon as she got out of bed. Threatened by progressive anemia, tuberculosis and madness, she held on to life by a fine thread, feeling her way with her baby in her arms, without news of her husband, searching for him in mirrors (the only place of return for drowned men) in her son's eyes and in her own as she slept and dreamed of him in New York or Singapore.

At last a day came which shed light on the dark night of her grief, as she wandered like a shadow between the pines, the orchard fruit-trees and the tall trees in the fields: it was Whit Sunday, when her son was anointed with salt, oil, water and the priest's saliva, and given the name of Miguel. The mocking-birds were caressing each other with their beaks— two ounces of feathers and endless trills. The sheep were busy licking their lambs. What a perfect sensation of Sunday well-being the movements of its mother's tongue over its body produced in the suckling lamb, flickering its long-lashed eyes under her caress! Foals raced after moist-eyed mares. Calves mooed with delight, their jaws slavering, as they nuzzled the swollen udders. Without knowing why, she pressed her baby to her heart when the christening chimes had ended, as if life had been renewed in her.

Little Miguel grew up in the country and became a countryman. Camila never again set foot in the city.

CHAPTER XLI

Nothing to Report

Once in every twenty-two hours the light penetrated between the cobwebs and stone mullions into the underground vaults; and once in every twenty-two hours a rusty old petrol tin was let down on a rotten, knotted cord with food for the prisoners in the underground cells. At the sight of the can full of greasy broth with scraps of fat meat and pieces of pancake in it, the prisoner in No. 17 turned away his head. He would rather die than eat even a mouthful, and day after day the tin descended and went up again untouched. But he was driven by sheer need, hunger had him with his back to the wall, his eyes had become enormous with glassy pupils, he talked aloud and ramblingly as he paced up and down his tiny cell, he rubbed his teeth with his fingers, tugged at his cold ears, and the day came at last when he rushed at the descending tin as if it might be withdrawn any moment and plunged his mouth, nose, face and hair into it, nearly drowning himself in his efforts to swallow and chew at the same time. He finished the lot, and when the rope was pulled up he watched the empty tin ascending with the pleasure of a satisfied animal. He could not stop sucking his fingers and licking his lips. But his gratification was short-lived, for he soon vomited up his meal amid curses and groans. The meat and the pancake glued themselves to his stomach and refused to budge, but each spasm left him leaning against the wall open-mouthed like someone leaning over the edge of a cliff. At last he got his breath again, but his head was spinning; he combed his damp hair with his hand, slipping it down behind his ears to clean the vomit from his beard. There was a ringing in his ears.

His face was bathed in cold, sticky, sour sweat, like the water in an electric battery. And the light was already going— the light always began to go as soon as it came. By clutching on to his wasted body, as if struggling with himself, he succeeded in half sitting down, stretching his legs, resting his head against the wall and succumbing to the weight of his eyelids as to some powerful narcotic. But there was no comfort in sleep for him; his struggles to breathe in spite of the lack of air were followed by restless movements of his hands over his body, a compulsive drawing up and stretching out of each leg in turn, and feverish efforts to tear out the live coal which seemed to be burning his throat, with the little helmets of his finger-nails. As soon as he was half awake he began to open and shut his mouth like a fish out of water, to taste the icy air with his dry tongue; and, once fully awake, he began to shout in a feverish delirium, standing on tiptoe and stretching to his full height so that everyone should hear him. His cries grew fainter and fainter as they echoed through the vaults. He beat on the walls, stamped on the floor with his feet and shouted again and again, until soon his shouts had become yells . . . "Water, soup, salt, fat, anything; water, soup . . ."

A trickle of blood fell on his hand— the blood of a crushed scorpion . . . of many scorpions, for it was still flowing . . . of all the crushed scorpions in heaven turning to rain . . . He quenched his thirst without knowing whence came this gift of liquid, which was afterwards to be his chief torment. For he spent hours and hours crouching on the stone he used as a pillow, to keep his feet out of the puddle of water which collected in his cell in winter; hours and hours, wet to the very hair, distilling water, wet to the very bones, yawning

and shivering, suffering torments of hunger whenever the tin of greasy broth was late in arriving. He ate as thin people do, to nourish his dreams, and he fell asleep standing up after the last mouthful. Afterwards another tin was lowered in which prisoners in solitary confinement satisfied their physical needs. The first time the prisoner in No. 17 heard it come down he thought it was a second meal, and as this was during the time he was refusing to eat he let it go up again without dreaming that it contained excrement; its stench was much the same as that of the soup. This tin used to pass from cell to cell and when it reached No. 17 it was half full. How terrible to hear it come down when he had no need of it, or to need it when he had perhaps deafened himself with beating on the wall like the clapper of a useless bell! Sometimes, as a further refinement of torture, his desire left him when he even thought of the tin, wondering if it would arrive or not arrive, or be late or even forgotten (this was not uncommon) or break its cord (this happened nearly every day) and give one of the prisoners a shower-bath. The thought of the fumes that came from it, the human warmth, the sharp edges of the square receptacle, the necessary effort, was enough to inhibit his desire and then he had to wait for the next time, to live through twenty-two hours of colic, strangury, tears, contortions, and obscenities, with the taste of copper in his saliva, and in the last extremity to relieve himself on the floor, emptying the stinking contents of his bowel like a dog or a child, alone with death.

Two hours of light, twenty-two hours of utter darkness, one tin of soup and one of excrement, thirst in summer, flood in winter; that was life in the underground cells.

"You weigh less every day," said the

prisoner in No. 17 to himself in a voice he hardly recognized; "and soon the wind will be able to blow you to where Camila is waiting for you to come home! She must be tired out with waiting, she must have shrunk into something almost invisible! What will it matter if your hands are thin? She will warm them in her bosom! Dirty? She'll wash them with her tears! Her green eyes? Yes, like those pictures of fields in the Austrian Tyrol in *La Ilustracion,* or the green of sugar-cane, flecked with bright yellow and indigo. And the taste of her words, and the taste of her lips, and the taste of her teeth, and the taste of her taste . . . And her body, like a figure of eight with her slender waist, or the guitar-shaped cloud of smoke left by fireworks as they go out and lose their impetus. There were fireworks the night I stole her from death . . . The angels were walking, the clouds were walking, the roofs were walking with little steps like a night-watchman, the houses, the trees, everything was walking on air with her and with me."

And he used to feel Camila close beside him, like silken powder to his touch, in each breath he drew, in his ears, between his fingers, against his ribs as they were shaken like eyelashes by the blind eyes of his viscera.

And he possessed her . . .

The spasm would come about gently, without the slightest contortion; a slight shiver would pass along the twisted thorns of his spine, there would be rapid contraction of the glottis, and his arms would drop to the ground as though amputated . . .

The disgust it caused him to satisfy his needs in the tin, multiplied by the guilt that devoured him for satisfying his physical needs in so barren a manner with the memory of his wife, left him without the strength to move.

With the only metal utensil at his disposal, a little piece of brass torn from one of his shoe-laces, he engraved Camila's name and his own intertwined on the wall, and making use of the light which came every twenty-two hours, he added a heart, a dagger, a crown of thorns, an anchor, a cross, a little sailing-boat, a star, two swallows like the tilde on an ñ, and a railway-train with a spiral of smoke.

Fortunately his weakness spared him the torments of the flesh. Physically destroyed as he was, he thought of Camila as one smells a flower or hears a poem. He thought of her as the rose which used to flower every April and May in the window of the dining-room where he breakfasted with his mother as a child— an inquisitive little rose-tree branch. A series of childish mornings left him bewildered. The light was going . . . it was going . . . the light always began to go as soon as it came. The darkness swallowed up the thick walls as if they were wafers and soon afterwards the bucket of excrement would arrive. Oh for his rose! The harsh sound of the rope and the tin hanging crazily between the intestinal walls of the vaults. He shivered at the thought of the stench which would accompany this important visitor. Oh for his rose, as white as the milk in his breakfast jug!

In the course of years the prisoner in No. 17 had aged considerably, though more from suffering than from the passage of time. Countless deep wrinkles grooved his face and he sprouted white hairs as ants sprout wings in winter. Nothing left of his body . . . Nothing left of his corpse . . . without air, without sun, without movement, suffering from dysentery, rheumatism and neuralgia, practically blind, the last and only thing that remained alive in him was the hope of seeing his wife again, that love which sustains the heart against the emery-powder of suffering.

The Chief of the Secret Police pushed back his chair, tucked his feet under it, leaned his elbows on the black-topped table, brought his pen closer to the light and with bared teeth and a sudden pinching movement of two fingers, succeeded in extracting the hair which had been giving his letters prawns' whiskers. Then he went on writing:

". . . and according to instructions received," the pen scratched its way over the paper from stroke to stroke, "the aforenamed Vich made friends with the prisoner in cell No. 17, after he had been shut up with him for two months and made a pretense of weeping at all hours, shouting all day long and wanting to commit suicide every few moments. From friendship to words; the prisoner in No. 17 asked him what crime against the President he had committed to be sent to this place where all hope was at an end. The aforenamed Vich did not answer, but merely beat his head on the ground and broke into obscenities. But he insisted, until in the end Vich's tongue was loosened: A polyglot born in a land of polyglots, he heard of the existence of a country where there were no polyglots. Journey. Arrival. An ideal country for foreigners. Jobs here, friends there, money, everything. Then suddenly a woman in the street; the first hesitating steps in pursuit, almost against his will. Married? Single? Widow? The only thing he knows is that he has to follow her! What beautiful green eyes! A mouth like a rose! How gracefully she walks! He determines to get in touch with her, he walks past her house, manages to get inside, but from the moment he tries to speak to her he never sees her again, and an unknown man begins following him everywhere like his shadow. What does it mean, my friends? His friends turn away.

Paving-stones, what does it mean? The walls tremble to hear him speak. The only thing that becomes clear is that he has been so rash as to want to make love to the President's mistr—a lady who was the daughter of a general and had done this out of revenge because her husband had deserted her, so they told him, before he was put in prison as an anarchist.

"The aforementioned Vich states that at this point he heard a noise like a snake rustling through the darkness, that the prisoner came up to him and begged him in a voice as weak as a fish's fin to tell him the lady's name, and the aforementioned Vich repeated it twice . . .

"From this moment the prisoner began to scratch himself as if his whole body itched, although he had no more sensation in it; he tore at his face to wipe away tears where there was nothing but dry skin, and raised his hand to his breast but could not find it: a spiders-web of damp dust had fallen to the ground . . .

"According to instruction received I handed personally to the aforementioned Vich, whose statement I have tried to set down exactly, eighty-seven dollars for the time he was imprisoned, a second-hand cashmere suit and his passage to Vladivostok. The death certificate of the prisoner in No. 17 has been filled in as follows: Died of infectious dysentery.

"This is all I have the honor to impart to the President . . ."

Epilogue

The student was standing rooted to the edge of the pavement as if he had never seen a man in a cassock before. It was not the cassock that astonished him, however, so much as what the sacristan whispered in his ear, as they embraced with delight at meeting one another at liberty:

"I've received orders to dress like this."

And he would have stopped there had it not been that a string of prisoners just then went by between two files of soldiers, in the middle of the street.

"Poor wretches," murmured the sacristan, while the student stepped on to the pavement, "this is the price they have to pay for pulling down the Cathedral Porch! Some things must be seen to be believed!"

"One sees them," the student exclaimed, "touches them, and still doesn't believe them! I'm talking about the Municipality."

"I thought you meant my cassock."

"They weren't content with forcing the Turks to pay for painting the Porch; they must needs carry their protest against the assassination of the 'man with a little mule' to the lengths of destroying the structure itself."

"Take care no one hears you, you chatterbox. Be quiet for God's sake! It's not certain."

The sacristan had more to say, but a little man who was running about the Plaza without a hat on came up, planted himself in front of them and sang at the top of his voice:

"Figurine, what figure-maker
figured you?
who gave you the face
of a figure of fun?"

"Benjamin! Benjamin!" called a woman running after him, who looked as though she would burst into tears any minute.

"Not Benjamin the puppet-master?
no not he;
who made you a policeman
and a figure of fun?"

"Benjamin! Benjamin!" cried the woman, almost in tears now. "Don't take any notice, please, don't pay any attention to him; he's quite mad; he can't get it into his head that there's no Cathedral Porch any longer!" And while the puppet-master's wife made excuses for him to the sacristan and the student, Don Benjamin hurried off to sing his song to an ill-tempered gendarme:

"Figurine, what figure-maker
figured you?
who gave you the face
of a figure of fun?
Not Benjamin the puppet-master,
no not he,
who made you a policeman
and a figure of fun?"

"Please don't take him away, he doesn't mean any harm; don't you see he's mad?" begged Don Benjamin's wife, getting between the puppet-master and the policeman. "He is mad, I tell you, don't take him away—no, don't hit him please! He's so mad that he says he can see the whole town laid flat like the Porch!"

The prisoners were still going past. What must it be like to be them instead of the lookers-on who were so deeply thankful not to be them? Behind the procession of men pushing hand-carts came some who carried heavy tools over their shoulders like a cross, and behind them again were second rows of men dragging their chains like noisy rattlesnakes.

Don Benjamin tore himself away from the gendarme, who was arguing with ever-increasing violence with his wife, and ran to greet the prisoners with the first words that came into his head: "Just look at you now, Pancho Tonancho, and that knife of yours which eats into leather and likes making holes in a cork bedroom! Just look at you now, Lolo Cusholo, with your fan-tailed machete! Just look at you walking now, Mixto Melindres, when you used to ride on horseback; fresh water for your dagger, you sodomite and traitor! Who saw you with your pistol when your name was

Domingo and who sees you now, as sad as a week-day, without it! She gave them nits, let her delouse them! Guts dressed in rags make no stew for soldiers! Anyone who's got no padlock to fasten his mouth had better put on handcuffs!"

The shop assistants were beginning to go home; the trams were full to bursting-point. An occasional cab, car, or bicycle . . . A little surge of life, which lasted as long as it took the sacristan and the student to cross the Cathedral square—the beggars' refuge and the rubbish-dump of the irreligious—and say goodbye outside the door of the Archbishop's Palace.

The student looked scornfully down at the debris of the Porch from a bridge of planks laid over it. A gust of icy wind had just raised a thick cloud of dust, like smoke without fire, or the remains of a distant eruption. Another gust brought a shower of pieces of useless official paper raining down on what had once been the assembly-room of the Town Hall. The remains of the tapestries on the fallen walls waved like flags in the current of air. Suddenly the shadow of the puppet-master appeared riding on a broom against a blue background covered with stars, with five little volcanoes of gravel and stone at his feet.

Splash! The chimes announcing that it was eight o'clock in the evening plunged into the silence—Splash! Splash!

The student arrived at his house at the end of a blind alley, and as he opened the door he heard (interspersed with the servants' coughs as they prepared to make the responses to the Litany) his mother's voice telling her rosary:

"For the dying and for travelers. So that Peace shall reign among Christian rulers. For those who suffer persecution by the law. For the enemies of the Catholic faith. For the desperate needs of Holy Church and for our own needs . . . For the blessed souls of Holy Purgatory . . . Kyrie eleison."

THE LIFE AND WORKS OF
MIGUEL ANGEL ASTURIAS

By *GREGORY RABASSA*

AMONG THE Mayan Indians of Guatemala and Yucatan, both ancient and modern, there is a figure called the *Gran Lengua* (Great Tongue), who is committed by natural endowment and communal agreement to create and preserve the great legends that are handed down as the people's heritage and religion. This is how Miguel Angel Asturias has described himself. The people he speaks for are not only those of his native Guatemala but the whole diverse population of Latin America, whose lands he has known and whose problems he has shared.

Asturias was born in Guatemala City on October 10, 1899. His father was a judge and his mother a schoolteacher. His life and his art were linked by fate from the very beginning. The year before he was born the dictator Estrada Cabrera came to power. He would be the inspiration and model for the tyrant in Asturias's first and best known novel, *El Señor Presidente* (1947). With the establishment of the dictatorship began the era of economic imperialism as Estrada Cabrera opened the country up to exploitation by United States enterprises, notably the United Fruit Company. Popular resentment soon took concrete shape, with results that deeply affected

Asturias's future. In 1902 and 1903 there were student demonstrations against the dictator. The elder Asturias, as a magistrate, was expected to take measures against the students, but he refused and lost his position. Asturias's mother was also discharged from her teaching post and the family was forced to move from the capital to the inland town of Salamá.

It was there that the young boy had his first real contact with the land and people of his country. He grew very close to his grandfather, a landowner in Salamá, and accompanied the old man on horseback rides across the countryside. Although he returned with his family to Guatemala City in 1907, those early rural memories became constant in his vision of life and legend in Guatemala. The country was in almost complete isolation from the outside world and the capital was like an eerie tomb, dominated by a recluse tyrant who was changing from man to name to myth. There was a tremendous bloodletting and purge after an attempted coup by the professional class and a subsequent student uprising. Nearly a whole generation was wiped out and the jails were full.

Almost as a portent of the dictator's downfall, on December 25, 1917, an earthquake laid waste to Guatemala City.

The ugly city was nearly demolished completely and people were forced to live close together. This was no doubt influential in bringing on the fall of the dictator in 1920. Student demonstrations and a movement for Central American unity kept the tyrant boxed in and his ineptness in attempting to cope with them finally led the National Assembly to declare him unfit to govern. He refused to leave the country, was brought to trial and sentenced to prison, where he died a few years later.

During this time Asturias came to know the dictator; as a law student he was secretary of the court which tried Estrada Cabrera and in that capacity saw him almost daily in jail. Cabrera had come completely under the spell of his own myth and had surrounded himself with witch doctors and other mystics. It was during his association with Cabrera that Asturias's most famous character was formed.

In 1920 Asturias was one of a group of students who founded the Association of Unionist Students, a branch of the political party whose aim was the reunification of Central America. General Orellana, the new president, favored the group and also the foundation of the Popular University, which embarked upon a campaign of literacy and adult education.

Asturias as a student of law was deeply interested in the social problem of the Indians. His father, since his return to the city, had prospered as a dealer in sugar and flour, and the house was continuously filled with traders from the interior. His contact with these Indians brought Asturias back to his earlier sojourn in the country.

Times were becoming ominous again, however, and after the assassination of Orellana, Asturias and another lawyer were appointed to defend the officer accused of his murder, who was subse-quently adjudged guilty and executed. The military were gaining more and more influence in the government. When Asturias and some friends published articles criticizing the military in *Tiempos Nuevos,* a weekly they had founded, one of them was seriously beaten. Concerned for the safety of their son, Asturias's parents sent him off to London, where he was to study economics.

He went almost immediately to the British Museum to see the Mayan collection there. The objects recalled to him his childhood and his contact with country people. Then, by accident, while on a vacation in Paris in 1923, he met Georges Raynaud, a professor at the Sorbonne and an expert in Mayan religion and culture. For the next five years he studied under Raynaud, who had spent his life translating the Mayan sacred book, the *Popol Vuh,* into French. Asturias, with the help of a Mexican friend, González de Mendoza, began work on a new Spanish version of the sacred book. As he pursued his scholarly studies he also was working as a journalist for Guatemalan and Mexican newspapers. The work on the *Popol Vuh* was finished in 1926.

During this time he also began to write poetry and in 1925 his first collection, *Rayito de estrella* (Starbeam), was published in Paris. He called his poems "phantomimes." They are facile combinations of Indian legend and surrealistic techniques, a form that he later pursued in his prose. All the while, as he worked with Raynaud, he began organizing his childhood memories and combining them with his research into ancient Mayan lore. The result of this was his first substantial work, *Leyendas de Guatemala* (Legends of Guatemala), which was published in Spain in 1930. This realistic book is quite close in theme to that which Asturias would return to in his later years as his style came to fulfillment.

He was still close to his own past, and as he mulled over the days of the dictatorship of Estrada Cabrera, and as his circle of friends widened, he realized that such a regime was not peculiar to Guatemala but could almost be considered endemic to a great part of Latin America. This reworking in his mind delayed the final version of his thoughts and impressions which he had begun in 1922 as a short story, *"Los mendigos políticos"* (Political Beggars), but which would not be published until 1947 as the novel *El Señor Presidente,* still his best known and most widely read work.

In 1933 he did some extensive traveling in Europe and the Near East and finally returned to Guatemala to find it once more under the sway of dictatorship, this time that of Jorge Ubico. The Popular University was soon dissolved and Asturias found himself writing a cryptic poetry understood only by those who closely followed his imagery. Ubico was overthrown in 1944, and after a brief hiatus the reformist and revolutionary Arévalo government came to power. Asturias was at last in accord with the ruler of his country and was active in its foreign service. He was in Mexico in 1945 and 1946 and completed *El Señor Presidente* for publication in 1947. That same year he went to Buenos Aires to serve in the Guatemalan embassy there. It was in Argentina that he worked on *Hombres de maíz* (Men of Corn), published in 1949, and considered by many critics to be his finest work.

While still in Argentina he embarked upon an ambitious venture which held him for several years and established his fame as a political polemicist. This was his "banana trilogy," a long, complex, and somewhat disjointed tale of the exploitation of a Central American republic (easily recognized as Guatemala although never named) by a powerful company in the United States (equally recognizable as the United Fruit Co.). The three connected volumes are *Viento fuerte (Strong Wind,* 1950), *El papa verde (The Green Pope,* 1954), and *Los ojos de los enterrados (The Eyes of the Interred,* 1960). In the meantime, the constitutional revolutionary government of Jacobo Arbenz, the successor to President Arévalo, was overthrown in 1954 by an armed invasion with the alleged connivance of the United States. As a result Asturias had his citizenship revoked and went back to Buenos Aires as an exile.

In 1962, with the downfall of the Frondizi government in Argentina, he moved to Italy, settling in Genoa. He had served the Arbenz government as Ambassador to El Salvador and had been close to events that were in the making. His view of the invasion and overthrow of the Guatemalan government by Colonel Castillo Armas is put forth in the collection of short stories entitled *Weekend en Guatemala* (1956).

As before, during this second period of adversity he returned once more to poetry while earning his living as journalist and editor. He considers poetry a more intimate form, in the Hispanic tradition, and in this sense he has kept his verse closer to himself, although he does feel that poetry is an important aspect of the work of all Latin American novelists and that his own prose, even some of the most political and contentious, is softened and lifted by his lyricism. It was also at this time that he published some of his theatrical works for the first time, the most notable of which is a folkloric play with a modern setting but rather medieval format called *Soluna* (1955), a title which is a combination of the words for sun and moon and a theme that appears later in his novels. He still does not feel comfortable in the theater, saying that it is "from the mouth outward," while the novel is "from the lips inward."

A cycle of sorts came full turn in 1963 with the publication of his novel *Mulata de tal (Mulata,* 1963). Here he returned to Mayan mythology and rekindles the spirit of it in a modern setting but with a surrealist vision. This was already evident in *El alhajadito* (a title something close to "Little Boy Blue"), a prose-poem rendering of some children's stories, and was continued in *El espejo de Lida Sal* (The Mirror of Lida Sal, 1967). In his latest work, *Maladrón* (Badthief, 1969), he takes a concept from *Mulata* and places it in a colonial context during the time of the Spanish Conquest.

In 1966 Asturias was named Ambassador to France by the centrist Guatemalan government of Julio César Méndez Montenegro, a position he held until 1970. His acceptance of the post was viewed as a betrayal by his friends on the Left, and he was never forgiven for his past activities by his foes on the Right. As a result he has been reluctant to return to his strife-torn homeland after so many years and has continued living in Paris, working at any number of literary projects, most of them derivative of the varied work he has done in the past. His winning of the Nobel Prize for Literature in 1967 gave him a long-awaited financial independence that has enabled him to withdraw to his writing and the many aims and possibilities that have been on his mind for so many years.

Apart from the miscellany of poetry, theater, translations, and journalistic work, the books of Miguel Angel Asturias tend to fall into three broad groupings: works based on a combination of peasant life and mores and the impact of ancient myth and legend, both Mayan and Spanish Christian (*Hombres de maíz Leyendas de Guatemala, Mulata, Maladrón*); works of social and political protest, albeit with a smattering of folkloric and mythic elements (the "banana trilogy," *Week-end en Guatemala*); the book that stands between these two tendencies stands alone in its type, with a more even balance of the two basic elements in Asturias's best-known work and his first novel, *El Señor Presidente.*

Magic realism is a term which has become almost a cliché in the discussion of Latin American writing of the past decade or so. It has been applied to writers as diverse as Asturias, Borges, the Brazilian Guimarães Rosa, the Cuban Alejo Carpentier, and especially to the newer generation, including Julio Cortazár, Mario Vargas Llosa, Nélida Piñon, and, above all, Gabriel García Marquez. The movement, if it can be called such, is a turnaway from the long-predominant school of documentary realism.

By some strange coincidence this new wave in the Latin American novel has incorporated the tremendous new depths of knowledge of the human psyche revealed by modern studies in psychology and psychiatry, even though the impact of Freud and his science has been much more indirect and derivative in Latin America than in other cultures. Another relatively new science, anthropology, has also been important in its role in Latin America, perhaps because the material in this study is closer to home. It is important to remember that Asturias had training as a cultural anthropologist.

In another aspect, magic realism represents a return not only to the culture of the writer's land, but also to the very roots of the novel which itself was a product of Hispanic tradition. After *Don Quixote,* which by any standard fits the pattern of magic realism, the novel virtually disappeared from the land of its origin, returning in the nineteenth century in the artificial and foreign shape of realism and naturalism, far-removed from popular Cervantine tradition, with the rare exceptions of such aberrant works as *Nazarín,* by Benito Pérez Galdós. Not only is Asturias's new trend a break away from a century of false tradition, but it is also a return to the original tradition of narrative expression exemplified by the first and greatest modern novel.

Guatemala has another tradition, however, one observed, partially adopted through acculturation, and therefore productive of a hybrid culture with roots deep in both sides. In *Mulata* Asturias gives an apocalyptic vision of the clash of the two cultures. The last chapter in this disjointed book is a welter of visions of chaos and break-up worthy of the Book of Revelations.

Along similar lines, but much more an exercise in refurbishing myth with the trappings of contemporary reality is *Hombres de maíz.* It is somewhere between a novel threaded together by certain coincidences and a collection of vaguely related tales. What Asturias set out to do here was to bring into a more perfect literary style and mode the rather strictly anthropological material of his earliest attempt at prose fiction. Here we have a preview of the ribaldry that comes into full bloom in the various Rabelaisan episodes of *Mulata.* Asturias has shown the important place of humor in folkloric tradition. The title "Men of Corn" is derived from the Mayan tradition that man was created from corn, the staple food, a seemingly more positive idea in a sense than the Judeo-Christian myth of clay, apt as it might have been for a desert culture.

The variety of Asturias's ability becomes evident in his banana trilogy, which, although inserted among the production of his more mythological and folkloric works and with touches of their spirit, is really quite different in intent. The aim is heroic, but unlike some other Latin American writers where the theme of protest takes on an epic tone, as in the works of the Ecuadorian Demetrio Aguilera-Malta, the figures fall short of truly heroic stature. In the banana trilogy, realism (or Asturias's version of it) is more important than myth.

Asturias blends Mayan and Spanish legends. In *Mulata* there is a druggist who worships the Bad Thief (*mal ladrón*) at Easter time as the symbol of agnosticism and skepticism. The whole episode is a remarkable parody of religion, but the figure of the Bad Thief seems to have fascinated Asturias, for in his latest novel, *Maladrón,* he goes back to the time of the Spanish Conquest and shows how the cult of the Bad Thief, as old as the Crucifixion itself, had spread to Spain, where a sect of adepts grew up. Members of this group were among the conquerors of Mexico, and Asturias tells how certain of them reached Guatemala, where they broke away in isolation from the main force of Conquistadores and established their own settlement after mixing with the Indian population.

Mario Vargas Llosa has spoken of Latin American society as one not heading for future fulfillment but toward complete dissolution as it now stands. In other words, Latin America, which was established by a rapidly decaying Iberian culture, has now come close to the complete collapse of that culture along with those other cultures that have been blended in through acculturation.

Gregory Rabassa, professor of Spanish languages and literature at Columbia University and Queens College, has translated Asturias's works.

THE 1967 PRIZE

By KJELL STRÖMBERG

IN THE AUTUMN of 1967 André Malraux made a brilliant comeback to the world of letters by publishing his *Anti-Mémoires,* a powerful work which undeniably proved that his creative vein had not been exhausted. He had been proposed as a candidate for the Nobel Prize year after year, and general opinion, not only in the French press, was that this year his name should have been honored by this great distinction. But the Swedish Academy had established the principle that no active member of a government could be given the Prize. True, Winston Churchill had been awarded the Prize in 1953 when, as Prime Minister, he was in charge of his country's destiny: but this remained a precedent that was never repeated, the more so as this award was sharply criticized. One would have thought that in the case of Malraux extenuating circumstances could have been produced, because his governmental activities were confined to the protection and development of works of art; but the Nobel Committee did not accept this view.

The Swedish Academy had for a long time been concentrating its attention on the flourishing literature of South America, where there were several equally deserving candidates from which to choose: the Chilean poet Pablo Neruda, a militant Communist who had

been launched and hotly defended by influential critics in the Swedish press; the subtle Argentinian writer Jorge Luis Borges; and his exuberant Guatemalan colleague Miguel Angel Asturias, heir to the ancient Mayan civilization, who was at that time his country's Ambassador in Paris. The 1967 Nobel Prize, which in that year came to well over fifty thousand dollars, was awarded to Asturias, according to the official report, for "the vividness of his literary work, rooted in national traits and Indian traditions." In the previous year, he had received the Lenin Prize for Peace.

Thus Asturias became the second Latin American holder of the Nobel Prize for Literature, after the Chilean poetess Gabriela Mistral, who was the 1945 laureate. The prolonged visit which Asturias made to Sweden in 1964, at the invitation of several of the universities, must have helped to publicize his candidacy. He took the opportunity to supervise the translation into Swedish of his great banana trilogy, *Strong Wind, The Green Pope,* and *The Eyes of the Interred.*

During this same year the Swedish Academy had commissioned a young critic who specialized in Spanish, Kjell A. Johansson, to make a thorough examination of Asturias's output. He came to the conclusion that Asturias was "one of the most fruitful and vivid [writers] in Latin American literature of today, without a rival in the art of fusing Latin American myth and reality." He reserved the prize for perfection for Asturias's first novel, *El Señor Presidente*.

The news of his award was brought to Asturias at a bar in the Place des Termes, where some journalists managed to track him down while he was quietly celebrating his sixty-eighth birthday. He was asked if he did not consider himself to be the worthiest among his Latin American colleagues to receive the Prize. At first, he refused to answer this question, which was, to say the least, indiscreet. Then he gave the names of two or three writers to whom he would gladly have seen the Prize awarded—either Pablo Neruda, or one of two Mexican novelists, Octavio Paz and Juan Rulfo, who he felt were allied to him by the volcanic force of their political involvement.

With very few exceptions, the new laureate received a good press almost everywhere, and in Guatemala he enjoyed a real triumph. His portrait appeared on a stamp and a medal, a street was named after him, and the whole of his little country was given over to rejoicing, while waiting for her great son to return sooner or later for his triumphant entry into the capital. Similar reactions of sympathy and unreserved admiration were registered in most of the South American countries where, not unreasonably, people considered the Nobel Prize awarded to Asturias as homage paid to Latin American literature as a whole. This was, indeed, the opinion of the laureate himself, which he expressed on many occasions to his interviewers, both in Paris and later in Stockholm. However, this modesty had its limits, to judge by his arrogant statement quoted by the Communist *Humanité* of Paris: "My work will continue to echo the voices of nations, gathering together myths and popular beliefs, and at the same time concentrating on giving birth to a universal conscience concerning Latin-American problems."

Eight laureates were gathered together at the Nobel ceremony on December 10, 1967. This unusually large number is explained by the fact that the Prizes for Chemistry and Medicine had each been divided between three scientists. Ulf von Euler, president of the Nobel Foundation, recalled in his opening speech that it was exactly one hundred years since Alfred Nobel had patented dynamite, the most famous of his inventions. Asturias made his acceptance speech in Spanish and went on to speak of the tragic destinies of the South American continent and of their repercussions on its literature.

Translated by Camilla Sykes.

Jacinto Benavente

1922

"For the happy manner in which he has

continued the illustrious traditions

of the Spanish drama"

Illustrated by D'ORCINO

PRESENTATION ADDRESS

By *PER HALLSTRÖM*

CHAIRMAN OF THE NOBEL COMMITTEE
OF THE SWEDISH ACADEMY

———

JACINTO BENAVENTE has devoted his imaginative gifts mainly to the theater, and it seems as if he has systematically guided the course of his development in this direction through many varieties of experience. But with this imaginative artist, system seems to be a free and direct expression of his whole being. It appears that no one could have reached his goal with less effort and brooding in comparison with the value of the achievement.

The feeling which has carried him on has also been of an unusually complete and harmonious nature: it is not only the dramatic art and the atmosphere of the theater that he has loved; he has cherished an equally warm affection for life outside, for the world of realities which it was his task to bring to the stage. It is not a matter of mere uncritical and superficial worship of life. He has observed his world with extremely clear and keen eyes, and what he has seen he has measured and weighed with an alert and flexible intelligence. He has not allowed himself to be duped either by men or by ideas, not even by his own ideas or his own pathos. Nevertheless, he does not strike one as being in the least bitter, or even blasé.

His writing has thus obtained its most distinctive quality—grace. This is such a rare value, especially in our own times, that there is little demand for it on the market and it is not recognized by most people. Grace, however, is as precious as it is uncommon. It is the token of the balance of powers, of the self-discipline and assurance of art, especially when it is not an end in itself and a mere frivolity, but when, without apparent effort, it stamps its mark on the entire form-giving process. It does not, then, merely play on the surface, affecting the style; it also determines each proportion in the treatment of the subject and every line in its depiction.

This is precisely the case with Benavente. The effect he attains may vary greatly in strength, but it is based on unfailing tact and strict loyalty to the subject. He gives what the subject is able to give without effort and without bombast. The fare he provides may be more or less rich and interesting, but it is always unadulterated. This is a classic feature in Benavente.

Nevertheless, his bent is above all realistic, if we eliminate from that label all the customary flavor of social tendency, commonplace philosophy, or gross striving for effect. To reproduce the wealth and mobility of life, the play of characters, and the struggle between wills, in a way that comes as near truth as possible—that is his chief aim. When he aims at something beyond this—to stimulate thought, to solve problems, to demolish prejudices, to enlarge human sympathy—he does so with the most scrupulous care not to tamper with the objective accuracy of the literary description. He exercises this unusual discipline even when he is faced with the strongest temptation for a dramatist—dramatic and scenic effect. However easily a scene could be made more telling by increasing the tension of the conflict and plot, by putting on more flaring colors, by flogging up the emotions to their highest pitch, Benavente never does this at the expense of truth: he permits no blurring of the tone. He is a rare example of a born dramatist, one whose imagination, by itself, creates in accordance with the laws of the stage, but yet avoids anything theatrical as fully as all other false conventions.

His activity lies especially in comedy, but that term in Spanish is more inclusive than with us; it comprises what we may in general call middle-class plays without tragic conclusions. If there is such a conclusion, the pieces are called dramas, and Benavente has also written such plays, including the remarkable and moving play, *La Malquerida* (The Wrongly Loved, 1913). He has also composed many romantic and fantastic pieces, among which are exquisite achievements of poetic art, especially on a small scale.

But his central significance lies in his comedies, which, as we have seen, may well be as serious as they are gay; and in the short forms of comedy, which in Spanish literature have been developed into special species with old and glorious traditions. In the latter Benavente is an enchanting master because of his unlabored wit and comic verve, his radiant good nature, and his grace, which combines all these qualities. I have time for only a few names: *De pequeñas causas* (For Small Reasons, 1908); *El amor asusta* (Love Frightens, 1907); *No fumadores* (Smoking Prohibited, 1904). But there are many others, an entire treasury of merry jest, where the battle is waged so lightly and so elegantly that it is always good-tempered, however sharp the weapon itself may be.

In the larger works we encounter an amazing range of spheres of life and subject matter. They are taken from peasant life, from all circles of society in the town, from the artist's world down to the traveling circus people whom the poet embraces with a strong human sympathy and whom he values more highly than many other classes.

But it is mainly the life of the upper classes that he has treated in its two characteristic centers, Madrid and Moraleda, the latter a place not found on the map, but which in its sunny and alluring variety comprises the typical features of a provincial town in Castile. In *La farándula* (The Company of Comedians, 1897) the ambitious politician goes to this town in order to rally and to gain the support of the uncorrupted energies of the people for a somewhat vaguely defined ideal; in the play *La Gobernadora* (The Governor's Wife, 1901), conceited ambition dreams of a larger stage for its greater talents. Moraleda is really a planetary world, which is attracted and illuminated by Madrid and does not reveal the full force of its comedy except in comparison with Madrid.

The capital and its spiritual content are made understandable much more fully through personal vicissitudes of fortune which are determined, as are its fashions and its culture, by the strata of its society. We see a distinct development in the art of Benavente. He begins by stressing the description of environment, with an abundant wealth of color and life and features that reveal character. The dramatic element proper —unsought, like all the rest of the apparatus—exists for the most part merely to keep the action going. Its function is to arrange the whirl of life in a picture, composed in groups, with strong individual scenes. He has taken pains to create a faithful and artistic mirror of reality, which is then left to speak for itself.

Later his composition becomes more rigid. Although it is arranged firmly around a stronger, deeper, and more spiritual dramatic conflict, it is, nevertheless, almost as simple as when Benavente was merely writing episodes describing society. There is nothing artificial, nothing abstract and isolated, in the human fates which are represented. As before, they are still connected with the world around them, but the light is strictly limited, revealing only what is central from a dramatic point of view. The sharp characterization is carried just far enough to make the action clear; the psychology is merely a means, not an end. Nothing is laboriously prepared beforehand; nothing strikes one really as being prepared at all: every feature in the action comes, as it were, with the improvisation of life and may take one by surprise until one has reflected for a moment, just as happens in life itself. The technique, too, is purely realistic and has not searched for models in ancient tragedy. Summing up the past is not the main function of this kind of drama, nor is the dialogue a kind of cross-examination to discover the past. The required discoveries are made by life itself by means of the unforced course of the action.

Broadly speaking, Benavente does not seek to harrow the spectator; his object is a solution of conflicts that is harmonious even in melancholy and sorrow. This harmony is usually gained by resignation, not weary or aloof or pathetic, and without great gestures. The characters suffer, tear at their bonds, are attracted by fortune (the way to which is to pass over others' fortune), wrestle in conflicts, measure their world and themselves, and gain a clearer and wider vision through their constraint. That which has the last word is not passion, in fact not the ego at all, but the spiritual value that proves so great that, were it lost, the ego would be poor and fortune empty. The decision is made without capitulation, merely through the fact that the personality is face to face with the consequences of its choice of fate and chooses freely, on the basis of instinctive feeling rather than in accordance with theories.

I have time for only one or two titles of his strange, simple, and quiet dramas: *Alma triumfante* (Conquering Soul, 1902), *La propria estimacion* (Self-respect, 1915), and *Campo de armiño* (The White Scutcheon, 1916). There are many others of equal value which are more or less like these. The distinctive mark of them all is a peculiarly pure humanity, which at first glance is surprising in the keen and flashing satirist, while the moderation and the freedom from all sentimentality in the mode of expression are in complete accordance with his schooling. As a matter of fact his qualities go well together: as his grace of form is a classic feature, so are his feeling and his insight classic, strictly schooled, well balanced, farsighted, and clear. His simplicity of expression and hushed tone come from the same source.

Nevertheless, Teutonic readers are often reminded, even when it comes to an art as good as this, that it has sprung from a national temperament other than ours and from other poetic traditions. The kind of lyric we desire, at least in the atmosphere of the world of drama, is on the whole probably unknown to the Romance nations. Half-light, both in nature and in the human soul, is lacking in them: all that human beings contain is expressed, or it seems that it *can* be expressed. Their thoughts may have brilliance, rapidity, and, of course, clarity; but they strike us as lacking in power, as belonging to a somewhat more vacant atmosphere, and as having less life in their inner being. What southerners say of our art may reveal equally great defects; but we must mutually accustom ourselves to admire what we understand and to leave outside our aesthetic judgments things which, for the reasons mentioned, fail to satisfy us.

In the works in which the Spaniard Benavente has abandoned his comedy descriptive of society and individuals, and instead has ranged over larger complexes of ideas and has sought to interpret all the unrest and yearning of our times, we cannot follow him with the admiration that has been bestowed upon him by his countrymen. This is true of *El collar de estrellas* (The Belt of Stars, 1915) and several other pieces.

I have not dwelt on the limitations of his art, but sought to indicate the central qualities of his craftsmanship in his country and in his time. I believe that scarcely any other contemporary dramatist has anywhere captured the life about him in such a many-sided and faithful manner and given it a form so immediate and, through its simple and noble art, so durable. The traditions of Spanish poetry comprise a strong, bold, and sound realism, a prolific power of growth, and an inimitable charm in the comic spirit which is merry and built on realities, not on conversational wit. Benavente has shown that he belongs to this school and, in a form peculiar to himself, has worked out a modern comedy of character containing much of the classic spirit. He has proved himself to be a worthy adherent of an ancient and elevated style of poetry; and that is to say a great deal.

There was no formal Acceptance Speech by Benavente.

THE BONDS OF INTEREST

A COMEDY IN A PROLOGUE AND THREE ACTS

By JACINTO BENAVENTE

Translated by John Garrett Underhill

CHARACTERS

DOÑA SIRENA
SILVIA
THE WIFE OF POLICHINELLE
COLUMBINE
LAURA
RISELA
LEANDER
CRISPIN
THE DOCTOR
POLICHINELLE
HARLEQUIN
THE CAPTAIN
PANTALOON
THE INNKEEPER
THE SECRETARY
1st and 2nd SERVANTS AT THE INN
1st and 2nd CONSTABLES

The action takes place in an imaginary country at the beginning of the Seventeenth Century.

THE BONDS OF INTEREST

PROLOGUE

Spoken by CRISPIN

A conventional drop at the front, having a door in the middle, curtained.

Here you have the mummer of the antique farce who enlivened in the country inns the hard-earned leisure of the carter, who made the simple rustics gape with wonder in the square of every rural town and village, who in the populous cities drew about him great bewildering assemblages, as in Paris where Tabarin set up his scaffold on the *Pont-Neuf* and challenged the attention of the passers-by, from the learned doctor pausing a moment on his solemn errand to smooth out the wrinkles on his brow at some merry quip of old-time farce, to the light-hearted cutpurse who there whiled away his hours of ease as he cheated his hunger with a smile, to prelate and noble dame and great grandee in stately carriages, soldier and merchant and student and maid. Men of every rank and condition shared in the rejoicing—men who were never brought together in any other way—the grave laughing to see the laughter of the gay rather than at the wit of the farce, the wise with the foolish, the poor with the rich, so staid and formal in their ordinary aspect, and the rich to see the poor laugh, their consciences a little easier at the thought: "Even the poor can smile." For nothing is so contagious as the sympathy of a smile.

Sometimes our humble farce mounted up to Princes' Palaces on the whims of the mighty and the great; yet there its rogueries were not less free. It was the common heritage of great and small. Its rude jests, its sharp and biting sentences it took from the people, from that lowly wisdom of the poor which knows how to suffer and bear all, and which was softened in those days by resignation in men who did not expect too much of the world and so were able to laugh at the world without bitterness and without hate.

From its humble origins Lope de Rueda and Shakespeare and Molière lifted it up, bestowing upon it high patents of nobility, and like enamored princes of the fairy-tales, elevated poor Cinderella to the topmost thrones of Poetry and of Art. But our farce tonight cannot claim such distinguished lineage, contrived for your amusement by the inquiring spirit of a restless poet of today.

This is a little play of puppets, impossible in theme, without any reality at all. You will soon see how everything happens in it that could never happen, how its personages are not real men and women, nor the shadows of them, but dolls or marionettes of paste and cardboard, moving upon wires which are visible even in a little light and to the dimmest eye. They are the grotesque masks of the Italian *Commedia dell'Arte*, not as boisterous as they once were, because they have aged with the years and have been able to think much in so long a time. The author is aware that so primitive a spectacle is unworthy of the culture of these days; he throws himself upon your courtesy and upon your goodness of heart. He only asks that you should make yourselves as young as possible. The world has grown old, but art never can reconcile itself to growing old, and so, to seem young again, it descends to these fripperies. And that is the reason that these outworn puppets have presumed to come to amuse you tonight with their child's play.

THE FIRST ACT

A plaza in a city. The façade of an Inn is at the right, having a practicable door, with a knocker upon it. Above the door is a sign which reads INN.

LEANDER *and* CRISPIN *enter from the left.*

LEANDER. This must be a very great city, Crispin. Its riches and its power appear in everything.

CRISPIN. Yes, there are two cities. Pray God that we have chanced upon the better one!

LEANDER. Two cities do you say, Crispin? Ah! Now I understand—an old city and a new city, one on either side of the river.

CRISPIN. What has the river to do with it, or newness or age? I say two cities just as there are in every city in the world; one for people who arrive with money and the other for persons who arrive like us.

LEANDER. We are lucky to have arrived at all without falling into the hands of Justice. I should be heartily glad to stop here awhile and rest myself, for I am tired of this running about the world so continually.

CRISPIN. Not I! No, it is the natural condition of the free-born subjects of the Kingdom of Roguery, of whom am I, not to remain seated long in any one place, unless it be through compulsion, as to say in the galleys, where, believe me, they are very hard seats. But now since we have happened upon this city, and to all appearances it is a well fortified and provisioned one, let us like prudent captains map out our plan of battle beforehand, if we are to conquer it with any advantage to ourselves.

LEANDER. A pretty army we shall make to besiege it.

CRISPIN. We are men and we have to do with men.

LEANDER. All our wealth is on our backs. You were not willing to take off these clothes and sell them, when by doing so we could easily have obtained money.

CRISPIN. I would sooner take off my skin than my good clothes. As the world goes nothing is so important as appearances, and the clothes, as you must admit, are the first things to appear.

LEANDER. What are we going to do, Crispin? Hunger and fatigue have been too much for me. I am overcome; I cannot talk.

CRISPIN. There is nothing for us to do but to take advantage of our talents and our effrontery, for without effrontery talents are of no use. The best thing, as it seems to me, will be for you to talk as little as possible, but be very impressive when you do, and put on the airs of a gentleman of quality. From time to time then I will permit you to strike me across the back. When anybody asks you a question, reply mysteriously and if you open your mouth upon your own account, be sure that it is with dignity, as if you were pronouncing sentence. You are young; you have a fine presence. Until now you have known only how to dissipate your resources; this is the time for you to begin to profit by them. Put yourself in my hands. There is nothing so useful to a man as to have some one always at his heels to point out his merits, for modesty in one's self is imbecility, while self-praise is madness, and so between the two we come into disfavor with the world. Men are like merchandise; they are worth more or less according to the skill of the salesman who markets them. I tell you, though you were but muddy glass, I will so contrive that in my hands you shall pass for pure diamond. And now let us knock at the door of this inn, for surely it is the proper thing to have lodgings on the main square.

LEANDER. You say at this inn? But how are we going to pay?

CRISPIN. If we are to be stopped by a little thing like that then we had better search out an asylum or an almshouse or else beg on the streets, if so be that you incline to virtue. Or if to force, then back to the highway and cut the throat of the first passer-by. If we are to live upon our means, strictly speaking, we have no other means to live.

LEANDER. I have letters of introduction to persons of importance in this city, who will be able to lend us aid.

CRISPIN. Then tear those letters up; never think of such baseness again! Introduce yourself to no man when you are in need. Those would be pretty letters of credit indeed! Today you will be received with the greatest courtesy; they will tell you that their houses and their persons are to be considered as yours. The next time you call, the servant will tell you that his master is not at home. No, he is not expected soon. . . . and at the next visit nobody will trouble so much as to open the door. This is a world of giving and taking, a shop, a mart, and before you ask you have to offer.

LEANDER. But what can I offer when I have nothing?

CRISPIN. How low an opinion you must have of yourself! Is a man in himself, then, worth nothing? A man may be a soldier, and by his valor win great victories. He may be a husband or a lover, and with love's sweet, oblivious medicine, restore some noble dame to health, or some damsel of high degree, who has been pining away through melancholy. He may be the servant of some mighty and powerful lord, who becomes attached to him and raises him up through his favor, and he may be so many other things besides that I have not the breath even to begin to run them over. When one wants to climb, why any stair will do.

LEANDER. But if I have not even that stair?

CRISPIN. Then accept my shoulders, and I will lift you up. I offer you the top.

LEANDER. And if we both fall down upon the ground?

CRISPIN. God grant that it may be soft! (*Knocking at the inn-door*) Hello! Ho, within there! Hello, I say, in the inn! Devil of an innkeeper! Does no one answer? What sort of a tavern is this?

LEANDER. Why are you making all this noise when as yet you have scarcely begun to call?

CRISPIN. Because it is monstrous that they should make us wait like this! (*Calling again more loudly*) Hello within! Who's there, I say? Hello in the house! Hello, you thousand devils!

INNKEEPER. (*Within*) Who's there? What knocking and what shouting at my door! Is this the way to stand and wait? Out, I say!

CRISPIN. It is too much! And now he will tell us that this dilapidated old tavern is a fit lodging for a gentleman.

(*The* INNKEEPER *and* TWO SERVANTS *come out of the Inn.*)

INNKEEPER. Softly, sirs, softly; for this is not a tavern but an inn, and great gentlemen have been lodged in this house.

CRISPIN. I would like to have seen those same great gentlemen—gentle, a little more or less. What? It is easy enough to see by these rascals that they are not accustomed to waiting on persons of quality. They stand there like blockheads without running to do our service.

INNKEEPER. My life! But you are impertinent!

LEANDER. My servant is a little forward, perhaps. You will find him somewhat hasty in his temper. However, your inn will be good enough for the brief time that we shall be able to remain in it.

Prepare an apartment for me and another for my servant, and let us spare these idle words.

INNKEEPER. I beg your pardon, sir. If you had only spoken before. . . . I don't know how it is, but somehow gentlemen are always so much more polite than their servants.

CRISPIN. The fact is my master is so good-natured that he will put up with anything. But I know what is proper for his service, and I have no mind to wink at villainy. Lead us to our apartments.

INNKEEPER. But where is your luggage?

CRISPIN. Do you suppose that we are carrying our luggage with us on our backs, like a soldier's knapsack, or trundling it like students' bundles in our hands? Know that my master has eight carts coming after him, which will arrive if he stays here long enough, and at that he will only remain for the time which is absolutely necessary to conclude the secret mission with which he has been entrusted in this city.

LEANDER. Will you be silent and hold your tongue? What secret is it possible to keep with you? If I am discovered through your impudence, through your misguided talk. . . . (*He threatens and strikes* CRISPIN *with his sword.*)

CRISPIN. Help! He is killing me! (*Running.*)

INNKEEPER. (*Interposing between* LEANDER *and* CRISPIN) Hold, sir!

LEANDER. Let me chastise him! The most intolerable of vices is this desire to talk.

INNKEEPER. Do not beat him, sir!

LEANDER. Let me at him! Let me at him! Will the slave never learn?

(*As he is about to strike* CRISPIN, CRISPIN *runs and hides himself behind the* INNKEEPER, *who receives all the blows.*)

CRISPIN. (*Crying out*) Ay! Ay! Ay!

INNKEEPER. Ay, say I! For I got all the blows!

LEANDER. (*To* CRISPIN) Now you see what you have done. This poor man has received all the blows. Down! Down! Beg his pardon!

INNKEEPER. It will not be necessary, sir. I pardon him willingly. (*To the servants*) What are you doing standing there? Prepare the rooms in which the Emperor of Mantua is accustomed to reside when he is stopping in this house, and let dinner be made ready for these gentlemen.

CRISPIN. Perhaps it would be as well if I saw to that myself, otherwise they may delay and spoil everything, and commit a thousand blunders for which I shall be held responsible, for my master, as you see, is not a man to submit to insult. I am with you, sirrahs—and remember who it is you serve, for the greatest good fortune or the direst calamity in the world enters at this moment behind you through these doors.

(*The servants, followed by* CRISPIN, *re-enter the Inn.*)

INNKEEPER. (*To* LEANDER) Will you be good enough to let me have your name, where you come from, and the business which brings you to this city?

LEANDER. (*Seeing* CRISPIN *re-enter from the Inn*) My servant will let you have them. Learn not to bother me with foolish questions. (*He goes into the Inn.*)

CRISPIN. What have you done now? You have not dared to question my master? If you want to keep him so much as another hour in your house, never speak to him again. No! Not one word!

INNKEEPER. But the laws are very strict. It is absolutely necessary that the questions should be answered. The law in this city. . . .

CRISPIN. Never mention the law to my master! Silence! Silence! And for shame! You do not know whom you have in

[190]

your house; no, and if you did, you would not be wasting your time on these impertinences.

INNKEEPER. But am I not to be told at least——

CRISPIN. Bolt of Heaven! Silence! Or I will call my master, and he will tell you whatever he sees fit—and then you will not understand. Take care! Look to it that he wants for nothing! Wait on him with every one of your five senses, or you will have good reason to regret it! Have you no knowledge of men? Can't you read character? Don't you see who my master is? What? How is that? What do you say? No reply? . . . Come! Come! . . . . In! . . . .

(*He goes into the Inn, pushing the* INNKEEPER *before him. The* CAPTAIN *and* HARLEQUIN *enter from the left.*)

HARLEQUIN. As we return from the fields which surround this fair city—and beyond a doubt they are the best part of it—it seems that without intending it we have happened upon this Inn. What a creature of habit is man! And surely it is a vile habit, this being obliged to eat every day.

CAPTAIN. The sweet music of your verses had quite deprived me of all thought. Delightful privilege of the poet!

HARLEQUIN. Which does not prevent him from being equally lacking upon his own part. The poet wants everything. I approach this Inn with fear. Will they consent to trust us today? If not, we must rely upon your sword.

CAPTAIN. My sword? The soldier's sword, like the poet's lyre, is little valued in this city of merchants and traders. We have fallen upon evil days.

HARLEQUIN. We have. Sublime poesy, which sings of great and glorious exploits, is no more. It is equally profitless to offer your genius to the great to praise or to lampoon them. Flattery and satire are both alike to them. They neither thank you for the one nor fear the other, nor do they read them. Aretino himself would have starved to death in these days.

CAPTAIN. But tell me, how is it with us? What is the position of the soldier? Because we were defeated in the late wars—more through these base traffickers who govern us and send us to defend their interests without enthusiasm and without arms, than through any power of the enemy, as if a man could fight with his whole heart for what he did not love—defeated by these traffickers who did not contribute so much as a single soldier to our ranks or lend one single penny to the cause but upon good interest and yet better security; who, as soon as they scented danger and saw their pockets in jeopardy, threatened to make common cause with the enemy—now they blame us, they abuse us and despise us, and seek to economize out of our martial misery, which is the little pay that they give us, and would dismiss us if they dared, if they were not afraid that some day all those whom they have oppressed by their tyranny and their greed would rise up and turn against them. And woe to them when they do, if we remember that day on which side lie duty and justice!

HARLEQUIN. When that day comes you will find us at your side.

CAPTAIN. Poets cannot be depended upon for anything. Your spirits are like the opal, which looks different in every light. You are in an ecstasy today over what is about to be born, and tomorrow over what is in the last stages of dissolution. You have a special weakness for falling in love with ruins, which to my mind is a melancholy thing. And since as a rule you sit up all night, you more often see the sun set than the day break; you know more about going down **than** you do of rising.

[191]

HARLEQUIN. That cannot truthfully be said of me. I have often seen the sun rise when I had no place to lay my head. Besides, how can you expect a man to hail the day as blithely as the lark when it always breaks so unfortunately for him?—What say you? Shall we try our fate?

CAPTAIN. It cannot be avoided. Be seated, and let us await what our good host has in store.

HARLEQUIN. (Calling into the Inn) Hello, there! Ho! Who serves today?

(The INNKEEPER enters.)

INNKEEPER. Ah, gentlemen! Is it you? I am sorry, but there is no entertainment at the Inn today.

CAPTAIN. And for what reason, if it is proper to ask the question?

INNKEEPER. A proper question for you to ask. Do you suppose that I trust nobody for what is consumed in this house?

CAPTAIN. Ah! Is that the reason? And are we not persons of credit, who are to be trusted?

INNKEEPER. No; not by me. And as I never expect to collect anything, you have had all that courtesy requires out of me already. This being the case, you will be so kind as to remove yourselves from my door.

HARLEQUIN. Do you imply that there is nothing to be counted between us but money? Are all the praises that we have lavished upon your house in all parts of the country to go for nothing? I have even composed a sonnet in your honor, in which I celebrate the virtues of your stewed partridges and hare pie! And as for my friend, the Captain, you may rest assured that he alone would uphold the reputation of your hostelry against an army. Is that a feat which is worth nothing? Is there nothing but clinking of coins in your ears?

INNKEEPER. I am not in a jesting mood; it does not suit my humor. I want none of your sonnets, nor the Captain's sword either, which might better be employed in other business.

CAPTAIN. Name of Mars! You are right. Better employed upon an impudent rascal's back, flaying off his hide! (Threatening him and striking him with his sword.)

INNKEEPER. (Crying out) What? How is this? You strike me? Help! Justice!

HARLEQUIN. (Restraining the CAPTAIN) Don't run your head into a noose on account of such a worthless scamp.

CAPTAIN. I shall kill him. (Striking him.)

INNKEEPER. Help! Justice!

(The TWO SERVANTS enter, running, from the Inn.)

SERVANTS. They are killing our master!

INNKEEPER. Save me!

CAPTAIN. Not one of them shall remain alive!

INNKEEPER. Will no one come?

(CRISPIN and LEANDER enter.)

LEANDER. What is this brawl?

CRISPIN. In the presence of my master? Before the house where he resides? Is there no rest possible, nor quiet? Hold! Or I shall summon Justice. Order! Quiet!

INNKEEPER. This will be the ruin of me! With such a dignitary stopping in my house!——

HARLEQUIN. Who is he?

INNKEEPER. Never dare to ask me his name!

CAPTAIN. Your pardon, sir, if we have disturbed your rest, but this rascally villain——

INNKEEPER. It wasn't my fault, my lord. These unblushing scoundrels——

CAPTAIN. What? I? Unblushing—I? I can bear no more!

CRISPIN. Hold, sir Captain, for one is here who is able to redress your wrongs, if so be you have had them of this man.

INNKEEPER. Consider, sir, that for more than a month these fellows have eaten at my expense without the payment of one penny—without so much as the thought of payment; and now because I refuse to serve them today, they turn upon me.

HARLEQUIN. I do not turn because I am accustomed to face that which is unpleasant.

CAPTAIN. Is it reasonable that a soldier should not be given credit?

HARLEQUIN. Is it reasonable that a sonnet should be allowed to pass for nothing, although it is written with the best of flourishes in praise of his stewed partridges and hare pies? And all this upon credit on my part, for I have never tasted one of them, but only his eternal mutton and potatoes.

CRISPIN. These two noble gentlemen are right. It is infamous that a poet and a soldier should be denied in this manner.

HARLEQUIN. Ah, sir! You have a great soul!

CRISPIN. No, I have not—but my master, who is here present. Being a grand gentleman, there is nothing which appeals to him so much in the world as a poet or a soldier.

LEANDER. To be sure. I agree with you.

CRISPIN. You need have no doubt but that while he remains in this city you will be treated with the consideration you deserve. You shall want for nothing. Whatever expense you may be at in this Inn, is to be placed upon his account.

LEANDER. To be sure. I agree with you.

CRISPIN. And let the landlord look to it that you get your desserts!

INNKEEPER. Sir! . . .

CRISPIN. And don't be so stingy with those partridges and hairy pies. It is not proper that a poet like Signor Harlequin should be obliged to draw upon his imagination in his descriptions of such material things.

HARLEQUIN. What? Do you know my name?

CRISPIN. No, I do not; but my master, being such a great gentleman, knows all

the poets who exist or who ever did exist in the world, provided always that they were worthy of the name.

LEANDER. To be sure. I agree with you.

CRISPIN. And none of them is more famous than you, Signor Harlequin. Whenever I consider that you have not been treated here with the respect which is your due——

INNKEEPER. Your pardon, sir. They shall be made welcome, as you desire. It is sufficient that you should be their security.

CAPTAIN. Sir, if I can be of service to you in any way. . . .

CRISPIN. What? Is it a small service to be permitted to know you? O glorious Captain, worthy only to be sung by this immortal poet!

HARLEQUIN. Sir!

CAPTAIN. Sir!

HARLEQUIN. So my verses are known to you?

CRISPIN. How? Known? And if known would it ever be possible to forget them? Is not that wonderful sonnet yours, which begins:

"The soft hand which caresses and
    which slays". . . .

HARLEQUIN. What?
CRISPIN.

"The soft hand which caresses and
    which slays". . . .

It does not say what.

HARLEQUIN. Nonsense! No, that is not my sonnet.

CRISPIN. Then it is worthy of being yours. And you, Captain! Who is not familiar with your marvelous exploits? Was it not you who, alone, with twenty men, assaulted the Castle of the Red Rock in the famous battle of the Black Field?

CAPTAIN. You know, then?

CRISPIN. How? . . . . Do I know?

Oh! Many a time, transported, I have listened to my master recount the story of your prowess! Twenty men, twenty, and you in front of them, and in front of you the castle. Boom! Boom! Boom! from the castle, shots and bombards, darts and flaming squibs and boiling oil! And the twenty men all standing there like one man, and you in front of them! And from above: Boom! Boom! Boom! And the roll of the drums: Rum-a-tum-tum! And the blare of the trumpets: Tara! Tara-ra! And you all the while there alone with your sword: Swish! Swish! Swish! A blow here, a blow there. Or without your sword. . . . Above, below. . . . A head, an arm. . . .

(*He begins to rain blows about him right and left, and to kick, using his fists, his feet, and the flat side of his sword indifferently.*)

SERVANTS. Ay! Ay! Oh! Oh!

INNKEEPER. Hold! Hold! Restrain yourself! You don't know what you are doing. You are all excited. . . . It is as if the battle were really taking place. . . .

CRISPIN. How? I am excited? Know that I always feel in my breast the *animus belli,* the thirst for war!

CAPTAIN. It seems almost as if you must have been there.

CRISPIN. To hear my master describe it is the same as being there. No, it is preferable to it. And is such a soldier, the hero of the Red Rocks in the Black Fields, to be insulted thus? Ah! How fortunate it is that my master was present, and that important business had brought him to this city, for he will see to it that you are accorded the consideration you deserve. So sublime a poet, so great a captain! . . . (*To the servants*) Quick! What are you doing there? Bring the best food that you have in the house and set it before these gentlemen. And first of all get a bottle of good wine; it will be a rare pleasure to my master to drink with them. He will esteem himself indeed fortunate. Don't stand there and stare! Quick! Bestir yourselves!

INNKEEPER. Run, run! I go. . . . We are getting something out of this after all.

(*The* INNKEEPER *and the* TWO SERVANTS *run into the Inn.*)

HARLEQUIN. Ah, sir! How can we ever repay you?

CAPTAIN. How? We certainly never shall. . . .

CRISPIN. Let nobody speak of payment before my master. The very thought gives offense. Be seated, be seated. My master, who has wined and dined so many princes, so many noblemen at his table, will deem this an even greater pleasure.

LEANDER. To be sure. I agree with you.

CRISPIN. My master is not a man of many words; but, as you see, the few that he does speak, are, as it were, fraught with wisdom.

HARLEQUIN. His grandeur appears in everything.

CAPTAIN. You have no idea what a comfort it is to our drooping spirits to find a noble gentleman like you who condescends to treat us with consideration.

CRISPIN. Why, this is nothing to what he will condescend to do! I know that my master will never rest satisfied to stop at such a trifle. He will elevate you to his own level, and then hold you up beside him on the same exalted plane. He is just that kind of a man.

LEANDER. (*To* CRISPIN) Don't let your tongue run away with you, Crispin.

CRISPIN. My master is averse to foolish talk; but you will soon know him by his deeds.

(*The* INNKEEPER *and the* SERVANTS *re-enter, bringing wine and provisions which they place upon the table.*)

INNKEEPER. Here is the wine—and the dinner.

CRISPIN. Drink, drink and eat! See that they want for nothing; my master is agreeable. He will be responsible. His responsibility is fortunately not in question. If you would like anything you don't see, don't hesitate to ask for it. My master will order it. And let the landlord look to it that it is brought promptly, for verily at this business, he is the sorriest kind of a knave.

INNKEEPER. To be sure. . . . I don't agree with you.

CRISPIN. Not another word! You insult my master.

CAPTAIN. Your very good health!

LEANDER. Your good healths, gentlemen! To the health of the greatest poet and the best soldier in the world!

HARLEQUIN. To the health of the noblest gentleman!

CAPTAIN. The most liberal and the most generous!

CRISPIN. In the world! Excuse me, but I must drink too, though it may seem presumptuous. But on a day like this, this day of days, which has brought together the sublimest poet, the bravest captain, the noblest gentleman, and the most faithful servant in the universe. . . . (*They drink*) Now you will permit my master to retire. The important business which brings him to the city admits of no further delay.

LEANDER. To be sure.

CRISPIN. You will not fail to return every day and present your respects to him?

HARLEQUIN. Every hour! And I am going to bring with me all the poets and all the musicians of my acquaintance, **to** serenade him with music and songs.

CAPTAIN. I shall bring my whole company with me with torches and banners.

LEANDER. You will offend my modesty.

CRISPIN. And now eat, drink! Mind you, sirrahs! About it! Quick! Serve these gentlemen. (*To the* CAPTAIN) A word in your ear. Are you out of money?

CAPTAIN. What shall I say?

CRISPIN. Say no more. (*To the* INN-KEEPER) Eh! This way! Let these gentlemen have forty or fifty crowns on my master's account, as a present from him. Omit nothing! See that they are satisfied.

INNKEEPER. Don't worry, sir. Forty or fifty, did you say?

CRISPIN. While you are about it, better make it sixty. Your health, gentlemen!

CAPTAIN. Long life to the noblest gentleman in the world!

HARLEQUIN. Long life!

CRISPIN. Shout long life, too, you uncivil people.

INNKEEPER AND SERVANTS. Long life! Long life!

CRISPIN. Long life to the sublimest poet and the best soldier in the world!

ALL. Long life!

LEANDER. (*To* CRISPIN) Are you mad, Crispin? What are you doing? How are we ever going to get out of this?

CRISPIN. The same way that we got in. You see now poesy and arms are ours. On! We shall achieve the conquest of the world!

(*All exchange bows and salutations, after which* LEANDER *and* CRISPIN *go out upon the left, as they came in. The* CAPTAIN *and* HARLEQUIN *attack the dinner which is set before them by the* INNKEEPER *and the* SERVANTS, *who wait upon them assiduously with anticipation of their every want.*)

CURTAIN

THE SECOND ACT

A garden with the façade of a pavilion opening upon it.

DOÑA SIRENA *and* COLUMBINE *enter from the pavilion.*

SIRENA. Is it not enough to deprive a woman of her five senses, Columbine? Can it be possible that a lady should see herself placed in so embarrassing a position and by low, unfeeling people? How did you ever dare to show yourself in my presence with such a tale?

COLUMBINE. But sooner or later wouldn't you have had to know it?

SIRENA. I had rather have died first. But did they all say the same?

COLUMBINE. All, one after the other, exactly as I have told it to you. The tailor absolutely refuses to send you the gown until you have paid him everything that you owe.

SIRENA. Impudent rascal! Everything that I owe *him*. The barefaced highwayman! And does he not stand indebted for his reputation and his very credit in this city to me? Until I employed him in the decoration of my person he did not know, so to speak, what it was to dress a lady.

COLUMBINE. All the cooks and musicians and servants say the same. They refuse to play tonight or to appear at the fête unless they are all paid beforehand.

SIRENA. The rogues! The brood of vipers! Whence does such insolence spring? Were these people not born to serve? Are they to be paid nowadays in nothing but money? Is money the only thing which has value in the world? Woe unto her who is left without a husband to look after her, as I am, without male relatives, alas, without any masculine connection! A woman by herself is worth nothing in the world, be she never so noble or virtuous. O day foretold of the Apocalypse! Surely Antichrist has come!

COLUMBINE. I never saw you so put out before. I hardly know you. You have always been able to rise above these calamities.

SIRENA. Those were other days, Columbine. Then I had my youth to count on, and my beauty, as powerful allies. Princes and great grandees cast themselves at my feet.

COLUMBINE. But on the other hand you did not have the experience and knowledge of the world which you have now. And as far as beauty is concerned, surely you never shone with such refulgence as today—that is, if you will listen to me.

SIRENA. Don't attempt to flatter me. Do you suppose that I should ever have got myself into such a fix if I had been the Doña Sirena of my twenties?

COLUMBINE. Your twenty suitors?

SIRENA. What do you think? I had no end of suitors. And you who have not yet begun upon twenty, you have not the sense to perceive what that means and to profit by it. I would never have believed it possible. Otherwise should I have adopted you for my niece if I had, though I saw myself abandoned by every man in the world and reduced to live alone with a maid servant? If instead of wasting your youth on this impecunious Harlequin, this poet who can bring you nothing but ballads and verses, you had had the sense to make a proper use of your time, we should not be languishing now in this humiliating dilemma.

COLUMBINE. What do you expect? I am too young to resign myself to being loved without loving. If I am ever to become skillful in making others suffer for love of me, surely I must learn first what it is one suffers when one loves. And when I do, I am positive I shall be able to profit by it. I have not yet turned twenty, but you must not think because of that I have so little sense as to marry Harlequin.

SIRENA. I would not trust you. You are capricious, flighty, and allow yourself to be run away with by your imagination. But first let us consider what is to be done. How are we to extricate ourselves from this horrible dilemma? In a short time the guests will arrive—all persons of quality and importance, and among them Signor Polichinelle and his wife and daughter, who, for various reasons, are of more account to me than the rest. You know my house has been frequented of late by several noble gentlemen, somewhat frayed in their nobility, it is true, as I am, through want of means. For any one of them, the daughter of Signor Polichinelle, with her rich dowry and the priceless sum which she will inherit upon her father's death, would be an untold treasure. She has many suitors, but I interpose my influence with Signor Polichinelle and with his wife in favor of them all. Whichever one should be fortunate I know that he will requite my good offices with his bounty, because I have made them all sign an agreement which assures me of it. I have no other means than this to repair my state. If now some rich merchant or some trader by some lucky chance should fall in love with you. . . . Ah, who can say? This house might become again what it was in other days. But if the insolence of these people breaks out tonight, if I cannot give the fête. . . . No! I cannot think of it! It would be the death of me!

COLUMBINE. Do not trouble yourself, Doña Sirena. We have enough in the house to provide the entertainment. As for the music and the servants, Signor Harlequin will be able to supply them— he is not a poet and in love with me for nothing. Many singers and choice spirits of his acquaintance will willingly lend themselves to any adventure. You will see that nothing will be lacking, and your guests will all say that they have never been present at so marvelous a fête in their lives.

SIRENA. Ah, Columbine! If that could only be, how greatly you would rise in my estimation! Run, run and seek out your poet. . . . There is no time to lose.

COLUMBINE. My poet? Surely he is walking up and down now on the other side of the garden, waiting for a sign.

SIRENA. I fear it would not be proper for me to be present at your interview. I ought not to demean myself by soliciting

his favors. I leave all that to you. Let nothing be wanting at the fête and you shall be well repaid, for these terrible straits through which we are passing tonight cannot continue forever—or else I am not Doña Sirena!

COLUMBINE. All will be well. Have no fear.

(DOÑA SIRENA *goes out through the pavilion.*)

COLUMBINE. (*Stepping toward the right and calling*) Harlequin! Harlequin! (CRISPIN *enters*) It isn't he!

CRISPIN. Be not afraid, beautiful Columbine, mistress of the mightiest poet, who yet has not been able to heighten in his verses the splendors of your charm. If the picture must always be different from reality, the advantage in this case is all on the side of reality. You can imagine, no doubt, what the picture must have been.

COLUMBINE. Are you a poet, too, or only a courtier and a flatterer?

CRISPIN. I am the best friend of your lover Harlequin, although I only met him today; but he has had ample proof of my friendship in this brief time. My greatest desire has been to salute you, and Signor Harlequin would not have been the poet that I take him for, had he not trusted to my friendship implicitly. But for his confidence I should have been in danger of falling in love with you simply upon the opportunity which he has afforded me of seeing you.

COLUMBINE. Signor Harlequin trusted as much in my love as he did to your friendship. Don't take so much credit to yourself. It is as foolish to trust a man while he lives as a woman while she loves.

CRISPIN. Now I see that you are not so fatal to the sight as to the ear.

COLUMBINE. Pardon me. Before the fête tonight I must speak with Signor Harlequin, and. . . .

CRISPIN. It will not be necessary. That

is why I have come, a poor ambassador from him and from my master, who stoops to kiss your hand.

COLUMBINE. Who is your master, if I may ask that question?

CRISPIN. The noblest and most powerful gentleman in the world. Permit me for the present not to mention his name. Soon it will be known. My master desires to salute Doña Sirena and to be present at her fête tonight.

COLUMBINE. At her fête? Don't you know. . . .

CRISPIN. I know everything. That is my business—to investigate. I know that there were certain inconveniences which threatened to becloud it; but there will be none. Everything is provided for.

COLUMBINE. What! Then you do know?

CRISPIN. I assure you everything is provided for—a sumptuous reception, lights and fireworks, musicians and sweet song. It will be the most brilliant fête which ever was in the world.

COLUMBINE. Ah, then you are an enchanter?

CRISPIN. Now you begin to know me. But I shall only tell you that I do not bring good fortune with me for nothing. The people of this city are so intelligent that I am sure they will be incapable of frowning upon it and discouraging it with foolish scruples when they see it arrive. My master knows that Signor Polichinelle and his only daughter, the beautiful Silvia, the richest heiress in the city, are to be present at the fête tonight. My master has to fall in love with her, my master has to marry her; and my master will know how to requite in fitting fashion the good offices of Doña Sirena and of yourself in the matter, if so be that you do him the honor to assist in his suit.

COLUMBINE. Your speech is impertinent. Such boldness gives offense.

CRISPIN. Time presses and I have no leisure to pay compliments.

COLUMBINE. If the master is to be judged by the man. . . .

CRISPIN. Reassure yourself. You will find my master the most courteous, the most affable gentleman in the world. My effrontery permits him to be modest. The hard necessities of life sometimes compel the noblest cavalier to descend to the devices of the ruffian, just as sometimes they oblige the noblest ladies, in order to maintain their state, to stoop to menial tricks, and this mixture of ruin and nobility in one person is out of harmony with nature. It is better to divide among two persons that which is usually found confused clumsily and joined in one. My master and myself, as being one person, are each a part of the other. Would it could be always so! We have all within ourselves a great and splendid gentleman of lofty hopes and towering ideals, capable of everything that is noble and everything that is good—and by his side, a humble servant born to forlorn hopes and miserable and hidden things, who employs himself in the base actions to which we are enforced by life. The art of living is so to separate the two that when we fall into any ignominy we can say: "It was not my fault; it was not I. It was my servant." In the greatest misery to which we sink there is always something in us which rises superior to ourselves. We should despise ourselves too much if we did not believe that we were better than our lives. Of course you know who my master is: he is the one of the towering thoughts, of the lofty, beautiful ideals. Of course you know who I am: I am the one of the forlorn and hidden things, the one who grovels and toils on the ground, delving among falsehood and humiliation and lies. Only there is something in me which redeems me and elevates me in my own eyes. It is the loyalty of my service, this loyalty which humiliates and abases itself that another may fly, that he may always be the lord of the towering thoughts, of the lofty, beautiful ideals.

(*Music is heard in the distance.*)

COLUMBINE. What is this music?

CRISPIN. The music which my master is bringing with him to the fête with all his pages and all the attendants of his train, accompanied by a great court of poets and singers presided over by Signor Harlequin, and an entire legion of soldiers with the Captain at their head, illuminating his coming with torches, with rockets and red fire.

COLUMBINE. Who is your master, that he is able to do so much? I run to tell my lady. . . .

CRISPIN. It will not be necessary. She is here.

(DOÑA SIRENA *enters from the pavilion.*)

SIRENA. What is this? Who has prepared this music? What troop of people is arriving at my door?

COLUMBINE. Ask no questions. Know that today a great gentleman has arrived in this city, and it is he who offers you this fête tonight. His servant will tell you everything. I hardly know myself whether I have been talking to a great rogue or a great madman. Whichever it is, I assure you that he is a most extraordinary man.

SIRENA. Then it is not Harlequin?

COLUMBINE. Ask no questions. It is all a work of magic!

CRISPIN. Doña Sirena, my master begs permission to kiss your hand. So great a lady and so noble a gentleman ought not, when they meet, to descend to indignities inappropriate to their state. That is why, before he arrives, I have come to tell you everything. I am acquainted with a thousand notable exploits of your history, which should I but refer to them, would be sufficient to assure me attention. But it might seem impertinence to mention them. (*Handing her a paper*) My master acknowledges in this paper over his signature the great sum which he will be in your debt should you be able to fulfill upon your part that which he has here the honor to propose.

SIRENA. What paper and what debt is this? (*Reading the paper to herself*) How? A hundred thousand crowns at once and an equal quantity upon the death of Signor Polichinelle, if your master succeeds in marrying his daughter? What insolence and what infamy have we here? And to a lady! Do you know to whom you are speaking? Do you know what house this is?

CRISPIN. Doña Sirena! Forego your wrath. There is nobody present to warrant such concern. Put that paper away with the others, and let us not refer to the matter again. My master proposes nothing which is improper to you, nor would you consent that he should do so. Whatever may happen hereafter will be the work of chance and of love. I, the servant, was the one who set this unworthy snare. You are ever the noble dame, my master the virtuous cavalier, and as you meet in this festival tonight, you will talk of a thousand gallant and priceless things, as your guests stroll by and whisper enviously in praise of the ladies' beauty and the exquisite artfulness of their dress, the splendor and magnificence of the entertainment, the sweetness of the music, the nimble grace of the dancers' feet. And who is to say that this is not the whole story? Is not life just this—a fête in which the music serves to cover up the words, the words to cover up the thoughts? Then let the music sound, let conversation flash and sparkle with its smiles, let the supper be well served—this is all that concerns the guests. See, here is my master, who comes to salute you in all courtesy.

[199]

(LEANDER, HARLEQUIN, *and the* CAPTAIN *enter from the right.*)

LEANDER. Doña Sirena, I kiss your hand.

SIRENA. Sir. . . .

LEANDER. My servant has already told you in my name much more than I myself could say.

CRISPIN. Being a gentleman of discretion, my master is a man of few words. His admiration is mute.

HARLEQUIN. He wisely knows how to admire.

CAPTAIN. True merit.

HARLEQUIN. True valor.

CAPTAIN. The divine art of poesy.

HARLEQUIN. The incomparable science of war.

CAPTAIN. His greatness appears in everything!

HARLEQUIN. He is the noblest gentleman in the world.

CAPTAIN. My sword shall always be at his service.

HARLEQUIN. I shall dedicate my greatest poem to his glory.

CRISPIN. Enough! Enough! You will offend his native modesty. See how he tries to hide himself and slip away. He is a violet.

SIRENA. Surely he has no need to speak for himself who can make others talk like this in his praise.

(*After bows and salutations the men all withdraw upon the right,* DOÑA SIRENA *and* COLUMBINE *remaining alone.*)

SIRENA. What do you think of this, Columbine?

COLUMBINE. I think that the master is most attractive in his figure and the servant most captivating in his impertinence.

SIRENA. We shall take advantage of them both. For either I know nothing of the world or about men, or else fortune this day has set her foot within my doors.

COLUMBINE. Surely then it must be fortune, for you do know something of the world, and about men—what don't you know!

SIRENA. Here are Risela and Laura, the first to arrive.

COLUMBINE. When were they the last at anything? I leave them to you; I must not lose sight of our cavalier.

(*She goes out to the right.* LAURA *and* RISELA *enter.*)

SIRENA. My dears! Do you know, I was beginning to worry already for fear that you would not come?

LAURA. What? Is it really so late?

SIRENA. Naturally it is late before I worry about you.

RISELA. We were obliged to disappoint at two other fêtes so as not to miss yours.

LAURA. Though we understood that you might not be able to give it tonight. We heard that you were indisposed.

SIRENA. If only to rebuke gossipers I should have given it though I had died.

RISELA. And we should have been present at it even though we had died.

LAURA. But of course you have not heard the news?

RISELA. Nobody is talking of anything else.

LAURA. A mysterious personage has arrived in the city. Some say that he is a secret ambassador from Venice or from France.

RISELA. Others say that he has come to seek a wife for the Grand Turk.

LAURA. They say he is beautiful as an Adonis.

RISELA. If we could only manage to meet him!—What a pity! You ought to have invited him to your fête.

SIRENA. It was not necessary, my dears. He himself sent an ambassador begging permission to come. He is now in my house, and I have not the slightest doubt but that you will be talking to him soon.

LAURA. What is that? I told you that we made no mistake when we came. Something was sure to happen.

RISELA. How we shall be envied tonight!

LAURA. Everybody is mad to know him.

SIRENA. It was no effort for me. It was sufficient for him to hear that I was receiving in my house.

RISELA. Of course—the old story. No person of importance ever arrives in the city, but it seems he runs at once and pays his attentions to you.

LAURA. I am impatient to see him. Lead us to him, on your life!

RISELA. Yes! Take us where he is.

SIRENA. I beg your pardons—Signor Polichinelle arriving with his family. But, my dears, you will not wait. You need no introductions.

RISELA. Certainly not! Come, Laura.

LAURA. Come, Risela, before the crowd grows too great and it is impossible to get near.

(LAURA *and* RISELA *go out to the right.* POLICHINELLE, *the* WIFE OF POLICHINELLE, *and* SILVIA *enter.*)

SIRENA. O, Signor Polichinelle! I was afraid you were not coming. Until now I really did not know whether or not I was to have a fête!

POLICHINELLE. It was not my fault; it was my wife's. With forty gowns to select from, she can never make up her mind which to put on.

WIFE OF POLICHINELLE. Yes, if I were to please him I should make an exhibition of myself. Any suggestion will do. As it is, you see that I have really not had time to put on anything.

SIRENA. But you never were more beautiful!

POLICHINELLE. Well, she is not displaying one half of her jewels. If she were, she could not support the weight of the treasure.

SIRENA. Who has a better right to be proud than you have, Signor Polichinelle? What your wife displays are the riches which you have acquired by your labor.

WIFE OF POLICHINELLE. I tell him this is the time to enjoy them. He ought to be ambitious and seek to rise in the world. Instead, all he thinks about is how he can marry his daughter to some trader.

SIRENA. O, Signor Polichinelle! Your daughter deserves a great deal better than a trader. Surely you hold your daughter far too high for trade. Such a thing is not to be thought of for one moment. You have no right to sacrifice her heart to a bargain. What do you say, Silvia?

POLICHINELLE. She would prefer some waxed-up dandy. Instead of listening to my advice, she reads novels and poetry. It disgusts me.

SILVIA. I always do as my father says, unless it is displeasing to my mother or distasteful to me.

SIRENA. You speak very sensibly.

WIFE OF POLICHINELLE. Her father has an idea that there is nothing but money to be had in the world.

POLICHINELLE. I have an idea that without money there is nothing to be had out of the world. Money is the one thing which counts. It buys everything.

SIRENA. Oh, I cannot hear you talk like that! What of virtue, what of intelligence, what of noble blood?

POLICHINELLE. They all have their price. You know it. And nobody knows it better than I do, for I have bought heavily in those lines, and found them reasonable.

SIRENA. O, Signor Polichinelle! You are in a playful humor this evening. You know very well that money will not buy everything, and if your daughter should fall in love with some noble gentleman, you would not dream of attempting to oppose her. I can see that you have a father's heart.

POLICHINELLE. I have. I would do anything for my daughter.

SIRENA. Even ruin yourself?

POLICHINELLE. That would not be anything for my daughter. Why, I would steal first, rob, murder—anything. . . .

SIRENA. I felt sure that you must know some way to recoup yourself. But the fête is crowded already! Come with me, Silvia. I have picked out a handsome gentleman to dance with you. You will make a striking couple—ideal!

(*All go out upon the right except* SIGNOR POLICHINELLE, *who is detained as he is about to do so by* CRISPIN, *who enters and accosts him.*)

CRISPIN. Signor Polichinelle! With your permission. . . . A word with you. . . .

POLICHINELLE. Who calls me? What do you want?

CRISPIN. You don't remember me? It is not surprising. Time blots out everything, and when what has been blotted out was unpleasant, after a while we do not remember even the blot, but hurry and paint over it with bright colors, like these with which you now hide your capers from the world. Why, when I knew you, Signor Polichinelle, you had hard work to cover your nakedness with a couple of muddy rags!

POLICHINELLE. Who are you and where did you know me?

CRISPIN. I was a mere boy then; you were a grown man. But you cannot have forgotten so soon all those glorious exploits on the high seas, all those victories gained over the Turks, to which we contributed not a little with our heroic strength, both pulling chained at the same noble oar in the same victorious galley?

POLICHINELLE. Impudent scoundrel! Silence, or—

CRISPIN. Or you will do with me as you did with your first master in Naples, or with your first wife in Bologna, or with that usurious Jew in Venice?

POLICHINELLE. Silence! Who are you who know so much and talk so freely?

CRISPIN. I am—what you were. One who will come to be what you are—as you have done. Not with the same violence as you, for these are other days and only madmen commit murder now, and lovers, and poor ignorant wretches who fall armed upon the wayfarer in dark alleys or along the solitary highway. Despicable gallows-birds! Negligible!

POLICHINELLE. What do you want of me? Money, is it not? Well, we can meet again; this is not the place. . . .

CRISPIN. Do not trouble yourself about your money. I only want to be your friend, your ally, as in those days.

POLICHINELLE. What can I do for you?

CRISPIN. Nothing; for today I am the one who is going to do for you, and oblige you with a warning. (*Directing him to look off upon the right*) Do you see your daughter there—how she is dancing with that young gentleman? How coyly she blushes at his gallant compliments! Well, that gentleman is my master.

POLICHINELLE. Your master? Then he must be an adventurer, a rogue, a blackguard, like. . . .

CRISPIN. Like us, you were going to say? No, he is more dangerous than we, because, as you see, he has a fine figure, and there is a mystery and an enchantment in his glance and a sweetness in his voice which go straight to the heart, and which stir it as at the recital of some sad tale. Is not this enough to make any woman fall in love? Never say that I did not warn you. Run and separate your daughter from this man and never permit her to dance with him again, no, nor to speak to him, so long as she shall live.

POLICHINELLE. Do you mean to say that he is your master and is this the way you serve him?

CRISPIN. Are you surprised? Have you

forgotten already how it was when you were a servant? And I have not planned to assassinate him yet.

POLICHINELLE. You are right. A master is always despicable. But what interest have you in serving me?

CRISPIN. To come safe into some good port, as we often did when we rowed together at the oar. Then sometimes you used to say to me: "You are stronger than I, row for me." In this galley in which we are today, you are stronger than I. Row for me, for your faithful friend of other days, for life is a horrible vile galley and I have rowed so long.

(*He goes out by the way he came in.* DOÑA SIRENA, *the* WIFE OF POLICHINELLE, RISELA, *and* LAURA *re-enter.*)

LAURA. Only Doña Sirena could have given such a fête!

RISELA. Tonight she has outstripped all the others.

SIRENA. The presence of so distinguished a gentleman was an added attraction.

POLICHINELLE. But Silvia? Where is Silvia? What have you done with my daughter?

SIRENA. Do not disturb yourself, Signor Polichinelle. Your daughter is in excellent hands, and you may rest assured that she will remain in them as long as she is in my house.

RISELA. There were no attentions for any one but her.

LAURA. All the smiles were for her.

RISELA. And all the sighs!

POLICHINELLE. Whose? This mysterious gentleman's? I do not like it. This must stop——

SIRENA. But Signor Polichinelle!

POLICHINELLE. Away! Let me be! I know what I am doing. (*He rushes out.*)

SIRENA. What is the matter? What infatuation is this?

WIFE OF POLICHINELLE. Now you see what sort of man he is. He is going to commit an outrage on that gentleman. He wants to marry his daughter to a trader, does he—a clinker of worthless coin? He wants to make her unhappy for the rest of her life.

SIRENA. No, anything rather than that! Remember—you are her mother and this is the time for you to interpose your authority.

WIFE OF POLICHINELLE. Look! He has spoken to him and the cavalier drops Silvia's hand and retires, hanging his head.

LAURA. And now Signor Polichinelle is attacking your daughter!

SIRENA. Come! Come! Such conduct cannot be tolerated in my house.

RISELA. Signora Polichinelle, in spite of your riches you are an unfortunate woman.

WIFE OF POLICHINELLE. Would you believe it, he even forgets himself so far sometimes as to turn upon me?

LAURA. Is it possible? And are you a woman to submit to that?

WIFE OF POLICHINELLE. He makes it up afterward by giving me a handsome present.

SIRENA. Well, there are husbands of my acquaintance who never even think of making up. . . .

(*They all go out.* LEANDER *and* CRISPIN *enter.*)

CRISPIN. What is this sadness, this dejection? I expected to find you in better spirits.

LEANDER. I was never unfortunate till now; at least it never mattered to me whether or not I was unfortunate. Let us fly, Crispin, let us fly from this city before any one can discover us and find out who we are.

CRISPIN. If we fly it will be after everyone has discovered us and they are running after us to detain us and bring us back in spite of ourselves. It would be most discourteous to depart with such scant ceremony without bidding our attentive friends good-by.

LEANDER. Do not jest, Crispin; I am in despair.

CRISPIN. So you are. And just when our hopes are under fullest sail.

LEANDER. What could you expect? You wanted me to pretend to be in love, but I have not been able to pretend it.

CRISPIN. Why not?

LEANDER. Because I love—I love in spirit and in truth!

CRISPIN. Silvia? Is that what you are complaining about?

LEANDER. I never believed it possible a man could love like this. I never believed that I could ever love. Through all my wandering life along the dusty roads, I was not only the one who passed, I was the one who fled, the enemy of the harvest and the field, the enemy of man, enemy of sunshine and the day. Sometimes the fruit of the wayside tree, stolen, not given, left some savor of joy on my parched lips, and sometimes, after many a bitter day, resting at night beneath the stars, the calm repose of heaven would invite and soothe me to a dream of something that might be in my life like that calm night sky, brooding infinite over my soul—serene! And so tonight, in the enchantment of this fête, it seemed to me as if there had come a calm, a peace into my life—and I was dreaming! Ah! How I did dream! But tomorrow it will be again the bitter flight with justice at our heels, and I cannot bear that they should take me here where she is, and where she may ever have cause to be ashamed at having known me.

CRISPIN. Why, I thought that you had been received with favor! And I was not the only one who noticed it. Doña Sirena and our good friends, the Captain and the poet, have been most eloquent in your praises. To that rare excellent mother, the Wife of Polichinelle, who thinks of nothing but how she can relate herself by marriage to some nobleman, you have seemed the son-in-law of her dreams. As for Signor Polichinelle. . . .

LEANDER. He knows. . . . he suspects. . . .

CRISPIN. Naturally. It is not so easy to deceive Signor Polichinelle as it is an ordinary man. An old fox like him has to be cheated truthfully. I decided that the best thing for us to do was to tell him everything.

LEANDER. How so?

CRISPIN. Obviously. He knows me of old. When I told him that you were my master, he rightly supposed that the master must be worthy of the man. And upon my part, in appreciation of his confidence, I warned him not to permit you under any circumstances to come near to or speak with his daughter.

LEANDER. You did? Then what have I to hope?

CRISPIN. You are a fool! Why, that Signor Polichinelle will exert all his authority to prevent you from meeting her.

LEANDER. I do not understand.

CRISPIN. In that way he will become our most powerful ally, for if he opposes it, that will be enough to make his wife take the opposite side, and the daughter will fall in love with you madly. You have no idea what a young and beautiful daughter of a rich father, who has been brought up to the gratification of her every whim, can do when she finds out for the first time in her life that somebody is opposing her wishes. I am certain that this very night, before the fête is over, she will find some way of eluding the vigilance of her father at whatever cost, and return to speak with you.

LEANDER. But can't you see that Signor Polichinelle is nothing to me, no, nor the wide world either? It is she, only she! It is to her that I am unwilling to appear unworthy or mean, it is to her—to her that I cannot lie.

CRISPIN. Bah! Enough of this nonsense! Don't tell me that. It is too late to draw back. Think what will happen if we vacillate now and hesitate in going on. You say that you have fallen in love? Well, this real love will serve us better than if it were put on. Otherwise you would have wanted to get through with it too quickly. If insolence and effrontery are the only qualities which are of use elsewhere, in love a faint suggestion of timidity is of advantage to a man. Timidity in a man always makes the woman bolder. If you don't believe it, here is the innocent Silvia now, skulking in the shadows and only waiting for a chance to come near until I retire or am concealed.

LEANDER. Silvia, do you say?

CRISPIN. Hush! You may frighten her. When she is with you, remember, discretion—only a few words, very few. Adore her, admire her, contemplate her, and let the enchantment of this night of pallid blue speak for you, propitious as it is to love, and whisper to her in the music whose soft notes die away amid the foliage and fall upon our ears like sad overtones of this festival of joy.

LEANDER. Do not trifle, Crispin! Do not trifle with my love! It will be my death.

CRISPIN. Why should I trifle with it? I know, too, it is not always well to grovel on the ground. Sometimes we must soar and mount up into the sky better to dominate the earth. Mount now and soar—and I will grovel still. The world lies in our hands!

(*He goes out to the right.* SILVIA *enters.*)

LEANDER. Silvia!

SILVIA. Is it you? You must pardon me. I did not expect to find you here.

LEANDER. I fly from the festival. I am saddened by this joy.

SILVIA. What? You, too?

LEANDER. Too, do you say? Does joy sadden you, too?

SILVIA. My father is angry with me. He never spoke to me like this before. And he was discourteous to you. Will you forgive him?

LEANDER. Yes. I forgive him everything. But you must not make him angry upon my account. Return to the company. They will be looking for you. If they find you here with me. . . .

SILVIA. You are right. But you must come, too. Why should you be so sad?

LEANDER. No, I must slip away without anybody seeing me, without their knowing I am gone. I must go far away.

SILVIA. What? But you have important business in the city. I know you have. . . . You will have to stay a long, long time.

LEANDER. No, no! Not another day, not another hour!

SILVIA. But then. . . . You have not lied to me?

LEANDER. Lied? No! Don't say that I have lied! No; this is the one truth of my whole life—this dream from which there should be no awakening!

(*The music of a song is heard in the distance, continuing until the curtain falls.*)

SILVIA. It is Harlequin, singing. . . . What is the matter? You are crying. Is it the music which makes you cry? Why will you not tell me what it is that makes you cry?

LEANDER. What makes me cry? The song will tell you. Listen to the song!

SILVIA. We can hear only the music; the words are lost, it is so far away. But don't you know it? It is a song to the silence of the night. It is called the "Kingdom of the Soul." You must know it.

LEANDER. Say it over to me.

SILVIA:

The amorous night above the silent lover
Across the blue heaven spreads a nuptial
veil.

The night has strewn its diamonds on the
  cover
Of a moonlit sky in drowsy August pale.
The garden in the shade now knows no
  color,
Deep in the shadow of its obscurity
Lightly the leaflets flutter, sweetly smells
  the flower,
And love broods there in silent
  sympathy.

You voices which sigh, you voices which
  sing,
You voices which whisper sweet phrases
  of love,
Intruders you are and a blasphemous
  thing,
Like an oath at night-tide in a prayer
  sped above.
Great Spirit of Silence, whom I adore,
There is in your silence the ineffable
  voice
Of those who have died loving in silence
  of yore,
Of those who were silent and died of
  their love;
Of those in their lives whose great love
  was such
They were unable to tell it, their love was
  so much!
Yours are the voices which nightly I
  hear,
Whispers of love and eternity near.

Mother of my soul, the light of this
  star,
  Is it not the light of your eyes,
Which, like a drop of God's blood,
  Trembles in the night
  And fades at sunrise?
Tell him whom I love, I never shall
  love
  More than him on the earth,
And when he fades away, light of my
  eyes,
  I shall kiss at sunrise
  But the light of thy star!

LEANDER:

Mother of my soul, I never have loved
  More than you on the earth.
And when you fade away, light of my
  eyes,
  I shall kiss at sunrise
  The light of thy star.

(*They remain in silence, embracing
and gazing into each other's eyes.*)

CRISPIN. (*Who appears at the right—
to himself*)

Poesy and night and madness of the
  lover. . . .
  All has to serve us that to our net shall
  come.
The victory is sure! Courage, charge and
  over!
  Who shall overcome us when love
  beats the drum?

(SILVIA *and* LEANDER *move slowly off
to the right, locked in each other's arms.*
CRISPIN *follows them in silence, without
being seen. Slowly the curtain descends.*)

THE THIRD ACT

A room in LEANDER'S *house.*
CRISPIN, *the* CAPTAIN, *and* HARLEQUIN
enter from the right.

CRISPIN. Enter, gentlemen, and be
seated. Will you take something? Let me
give orders to have it brought. Hello
there! Ho!
CAPTAIN. No! By no means! We can
accept nothing.
HARLEQUIN. We came merely to offer
our services to your master after what we
have just heard.

CRISPIN. Incredible treachery, which, believe me, shall not be suffered to remain unpunished! I promise you if Signor Polichinelle ever puts himself within the reach of my hands——

HARLEQUIN. Ah! Now you see what an advantage is possessed by us poets! I have him always within the reach of my verses. Oh! What a terrible satire I am thinking of writing against him! The cutthroat! Old reprobate!

CAPTAIN. But you say your master was not so much as even wounded?

CRISPIN. It might have killed him just the same. Imagine! Set upon by a dozen ruffians absolutely without warning. . . . Thanks, though, to his bravery, to his skill, to my cries. . . .

HARLEQUIN. Do you say that it happened at night as your master was talking to Silvia over the wall of her garden?

CRISPIN. Naturally, my master had already been advised of what might happen. But you know what sort of man he is. He is not a person to be deterred by anything.

CAPTAIN. He ought to have notified us, however.

HARLEQUIN. He ought, certainly, to have notified the Captain. He would have been delighted to have lent his aid.

CRISPIN. You know what my master is. He is a host in himself.

CAPTAIN. But you say that he caught one of the ruffians by the nape of the neck, and the rascal confessed that it had all been planned and arranged by Signor Polichinelle beforehand so as to rid himself of your master?

CRISPIN. Who else could have had any interest in it? His daughter is in love with my master; her father wants to marry her to suit himself. My master is opposing his plans, and Signor Polichinelle has known all his life how to get rid of disturbances. Didn't he become a widower twice in a very short time?

Hasn't he inherited all that his relatives had, irrespective of age, whether they were older or younger than he? Everybody knows it; nobody will say that I do him injustice. Ah! the riches of Signor Polichinelle are an affront to our intelligence, a discouragement to honest labor. A man like Signor Polichinelle could remain rich only among a base and degenerate people.

HARLEQUIN. I agree with you. I intend to say all this in my satire—of course, without mentioning names. Poetry does not admit of such license.

CRISPIN. Much good, then, your satire will do!

CAPTAIN. Leave him to me! Leave him to me! I promise you if he once puts himself within the reach of my sword— ah! But I am confident that he never will.

CRISPIN. My master would never consent to have an insult offered to Signor Polichinelle. After all, he is Silvia's father. The point is to let people in the city understand that an attempt has been made to assassinate my master. Is that old fox to be allowed to stifle the honest affection, the generous passion of his daughter? It is impossible.

HARLEQUIN. It is impossible. Love will find a way.

CRISPIN. If my master had been some impecunious beggar. . . . Tell me, isn't Signor Polichinelle the one who ought to be congratulated that my master has condescended to fall in love with his daughter, and is willing to accept him for his father-in-law?—my master, who has rejected the advances of so many damsels of high degree; my master, for whom over four princesses have committed I know not how many absurdities! But who is here? (*Looking toward the right*) Ah, Columbine! Come in, my beautiful Columbine! Do not be afraid. (COLUMBINE *enters from the right*) We are all your friends, and our mutual friendship will protect you from our mutual admiration.

COLUMBINE. Doña Sirena has sent me for news of your master. It was scarcely day when Silvia came to our house and confided everything that had happened to my mistress. She says that she will never return to her father, nor leave my mistress, unless it is to become the bride of Signor Leander.

CRISPIN. Does she say that? O, noble girl! O, constant, true-hearted lover!

HARLEQUIN. What an epithalamium I shall write for their wedding!

COLUMBINE. Silvia is positive that Leander is wounded. She heard the clash of swords beneath the balcony, your cries for help; then she fell senseless and they found her in a swoon at daybreak. Tell me how Signor Leander is, for she is beside herself with anxiety to hear, and my lady also is much distressed.

CRISPIN. Tell her that my master escaped with his life only through the unutterable power of love. Tell her that he is dying now only from the incurable wounds of love. Tell her that to the last. . . . (Seeing LEANDER approach) Ah, but here he is himself, and he will be able to give you later news than I.

(LEANDER enters.)

CAPTAIN. (Embracing him) My dear, good friend!

HARLEQUIN. (Embracing him) My friend and master!

COLUMBINE. Ah, Signor Leander, what happiness! You are safe!

LEANDER. What? How did you know?

CRISPIN. Nothing else is talked about in the city. People gather in groups in the squares murmuring vengeance and venting imprecations upon Signor Polichinelle.

LEANDER. What is this?

CAPTAIN. He had better not dare to attempt your life a second time.

HARLEQUIN. He had better not dare to attempt to arrest the true course of your love.

COLUMBINE. It would be useless. Silvia is in my mistress's house and she swears that she will leave it only to become your bride.

LEANDER. Silvia in your house? But her father. . . .

COLUMBINE. Signor Polichinelle has all he can do to look after himself.

CAPTAIN. What? I knew that man would be up to something. Oh, of what base uses money is capable!

HARLEQUIN. It is capable of everything but love; of that it is incapable.

COLUMBINE. He tried to have you assassinated dishonorably in the dark.

CRISPIN. By twelve cutthroats. Twelve! I counted them.

LEANDER. I made out only three or four.

CRISPIN. My master will end by telling you that there was no danger so as not to receive credit for his coolness and his bravery—but I saw it. There were twelve; twelve armed to the teeth, prepared to do murder. It seemed impossible that he could escape with his life.

COLUMBINE. I must run and calm Silvia and my mistress.

CRISPIN. Listen, Columbine. As to Silvia—wouldn't it be as well, perhaps, not to calm her?

COLUMBINE. Leave that to my mistress. Silvia is convinced that your master is dead, and although Doña Sirena is making the most unheard-of efforts to console her, it will not be long before she is here in spite of the consequences.

CRISPIN. I ought to have known of what your mistress was capable.

CAPTAIN. We must be going, too; there is nothing here that we can do. The point is to arouse the indignation of the people against Signor Polichinelle.

HARLEQUIN. We shall stone his house; we shall raise the whole city. Until today not a single man has dared to lift his hand against him; today we will all dare to do it together. There is an uplift, a moral earnestness in a crowd.

COLUMBINE. He will come creeping on his knees and beg you to accept his daughter as your wife.

CRISPIN. Yes, yes, he will indeed! Run, friends, run! The life of my master is not secure. A man who has once made up his mind to assassinate him is not likely to be turned aside for a trifle.

CAPTAIN. Have no fear, my good friend.

HARLEQUIN. My friend and master!

COLUMBINE. Signor Leander!

LEANDER. Thanks to you all, my friends. My loyal friends!

(*All go out but* LEANDER *and* CRISPIN.)

LEANDER. What is this, Crispin? What are you trying to do? Where do you expect to come out with all your lies? Do you know what I believe? You paid those fellows yourself; it was your idea. I should have got off badly enough among so many if they had been in earnest.

CRISPIN. Have you the temerity to reproach me when I precipitate the fulfillment of your desires so skillfully?

LEANDER. No, Crispin, no. You know you do not. I love Silvia. I am resolved: I shall never win her love through deception, come what may.

CRISPIN. You know very well, then, what will come. Do you call it love to sit down and resign yourself to losing what you love for the sake of these quibbles of conscience? Silvia herself would not thank you for it.

LEANDER. What do you mean? If she once learns who I am. . . .

CRISPIN. By the time she finds out you will no longer be the one that you are. You will be her husband then, her beloved husband, who is everything that is noble and faithful and true, and whatever else you like besides, or that her heart desires. Once you are master of her heart —and her fortune—will you not be a complete and perfect gentleman? You will not be like Signor Polichinelle, who, with all his wealth which permits him so many luxuries, has not yet been able to permit himself the luxury of being honest. Deceit is natural to him, but with you it was only necessity. If you had not had me at your side you would have starved to death before this out of pure conscientiousness. Ah! do you suppose that if I had thought for one moment that you were a man of another sort, I would have been satisfied to devote your abilities to love? No, I would have put you into politics, and not merely the fortune of Signor Polichinelle would have been ours, but a chastened and admiring world. But you are not ambitious. You will be satisfied to be happy.

LEANDER. But can't you see that no good, no happiness, can come out of this? If I could lie so as to make her love me and in that way become rich, then it could only be because I did not love. And if I did not love, then how could I be happy? And if I love, how can I lie?

CRISPIN. Don't lie, then. Love, love passionately, entirely, with your whole heart and soul. Put your love before everything else upon earth. Guard and protect it. A lover does not lie when he keeps to himself what he thinks might prejudice the blind affection of his mistress.

LEANDER. These are subtleties, Crispin.

CRISPIN. Which you would have known all about before if you had really been in love. Love is all subtleties and the greatest subtlety of them all is not that lovers deceive others—it is that they can so easily deceive themselves.

LEANDER. I do not deceive myself, Crispin. I am not one of those men who, when they have sold their conscience, think that they have also been able to dispose of their intelligence as well.

CRISPIN. That is the reason I said you

would never make a good politician. You are right. For the intelligence is the conscience of truth, and the man who parts with that among the lies of this life is as one who has lost himself. He is without compass or sail. He will never be able to find himself again, nor know himself, but become in all his being just one more living lie.

LEANDER. Where did you learn all these things, Crispin?

CRISPIN. I meditated a little while in the galleys, where this conscience of my intelligence accused me of having been more of a fool than a knave. If I had had more knavery and less stupidity, instead of rowing I might have commanded the ship. So I swore never again to return to the oar. You can see now what I am willing to do for your sake since I am on the point of breaking my oath.

LEANDER. In what way?

CRISPIN. Our situation has become desperate. We have exhausted our credit, and our dupes begin to demand something more substantial than talk: the innkeeper who entertained us so long with such munificence, expecting that you would receive your remittances; Signor Pantaloon, who, hearing of the credit extended by the innkeeper, advanced us whatever was necessary to install us sumptuously in this house; tradesmen of every description, who did not hesitate to provide us with every luxury, dazzled by such display; Doña Sirena herself, who has lent us her invaluable good offices in your love affair—they have all only asked what was reasonable; it would be unjust to expect more of them or to complain of such delightful people. The name of this fair city shall ever be engraven upon my heart in letters of gold. From this hour I claim it as my adopted mother! But more than this, have you forgotten that they have been searching for us in other parts and following on our heels? Can it be that all those glorious exploits of Mantua and Florence have been forgotten? Don't you recall that famous lawsuit in Bologna? Three thousand two hundred pages of testimony already admitted against us before we withdrew in alarm at the sight of such prodigious expansive ability! Do you imagine that it has not continued to grow under the pen of that learned doctor and jurist, who has taken it under his wing? How many whereases and therefores must there now be therefore, whereas they are all there for no good? Do you still doubt? Do you still hesitate and reprove me because I give the battle today which is to decide our fate forever at a single blow?

LEANDER. Let us fly!

CRISPIN. No! Let the despairing fly! This day decides. We challenge fortune. I have given you love; give me life!

LEANDER. But how can we save ourselves? What can I do? Tell me.

CRISPIN. Nothing yet. It will be enough to accept what others offer. We have intertwined ourselves with the interests of many, and the bonds of interest will prove our salvation.

(DOÑA SIRENA enters.)

SIRENA. Have I your permission, Signor Leander?

LEANDER. Doña Sirena! What? You in my house?

SIRENA. I am conscious of the risk I am running—the gossip of evil tongues. What? Doña Sirena in the house of a young and gallant gentleman?

CRISPIN. My master will know how to avoid all cause of scandal, if any indeed could attach to your name.

SIRENA. Your master? I would not trust him. Men are so boastful! But it is idle to anticipate. What, sir, is this talk about an attempt to kill you last night? I have not heard another thing since I got up in the morning. And Silvia! The poor child! How she loves you! I would give a great deal to know what it was that you did to make her fall in love with you like that.

CRISPIN. My master feels that it was what you did. He owes it all to you.

SIRENA. I should be the last one to deny that he owes me anything. I have always tried to speak well of him—a thing I had no right to do, not knowing him sufficiently. I have gone to great lengths in his service. Now if you are false to your promise. . . .

CRISPIN. You do not doubt my master? Have you not the papers signed in his own hand?

SIRENA. The hand is a good one and so is the name. I don't bother about them. I know what it is to trust, and I know that Signor Leander will pay me what he owes. But today has been a bitter day for me, and if you could let me have today one half of what you have promised, I would willingly forego the other half.

CRISPIN. Today, do you say?

SIRENA. A day of tribulation! And what makes it worse, it is twenty years ago today that my second husband died, who was my first—yes, my only love.

CRISPIN. May he rest in peace with all the honors of the first!

SIRENA. The first was forced upon me by my father. I never loved him, but in spite of it he insisted upon being faithful to me.

CRISPIN. What knowledge you have of men, Doña Sirena!

SIRENA. But let us leave these recollections, which are depressing, and turn to hope. Would you believe it? Silvia insisted upon coming with me.

LEANDER. Here? To this house?

SIRENA. Where do you suppose it was that she insisted upon coming? What do you say to that? What would Signor Polichinelle say? With all the city roused against him, there would be nothing for him to do but to have you marry.

LEANDER. No, no! Don't let her come. . . .

CRISPIN. Hush! You know my master has a way of not saying what he means.

SIRENA. I know. What would he give to see Silvia at his side, never to be separated from him more?

CRISPIN. What would he give? You don't know what he would give!

SIRENA. That is the reason I ask.

CRISPIN. Ah, Doña Sirena! If my master becomes the husband of Silvia today, today he will pay you everything that he has promised you.

SIRENA. And if he does not?

CRISPIN. Then you lose everything. Suit yourself.

LEANDER. Silence, Crispin, silence! Enough! I cannot submit to have my love treated as a bargain. Go, Doña Sirena! Say to Silvia that she must return to her father's house, that under no circumstances is she ever to enter mine; that she must forget me forever. I shall fly and hide myself in the desert places of the earth, where no man shall see me, no, nor so much as know my name. My name? I wonder—have I a name?

CRISPIN. Will you be silent?

SIRENA. What is the matter with him? What paroxysm is this? Return to your senses! Come to your proper mind! How? Renounce so glorious an enterprise for nothing? You are not the only person who is to be considered. Remember that there are others who have put their confidence in you. A lady of quality who has exposed herself for your sake is not to be betrayed with impunity. You will do no such thing. You will not be so foolish. You will marry Silvia or there will be one who will find a way to bring you to a reckoning for all your impostures. I am not so defenseless in the world as you may think, Signor Leander.

CRISPIN. Doña Sirena is right. But believe me, this fit of my master's—he is offended by your reproaches, your want of confidence.

SIRENA. I don't want confidence in

your master. And I might as well say it—I don't want confidence in Signor Polichinelle. He is not a man to be trifled with, either. After the outcry which you raised against him by your stratagem of last night——

CRISPIN. Stratagem, did you say?

SIRENA. Bah! Everybody knows it. One of the rascals was a relative of mine, and among the others I had connections. Very well, sirs, very well! Signor Polichinelle has not been asleep. It is said in the city that he has given information as to who you are to Justice, and on what grounds you may be apprehended. It is said that a process has arrived today from Bologna——

CRISPIN. And a devil of a doctor with it? Three thousand nine hundred folios. . . .

SIRENA. So it is said and on good authority. You see that there is no time to lose.

CRISPIN. Who is losing and who is wasting time but you? Return, return at once to your house! Say to Silvia——

SIRENA. Silvia? Silva is here. She came along with me and Columbine as one of the attendants in my train. She is waiting in the antechamber. I told her that you were wounded horribly.

LEANDER. Oh, my Silvia!

SIRENA. She has reconciled herself to your death. She hopes for nothing else. She expects nothing else. She thinks nothing of what she risks in coming here to see you. Well? Are we friends?

CRISPIN. You are adorable! (*To* LEANDER) Quick! Lie down here. Stretch yourself out in this chair. Seem sick, suffer, faint—be downhearted. And remember, if I am not satisfied with the appearance, I will substitute the reality! (*Threatening him and forcing him into a chair.*)

LEANDER. Yes, I am in your power! I see it, I know it! But Silvia shall never be! Yes, let me see her. Tell her to come in. I shall save her in spite of you, in spite of everything, in spite even of herself!

CRISPIN. You know my master has a way of not meaning what he says.

SIRENA. I never thought him such a fool. Come with me. (*She goes out with* CRISPIN.)

(SILVIA *enters.*)

LEANDER. Silvia! My Silvia!

SILVIA. But aren't you wounded?

LEANDER. No, don't you see? It was a lie, another lie to bring you here. But don't be afraid. Your father will come soon; soon you will leave this house with him without having any cause to reproach me. . . . Ah! None but that I have disturbed the serenity of your soul with an illusion of love which will be to you in the future no more than the remembrance of a dark and evil dream!

SILVIA. But Leander? Then your love was not real?

LEANDER. My love was, yes. That is why I could not deceive you. Leave this place at once—before any but those who brought you here discover that you came.

SILVIA. What are you afraid of? Am I not safe in your house? I was not afraid to come. What harm can happen to me at your side?

LEANDER. You are right. None! My love will protect you even from your innocence.

SILVIA. I can never go back to my father's house—not after the horrible thing which he did last night.

LEANDER. No, Silvia, do not blame your father. It was not his fault; it was another deception, another lie. Fly from me; forget this miserable adventurer, this nameless outcast, a fugitive from justice. . . .

SILVIA. No, it isn't true. No! It is the conduct of my father which makes me unworthy of your love. That is what it is. I see it all now. I understand. Ay, for me!

LEANDER. Silvia! My Silvia! How cruel your sweet words are! How cruel this noble confidence of your heart, so innocent of evil and of life!

(CRISPIN *enters, running.*)

CRISPIN. Master! Master! Signor Polichinelle is coming!

SILVIA. My father!

LEANDER. It doesn't matter. I shall lead you to him with my own hand.

CRISPIN. But he is not coming alone. There is a great crowd with him; the officers of justice. . . .

LEANDER. What? Ah! If they should find you here? In my house! (*To* CRISPIN) I see it all now. You have told them. But you shall not succeed in your design!

CRISPIN. I? No. Certainly not! For this time this is in earnest and nothing can save us now.

LEANDER. No, not us. Nor shall I try. But her. . . . Yes! Hide her, conceal her! We must secrete her here.

SILVIA. But you?

LEANDER. Have no fear. Quick! They are on the stair. (*He hides* SILVIA *in a room at the rear, meanwhile saying to* CRISPIN) See what these fellows want. On your life let no man set his foot within this room after I am gone! . . . The game is up! It is the end for me. (*He runs to the window.*)

CRISPIN. (*Holding him back*) Master! Master! Hold! Control yourself. Come to your senses. Don't throw your life away!

LEANDER. I am not throwing my life away. . . . There is no escape. . . . I am saving her. . . .

(*He climbs through the window and rapidly up outside and disappears.*)

CRISPIN. Master! Master! H'm! Not so bad after all. I thought he was going to dash himself to pieces on the ground. Instead he has climbed higher. . . . There is hope yet—he may yet learn to fly. It is his region, the clouds. . . . Now I to mine, the firm ground. And more

need than ever that I should make certain that it is solid beneath my feet. (*He seats himself complacently in an armchair.*)

POLICHINELLE. (*Without, to those who are with him*) Guard the doors! Let no man escape! No, nor woman either. . . . Nor dog nor cat!

INNKEEPER. Where are they? Where are these bandits? These assassins?

PANTALOON. Justice! Justice! My money! My money!

(SIGNOR POLICHINELLE, *the* INNKEEPER, SIGNOR PANTALOON, *the* CAPTAIN, HARLEQUIN, *the* DOCTOR, *the* SECRETARY, *and two* CONSTABLES *enter, bearing in their arms enormous scrolls and protocols, or papers of the suit. All enter from the right in the order named. The* DOCTOR *and the* SECRETARY *pass at once to the table and prepare to take testimony. Such rolls and papers as cannot be accommodated upon the table the two* CONSTABLES *retain in their hands, remaining standing for that purpose at the rear.*)

CAPTAIN. But can this be possible, Crispin?

HARLEQUIN. Is it possible that such a thing can be?

PANTALOON. Justice! Justice! My money! My money!

INNKEEPER. Seize them! Put them in irons!

PANTALOON. Don't let them escape! Don't let them escape!

CRISPIN. What? How is this? Who dares to desecrate with impious clamor the house of a gentleman and a cavalier? Oh, you may congratulate yourselves that my master is not at home!

PANTALOON. Silence! Silence! For you are his accomplice and you will be held to answer to the same reckoning as he.

INNKEEPER. Accomplice, did you say? As guilty as his pretended master!—for he was the one who deceived me.

CAPTAIN. What is the meaning of this, Crispin?

HARLEQUIN. Is there any truth in what these people say?

POLICHINELLE. What have you to say for yourself now, Crispin? You thought you were a clever rogue to cut up your capers with me. I tried to murder your master, did I? I am an old miser who is battening on his daughter's heart? All the city is stirred up against me, is it, heaping me with insults? Well, we shall see.

PANTALOON. Leave him to us, Signor Polichinelle, for this is our affair. After all, you have lost nothing. But I—all my wealth which I lent him without security. I am ruined for the rest of my life. What will become of me?

INNKEEPER. What will become of me, tell me that, when I spent what I never had and even ran into debt so that he might be served—as I thought—in a manner befitting his station? It was my destruction, my ruin.

CAPTAIN. We too were horribly deceived. What will be said of me when it is known that I have put my sword at the disposition of an adventurer?

HARLEQUIN. And of me, when I have dedicated sonnet after sonnet to his praise, just as if he had been any ordinary gentleman?

POLICHINELLE. Ha! Ha! Ha!

PANTALOON. Yes, laugh, laugh, that is right. You have lost nothing.

INNKEEPER. Nobody robbed you.

PANTALOON. To work! To work! Where is the other villain?

INNKEEPER. Better see what there is in the house first.

CRISPIN. Slowly, slowly, gentlemen. If you advance one other step——(*Threatening them with his sword.*)

PANTALOON. What? You threaten us? Again? Is such a thing to be endured? Justice! Justice!

INNKEEPER. Yes, justice!

DOCTOR. Gentlemen, unless you listen to me we shall get nowhere. No man may take justice into his own hands, inasmuch as justice is not haste nor oppression nor vengeance nor act of malice. *Summum jus, summum injuria;* the more wrong, the more justice. Justice is all wisdom, and wisdom is all order, and order is all reason, and reason is all procedure, and procedure is all logic. Barbara, Celarent, Darii, Ferio, Baralipton, deposit all your wrongs and all your disputations with me, for if they are to be of any validity they must all form a part of this process which I have brought in these protocols with me.

CRISPIN. The devil, you say! Hasn't it grown enough already?

DOCTOR. Herein are set down and inscribed divers other offenses of these defendants, whereunto must be added and conjoined each and every one of those of which you may accuse them now. And I must be the advocate in all of them, for that is the only way in which it will be possible for you to obtain satisfaction and justice. Write, Signor Secretary, and let the said complainants depose.

PANTALOON. It might be better to settle our differences among ourselves. You know what justice is.

INNKEEPER. Write nothing. It will only be making the white black, and in the end we shall be left without our money and these rogues without punishment.

PANTALOON. Exactly. My money! My money! And justice afterward.

DOCTOR. You unlearned, you uncivil, you ignorant generation! What do you know of justice? It is not enough for you to say that you have suffered a wrong, unless there be plainly apparent therein an intention to make you suffer that wrong; that is to say, fraud or deceit, which are not the same, although they are confounded in the popular acceptation. But I say unto you that only in the single case——

PANTALOON. Enough! Enough! You

will end by telling us that we are the guilty ones.

DOCTOR. What else am I to think when you persist in denying such a plain and obvious fact?

INNKEEPER. I like that. Good! We were robbed. Do you want any plainer or more obvious fact?

DOCTOR. Know, then, that robbery is not the same as theft, much less is it the same as fraud or deceit, which again are not the same as aforesaid. From the laws of the Twelve Tables down to Justinian, to Tribonian, to Emilian, to Triberian. . . .

PANTALOON. We shall be cheated out of our money. There is no one who can reason me out of that.

POLICHINELLE. The Signor Doctor is right. We can safely leave the matter to him and everything will be attended to in the process.

DOCTOR. Then write, Signor Secretary, write.

CRISPIN. Will any one listen to me?

PANTALOON. No one, no one. Let that rascal be quiet! Silence for that villain!

INNKEEPER. You will have a chance to talk soon enough when you don't want to.

DOCTOR. He will speak at the proper moment, for justice requires that everybody should be afforded an opportunity to talk. Write, write: In the city of . . . . in the matter of. . . . But it would certainly not be amiss if we proceeded first to an inventory of whatever there is in the house.

CRISPIN. (*Before the door*) It certainly would be a miss. . . .

DOCTOR. Thence to progress to the deposit of security on the part of the complainants, so that there may be no question as to their good faith when they assert that they have suffered a loss. Two thousand crowns will be sufficient from each of you, to be secured by guarantees upon all your goods and chattels.

PANTALOON. What is that? Two thousand crowns from us?

DOCTOR. I ought to make it eight; however, as you are persons of responsibility, I take that fact into account. I allow nothing to escape me.

INNKEEPER. Hold! And write no more! We cannot submit to this.

DOCTOR. What? Do you threaten justice? Open a separate process for battery and the hand of violence raised against an officer of the law in full performance of his duties.

PANTALOON. This man will be the ruin of us.

INNKEEPER. He is mad.

DOCTOR. What? Do you call me a man and mad? Speak with more respect. Write! Write! Open two more counts. There was also an assault by word of mouth. . . .

CRISPIN. Now see what you have done through not listening to me.

PANTALOON. Talk, talk, for heaven's sake! Talk! Anything would be better than what is happening to us now.

CRISPIN. Then shut off this fellow, for the love of mercy! He is raising up a mountain with his protocols.

PANTALOON. Stop! Stop, I say!

INNKEEPER. Put down that pen!

DOCTOR. Let no man dare to raise his hand.

CRISPIN. Signor Captain, then lend us your sword. It also is the instrument of justice.

CAPTAIN. (*Going up to the table and delivering a tremendous blow with his sword upon the papers on which the* DOCTOR *is engaged*) Have the kindness to desist.

DOCTOR. You see how ready I am to comply with a reasonable request. Suspend the actions. (*They stop writing*) There is a previous question to be adjudged. The parties dispute among themselves. Nevertheless it will be proper to proceed with the inventory. . . .

PANTALOON. No! No!

DOCTOR. It is a formality which cannot be waived.

CRISPIN. I don't think it would be proper. When the proper time comes you can write as much as you like. But let me have permission first to speak for a moment with these honorable gentlemen.

DOCTOR. If you wish to have what you are about to say recorded as testimony. . . .

CRISPIN. No! By no means. Not a single word, or I shall not open my mouth.

CAPTAIN. Better let the fellow talk.

CRISPIN. What shall I say? What are you complaining about? That you have lost your money? What do you want? To get it back?

PANTALOON. Exactly! Exactly! My money!

INNKEEPER. Our money!

CRISPIN. Then listen to me. Where do you suppose that it is coming from when you insist upon destroying the credit of my master in this fashion, and so make his marriage with the daughter of Signor Polichinelle impossible? Name of Mars! I had rather deal with a thousand knaves than one fool. See what you have done now and how you will be obliged to compound with justice for a half share of what we owe you—I say *owe* you. How will you be any better off if you succeed in sending us to the galleys or to some worse place? Will it put money in your pockets to collect the welts on our skins? Will you be richer or nobler or more powerful because we are ruined? On the other hand, if you had not interrupted us at such an inopportune moment, today, this very day, you would have received your money with interest, which God knows is enough to send you all to hang on the gallows to remain suspended forever, if justice were not in these hands —and these pens. Now do as you see fit; I have told you what you ought to do.

DOCTOR. They will remain suspended until further notice.

CAPTAIN. I would never have believed it possible that their crimes could have been so great.

POLICHINELLE. That Crispin. . . . He will be capable of convincing them.

PANTALOON. (*To the* INNKEEPER) What do you think of this? Looking at it calmly. . . .

INNKEEPER. What do you think?

PANTALOON. You say that your master was to have married the daughter of Signor Polichinelle today? But suppose he refuses to give his consent?

CRISPIN. What good would that do him? His daughter has run away with my master. All the world will soon know it. It is more important to him than it is to any one else not to have it known that his daughter has thrown herself away upon a rapscallion, a man without character, a fugitive from justice.

PANTALOON. Suppose this should turn out to be true? What do you think?

INNKEEPER. Better not weaken. The rogue breathes deceit. He is a master.

PANTALOON. You are right. No one can tell how far to believe him. Justice! Justice!

CRISPIN. I warn you—you lose everything!

PANTALOON. Wait! . . . . just a moment. We will see. A word with you, Signor Polichinelle.

POLICHINELLE. What do you want with me?

PANTALOON. Suppose that we had made a mistake in this complaint. Suppose that Signor Leander should turn out to be, after all, a noble, virtuous gentleman, incapable of the slightest dishonest thought. . . .

POLICHINELLE. What is that? Say that again.

PANTALOON. Suppose that your daughter was in love with him madly, passionately, even to the point where she had run away with him from your house?

POLICHINELLE. My daughter ran away from my house with that man? Who says so? Show me the villain! Where is he?

PANTALOON. Don't get excited. It is only in supposition.

POLICHINELLE. Well, sir, I shall not tolerate it even in supposition.

PANTALOON. Try to listen more calmly. Suppose all this should have happened. Wouldn't the best thing for you to do be to let them marry?

POLICHINELLE. Marry? I would see them dead first. But it is useless to consider it. I see what you want. You are scheming to recoup yourselves at my expense, you are such rogues yourselves. But it shall not be! It shall not be!

PANTALOON. Take care! We had better not talk about rogues while you are present.

INNKEEPER. Hear! Hear!

POLICHINELLE. Rogues, rogues!—conspiring to impoverish me. But it shall not be! It shall not be!

DOCTOR. Have no fear, Signor Polichinelle. Even though they should be dissuaded and abandon their design, do you suppose that this process will amount to nothing? Do you imagine that one line of what is written in it can ever be blotted out, though two and fifty crimes be alleged therein and proved against them, besides as many more which require no proof?

PANTALOON. What do you say now, Crispin?

CRISPIN. That though all those crimes were proved three times and those that require no proof yet three times more than the others, you would still be losing your money and wasting your time, for we cannot pay what we do not have.

DOCTOR. Not at all. That is not good law. For I have to be paid, whatever happens.

CRISPIN. Then the complainants will have to pay you. We shall have more than we can do to pay our offenses with our backs.

DOCTOR. The rights of justice are inviolable, and the first of them is to attach in its interest whatever there is in this house.

PANTALOON. But what good will that do us? How shall we get anything?

INNKEEPER. Of course not! Don't you see?

DOCTOR. Write, write, for if we were to talk forever we should never arrive at a conclusion which would be more satisfactory.

PANTALOON AND INNKEEPER. No! No! Not a word! Not a word!

CRISPIN. Hear me, first, Signor Doctor! In your ear. . . . Suppose you were to be paid at once, on the spot and without the trouble of all this writing, your . . . what is it that you call them?—crumbs of justice?

DOCTOR. Perquisites of the law.

CRISPIN. Have it your own way. What would you say to that?

DOCTOR. Why, in that case. . . .

CRISPIN. Listen:—my master will be rich today, influential, if Signor Polichinelle consents to his marrying his daughter. Remember that the young lady is the only child of Signor Polichinelle; remember that my master will be master indeed not only of her. . . . Remember. . . .

DOCTOR. H'm! It certainly does deserve to be remembered.

PANTALOON. (*To* CRISPIN) What does he say?

INNKEEPER. What are you going to do?

DOCTOR. Let me consider. That fellow clearly is not thick-witted. It is easy to see that he is acquainted with legal precedent. For if we remember that the wrong which has been done was purely a pecuniary one, and that every wrong which can be redressed in kind suffers in the reparation the most fitting punishment; if we reflect that in the barbaric and primitive law of vengeance it was written: an eye for an eye and a tooth for a tooth, but not a tooth for an eye nor an eye for a tooth, so in the present instance it might be argued a crown for a crown and money for money. He has not taken your lives. Why not? The fact is evidence that he did not wish you to take his in return. He has not insulted your persons, impugned your honor, your reputations. Why not? Plainly because he was not willing to submit to a like indignity from you. Equity is the supremest justice. *Equitas justiciam magna est.* And from the Pandects to Tribonian, including Emilianus Tribonianus. . . .

PANTALOON. Include him. So long as we get our money. . . .

INNKEEPER. So long as he pays us. . . .

POLICHINELLE. What is this nonsense? How can he pay? What is the use of all this talk?

CRISPIN. A great deal of use. As I was saying, you are all deeply interested in saving my master, in saving both of us, for your own advantage, for the common good of all. You, so as not to lose your money; the Signor Doctor so as not to see all this vast store of doctrine go for nothing, which he is heaping up in those sarcophagi of learning; the Signor Captain because everybody knows that he was the friend of my master, and it would not be creditable to his valor to have it said that he had been the dupe of an adventurer; you, Signor Harlequin, because your poetic dithyrambs would lose all their merit as soon as it became known with what little sense you composed them; you, Signor Polichinelle, my dear old friend, because your daughter is now, in the sight of God and before man, Signor Leander's wife.

POLICHINELLE. You lie! You lie! Impudent rascal! Cutthroat!

CRISPIN. I think then that we had better proceed with the inventory of what there is in the house. Write, write, and let all these gentlemen be our witnesses. We can begin with this apartment.

(*He throws back the tapestry from the door at the rear, and* SILVIA, LEANDER, DOÑA SIRENA, COLUMBINE, *and the* WIFE OF POLICHINELLE *appear, forming a group.*)

PANTALOON AND THE INNKEEPER. Silvia!

CAPTAIN AND HARLEQUIN. Together! Both of them!

POLICHINELLE. Is it possible? What? Are they all against me? My wife and daughter, too? All, all, for my ruin? Seize that man, these women, this impostor, or I with my own hand. . . .

PANTALOON. Signor Polichinelle, are you out of your head?

LEANDER. (*Advancing toward the proscenium, accompanied by the others*) Your daughter came to my house under the protection of Doña Sirena, believing that I was wounded; and I ran immediately in search of your wife, so that she too might be present with her and protect her. Silvia knows who I am, she knows the whole story of my life of misery and wandering, of cheats and deceptions and lies—how it has been utterly vile; and I am sure that no vestige of our dream of love any longer remains in her heart. Take her away from this place, take her away! That is my only request before I deliver myself up into the hands of justice.

POLICHINELLE. The punishment of my daughter shall be my affair, but as for this villain. . . . Seize him, I say!

SILVIA. Father! If you do not save him it will be my death. I love him, I shall love him always; I love him now more than I ever did, because his heart is noble. He has been cruelly unfortunate; and he might have made me his by a lie—but he would not lie.

POLICHINELLE. Silence! Silence, foolish, unhappy girl! This is the result of the bringing up of your mother, of her van-

ity, her hallucinations, of all your romantic reading, your music to the light of the moon.

WIFE OF POLICHINELLE. Anything would be preferable to having my daughter marry a man like you, to be unhappy afterward all the rest of her life, like her mother. Of what use are my riches to me?

SIRENA. You are right, Signora Polichinelle. Of what use are riches without love?

COLUMBINE. The same use as love without riches.

DOCTOR. Signor Polichinelle, under the circumstances, the only thing for you to do is to let them marry.

PANTALOON. Or there will be a scandal in the city.

INNKEEPER. And everybody will be on his side.

CAPTAIN. And we can never consent to have you use force against your daughter.

DOCTOR. It will have to stand in the process that they were surprised here together.

CRISPIN. And after all, the only trouble with my master was that he had no money; no one could outdo him in nobility of character; your grandchildren will be gentlemen—even if that quality does not extend up to the grandfather.

ALL. Let them marry! Let them marry!

PANTALOON. Or we will all turn upon you.

INNKEEPER. And your history will be brought to light—the secret story of your life. . . .

HARLEQUIN. And you will gain nothing by that.

SIRENA. A lady begs it of you on her knees, moved to tears by the spectacle of a love so unusual in these days.

COLUMBINE. Which seems more like love in a story.

ALL. Let them marry! Let them marry!

POLICHINELLE. Yes! let them marry in an evil hour. My daughter shall be cut off without dowry and without inheri-

tance. I will ruin my estate rather than that this reprobate. . . .

DOCTOR. You certainly will not do anything of the kind, Signor Polichinelle.

PANTALOON. Who ever heard of such nonsense?

INNKEEPER. I shouldn't think of it for a moment.

HARLEQUIN. What would people say?

CAPTAIN. We could never consent to it.

SILVIA. No, my dear father, I am the one who cannot accept anything. I am the one who must share the poverty of his fate. I love him so.

LEANDER. That is the only condition upon which I can accept your love.

(All run toward SILVIA and LEANDER.)

DOCTOR. What do you say? Are you crazy?

PANTALOON. Preposterous! Absurd!

INNKEEPER. You are going to accept everything.

HARLEQUIN. You will be happy and you will be rich.

WIFE OF POLICHINELLE. What? My daughter in poverty? Is this wretch the hangman?

SIRENA. Remember that love is a delicate babe and able to endure but few privations.

DOCTOR. It is clearly illegal. Signor Polichinelle, you will sign a munificent donation immediately as befits a person of your dignity and importance, who is a kind and loving father. Write, write, Signor Secretary, for this is something to which nobody will object.

ALL. (Except POLICHINELLE) Write! Write!

DOCTOR. And you, my dear, my innocent young lovers, resign yourselves to riches. You have no right to carry your prejudices to an extreme at which they become offensive to others.

PANTALOON. (To CRISPIN) Now will you pay us?

CRISPIN. Do you doubt it? But you will have to swear first that Signor Leander never owed you anything. See how he is sacrificing himself upon your account, accepting this money which is repugnant to him.

PANTALOON. We always knew that he was a perfect gentleman.

INNKEEPER. Always.

HARLEQUIN. We all believed it.

CAPTAIN. And we shall continue to maintain our belief.

CRISPIN. Now, Doctor, this process. . . . Do you suppose there is waste space enough anywhere in the world for it to be thrown away upon?

DOCTOR. My foresight has provided for everything. All that will be necessary is to change the punctuation. For example, here where it says: "Whereas I depose and declare, not without due sanction of law" . . . . take out the comma and it reads: "Whereas I depose and declare not without due sanction of law." And here: "Wherefore he is not without due judgment condemned" . . . put in a comma and it reads: "Wherefore he is not, without due judgment condemned" . . . .

CRISPIN. O excellent comma! O wonderful, O marvelous comma! Stupendous Genius and Miracle of Justice! Oracle of the Law! Thou Monster of Jurisprudence!

DOCTOR. Now I can rely upon the generosity of your master.

CRISPIN. You can. Nobody knows better than you do how money will change a man.

SECRETARY. I was the one who put in and took out the commas.

CRISPIN. While you are waiting for something better, pray accept this chain. It is of gold.

SECRETARY. H'm! How many carats fine?

CRISPIN. You ought to know. You understand commas and carats.

POLICHINELLE. I impose only one condition:—that this rogue leave your service forever.

CRISPIN. That will not be necessary, Signor Polichinelle. Do you suppose that

I am so poor in ambition as my master?

LEANDER. What? You are not going to leave me, Crispin? It will not be without sorrow on my part.

CRISPIN. It will not last long. I can be of no further use to you. With me you will be able to lay aside your lion's skin and your old man's wisdom. What did I tell you, sir? Between them all we were sure to be saved. And believe me now, when you are getting on in the world, the ties of love are as nothing to the bonds of interest.

LEANDER. You are wrong. For without the love of Silvia I should never have been saved.

CRISPIN. And is love a slight interest? I have always given due credit to the ideal and I count upon it always. With this the farce ends.

SILVIA. (*To the audience*) You have seen in it how these puppets have been moved by plain and obvious strings, like men and women in the farces of our lives—strings which were their interests, their passions, and all the illusions and petty miseries of their state. Some are pulled by the feet to lives of restless and weary wandering; some by the hands, to toil with pain, to struggle with bitterness, to strike with cunning, to slay with violence and rage. But into the hearts of all there descends sometimes from heaven an invisible thread, as if it were woven out of the sunlight and the moonbeams, the invisible thread of love, which makes these men and women, as it does these puppets which seem like men, almost divine, and brings to our foreheads the smile and splendors of the dawn, lends wings to our drooping spirits, and whispers to us still that this farce is not all a farce, that there is something noble, something divine in our lives which is true and which is eternal, and which shall not close when the farce of life shall close.

CURTAIN

LA MALQUERIDA

A DRAMA IN THREE ACTS

By JACINTO BENAVENTE

Translated by John Garrett Underhill

CHARACTERS

RAIMUNDA

ACACIA

JULIANA

DOÑA ISABEL

MILAGROS

FIDELA

ENGRACIA

BERNABEA

GASPARA

ESTEBAN

NORBERT

FAUSTINO

TÍO EUSEBIO

BERNABÉ

RUBIO

The action of the play takes place in Castile.

LA MALQUERIDA

THE FIRST ACT

A room in a rich farmer's house, situated on the outskirts of a pueblo, or small town.

As the curtain rises, RAIMUNDA, ACACIA, DOÑA ISABEL, MILAGROS, FIDELA, ENGRACIA, GASPARA, *and* BERNABEA *are bidding farewell to four or five women and young girls who are taking leave. While the others stand,* DOÑA ISABEL *remains seated.*

GASPARA. God be with you! Good-by, Raimunda.

BERNABEA. God be with you, Doña Isabel—and you, too, Acacia, and your mother. May everything turn out for the best.

RAIMUNDA. Thanks. May we all live to see it. Go down with them, Acacia.

ALL. Good-by! Good-by!

(*The women and girls retire, keeping up an animated chatter.* ACACIA *accompanies them.*)

DOÑA ISABEL. Bernabea is a nice girl.

ENGRACIA. It is only a year since she got over that trouble. No one would ever believe it to look at her now.

DOÑA ISABEL. I hear that she is going to be married.

FIDELA. Yes, come next fiesta—God willing and San Roque.

DOÑA ISABEL. I am always the last person in the village to pick up gossip. When you have nothing but trouble at home, naturally you lose interest in what is taking place outside.

ENGRACIA. How is your husband?

DOÑA ISABEL. He varies—up and down. The rest of us are thoroughly worn out. We are not able to leave the house, not even to attend mass upon Sundays. I am used to it myself, but it is hard on my daughter.

ENGRACIA. I think you make a mistake to keep her at home so much. This is a great year for weddings.

DOÑA ISABEL. But not for her. I am afraid that we shall never be able to find a man who measures up to her expectations.

FIDELA. All the same, it never struck me that she was born to be a nun. Some day she will happen on the right one.

DOÑA ISABEL. How are you pleased with this match, Raimunda? I must say you don't seem altogether cheerful about it.

RAIMUNDA. A wedding is always something of an experiment.

ENGRACIA. If you aren't satisfied, I am sure I don't know who could ever be. Your daughter has had the pick of the entire village.

FIDELA. She's not likely to want for anything, either. We all know how well they will both be provided for, which is not a thing you can afford to overlook.

RAIMUNDA. Milagros, run downstairs and enjoy yourself with Acacia and the boys. I hate to see you sitting there all alone in a corner.

DOÑA ISABEL. Yes, do go down.—The child is as innocent as the day that God made her.

MILAGROS. Excuse me. (*Goes out.*)

RAIMUNDA. We might all take another glass and some *bizcochos*.

DOÑA ISABEL. Thanks, I have had enough.

RAIMUNDA. No, no, come, everybody. This is nothing.

DOÑA ISABEL. Acacia doesn't seem as happy as you might expect, either, considering that her engagement was only announced today.

RAIMUNDA. She is as innocent, too, as God made her. I never saw any one like her; she is so silent. She distracts me. For weeks together she has not one word to say. Then there are times when she begins to talk, and her tongue runs until it fairly takes your breath away. It is a terrible thing to hear.

ENGRACIA. Naturally, you have spoiled her. After you lost the three boys she was all that you had, and you were too careful. Her father would have plucked the birds out of the air if she had asked for them, and you were no better. When he died—God rest his soul—then the child was jealous of you. She didn't like it when you married again, and she has never gotten over that grudge either.

RAIMUNDA. But what was I to do? I didn't want to marry again. I should never have thought of it if my brothers hadn't turned out the way that they did. If we had not had a man in the house to look after us, my daughter and I would have been in the street before this, and you know it.

DOÑA ISABEL. Yes, this world is no place for single women. You were left a widow very young.

RAIMUNDA. But I can't see why my daughter should be jealous. I am her mother, yet it would be hard to say which of us loves or spoils her the most. Esteban has never treated her like a stepdaughter.

DOÑA ISABEL. No wonder; you had no children of your own.

RAIMUNDA. He never comes nor goes without bringing her a present. He never thinks of such a thing with me—although, of course, I have no feeling. She is my daughter; it only makes me love him more to see how fond he is of her. You won't believe it when I tell you, but she would never let him kiss her even when she was a child, much less now. I

have seldom had to lay my hand on her, but whenever I have, it was on that account.

FIDELA. Nobody can make me believe, just the same, that your daughter isn't in love with her cousin.

RAIMUNDA. Norbert? She turned him off herself between night and morning, and that was the end of it. That is another thing I can't understand. We never could find out what did happen between them.

FIDELA. Nor anybody else. Nobody has ever been able to explain it. There must have been some reason, but what it was is a mystery.

ENGRACIA. Well, she never seemed to regret it, which is more than I can say for him. She never looked at him again, but he hasn't changed. When he heard that Faustino was coming over with his father today to settle the matter and arrange things, he turned on his heel, took his gun, and went straight up to Los Berrocales. People who saw him said that you would have thought that it had broken his heart.

RAIMUNDA. Neither Esteban nor I influenced her in the least. She broke with Norbert herself, just as they were ready to publish the banns. Everybody knows it. Then she consented to see Faustino. He always had a fancy for her. His father is a great friend of Esteban's —they belong to the same party and always work together. They have known each other for a long time. Whenever we went to Encinar for the Feast of the Virgin—or for any other fiesta—or if they were the ones who came here, it was easy to see that the boy was nervous. When she was around he didn't know what to do. He knew that there was something between her and her cousin, but he never said one word until the break came, whatever the reason was, which we don't know—no, not one; but as soon as they heard that she was done with her cousin,

Faustino's father spoke to Esteban, and Esteban spoke to me, and I spoke to my daughter, and she seemed to be pleased; so now they are going to be married. That is all there is to it. If she is not satisfied, then God have mercy on her soul, because we are only doing it to please her. She has had her own way in everything.

DOÑA ISABEL. Then she ought to be happy. Why not? The boy is a fine fellow. Everybody says so.

ENGRACIA. Yes, we all feel as if he belonged in the village. He lives so near by, and his family is so well known that nobody ever thinks of them as strangers.

FIDELA. Tío Eusebio owns more land here than at Encinar.

ENGRACIA. Certainly, if you stop to count. He inherited everything from his Uncle Manolito, and when the town lands were sold, two years ago, they went to him.

DOÑA ISABEL. The family is the richest in the neighborhood.

FIDELA. Undoubtedly. There may be four brothers, but each of them will come into a fortune.

ENGRACIA. Your daughter is not going barefoot, either.

RAIMUNDA. No, she is an only child and will inherit everything. Esteban has taken good care of the farm which she had from her father; he could not have done more if she had been his own child.

(*The Angelus sounds.*)

DOÑA ISABEL. The Angelus! (*The women mumble the words of the prayer*) It is time for us to be going, Raimunda. Telesforo expects his supper early—if the nibble of nothing which he takes can be called supper.

ENGRACIA. It is time for us all to go.

FIDELA. We were all thinking the same thing.

RAIMUNDA. But won't you stay to sup-per? I don't urge Doña Isabel—I know she ought not to leave her husband. He is impatient to see her back.

ENGRACIA. Yes. We all have husbands to look after. Thanks just the same.

DOÑA ISABEL. I suppose the young man stays to supper?

RAIMUNDA. No, he is going home with his father to Encinar. They cannot spend the night. There is no moon, so they should have been on the road long ago. It is getting late and the days are growing shorter. Before you know it, it is black night.

ENGRACIA. I hear them coming up now to say good-by.

RAIMUNDA. I thought so.

(ACACIA, MILAGROS, ESTEBAN, TÍO EUSEBIO, and FAUSTINO *enter.*)

ESTEBAN. Raimunda, here are Tío Eusebio and Faustino to say good-by.

EUSEBIO. We must be off before dark. The roads are in terrible shape after the heavy rains.

ESTEBAN. There are some bad stretches.

DOÑA ISABEL. Well, what has the boy to say for himself? I suppose he doesn't remember me. It is five years since I have seen him.

EUSEBIO. Don't you remember Doña Isabel?

FAUSTINO. I do, *sí, señor*. I was afraid she didn't remember me.

DOÑA ISABEL. No fear of that! My husband was *alcalde* at the time, when you gave us that awful fright, running after the bull. If you had been killed, I don't know what would have happened. I didn't enjoy it. God help San Roque! —it would have put an end to his fiesta. We certainly thought you were dead.

ENGRACIA. Julian, Eudosia's husband, was caught that year too.

FAUSTINO. I remember; *sí, señora*.

EUSEBIO. He remembers perfectly, because I gave him a sound thrashing when he got home—which he richly deserved.

FAUSTINO. I was a boy at the time.

DOÑA ISABEL. Yes—the boy of it! However, you have picked out the finest girl in the village, and she will have no reason to regret her choice either. But we must be going. You have business of your own to attend to.

ESTEBAN. No, they have attended to everything already.

DOÑA ISABEL. Good night, then. Come, Milagros.

ACACIA. I want her to stay to supper, but she is afraid to ask you. Do let her stay, Doña Isabel!

RAIMUNDA. Yes, do. Bernabé and Juliana will see her home afterward, and Esteban can go along, too, if necessary.

DOÑA ISABEL. No, we will send for her. You can stay, to please Acacia.

RAIMUNDA. They have so many things to talk over.

DOÑA ISABEL. God be with you. Adios, Tío Eusebio and Esteban.

EUSEBIO. Adios, Doña Isabel. My best sympathy to your husband.

DOÑA ISABEL. Which he appreciates, coming from you.

ENGRACIA. Good-by! A safe return!

FIDELA. God be with you!

(*The women go out.*)

EUSEBIO. Doña Isabel looks remarkably young. She must be my age at least. Well, "To have and to hold is to prepare to grow old," as the proverb has it. Doña Isabel was one of the best of them in her day, and in her day there were plenty.

ESTEBAN. Sit down, Tío Eusebio. What is your hurry?

EUSEBIO. No, don't tempt me; it's time to go. Night is coming on. Don't bother about us. We have the hands along and shan't need you.

ESTEBAN. No, the walk will do me good. I'll see you to the *arroyo* at least.

(RAIMUNDA, ACACIA, *and* MILAGROS *re-enter.*)

EUSEBIO. If you young folks have any-thing to say, now is the time for you to say it.

ACACIA. No, we have settled every-thing.

EUSEBIO. So you think.

RAIMUNDA. Come, come! Don't you try to embarrass my daughter, Tío Eusebio.

ACACIA. Thanks for everything.

EUSEBIO. What? Is that a way to thank me?

ACACIA. It was a lovely present.

EUSEBIO. The showiest thing we could find.

RAIMUNDA. Entirely too much so for a farmer's daughter.

EUSEBIO. Too much? Not a bit of it! If I'd had my way, it would have had more jewels in it than the Holy Monstrance at Toledo. Give your mother-in-law a good hug.

RAIMUNDA. Yes, come, boy. I must learn to love you or I shall never forgive you for taking her away. My heart goes with her.

ESTEBAN. Now don't begin to cry! Come, Acacia! You don't want to pass yourself off for a Magdalen.

MILAGROS. Raimunda! Acacia! (*Bursts into tears also*).

ESTEBAN. That's right—all together! Come, come!

EUSEBIO. Don't be foolish! Tears are for the dead. You are only going to be married. Try to be happy and enjoy yourselves; everybody is willing. Adios and good night!

RAIMUNDA. Adios, Tío Eusebio. Tell Julia that I don't know whether I shall ever be able to forgive her for not com-ing over today.

EUSEBIO. You know how bad her sight is. We'd have had to hitch up the cart, and it was up at Los Berrocales. We are beginning to slaughter.

RAIMUNDA. Tell her how sorry I am. May she be better soon.

EUSEBIO. Thanks to you.

RAIMUNDA. Now you had better be going. It is getting dark. (*To* ESTEBAN) Don't be long.

EUSEBIO. I tell him not to come.

ESTEBAN. Nonsense! It isn't any trouble. I'll go as far as the *arroyo*. Don't wait supper for me.

RAIMUNDA. No, we will wait. We're not anxious to eat alone tonight. Milagros won't mind if we are late.

MILAGROS. It makes no difference to me.

EUSEBIO. God be with you all! Good-by!

RAIMUNDA. No, we are coming down to see you out.

FAUSTINO. I . . . I have something to say to Acacia first. . . .

EUSEBIO. It will have to wait until tomorrow. You have had the whole day to yourselves.

FAUSTINO. Yes, but with so many people around, I had no chance. . . .

EUSEBIO. Before we were through I knew we were going to get some of this nonsense.

FAUSTINO. It isn't nonsense. Only I promised mother before we started to give Acacia this scapulary. The nuns in the convent made it on purpose for her.

ACACIA. How lovely!

MILAGROS. Oh! The Blessed Virgin of Carmen—with spangles all over!

RAIMUNDA. Very pretty. My daughter was always devoted to the Virgin. Thank your mother for us. We appreciate it.

FAUSTINO. It has been blessed.

EUSEBIO. Good! Now you have got that off your mind. I wonder what your mother would have thought if we'd taken it home again with us? I never saw such a boy! I wasn't so backward in my day. I am sure I don't know whom he does take after.

(*All go out. For a moment the stage remains deserted. Meanwhile it continues to grow darker. Presently* RAIMUNDA, ACACIA, *and* MILAGROS *reappear.*)

RAIMUNDA. They have made a long day of it. It is night before they start. How do you feel, my dear? Are you happy?

ACACIA. You can see for yourself.

RAIMUNDA. I can, can I? That is exactly what I want to do: see for myself. Nobody can ever tell how you feel.

ACACIA. I am tired out.

RAIMUNDA. It has certainly been a long day. I haven't had a minute's rest since five o'clock in the morning.

MILAGROS. Everybody has been here to congratulate you.

RAIMUNDA. The whole village, you might say, beginning with the priest, who was among the first. We paid him for a mass, and gave him ten loaves of bread besides for the poor. In our happiness it is only right to remember others who are not so fortunate. Praise God, we want for nothing! Where are the matches?

ACACIA. Here they are, mother.

RAIMUNDA. Light the lamp, dear. It makes me feel sad to sit in the dark. (*Calling*) Juliana! Juliana! I wonder where she is?

JULIANA. (*Downstairs*) What do you want?

RAIMUNDA. Bring up the broom and dust-pan.

JULIANA. (*Downstairs*) In a minute.

RAIMUNDA. I had better change my skirt while I think of it. Nobody will be in now; it's so late.

ACACIA. I might take off my dress.

RAIMUNDA. What for? There is nothing for you to do. You have been busy all day.

(JULIANA *enters.*)

JULIANA. Show me that dust——

RAIMUNDA. Stand the broom in the corner and take these things away. Mind you scour them until they are clean; then put them back in the cupboard. Be careful with those glasses! They are our very best.

JULIANA. Could I eat a cake?

RAIMUNDA. Of course you can!—though I don't see how you manage to hold so much.

JULIANA. I haven't touched a thing this whole day, God help me! I am my mother's own daughter. Haven't I passed cake and wine to the entire village? Everybody has been here today. That shows you what people think of this house—yes, and what they think of Tío Eusebio and his family. Wait till you see the wedding! I know somebody who is going to give her a new gold piece, and somebody who is going to give her a silk embroidered quilt that has flowers all over it, so lifelike that the first thing she will want to do is pick them off of it. That will be a great day for her, praise God! Not one of us but will laugh and cry then, and I will be the first—after her mother; she will be first because it is her right, but you know me. I love you all in this house. Besides, you make me think of my dead daughter. She looked just like you do when she died, and we buried her.

RAIMUNDA. Never mind that, Juliana. Go along and don't dig up any more of your troubles. We have enough of our own already.

JULIANA. God grant that I may never be a trouble to you! But everything goes topsy-turvy with me today, around and around, and every which way. The more you enjoy yourself the sadder it makes you feel. God forbid that I should ever drag in this child's poor dead father, who rests in heaven now, God bless him! But I wish he could have seen her today! He was fond of her.

RAIMUNDA. That will do, Juliana! That will do.

JULIANA. Don't talk like that to me, Raimunda. It's like a blow in the face, like beating a faithful hound. That's what I have been to you and your daughter and your house—a faithful hound, that has eaten your bread, God willing, in season and out—yes, and kept her self-respect while she was about it, and you know it. (*Goes out.*)

RAIMUNDA. Juliana!—She is right, though. She has always been like a faithful hound—faithful and loyal to us and our house. (*She begins to sweep.*)

ACACIA. Mother——

RAIMUNDA. Did you speak?

ACACIA. Will you let me have the key to this chest of drawers? I want to show Milagros some of my things.

RAIMUNDA. Yes, here it is; take the bunch. Sit down and rest while I go and keep an eye on the supper. (*She takes the broom and goes out.*)

(ACACIA *and* MILAGROS *seat themselves on the floor before the chest of drawers and open the lower drawer or compartment.*)

ACACIA. These earrings were a present from—well, from Esteban, since my mother isn't here. She always wants me to call him father.

MILAGROS. Don't you know that he loves you?

ACACIA. Yes, but you can have only one father and mother. He brought me these handkerchiefs, too, from Toledo. The nuns embroidered the initials. See all these postcards—aren't they pretty?

MILAGROS. What lovely ladies!

ACACIA. Yes, they're actresses from Madrid, or from Paris in France. Look at these boys— He brought me this box, too it had candy in it.

MILAGROS. I don't see how you can say then. . . .

ACACIA. I don't say anything. I know he loves me, but I'd rather have been left alone with my mother.

MILAGROS. You don't mean to tell me that your mother loves you any less on his account?

ACACIA. I don't know. She's wrapped up in him. How do I know, if she had to choose between me and that man. . . .

MILAGROS. I think it's wicked to talk

like that. Suppose your mother hadn't married again, what would she do now when you get married? She would have no one to live with.

ACACIA. You don't suppose that I would ever have gotten married, do you, if I had been living alone with my mother?

MILAGROS. Of course you would! What difference would it make?

ACACIA. Could I be as happy anywhere else as living here alone with my mother?

MILAGROS. Don't be foolish. Everybody knows what a nice stepfather you have. If he hadn't been good there would have been talk, and I would have heard it. So would you and your mother.

ACACIA. I don't say that he isn't good. But all the same I wouldn't have married if my mother hadn't married again.

MILAGROS. Do you know what I think?

ACACIA. What?

MILAGROS. People are right when they say that you don't love Faustino. The one that you love is Norbert.

ACACIA. That's a lie! How could I love him?—after the way that he treated me.

MILAGROS. Everybody says that you were the one who turned him off.

ACACIA. I did, did I? Yes, I suppose it was my fault! Anyway, we won't talk about it. What do they know? I love Faustino better than I ever did Norbert.

MILAGROS. I hope you do. Otherwise you oughtn't to marry him. Did you hear that Norbert left the village this morning? He didn't want to be around.

ACACIA. What does he care? Why today more than any other? It is nothing to him. Here is the last letter he wrote me— after everything was over. I never mean to see him again; I don't know what I am keeping it for. It would be more sensible to tear it up. (*She tears the letter into small pieces*) There! That ends it.

MILAGROS. What is the matter with you? You are all excited.

ACACIA. It's what he says. Now I am going to burn the pieces.

MILAGROS. Look out! The lamp will explode.

ACACIA. (*Opening the window*) To the road with you! I'll scatter the ashes. . . . The wind blows them away. . . . It is over now, and I am glad of it. Did you ever see such a dark night?

MILAGROS. (*Following her to the window*) It is black as pitch—no moon, no stars. . . .

ACACIA. What was that?

MILAGROS. Somebody slammed a door.

ACACIA. It sounded to me like a shot.

MILAGROS. Nonsense! Who would be out shooting at this hour? Unless there is a fire somewhere. . . . No, I don't see any glow in the sky.

ACACIA. I am frightened. Yes, I am——

MILAGROS. Don't be silly!

ACACIA. (*Running suddenly to the door*) Mother! Mother!

RAIMUNDA. (*Downstairs*) What is it?

ACACIA. Did you hear anything?

RAIMUNDA. (*Downstairs*) Yes. I sent Juliana to find out. It's all right.

ACACIA. Oh, mother!

RAIMUNDA. Don't be afraid! I am coming up.

ACACIA. It was a shot! I know it was a shot!

MILAGROS. Suppose it was? What of it?

ACACIA. God help us!

(RAIMUNDA *enters*.)

RAIMUNDA. Did it frighten you? Nothing is the matter.

ACACIA. Mother, you are frightened yourself.

RAIMUNDA. Because you are. Naturally, I was frightened at first—your father hasn't come back. But it is silly. Nothing could have happened. What was that? Do you hear? Some one is downstairs! God help us!

ACACIA. Mother! Mother!

MILAGROS. What do they say? What are they talking about?

RAIMUNDA. Stay where you are. I am going down.

ACACIA. Mother, don't you go!

RAIMUNDA. I can't make out what they say. . . . I am too excited. . . . Oh, Esteban, my heart! May no harm have come to you! (*She rushes out.*)

MILAGROS. There is a crowd downstairs. They are coming in. I can't make out what they say. . . .

ACACIA. Something has happened! Something awful! I knew it all the time.

MILAGROS. So did I, only I didn't want to frighten you.

ACACIA. What do you think?

MILAGROS. Don't ask me! Don't ask!

RAIMUNDA. (*Downstairs*) Holy Virgin! God save us! Terrible, terrible! Oh, his poor mother when she hears that her poor boy is dead—murdered! I can't believe it! What a terrible thing for us all!

ACACIA. What does she say? Did you hear?—Mother! Mother! Mother!

RAIMUNDA. Acacia! Daughter! Don't you come down! Don't come down! I am coming up.

(RAIMUNDA, FIDELA, ENGRACIA, *and a number of other women enter.*)

ACACIA. What's the matter? What has happened? Some one is dead, isn't he? Some one is dead?

RAIMUNDA. My poor child! Faustino! Faustino!

ACACIA. What?

RAIMUNDA. Murdered! Shot dead as he left the village!

ACACIA. Mother! *Ay!* But who did it? Who did it?

RAIMUNDA. Nobody knows. It was too dark; they couldn't see. Every one thinks it was Norbert—so as to fill the cup of disgrace which we must drain in this house!

ENGRACIA. It couldn't have been anyone else.

WOMEN. It was Norbert! It was Norbert!

FIDELA. Here come the constables.

ENGRACIA. Have they caught him?

RAIMUNDA. And here is your father. (ESTEBAN *enters*) Esteban, my soul! Who did it? Do you know?

ESTEBAN. How do I know? I saw what the rest did. Don't leave the house, do you hear? I don't want to have you running around the village.

RAIMUNDA. But how is his father? Think of his poor mother when they carry her boy home to her dead—murdered! And he left her alive, happy, and well only this morning!

ENGRACIA. Hanging is too good for the wretch that did it!

FIDELA. They ought to have killed him on the spot! Such a thing never happened before in this village.

RAIMUNDA. Esteban, don't let them take the body away. I must see him—and so must my daughter. He was to have been her husband.

ESTEBAN. Keep cool! There is plenty of time. I don't want you to leave the house, do you hear? It's in the hands of the law now; the doctor and priest were too late. I must hurry back; we all have depositions to make. (ESTEBAN *retires.*)

RAIMUNDA. Your father is right. What can we do?—except commend his soul to God, who was his Maker. I can't get his poor mother out of my head! Don't take it so hard, Acacia. It frightens me to see you so still. It is worse than if you cried your heart out. Who would ever have believed this morning that such a thing could be? But it is! A curse has fallen upon us!

ENGRACIA. The shot went straight through his heart.

FIDELA. He fell off his horse, like a log.

RAIMUNDA. What a shame, what a disgrace to the village! I blush to think that the murderer was born in this place, that he was one of us, and walked about here with all that evil in his heart! He is one of our own family, to make it worse!

GASPARA. But we aren't sure of that.

RAIMUNDA. Who else could it be? Everybody says so.

ENGRACIA. Everybody says it was Norbert.

FIDELA. It couldn't have been anyone but Norbert!

RAIMUNDA. Light the candles, Milagros, before the image of the Virgin. Let us tell her a rosary, since we can do no more than pray for the dead.

GASPARA. God rest his soul!

ENGRACIA. He died without confession.

FIDELA. From Purgatory, good Lord, deliver us.

ALL. God rest his soul!

RAIMUNDA. (*To* MILAGROS) You begin the rosary; I cannot pray. I am thinking of his mother's broken heart!

(*The women begin to tell the rosary.*)

CURTAIN

THE SECOND ACT

Entrance Hall of a farmhouse. There is a large door at the rear, on either side of which is a window, having an iron grating. A door on the left, and another on the right.

ESTEBAN *is seated at a small table, taking lunch.* RAIMUNDA *waits upon him, seated also.* JULIANA *comes and goes, assisting with the service.* ACACIA *sits in a low chair near one of the windows, sewing. A basket of clothes stands beside her.*

RAIMUNDA. Don't you like it?

ESTEBAN. Of course I do.

RAIMUNDA. You haven't eaten any-thing. Do you want us to cook something else?

ESTEBAN. Don't bother me, my dear. I have had plenty.

RAIMUNDA. You don't expect me to believe that. (*Calling*) Juliana! Bring the salad!—Something is the matter with you.

ESTEBAN. Don't be silly.

RAIMUNDA. Don't you suppose that I know you by this time? You ought never to have gone to the village. You've heard talk. We came out here to the grove to get rid of it all, to be away from the excitement, and it was a good thing, too, that we did. Now you go back to the village and don't say one word to me about it. What did you want to do that for?

ESTEBAN. I wanted to see Norbert and his father.

RAIMUNDA. Yes, but you could have sent for them and have had them come out here. You ought to have spared yourself; then you wouldn't have heard all this talk. I know how they are talking in the village.

JULIANA. Yes, and that is all the good it does us to stay out here and shut our-selves up from everybody, because everybody that goes anywhere in the neighbor-hood passes through this grove, and then they stop, and smell around, and meddle in what is none of their business.

ESTEBAN. Yes, and you meddle with every one of them.

JULIANA. No, Señor; don't you make any mistake. I meddle with nobody. Didn't I scold Bernabea only yesterday for talking more than she had any right to with some men from Encinar who were coming down the road? If anyone asks questions send them to me, because I've learned what to do from my mother, who had good reason to know: When questioned much, answer little, and be sure you make it just the opposite.

RAIMUNDA. Hold your tongue! And get

out. (JULIANA *retires*) What do they say in the village?

ESTEBAN. Nothing. Tío Eusebio and his boys swear they are going to kill Norbert. They refuse to accept the decision of the court; he got off too easily. They are coming over some day, and then there will be trouble. You hear both sides in the village. Some think that Tío Eusebio is right, that it must have been Norbert; others think it wasn't Norbert. They say that the court let him go because he was innocent, and he proved it.

RAIMUNDA. That is what I think. No one could contradict his deposition; not even Faustino's father could find any flaws in it, nor the hands. You couldn't yourself, and you were with them.

ESTEBAN. Tío Eusebio and I had stopped to light our cigars. We were laughing like two fools because I had my lighter, and it wouldn't light; so Tío Eusebio got out his tinder and flint and said to me, laughing: "Here, get a light, and don't waste your time with that new-fangled machine. All it is good for is to help fools waste their money. I still make out with this." That was what blinded us. We were fooling over the light when the shot was fired. We started up and could see nothing. Then, when we saw that he had dropped dead, we stood stock-still, as dead as he was. They could have finished us, too, while they were about, and we would never have known it.

(ACACIA *gets up suddenly and starts to go out*).

RAIMUNDA. Where are you going, my dear? Don't be nervous.

ACACIA. You never talk about anything else. I don't see how you can stand it. Hasn't he told us how it happened over and over again? Do we have to hear the same thing all the time?

ESTEBAN. She is right. If I had my way, I'd never mention it again; it's your mother.

ACACIA. I even dream about it at night. I never used to be nervous when I was alone or in the dark, but now I am frightened to death, even in broad daylight.

RAIMUNDA. You are not the only one, either. I get no rest, day nor night. I never used to be afraid. I thought nothing of passing the cemetery after dark, not even on All Souls' Eve, but now the least thing makes me jump, no matter what—noise, silence. To tell the truth, as long as we thought it was Norbert, although he was one of the family, and it would have been a shame and a disgrace to us all, at the same time it couldn't be helped; there was nothing to do but resign oneself—and I had resigned myself. After all, it had an explanation. But now, if it wasn't Norbert, if nobody knows who it was, and nobody can explain why it was that that poor boy was shot—I can't be easy in my mind. If it wasn't Norbert, who could have wished him any harm? Maybe it was revenge, some enemy of his father's, or of yours—how do we know but that the shot was intended for you, and since it was night and pitch-dark, they made a mistake, and what they didn't do then they will another time, and. . . . I can't stand this suspense! I get no rest! Every time that you go out of the house and show yourself on the road, it seems to me that I will go crazy. Today, when you were late, I was just starting for the village myself.

ACACIA. She was out on the road already.

RAIMUNDA. Yes, only I saw you and Rubio from the top of the hill, so I turned and ran back before you passed the mill, so you wouldn't be angry. I know it is foolish, but now I want to be with you all the time, wherever you go—I can't bear to be separated from you for one moment. Otherwise I can't be happy. This isn't living.

ESTEBAN. I don't believe anybody wishes me any harm. I never wronged any man. I go wherever I please, without so much as giving it a thought, day or night.

RAIMUNDA. I used to feel the same; there is nobody who could wish us harm. We have helped so many. But all that you need is one enemy, one envious, evil mind. How do we know but that we have some enemy without our suspecting it? A second shot might come from the same quarter as the first. Norbert is free because they couldn't prove that he was guilty; and I am glad of it. Why shouldn't I be glad when he is my own sister's son—my favorite sister's? I could never have believed that Norbert could have done such a thing as murder a man in the dark! But is this to be the end of it? What is the law doing now? Why don't they investigate, why doesn't someone speak? Somebody must know, somebody must have seen whoever it was that was there that day, hovering along the road. When everything is all right, everybody knows who is passing, and what is going on—who comes and who goes—you hear it all without asking; but when you want to know, then nobody knows, nobody has seen anything.

ESTEBAN. I can't see why that is so strange. When a man is going about his business, he has nothing to conceal; but when his intentions are evil, naturally the first thing he does is to hide himself.

RAIMUNDA. Who do you think that it was?

ESTEBAN. I? To tell the truth, I thought it was Norbert, the same as you. If it wasn't Norbert, I don't know who it was.

. RAIMUNDA. I suppose you won't like it, but I'll tell you what I have made up my mind to do.

ESTEBAN. What?

RAIMUNDA. Talk to Norbert. Bernabé has gone to find him. I expect him any minute.

ACACIA. Norbert? What do you want to talk to him for?

ESTEBAN. That is what I say. What does he know about it?

RAIMUNDA. How can I tell? But I know he won't lie to me. By the memory of his mother, I will make him tell me the truth. If he did it, he knows I will never tell. I can't stand this any longer. I shake all over.

ESTEBAN. Do you suppose that Norbert is going to tell you if he was the one who did it?

RAIMUNDA. After I talk to him I shall know.

ESTEBAN. Well, have your own way. It will only make more talk and hard feeling, especially since Tío Eusebio is coming over today. If they meet. . . .

RAIMUNDA. They won't meet on the road, because they come from different directions. After they are here the house is big enough. We can take care of them both.

(JULIANA enters.)

JULIANA. Master. . . .

ESTEBAN. Why are you always bothering me?

JULIANA. Tío Eusebio is coming down the road. Maybe you don't want to see him; I thought you might like to know. . . .

ESTEBAN. Why shouldn't I want to see him? Didn't I tell you he was coming?— Now bring in the other one!

RAIMUNDA. Yes, he can't come too soon to please me.

ESTEBAN. Who told you that I didn't want to see Tío Eusebio?

JULIANA. Oh, don't blame it on me! It wasn't my fault. Rubio says you don't want to see him because he is mad at you. You didn't side with him in court, and that's the reason that Norbert went free.

ESTEBAN. I'll teach Rubio it's none of his business whom I side with.

JULIANA. Yes, and there are other

things you might teach him while you are about it. Have I nothing to do but wait on that man? God help me, he has had more to drink today than is good for him. And that isn't talk, either.

RAIMUNDA. This is the last straw! Where is he?

ESTEBAN. No, leave him to me.

RAIMUNDA. Everything goes wrong in this house. Everybody takes advantage of you as soon as anything is the matter. You don't need to turn your back—it's instinct. They know when you can't take care of yourself.

JULIANA. I'll not take that from you, Raimunda, if you mean me.

RAIMUNDA. You know who I mean. Take it any way you like.

JULIANA. Señor, señor! What curse has fallen on this house? We are all poisoned, snared, our feet are caught in some evil vine; we are changed. One takes it out on the other, and everybody is against me. God help me, I say, and give me the strength to endure it!

RAIMUNDA. Yes, and give me the strength to endure you.

JULIANA. Yes, me! It is all my fault.

RAIMUNDA. Look at me, will you? Do I have to tell you to your face to get out? That's all I want from you.

JULIANA. Yes, you want me to shut up like a tomb. Well, I'll shut up, God help me! Señor! Let me out! Don't talk to me! (*Goes out.*)

ESTEBAN. Here comes Tío Eusebio.

ACACIA. I am going. He breaks down and cries whenever he sees me. He doesn't know what he is doing, but it's always the wrong thing. Does he think he is the only one who has lost anything?

RAIMUNDA. I am sure I have cried as much as his mother has. Tío Eusebio is not the same man; he forgets. But never mind. You are right not to see him.

ACACIA. I have finished the shirts, mother. I'll iron them as soon as I have time.

ESTEBAN. Were you sewing for me?

ACACIA. You can see for yourself.

RAIMUNDA. I don't know how we'd get on if she didn't sew. I am not good for anything. I don't know whether I am alive or dead, God help me! But she can work. She gets through with it somehow. (*She caresses* ACACIA *affectionately as she passes out*) God bless you, Acacia, my child! (ACACIA *goes out*) It is a terrible responsibility to be a mother. For a long time I was afraid that she was going to get married and leave me. Now, what wouldn't I give to see her married?

(TÍO EUSEBIO *enters.*)

EUSEBIO. Hello! Where is everybody?

ESTEBAN. Come in, Tío Eusebio.

EUSEBIO. Good morning to both.

RAIMUNDA. Good morning, Tío Eusebio.

ESTEBAN. Where are your horses? I'll have them put up.

EUSEBIO. My man will tend to that.

ESTEBAN. Sit down. Come, a glass of that wine he likes so much, Raimunda.

EUSEBIO. No, no, thank you. I am not feeling well. Wine doesn't agree with me.

ESTEBAN. This wine will do you good. It's a tonic.

RAIMUNDA. Suit yourself. How are you, Tío Eusebio? How is Julia?

EUSEBIO. Julia? What do you expect? I am going to lose her just as I did the boy; I can see it.

RAIMUNDA. God forbid! Hasn't she four sons yet to live for?

EUSEBIO. Yes, the more worry! That is what is killing her—worry. Nobody knows what will happen next. Our hearts are broken. We were sure that we would get justice; but now we are bitter. Everybody said it would be like this, but we didn't believe it. The murderer is alive— you pass him on the street; he goes home to his house, shuts the door, and laughs at us. It only proves what I knew all the time. There is no such thing in this world as justice, unless a man takes it with his own hands, which is what they will drive us to do now. That is why I wanted to see you yesterday. If my boys come into the village, send them home. Don't let them stay around. Arrest them—anything rather than another tragedy in our house; although I don't want to see his murderer go free—the murderer of my boy—unless God avenges him, as he must, by God!—or else there is no justice in heaven.

RAIMUNDA. Don't turn against God, Tío Eusebio. Though the hand of justice never fall upon him after the foul murder he has done, yet there is not one of us that would be in his place. He is alone with his conscience. I would not have what he has on his soul upon mine, for all the blessings of this world. We have lived good lives, we have done evil to no man, yet all our days are purgatory and torment. He must have hell in his heart after what he has done—of that we can be sure—as sure as of the day of our death.

EUSEBIO. That is cold comfort to me. How does it help me prevent my boys from taking the law into their own hands? Justice has not been done—and it should have been done. Now they are the ones who will go to jail for it! They will make good their threats too. You ought to hear them. Even the little fellow, who is only twelve, doubles up his fists like a man, and swears that whoever killed his brother will have to reckon with him, come what may. I sit there and cry like a child. I needn't tell you how his mother feels. And all the while I have it in my heart to say: Go, my sons! Stone him until he is dead! Cut him to pieces like a hound! Drag his carcass home to me through the mire—what offal there is left of it! Instead I swallow it all and look grave, and tell them that it is wrong even to think of such a thing—it would kill their mother, it would ruin all of us!

RAIMUNDA. You are unreasonable, Tío Eusebio. Norbert is innocent; the law says so. No one could bring the least proof against him; he proved where he was, and what he was doing all that day, one hour after the other. He and his men were up at Los Berrocales. Don Faustino, the doctor, saw him there and talked with him at the very hour it took place, and he is from Encinar. You know yourself no man can be in two places at the same time. You might think that his own people had been told to say what they did, although it isn't an easy thing for so many to agree on a lie; but Don Faustino is a friend of yours; he is in your debt. And others who would naturally have been on your side said the same. Only one shepherd from Los Berrocales would testify that he had seen a man at that hour, and that was a great way off; but he had no idea who it was. From his clothes and the way that he carried himself he was sure that it could not have been Norbert.

EUSEBIO. If it wasn't, I say nothing. Does it make it any better for us that he hired some one else to do it? There can't be any doubt; there is no other explanation. I have no enemies who would do such a thing. I never harmed any man; I help everyone, whether they are our own people or not. I make it easy. If I were to sue for one half the damage that is done me every day, it would take all of my time. I will die a poor man. They killed Faustino because he was going to marry Acacia. That is all there is to it. Nobody could have had any such reason but Norbert. If everybody had told what they knew, the trial would have ended right there. But the ones who knew most said the least; they said nothing.

RAIMUNDA. Do you mean us?

EUSEBIO. I don't say who I mean.

RAIMUNDA. It is plain enough; you don't have to mention names nor point your finger. Do you mean to say that we keep quiet because Norbert is one of our family?

EUSEBIO. Do you mean to say that Acacia doesn't know more about this thing than she is willing to admit?

RAIMUNDA. No, sir, she knows no more about it than you do. You have made up your mind that it was Norbert because you want to make yourself believe that nobody else has anything against you. We are none of us saints, Tio Eusebio. You may have done a great deal of good in your time, but you must also have done some evil; you think that nobody remembers, but maybe the ones who have suffered don't think the same. If Norbert had been in love with my daughter to that extent, he would have shown it before now. Your son didn't take her away from him, remember that. Faustino never said one word until after she was done with Norbert, and she turned him off because she knew he was going with another girl. He never so much as took the trouble to excuse himself, so that when you come down to it, he was the one who left her. That is no reason why anyone should commit murder. You can see it yourself.

EUSEBIO. Then why did everybody say that it couldn't have been anyone else? You said so yourself; everybody said so.

RAIMUNDA. Yes, because at first he was the only one we could think of. But when you look at it calmly, it is foolish to say that he is the only one who could have done it. You insinuate that we have something to conceal. Once for all, let me tell you, we are more anxious than you are to have the truth known, to have this thing out and be done with it. You have lost a son, but I have a daughter who is alive, and she has nothing to gain, either, by this mystery.

EUSEBIO. No, she hasn't. Much less when she keeps her mouth shut. And you

haven't anything to gain. You don't know what Norbert and his father say about this house so as to divert suspicion from themselves? If I believed what they said. . . .

RAIMUNDA. About us? What do they say? (*To* ESTEBAN) You have been in the village. What do they say?

ESTEBAN. Nobody cares what they say.

EUSEBIO. No, I don't believe one word that comes from them. I am only telling you how they repay the kindness you do them by taking their part.

RAIMUNDA. So you are on that tack again? Tío Eusebio, I have to stop and force myself to think what it must mean to lose a child, or I would lose control of myself. I am a mother, God knows, yet you come here and insult my daughter. You insult all of us.

ESTEBAN. Wife! Enough of this. What is the use? Tío Eusebio. . . .

EUSEBIO. I insult nobody. I only repeat what other people say. You suppress the truth because he is one of the family. The whole village is the same. What you are afraid of is the disgrace. People here may think that it was not Norbert, but in Encinar, let me tell you, they think that it was. If justice isn't done—and done quick—blood will be spilled between these villages, and nobody can stop it, either. You know what young blood is.

RAIMUNDA. Yes, and you are the one who stirs it up. You respect neither God nor man. Why, didn't you just admit that Norbert couldn't have done it unless he had hired someone to commit the murder? Nonsense! It isn't so easy to hire a man to commit murder. What had a boy like Norbert to give, anyway?—Unless you want us to believe that his father had a hand in it.

EUSEBIO. Bah! Rogues come cheap. How about the Valderrobles? They live here. Didn't they kill two goatherds for three and a half duros?

RAIMUNDA. How long was it before

they were found out? They fought over the half duro. When you hire a man to do a deed like that, you put yourself in his power; you become his slave for the rest of your life. There may be people who can afford to do such things, but they must be rich, they must have power. Not a boy like Norbert!

EUSEBIO. Every family has a faithful servant who will do what he is told.

RAIMUNDA. No doubt yours has. No doubt you have had occasion to use him too; you know so much about it.

EUSEBIO. Take care what you say!

RAIMUNDA. Take care yourself!

ESTEBAN. Raimunda! Enough of this. What is the use of all this talk?

EUSEBIO. Well, you hear what she says. How about you?

ESTEBAN. If we dwell on this forever, we shall all of us go mad.

EUSEBIO. Yes. You heard what I said.

RAIMUNDA. If you mean by that that you don't intend to let this matter drop until you have found the murderer of your boy, it is only right and proper, and I respect you for it. But that is no reason why you should come here and insult us. Once for all, you may want justice, but I want it more than you do. I pray to God for it every day, I pray him on my knees not to let the murderer go free—and I should pray to him just the same if I had a boy—if it had been my own boy that did it!

(RUBIO *appears in the doorway.*)

RUBIO. How about me, master?

ESTEBAN. Well, Rubio?

RUBIO. Don't look at me like that; I'm not drunk. We started out before lunch, that was all. I had an invitation and took a drop; it went against me. I'm sorry you feel that way about it.

RAIMUNDA. What is the matter with him? Juliana was right.

RUBIO. Tell Juliana to mind her business, will you? I just wanted to tell the master.

ESTEBAN. Rubio! You can tell me later whatever you like. Tío Eusebio is here. Don't you see? We are busy.

RUBIO. Tío Eusebio? So he is. What does he want?

RAIMUNDA. Is it any of your business what he wants? Get out! Go along and sleep it off. You don't know what you are talking about.

RUBIO. I know, señora. Don't say that to me.

ESTEBAN. Rubio!

RUBIO. Juliana's a fool; I don't drink. It was my money, anyhow. I'm no thief. What I have is my own; and my wife is my own, too. She owes nobody anything, eh, master?

ESTEBAN. Rubio! Go along! Get to bed, and don't show yourself again until you have had a good sleep. What is the matter with you? What will Tío Eusebio think?

RUBIO. I don't know. I don't take anything, understand—from anybody. (*Goes out.*)

RAIMUNDA. What was it that you were just saying about servants, Tío Eusebio? This man has us with our hearts in our throats, yet he is nothing to us. Suppose we had trusted him with some secret? What is the matter with Rubio, anyway? Is he going to get drunk every day? He was never like this before. You ought not to put up with it.

ESTEBAN. Don't you see? He isn't used to it. That is the reason he is upset by a thimbleful. Somebody invited him into the tavern while I was tending to my business. I gave him a piece of my mind and sent him to bed, but he hasn't slept it off yet. He is drunk. That is all there is to it.

EUSEBIO. Perfectly natural. Is that all?

ESTEBAN. Drop in again, Tío Eusebio.

EUSEBIO. Thanks. I am sorry this happened—after I took the trouble to come.

RAIMUNDA. Nonsense! Nothing has happened. We have no hard feeling.

EUSEBIO. No, and I hope you won't have any. Remember what I've been through. My heart is broken—it's not scratched. It won't heal either until God claims another one of his own. How long do you expect to stay in the grove?

ESTEBAN. Till Sunday. We have nothing to keep us. We only wanted to be out of the village. Now that Norbert is home, it is nothing but talk, talk, talk.

EUSEBIO. That's right—nothing but talk. If you see my boys around, look out! I don't want them to get into any trouble, which afterward we might have cause to regret.

ESTEBAN. Don't you worry. They won't get into any while I am around. Blame it on me if they do.

EUSEBIO. They're working down by the river now. They'll be all right unless somebody happens along and stirs them up. God be with you, I say. Adios! Where is Acacia?

RAIMUNDA. I told her not to come down, so as to spare your feelings. It is hard on her, too; it brings back everything.

EUSEBIO. That's so. It must.

ESTEBAN. I'll send for your horses.

EUSEBIO. No, I can call myself.—Francisco!—Here he comes. Take care of yourselves. God be with you! (*They move toward the door.*)

RAIMUNDA. God be with you, Tío Eusebio. Tell Julia not to worry. I think of her every day. I have prayed more for her than I have for the boy—God has forgiven him by this time. Surely he never did anything to deserve such a bad end! My heart bleeds for him.

(ESTEBAN *and* TÍO EUSEBIO *have passed out while she is speaking.*)

(BERNABÉ *enters.*)

BERNABÉ. Señora!

RAIMUNDA. Is Norbert here? Could you find him?

BERNABÉ. Yes, I brought him along so as to save time. He wanted to see you himself.

RAIMUNDA. Didn't you meet Tío Eusebio?

BERNABÉ. No, we saw him coming up from the river when we were a long way off, so we turned and went in by the great corral. Norbert is hiding there until Tío Eusebio starts back to Encinar.

RAIMUNDA. There he goes up the road now.

BERNABÉ. Yes—under the great cross.

RAIMUNDA. Tell Norbert. No—wait! What do they say in the village?

BERNABÉ. No good, señora. The law is going to have its hands full before it gets to the bottom of this.

RAIMUNDA. Does anybody think it was Norbert?

BERNABÉ. You would get your head broke if you said it was. When he came back yesterday, half the town was out to meet him. Everybody was sitting by the roadside. They took him up on their shoulders and carried him home. The women all cried, and the men hugged him. I thought his father would die for joy.

RAIMUNDA. He never did it. Poor Norbert!

BERNABÉ. They say the men are coming over from Encinar to kill him; everybody here carries a club and goes armed.

RAIMUNDA. Mother of God! Did anything go wrong with the master while he was in the village this morning? What did you hear?

BERNABÉ. So they have been talking to you?

RAIMUNDA. No. That is—yes; I know.

BERNABÉ. Rubio was in the tavern and began to say things, so I ran for the master, and he came and ordered him out. He was insolent to the master. He was drunk.

RAIMUNDA. Do you remember what he said? I mean Rubio.

BERNABÉ. Oh! His tongue ran away with him. He was drunk. Do you know what I think? If I were you, I wouldn't go back to the village for two or three days.

RAIMUNDA. No, certainly not. If I had my way we would never go back. I am filled with a loathing for it all so great that I want to rush out, and down that long road, and then on and up and over those mountains to the other side, and after that I don't know where I would hide myself. I feel as if some one were running after me, after me, always after me, with more than death in his heart. But the master. . . . Where is the master?

BERNABÉ. Seeing to Rubio.

RAIMUNDA. Tell Norbert to come in. I can't wait.

(BERNABÉ *goes out*.)

(NORBERT *enters*.)

NORBERT. Aunt Raimunda!

RAIMUNDA. Norbert, my boy! Give me a hug.

NORBERT. I am so glad you sent for me. I've been treated like a dog. It's a good thing that my mother is dead and in heaven. I am glad she never lived to see this day. Next to my father, there is nobody in the world I think so much of as I do of you.

RAIMUNDA. I could never have believed that you did it—not though everybody said so.

NORBERT. I know it; you were the first to take my part. Where is Acacia?

RAIMUNDA. In her room. We have our fill of trouble in this house.

NORBERT. Who says I killed Faustino? If I hadn't proved, as I did prove, where I was all that day, if I'd done as I meant at first and taken my gun and gone off to hunt alone by myself, and then couldn't have proved where I was, because no-

body had seen me, I would have spent the rest of my life in prison. They would have had me.

RAIMUNDA. Are you crying?

NORBERT. No, I am not crying; but I cried when I found myself in that prison. If anybody had ever told me that I would ever go to prison, I would never have believed it; I'd have laughed in his face. But that isn't the worst. Tío Eusebio and his boys have sworn to kill me. They will never believe that I am innocent; they know I murdered Faustino. They are as sure of it as I am that my mother lies under the ground!

RAIMUNDA. Because nobody knows who did it. Nobody can find out anything. Don't you see? They will never rest at that. Do you suspect anyone?

NORBERT. I more than suspect.

RAIMUNDA. Then why didn't you say so? You were in court. You had the opportunity.

NORBERT. If I hadn't cleared myself I would have told. But what was the use? I am a dead man now if I speak. They will do the same thing to me.

RAIMUNDA. Eh? Will they? What do you mean? Was it revenge? But who did it? Tell me what you think. I must know, because Tío Eusebio and Esteban have always had the same friends; they have always stood together, for better or for worse, whichever it was. Their enemies would naturally be the same. Now, I can get no rest. This vengeance was intended for us just as much as it was for Tío Eusebio; it was to prevent a closer union of our families. Maybe they won't stop at that, either. Someday they will do the same to my husband!

NORBERT. I wouldn't worry about Uncle Esteban.

RAIMUNDA. Why, what do you mean? Do you think? . . .

NORBERT. I don't think.

RAIMUNDA. Then tell me what you

know. Somehow I believe you are not the only one who knows it. You think what the rest think—it must be the same—what everybody knows.

NORBERT. Well, they didn't get it out of me; that is one thing you can be sure of. Besides, how could they know? It's gossip, that's all—not worth that! Talk in the village! They will never get it out of me.

RAIMUNDA. Norbert, by the soul of your sainted mother in heaven, tell me what it is!

NORBERT. For God's sake, I can't talk! I was afraid to open my mouth in court. Now, if I say a word, I am a dead man. A dead man!

RAIMUNDA. But who would kill you?

NORBERT. Who killed Faustino?

RAIMUNDA. But who did kill Faustino? Some one was paid to do it, is that it? Rubio said something in the wineshop this morning.

NORBERT. Who told you?

RAIMUNDA. Esteban went in and dragged him out; it was the only way he could stop him.

NORBERT. He didn't want to be compromised.

RAIMUNDA. What is that? He didn't want to be compromised? Was Rubio saying that he. . . .

NORBERT. That he was the real master of this house.

RAIMUNDA. The master of this house? Because it was Rubio. . . .

NORBERT. Rubio.

RAIMUNDA. Who killed Faustino?

NORBERT. Sí señora.

RAIMUNDA. Rubio! I knew it all the time. But does anybody else know? That is the question. Do they know it in the village?

NORBERT. He gives himself away; he has money—bills, bank-notes—wherever he goes. He turned on them this morning while they were singing that song. That

was why they had to call Uncle Esteban, and he kicked him out of the wineshop.

RAIMUNDA. That song? Oh, yes! That song—I remember. It goes. . . . How does it go?

NORBERT.
"Who loves the maid that dwells by
    the Mill
Shall love in evil hour;
Because she loves with the love that
    she loves,
Call her the Passion Flower."

RAIMUNDA. We are the ones who dwell by the Mill; that is what they call us. It is here—our house. And the maid that dwells by the Mill must be Acacia, my daughter. This song that everybody sings. . . . They call her the Passion Flower? That is it, isn't it? But who loves her in any evil way? How could anybody love her? You loved her, Faustino loved her; but who else ever loved her? Why do they call her the Passion Flower? Look me in the eye! Why did you give her up if you really loved her? Why? I want you to tell me; you have got to tell me. You cannot tell me anything worse than what I already know.

NORBERT. Do you want them to kill me? To ruin all of us? I have never said one word—not even when they had me in prison would I say one word! I don't know how it got out—Rubio told, or my father. He is the only one who ever had it from me. He wanted to put the law on them, but I said no. They would have killed him; they would have killed me!

RAIMUNDA. Stop! Don't you talk! I see it now. I see it all. The Passion Flower! *La Malquerida!* Come here to me! Tell me everything. Before they kill you, by God, they will have to kill me! It cannot go on like this. Somebody must pay for it. Tío Eusebio and his boys will never rest till they have justice. If they can't get it in any other way, they will take it out of you—revenge! You can't escape.

Faustino was murdered so as to prevent him from marrying Acacia. You left her for the same reason—for fear that they would kill you. Was that it? Tell me the truth!

NORBERT. They told me to leave her because she was promised to Faustino; she had been for a long time. They said they had an understanding with Tío Eusebio, and if I didn't make the best of it, then I could take the worst of it. But if I ever opened my mouth. . . .

RAIMUNDA. They would kill you? Was that it? But you. . . .

NORBERT. I believed it—I was afraid—I didn't know what to do. Then I began to run after another girl, who was nothing to me, so as to break off with Acacia. Afterward, when I found out that not a word of it was true, that neither Tío Eusebio nor Faustino had ever spoken to Uncle Esteban. . . . Then, when they killed Faustino I knew why they killed him. It was because he dared lay eyes on Acacia. There was nothing they could tell him. They couldn't scare him off. Tío Eusebio wasn't a man to stand by and see his son refused. They couldn't refuse, so they agreed to it, and went through with it until the end came, and they killed him. They killed him because I was here to take the blame. Who else could have done it? Of course it was I! I loved Acacia—I was jealous. That was the plot. Praise God, some saint surely watched over me that day! But now the crime has come home to him. It lies like lead on his conscience. He betrays himself. . . .

RAIMUNDA. It is possible that such a thing could be? I must have been blind not to see. What veil hung over my eyes? Why, it is all as clear as day! How could I have been so blind?

NORBERT. What are you doing?

RAIMUNDA. I don't know—I don't know where I am—something so awful, so vast is passing through my mind that it seems as if it were nothing. I can only remember one thing of all that you have told me—that song—La Malquerida! The Passion Flower! I want you to teach me the music. We can sing it together, and dance—dance and drop dead!—Acacia! Acacia! Acacia!

NORBERT. No, don't you call her! Don't take it like this! It wasn't her fault!

(ACACIA enters.)

ACACIA. Did you call, mother?—Norbert!

RAIMUNDA. Come here! Look at me—straight in the eye.

ACACIA. What is the matter with you, mother?

RAIMUNDA. No, it was not your fault.

ACACIA. But what have they been doing? What did you tell her?

RAIMUNDA. What every one else knows already—La Malquerida! The Passion Flower! Your honor is a scorn and a byword. It is bandied about in men's mouths!

ACACIA. My honor? Never! No one can say that.

RAIMUNDA. Don't you deny it! Tell me what you know. Why was it that you never called him father? Why was it?

ACACIA. Because a child has only one father, you know that. This man could never be my father. I hated, I despised him from the day that he entered this house, and brought hell along after him!

RAIMUNDA. Well, you are going to call him now, and you are going to call him what I tell you; you are going to call him father. Do you hear? Your father! I tell you to call your father.

ACACIA. Do you want me to go to the cemetery and call him? If that isn't what you want, I have no father. This man—this man is your husband; you love him, but all that he is to me is this man! This man! That is all he can ever be! Leave me alone if you know what is good for

[241]

you—you think you are so smart. Let the law take its course. I don't care. If he has sinned, he can pay for it.

RAIMUNDA. Do you mean for Faustino's murder? Yes—go on! Go on! What else? Out with it!

ACACIA. No, mother, no! For if I had consented, Faustino would never have been murdered! Do you think I don't know how to guard my honor?

RAIMUNDA. Then what have you been so silent about? Why didn't you come to me?

ACACIA. Would you have taken my word against this man, when you were mad for him? And you must have been mad not to see! He would eat me up with his eyes while you sat there; he followed me around the house like a cat. What more do you want? I hated him so, I had such a horror of him that I prayed to God that he would make himself even more of a beast than he was, so that it would open your eyes, if anything could have opened your eyes, and let you see what manner of man he was who had robbed me of your love, for you have loved him, you have loved him so much —more than you ever loved my father!

RAIMUNDA. No! That isn't true!

ACACIA. I wanted you to hate him as I hate him, as my father in heaven hates him! I have heard his voice from the skies.

RAIMUNDA. Silence! For shame! Come here to your mother. You are all that I have left in the world. And thank God that I can still protect you!

(BERNABÉ *enters.*)

BERNABÉ. Señora! Señora!

RAIMUNDA. What brings you running in such a hurry? No good, we may be sure.

BERNABÉ. Don't let Norbert leave the house! Don't let him out of your sight!

RAIMUNDA. How?

BERNABÉ. Tío Eusebio's boys are waiting outside with their men to kill him.

NORBERT. What did I tell you? You wouldn't believe it. They are here—they want to kill me! And they will kill me. Yes, they will!

RAIMUNDA. Not unless they kill us all first! Somebody has sent for them.

BERNABÉ. Yes, Rubio. I saw him running along the river bank where Tío Eusebio's boys were at work.

NORBERT. Didn't I tell you? They want to kill me, so as to save themselves. Then nothing will ever come out. Tío Eusebio's boys will think they have the man who murdered their brother. They will kill me, Aunt Raimunda! Yes, they will! They are too many for one; I can't defend myself. I haven't even a knife. I don't dare to carry a gun—I might kill someone. I'd rather die than be locked up in that cell again. Save me, Aunt Raimunda! I don't want to die. It wasn't my fault! They hunt me like a wolf.

RAIMUNDA. Don't be afraid. If they kill you, it will be over my dead body. Go in there with Bernabé and take that gun, do you hear? They won't dare to come in. If they do, shoot to kill! When I call, shoot —no matter who it may be! Do you understand? No matter who it may be! Don't shut the door. (*To* ACACIA) You stand here by me. Esteban! Esteban! Esteban!

ACACIA. What are you going to do?

(ESTEBAN *enters.*)

ESTEBAN. Did you call?

RAIMUNDA. Yes, I want to speak to you. Norbert is here in our house. Tío Eusebio's boys are waiting outside. You sent for them to kill him—because you are not man enough to do it yourself.

ESTEBAN. (*Making a movement to draw a weapon*) Raimunda!

ACACIA. Mother!

RAIMUNDA. No, don't you do it! Call Rubio and let him make an end of us all! He will have to make an end of us all to cover your guilt. Murderer! Assassin!

ESTEBAN. You are crazy!

RAIMUNDA. I was crazy! I was crazy the day that you first entered this house —my house—like a thief, to rob me of all I held dear!

ESTEBAN. What are you talking about?

RAIMUNDA. I am not talking; other people are talking. Soon the law will speak. If you don't want that, do as I tell you, or I will cry out—I will rouse the house. You brought them here—take them away again, you cowards that lie in wait for innocent men, to stab them in the back! Norbert leaves this house, but he leaves with me. If they kill him, they kill me. I am here to protect him, and I will protect my daughter—I, alone, against you, against all the assassins you can hire! Go! Here come my people. . . . Don't you touch me! Hide yourself in the uttermost recesses of those mountains, in caves where the wild beasts dwell. Now I know! You have nothing to hope for from me. Oh, I was alone with my child!—and you came. You knew that she was my child; there she stands— *La Malquerida!* The Passion Flower! Well! I am still here to guard her from you, to tell you that her father still lives in heaven—and to shoot you through the heart if you make one step to lay your hand on her!

CURTAIN

THE THIRD ACT

The scene is the same as in the Second Act. RAIMUNDA *stands at the door, peering anxiously out over the countryside. After a moment* JULIANA *enters.*

JULIANA. Raimunda!

RAIMUNDA. What do you want? Is he worse?

JULIANA. No, don't be nervous.

RAIMUNDA. How is he? Why did you leave him?

JULIANA. He's asleep. Acacia is with him; she can hear if he calls. You are the one I am worried about. Thank God, he's not dead. Do you expect to go all day without eating?

RAIMUNDA. Let me alone; don't bother me.

JULIANA. What are you doing out here? Come on in and sit with us.

RAIMUNDA. I was looking for Bernabé.

JULIANA. He can't be back so soon if he brings the men to take Norbert away. If the constables come with him. . . .

RAIMUNDA. Constables? Constables in this house? Ah, Juliana, surely a curse has fallen upon us all!

JULIANA. Come on in, and don't be looking out of the door all the time. It's not Bernabé that you are looking for; it's the other one—it's your husband. When all is said and done, he is your husband.

RAIMUNDA. Yes, the habits of a lifetime cannot be changed in one day. Although I know what I know, and that it must always be so, although if I saw him coming it would be to curse him, although I must loathe him for the rest of my life, yet here I stand looking out of the door and scanning every rock and cranny upon those mountains only for a sight of him! It seems to me as if I were waiting for him as I used to do, to see him come happy and smiling, and then turn and walk into the house with him arm in arm like two lovers, and sit down here at the table to eat, and go over everything that we had done during the day. Sometimes we would laugh, sometimes we would argue, but always it was so dear, as if we had been fonder of each other than anyone else who had ever lived in the world. Now it is all over; nothing remains. The peace of God has fled forever from this house!

JULIANA. You cannot believe what you see with your eyes. If you hadn't told me yourself, if I didn't know how you felt, how you were, I would never have believed it. Faustino is dead, God help him;

we can leave it. There might be more of the sort, too, for all I care; but this devil that has gotten into him with Acacia, it doesn't seem possible, I can't believe it—although I must believe it. There is no other explanation of the mystery.

RAIMUNDA. Did you never notice anything?

JULIANA. Nothing. When he first came to the house, it was to make love to you, and I needn't tell you how I felt. I was fond of your first husband; there never was a better nor juster man in the world, so I looked on him with disfavor. God have mercy on me, but if I had seen anything, what reason would I have had for keeping quiet? Of course, when you come to think, he gave her presents—and there were a good many of them, too—but we never thought anything of that. She was so haughty with him. They never had one good talk together from the day you were married. She was only a runt then anyway. She insulted him out of pure spite. Nobody could do anything with her. If you struck her, it made no difference. I'll say this while I am about it: if she had been nice to him when she was little, he might have looked on her as his own daughter. Then we would never have been where we are now.

RAIMUNDA. Are you trying to excuse him?

JULIANA. Excuse him? There can be no excuse for such a thing. It was enough that she was your daughter. What I say is that the girl was like a stranger to him from the beginning, although she was your own child. If she had treated him like a father, as she ought—it would have been different; he isn't a bad man. A bad man is bad through and through. When you were first married, I've seen him sit by himself and cry at the way the girl ran from him, as if he had had the plague.

RAIMUNDA. You are right. The only trouble we ever had was with the child.

JULIANA. After she was grown there wasn't a girl in the village that was her equal for looks. Nobody knows that better than you do. But she shrank from him as if he had been the devil. There she was all the time—right before his eyes! No wonder if he had an evil thought; none of us are above them.

RAIMUNDA. I don't say he might not have had an evil thought, although he ought never to have had such a thought. But you put an evil thought out of your mind unless you are evil. He must have had more than an evil thought to do what he did, to murder a man in cold blood to prevent my daughter from marrying and going away—away from him; his mind must have been evil, like the criminal's, waiting to break out, with all the evil of the world in his heart. I am more anxious than anybody to believe that it is not so bad, but the more I think, the more I see that there can be no excuse for it. When I remember what has been hanging over my daughter all these years, that any moment—because a man who will do murder will do anything. If he had ever laid hands on her I would have killed them both, as sure as my name is Raimunda—him, because he had been guilty of such a crime, and her because she did not let him kill her before she would consent to it.

(BERNABÉ enters.)

JULIANA. Here comes Bernabé.

RAIMUNDA. Are you alone?

BERNABÉ. Yes, they are deciding in the village what is best to be done. I was afraid to stay any longer.

RAIMUNDA. You were right. This is not life. What do they say now?

BERNABÉ. Do you want to go mad? Forget it. Pay no attention to what they say.

RAIMUNDA. Are they coming to take Norbert away?

BERNABÉ. His father will tend to that. The doctor won't let them put him in the cart for fear it will make him worse. He'll have to be carried on a stretcher. The judge and the prosecutor are coming to take his story, so they don't want a relapse. He was unconscious yesterday and couldn't testify. Everybody has his own idea; no two agree. Not a soul went to the fields today. The men stand around the streets in groups; the women talk in the houses and run to and fro. Nobody stops to eat. Not a meal has been served today, dinner or supper either, on the hour.

RAIMUNDA. Didn't you tell them that Norbert's wounds aren't serious?

BERNABÉ. What difference does that make? Now they can't do anything. Yesterday, when they thought Tío Eusebio's boys had fallen on him with the master, and he was going to die, the thing was simple; but today they hear he is better. How do they know but that he will soon be well again? Even Norbert's best friends say that it's a great pity that the wound wasn't serious. If he was wounded at all, it might better have been serious. Then Tío Eusebio's boys could have been made to pay for it, and they would have had their revenge, but now, if he gets well, the law will get into it, and then nobody will be satisfied.

JULIANA. They are so fond of Norbert, are they, that they wish he was dead? The idiots!

BERNABÉ. That is the way they are. I told them they could thank you for it, because you were the one who called the master, and the master threw himself between them and knocked up their guns, so they couldn't kill him.

RAIMUNDA. Did you tell them that?

BERNABÉ. Every mother's son that asked me. I said the first because it was true, and I said the rest—because you don't know what they are saying in the village, nor how they feel about what is going on in this house.

RAIMUNDA. No! I don't want to hear!

Where is the master? Have you seen him? Do you know where he is?

BERNABÉ. He and Rubio were up at Los Berrocales this morning with the goatherds from Encinar. They spent the night in a hut on the uplands. I don't like this going away. It's not right, if I know what is good for him. It looks as if he was afraid. This is no time to have people think what isn't so. Norbert's father talks too much. This morning he tried to persuade Tío Eusebio that his sons had had no cause to shoot his boy.

RAIMUNDA. Is Tío Eusebio in the village?

BERNABÉ. He came with his boys. They arrested them this morning, tied them together by the elbows, and brought them over from Encinar. Their father followed on foot and brought the little fellow with him, holding his hand all the way. They cried with every step that they took. There wasn't a man in the village but cried, too, when he saw them, even the strongest, no matter if he had never cried before.

RAIMUNDA. And his mother is alone at home, and here I am! What do you men know?

(ACACIA enters.)

ACACIA. Mother——

RAIMUNDA. Well? What is it?

ACACIA. Norbert wants you. He is awake now. He wants some water. He is thirsty; I was afraid to give him any for fear it wasn't right.

RAIMUNDA. The doctor says he can have all the orange-juice he can drink. Here's the jar. Does he suffer much?

ACACIA. No, not now.

RAIMUNDA. (To BERNABÉ) Did you get the things for the doctor?

BERNABÉ. Yes, they're in the saddle-bags. I'll bring them in. (Goes out.)

ACACIA. He is calling, mother. Do you hear?

RAIMUNDA. Coming, Norbert, my boy. (Goes out.)

ACACIA. Has that man come back?

JULIANA. No. He took his gun and rushed out like one mad as soon as it was over. Rubio ran after him.

ACACIA. Have they caught him?

JULIANA. You'll hear soon enough when they do. They'll have to bring charges against him first.

ACACIA. But doesn't everybody know? They heard what my mother said.

JULIANA. No, nobody heard except me and Bernabé, and he won't tell what isn't good for him; he is honest and loyal to this house. They heard your mother shout, that was all. They thought it was because Norbert was here, and Tío Eusebio's boys were waiting outside to kill him. Nobody will say a word when the judge comes unless your mother tells us to open our mouths.

ACACIA. Do you mean that my mother isn't going to let you tell the truth? Won't she tell what she knows?

JULIANA. Is that what you want? So you want to disgrace this house, do you, and yourself? Then every man will think what he likes; some will believe that you are innocent, and some will never believe it. A woman's honor is not a thing to be bandied about in men's mouths, not when it is none of their business.

ACACIA. My honor? I can take care of my honor. Let the others do the same. Now I shan't marry. I am glad it happened, because I shall never marry. I only agreed to it to get rid of him.

JULIANA. Acacia, I don't want to hear you—not another word. Surely the devil must be in you!

ACACIA. Yes, he is, and he has always been, since I first learned to hate that man!

JULIANA. Yes, and who is to say that wasn't where the trouble began? You had no cause to hate him. Mind you, nobody blamed your mother more than I did when she married again; but all the same,

I saw what a devil you were to this man when you were a little child, and how much it meant to him—which you were too young to know.

ACACIA. How much did it mean to me to see my mother always hanging around his neck? Do you suppose I liked it, sitting here and seeing her love him? I was always in the way.

JULIANA. You have no right to talk like that. You were always first with your mother, and you might have been with him.

ACACIA. Might have been? Never! Because I was, and I am.

JULIANA. But not like you mean, though you seem proud of it; in the way you should have been. He never would have loved you as he did if you had loved him as a daughter.

ACACIA. How could I love him? Didn't he turn me even against my own mother?

JULIANA. What do you mean? Turn you against your own mother?

ACACIA. Yes. Do you suppose I can love her now as I ought, as I should have loved her if that man had never entered this house? I remember once when I was a little girl, I spent all one night with a knife under my pillow, and I lay awake all night. The only thought that I had in my mind that night was to kill him.

JULIANA. *Jesús,* my child! What is that? Suppose you had? Suppose you had gotten up, and had dared, and had killed him?

ACACIA. I don't know who I might have killed next.

JULIANA. Holy Virgin! *Jesús!* Not another word. Don't you talk! You are beyond the pale of God's mercy. Do you know what I think? It was all your fault.

ACACIA. All my fault?

JULIANA. Yes, yours! It was your fault! And I'll go further: if you hated him as much as you say you do, then he would have been the only one you would

[246]

have hated—yes, the only one! *Jesús!* It's a good thing that your mother doesn't know!

ACACIA. Know what?

JULIANA. That he wasn't the one you were jealous of. It was her! You were in love with him and you didn't know it.

ACACIA. In love with him?

JULIANA. Yes, hate turned to love. Nobody can hate like that. A hate like that always grows out of a great love.

ACACIA. Do you mean to say that I was in love with that man? Do you know what you are telling me?

JULIANA. I am not telling you anything.

ACACIA. No. What you will do now is run and tell my mother.

JULIANA. Is that what you are afraid of? I thought so. Now you are the one who is telling. You needn't worry, though. I'll not tell. She has enough on her mind, poor soul. God help us!

(BERNABÉ *enters.*)

BERNABÉ. Here comes the master!

JULIANA. Did you see him?

BERNABÉ. Yes! You wouldn't know him. He looks as if he had stepped from the grave.

ACACIA. Let me out!

JULIANA. Yes, let us all out—and shut your mouth, do you hear? What is done is done. Your mother must never know. (*The women go out.*)

(ESTEBAN *and* RUBIO *enter, their guns over their shoulders.*)

BERNABÉ. Can—can I do anything?

ESTEBAN. Nothing, Bernabé.

BERNABÉ. I'll tell the mistress.

ESTEBAN. No, don't tell her; they'll find us.

RUBIO. How about his wounds, eh?

BERNABÉ. Better. The doctor sent for these things. I'll take them in—unless you need me. (*Goes out.*)

ESTEBAN. Here I am. What do you want me to do?

RUBIO. What do I want you to do? This is your house; you belong here. A man's house is his castle. Running away, being afraid to face it, is to confess. It will ruin us both.

ESTEBAN. Here I am; you have had your way. Now this woman will come and accuse me and raise the house. The judge will be here, and he will bring Tío Eusebio. What then?

RUBIO. Why didn't you let Tío Eusebio's boys handle it themselves? They would have finished it. Now he is only wounded. He will squeal, and so will his father; so will all the women. They are the ones I am afraid of. They will talk. Nobody can prove who shot Faustino. You were with his father; nobody saw me. I have a good pair of legs. I was with some friends two leagues away a few minutes before, and I set the clock ahead. When I left the house I took good care to have them notice it.

ESTEBAN. Yes, we would have been safe if that had been all. But you talked; you gave yourself away.

RUBIO. You ought to have killed me. That was the first time in my life that I ever was afraid. I never expected they would let Norbert go. I told you that we ought to go into court and have Acacia testify that Norbert had sworn he was going to kill Faustino, but you wouldn't listen. Do you mean to tell me that you couldn't have made her do it? We could have got others, too, to say the same. Then it would have been easy; they would never have let him go. I know I made a fool of myself, but when I saw that Norbert was free, that the law—yes, and Tío Eusebio—would never stop there, that they would look somewhere else, then I was afraid for the first time. I wanted to forget. So I began to drink, which I never do, and I talked. You ought to have killed me then; you had ground for it. They were talking already in the village; that was what scared me. When I heard that song—it put the blame here. Norbert and his father suspect. After what happened before, they have their eyes open. That is the talk that has got to be stopped, no matter what comes of it. That is the danger—the crime will be known by the cause. Nothing else counts. So long as nobody knows why he was killed, nobody will ever find out who killed him either.

ESTEBAN. But why? Why was he killed? What was the use of killing anybody?

RUBIO. I don't know. Don't ask me. Weren't you talking all the time? "If another man gets her, look out! Something happens." Then you told me she was going to be married. "I can't scare this one off; it's all over, he will take her away. I can't think. . . ." Didn't you come to me in the morning early again and again, before it was light, and wake me up and say: "Get up, Rubio; I haven't closed my eyes all night. I must get out. To the fields! I must walk!" And then we'd take our guns and go out and walk for hours, side by side, without speaking a word. At last, when the fit had passed, and we'd put a few shots in the air so that nobody could say that we did no hunting when we went out to hunt, I'd tell you that we scared away the game; but you said we frightened evil thoughts: and down we'd sit on some hummock and then you would burst out laughing like one mad, as if some weight had been lifted from your soul, and you'd catch me around the neck and talk, and talk, and talk—you didn't know how you talked, nor what you said, nor why, nor whether it had any sense at all; but it always came to the same thing: "I am mad, crazy, a wild man! I cannot live like this. I want to die. I don't know what devil has gotten into me. This is torment, hell!" And then you'd shuffle the words

again, over and over, but it was always the same, you were dying—death! And you talked death so long that one day death heard—and he came. And you know it.

ESTEBAN. Stop! Why do you have to talk?

RUBIO. Take care, master! Don't you touch me! I know what was in your mind when we were coming down the mountain. Make no mistake. You lagged behind. Another minute and your gun would have been at your shoulder. But don't you do it, master, don't you try! We'll stick together. I know how you feel; you're sick. You never want to see me again. If that would help, I'd get out. What did I care, anyway? It was nothing to me. Whatever I got you gave me afterward. It was your idea. I never asked. I don't need money. I don't drink, I don't smoke. All I want is to rove over the mountains, to do what I like, to be free. I want to be my own master. You trusted me, and I was proud of it. I know how you feel. We are like brothers. I'll take the blame. You needn't worry. They can grind me to powder but I'll never say a word. I'll tell them I did it—it was I—because—it's none of their business—just because. I don't care what they give me: they can make it ten years, fifteen. What's the difference? Then you fix it; you have influence. Only don't let them make it too much. Get busy; cut it down. Others have done the same. In four or five years everything will have blown over. Only I don't want you to forget. When I come out we will be brothers, the same as before. We can work together; we can do what we please. Only I mean to be my own master, to have power, to feel power in my hands! Nobody can stand alone. We'll be brothers. Hush! Some one is coming—the mistress!

(RAIMUNDA *enters, carrying a water-jar. She sees* ESTEBAN *and* RUBIO *and stops short, dazed. After hesitating for a moment she proceeds to fill the jar from a pitcher.*)

RUBIO. Señora!

RAIMUNDA. Get out of my house! Don't you come near me! What are you doing here? I never want to see you again.

RUBIO. Oh! You are going to see me again—and hear me.

RAIMUNDA. What do you mean? This is my house.

RUBIO. Just a word. Soon we will all be in court. We had better fix it beforehand. Because a few fools open their mouths is no reason why a good man should go to prison.

RAIMUNDA. More than one will go. You don't expect to get out of it?

RUBIO. I don't know. Only one will go, but that one will be I.

RAIMUNDA. It will?

RUBIO. But when I shut my mouth I don't want other people to talk. Take it from me: what you think is not so. Norbert and his father are back of these lies; they are the ones who do all the lying. They made up that song, too. It's a lie, and they know it.

RAIMUNDA. Is that so? You have agreed then on your story? Well, I don't believe one word of it. Gossip and songs are nothing to me. I believe nothing but the truth, the truth that I know—and I know it so well that I have known it all along. I guessed it from the beginning. I might have thought—but no, I never thought anything of you. He, he might have confessed; it would have been only fair. He might have known that I would hold my tongue, not for him, but for this house—which was my father's house—for my daughter, for my own sake. But why should I keep still when everybody knows it, and the very stones shout? They sing it from the housetops.

RUBIO. So long as you keep still, the rest can sing all they want to.

RAIMUNDA. Keep still? To save you? I could scream at the very sight of you! I could raise the village!

RUBIO. Don't be a fool! What's the use?

RAIMUNDA. Of course you weren't a fool when you murdered a man. And you nearly murdered another—in this house —or had him murdered.

RUBIO. I wouldn't have been a fool if I had.

RAIMUNDA. You are a coward! You are a murderer!

RUBIO. Your wife is speaking to you, master.

ESTEBAN. Rubio!

RUBIO. You see he can hear.

RAIMUNDA. Yes, hang your head before this man. What a humiliation! You are his slave for the rest of your life. Could any fate be more horrible? Now this house has a master. Thank God, he cannot be less jealous of its honor than you!

ESTEBAN. Raimunda!

RAIMUNDA. When I talk, you interrupt. You are not afraid of me.

ESTEBAN. If I had been man enough, I would have put a bullet through my head, and have been done with it.

RUBIO. Oh, master!

ESTEBAN. No! Stop there! That's all I'll take from you. Get out! What are you waiting for? Do you want me to beg you on my knees?

RAIMUNDA. Oh!

RUBIO. No, master. I am going. (*To* RAIMUNDA) If it hadn't been for me, there wouldn't have been any murder, but you might have lost a child. Now, you have another. The blood made him faint; a bad turn, that was all. But he's better. I am a good doctor. Sometime you can thank me for it. Don't forget. I'll show you how. (*Goes out.*)

ESTEBAN. Don't cry any more. I can't bear to see you cry. I am not worth all these tears. I ought never to have come back; I ought to have starved amid the brambles and thickets—they should have hunted me down like a wolf. I would not have raised my hand. Don't reproach me! Over and over again I have said to myself more than you can say. I have called myself murderer, assassin, times without number. Let me go. This is no longer my home. Turn me out! I am only waiting for them to take me. I don't go out on the road and give myself up, because I am too weak; my heart sinks; I am at the end of my tether. If you don't want me, tell me to go, and I will creep onto the highway and throw myself down in the fields, like carrion which you cast from your door.

RAIMUNDA. Yes, give yourself up! Bring shame and ruin on this house, drag my daughter's honor in the dust and mire of the village! I should have been the law to you; you ought to have thought of me. Do you suppose that I believe in these tears because this is the first time I ever saw you cry? Better you had cried your eyes out the day that wicked thought first entered your mind, rather than have turned them where you had no right. Now you cry—but what am I to do? Look at me. Nobody knows what I have been through. It could not be worse. I want to forget, but I must think—think how I can hide the shame which has fallen on this house, keep it out of men's sight, prevent a man from being dragged from this house to prison—a man I brought into it to be a father to my child! This was my father's house; here my brothers lived with the fear of God in their hearts, and from it they went to serve their King, or to marry, or to till other fields by their labor. When they re-entered these doors it was with the same honor with which they went forth. Don't cry; don't hang your head. Hold it high, as I do. In a few minutes the officers will be here to trap us all. Though the house burn, and they are in it, they shall not

smell the smoke. Dry your eyes; you have wept blood. Take a sip of water—I wish it was poison. Don't drink so fast; you are overheated. The thorns have torn your skin. You deserved knives. Let me wash you off; it makes my blood creep to look at you.

ESTEBAN. Raimunda! Wife! Pity me! You don't know. Don't talk to me. No, I am the one who must talk—I must confess as I shall confess at the hour of my doom! You don't know how I have struggled. I have wrestled all these years as with another man who was stronger than I, night and day, who was dragging me where I did not want to go.

RAIMUNDA. But when—when did that evil thought first enter your mind? When was that unhappy hour?

ESTEBAN. I don't know. It came upon me like a blight, all at once; it was there. All of us think some evil in our lives, but the thought passes away, it does no harm; it is gone. When I was a boy, one day my father beat me. Quick as a flash it came to me: "I wish he was dead!" But no sooner thought, than I was ashamed —I was ashamed to think that I had ever had such a thought. My heart stood still within me for fear that God had heard, that he would take him away. From that day I loved him more, and when he died, years afterward, I grieved as much for that thought as I did for his death, although I was a grown man. And this might have been the same; but this did not go away. It became more fixed the more I struggled to shake it off. You can't say that I did not love you. I loved you more every day! You can't say that I cast my eyes on other women—and I had no thought of her. But when I felt her by me my blood took fire. When we sat down to eat, I was afraid to look up. Wherever I turned she was there, before me—always! At night, when we were in bed, and I was lying close by you in the midnight silence of the house, all I could

feel was her. I could hear her breathe as if her lips had been at my ear. I wept for spite, for bitterness! I prayed to God, I scourged myself. I could have killed myself—and her! Words cannot tell the horror I went through. The few times that we were alone, I ran from her like a wild man. If I had stayed I don't know what might have happened: I might have kissed her, I might have dug my knife into her!

RAIMUNDA. Yes, you were mad—and you did not know it. It could only have ended in death. Why didn't we find some man for her? She could have married. You ought not to have kept her from Norbert.

ESTEBAN. It was not her marrying, it was her going away. I could not live without the feel of her; I craved her day and night. All her hate, her spite, her turning away—which she always did—cut me to the heart; then, I came to depend upon it. I could not live without it; it was part of my life. That is what it was—I didn't realize it myself, because it always seemed to me as if it could not be—such things could not really be. I was afraid to face it. But now, I have confessed it to you. It is true! It is true! I can never forgive myself, not even though you might forgive me.

RAIMUNDA. The evil cannot be cured by forgiveness; if I do not forgive you, it will not take the evil away. When I first heard of it, it seemed to me that no punishment could be too severe. Now, I don't know. To do what you did, you must have been all evil. But you were always kind and good, in season and out, to my daughter, when she was a child, when she was grown—and to me. I have seen it with my own eyes. You were good to all the servants from the day that you entered this house, to the men, to everybody who came near. You have been faithful and loyal, and worked hard for the honor of this house. A man cannot be good so long and become all bad in one day. Yet these things are; I know it. It chills my heart. When my mother was alive—God rest her soul!—we always laughed because she used to say that many a deed had been foretold in this world that afterward took place exactly as it had been foretold. We never believed it, but now I know it is true. The dead do not leave us when they die, though we lay them in the ground. They walk by the side of those that they loved in this life, of those that they hated with a hate that was stronger than death. They are with us, day and night. We do not see them, but they whisper in our ears. They put thoughts into our minds which are evil and wicked and strange, which we never can believe could be part of ourselves.

ESTEBAN. Do you mean? . . .

RAIMUNDA. Vengeance! This is vengeance from the other world. My daughter's father will not forgive me in heaven; he will never accept a second father for his child. There are some things which we cannot explain in this life. A good man like you cannot, all of a sudden, cease to be good; for you were good. . . .

ESTEBAN. I was—I was always. When you say it, you don't know what happiness, what boundless joy it is to me!

RAIMUNDA. Hush! Not so loud! I hear someone in the other part of the house. It is Norbert's father and his friends. They are going to take him away. If it had been the judge he would have come to this door. Stay here; I'll find out. Go in and wash; change your shirt. Don't let any one see you like this. You look. . . .

ESTEBAN. Like a murderer, eh? Say it.

RAIMUNDA. No, no, Esteban! We mustn't dwell on these things. We must stop this talk; that is first. Then we can think. Acacia can go to the nuns for a few days at Encinar. They are fond of her; they always ask how she is. Then I can write to my sister-in-law, Eugenia; she likes her. She can go to Andrada and live with her. She might marry, who knows? There are fine boys there—the town is rich—and she is the best match in our village. Then she could come back and have her children, and we would be grandfather and grandmother, and grow old with them around us, and be happy once more in this house. If only. . . .

ESTEBAN. What?

RAIMUNDA. If only. . . .

ESTEBAN. The dead man.

RAIMUNDA. Yes. He will always be here, between us.

ESTEBAN. Always. The rest we can forget. (*Goes into the room.*)

(ACACIA *enters.*)

RAIMUNDA. Acacia! Were you there?

ACACIA. Yes. Why not? Can't you see? Norbert's father is here with the men.

RAIMUNDA. What are they doing?

ACACIA. They seem more reasonable; they were surprised to find him better. Now they are waiting for the judge. He is down at Sotillo examining the men. He will come here as soon as he is done.

RAIMUNDA. I'll keep an eye on them.

ACACIA. I have something to say to you first, mother.

RAIMUNDA. You? Something to say? What is the matter with you? I am frightened. You never say anything.

ACACIA. I heard what you mean to do with me.

RAIMUNDA. You were listening at the keyhole, were you?

ACACIA. Yes, because it was my duty to hear. I had to know what you were doing with this man. It seems that I am the one who is in the way in this house. I have done nothing wrong, so I have to take the blame, while you stay here and enjoy yourself with your husband. You forgive him and turn me out, so that you can be alone together!

RAIMUNDA. What are you talking about? Who is turning you out? Who ever put that idea into your head?

ACACIA. I heard what you said. You want to send me to the convent at Encinar and shut me up, I suppose, for the rest of my life.

RAIMUNDA. How can you say such a thing? Didn't you tell me yourself that you wanted to go there and stay for a few days with the nuns? Didn't I refuse to let you go for fear that you would never come back, if you once saw the inside of the cloister? How often have you begged me to let you go to your Aunt Eugenia? Now, when it would be a good thing for us all, for the good of the family, which is your family—I tell you that we must hold our heads high—now what do you want me to do? Do you expect me to give up my husband—the man it was your duty to love as a father?

ACACIA. You are as bad as Juliana. I suppose it was all my fault?

RAIMUNDA. I don't say that. But he never looked on you as a daughter because you were never a daughter to him.

ACACIA. I suppose I flaunted myself in his face? I suppose I made him kill Faustino?

RAIMUNDA. Not so loud! Somebody might hear!

ACACIA. Well, this time you won't find it so easy to have your way. You want to save this man and hush it up, but I am going to tell what I know to the judge, to everybody. I have only my honor to think of, not that of a man who hasn't any, who never had any—who is a criminal!

RAIMUNDA. Silence! Not so loud! It freezes my heart to hear you. You hate him—and I had almost forgiven him!

ACACIA. Yes, I do hate him. I always did hate him, and he knows it. If he doesn't want me to speak, to denounce him, let him kill me. I can die—that is what I can do—die. Let him kill me!

Then, perhaps, once for all, you might learn to hate him.

RAIMUNDA. Hush, I say!—Here he comes. (ESTEBAN *enters*) Esteban!

ESTEBAN. She is right. She is not the one who ought to go. Only I don't want her to give me up. I will do it myself. I am strong now. I will go out on the road to meet them. Let me go, Raimunda. You have your child. You forgive me, but she never will. She hated me from the beginning.

RAIMUNDA. No, Esteban, don't you go! Esteban, my life!

ESTEBAN. No, let me go, or I will call Norbert's father. I will tell him. . . .

RAIMUNDA. (*To* ACACIA) Now you see what you have done. It was your fault. Esteban! Esteban!

ACACIA. Mother, don't let him go!

RAIMUNDA. Ah!

ESTEBAN. No, she wants to betray me. Why did you hate me like this? You never once called me father. You don't know how I loved you!

ACACIA. Mother, mother——

ESTEBAN. *La Malquerida!* The Passion Flower! I hang my head. But once—once how I could have loved you!

RAIMUNDA. For once, call him father.

ESTEBAN. She will never forgive me.

RAIMUNDA. But she must! Throw your arms about his neck. Call him father. Even the dead will forgive us then, and be happy in our happiness.

ESTEBAN. Daughter!

ACACIA. Esteban! . . . My God! Esteban!

ESTEBAN. Ah!

RAIMUNDA. But you don't call him father. Has she fainted? Ah! Lip to lip, and you clutch her in your arms! Let go, let go! Now I see why you won't call him father. Now I see that it was your fault—and I curse you!

ACACIA. Yes, it was. Kill me! It is true, it is true! He is the only man I ever loved.

ESTEBAN. Ah!

RAIMUNDA. What do you say? What is that? I will kill you—yes, and be damned with it!

ESTEBAN. Stand back!

ACACIA. Save me!

ESTEBAN. Stand back, I say!

RAIMUNDA. Ah! Now I see! It is plain to me now. And it is just as well! What is one murder to me? We can all die. Here! Come, everybody! The murderer! I have the murderer! Take this wicked woman, for she is not my child!

ACACIA. Run! Get away!

ESTEBAN. Yes, together—to hell! For I am damned for love of you. Come! They can hunt us like wild beasts among the rocks. To love you and hold you, I will be as the wild beasts, that know neither father nor mother!

RAIMUNDA. Help! Help! Come quick! The murderer! The murderer!

(RUBIO, BERNABÉ *and* JULIANA *appear simultaneously at different doors, followed by others from the village.*)

ESTEBAN. Out of my way! Take care who crosses me!

RAIMUNDA. Stay where you are!—The murderer!

ESTEBAN. Out of my way, I tell you!

RAIMUNDA. Over my dead body!

ESTEBAN. Yes—(*Raising his gun he shoots* RAIMUNDA.)

RAIMUNDA. Ah!

JULIANA. God in heaven!—Raimunda!

RUBIO. What have you done?

A MAN. Kill him!

ESTEBAN. Yes, kill me! I don't defend myself.

BERNABÉ. No! Put the law on him!

JULIANA. It was this man, this wretched man!—Raimunda!—He has killed her!—Raimunda! Don't you hear?

RAIMUNDA. Yes, Juliana. Don't let me die without confession. I am dying now. This blood. . . . No matter—Acacia! Acacia!

[253]

JULIANA. Acacia!—Where is she?

ACACIA. Mother, mother!

RAIMUNDA. Ah! Then you are not crying for him? It consoles me.

ACACIA. No, mother! You are my mother!

JULIANA. She is dying! Quick—Raimunda!

ACACIA. Mother, mother!

RAIMUNDA. This man cannot harm you now. You are saved. Blessed be the blood that saves, the blood of our Lord Jesus Christ!

CURTAIN

THE LIFE AND WORKS OF
JACINTO BENAVENTE

By LUIS JARAMILLO

JACINTO BENAVENTE was born in 1866, in the reign of Isabella II, daughter of Ferdinand VII. This was the period when, in the midst of balls and parties in Paris, Napoleon III was pursuing a policy of expediency and risk that was to lead him to disaster in 1870. Since Benavente lived to be eighty-eight, he had plenty of time, starting with that far-away, distant age, in which to observe and assimilate a great many things—surely an essential requirement for a dramatic author.

Benavente's father was born in the Spanish province of Murcia in 1818, and he became a doctor and surgeon greatly loved by the children who were his most numerous patients. Very little is known of Benavente's mother, Venancia Martinez. Benavente had two elder brothers; the first, Mariano, became a lawyer, while the second became a doctor like his father.

Little Jacinto was baptized in the ancient parish of Saint Sebastian, where several other dramatic writers are buried, the most famous among them being Lope de Vega. As a child Jacinto was gifted with precocious judgment, though hardly steeped in piety; indeed he was even inclined to rebellion. For instance, books recommended by his parents and teachers were not at all to his taste; he preferred to spend his time in secret with romantically inspired novels. Benavente also read Cervantes, but until he was ten, he yawned over the pages of Don Quixote. None of this prevented him from being a reasonably good pupil at Saint Joseph's College, and he always remained loyal to the memory of the director of this establishment, Carlos de Miguel, whom he called "a consistently good-tempered man."

Having passed his exams at the Institute of Saint Isidore, Benavente began to study law at the central university in Madrid in 1882. It would be an exaggeration to say that he showed exemplary application to the subject. It happened that during these days of study his passionate love of the theater was born. He was able to indulge his passion freely since he had the good fortune to live in Madrid, and to have a father who had become the personal physician of José Echegaray, another Nobel Prizewinner. This meant that Benavente was able to attend a great many first nights in Madrid theaters. In his biography, Sainz de Robles claims that Benavente used to make little cardboard stage sets where he performed his earliest playlets with marionettes to amuse his young friends.

This was a good start for a future play-wright, and completely in tradition. This love of the theater probably had something hereditary in it because when his father died of an attack of angina pectoris, the book which fell from his hands was *The Tempest*.

His father had hardly gone when Benavente abandoned his studies. He had the means to live a life similar to that of other sons of well-off Madrid families, but he did not lapse into destructive idleness. Instead, he used his freedom to cultivate a vocation that resulted in a life's work of about two hundred plays.

Before starting to write, Benavente steeped himself in the proper atmosphere. Unashamedly he turned night into day, spending time at the famous *tertulias de cafes,* which in Spain are rather what the gatherings of Saint-Germain-des-Prés and the Latin Quarter were in Paris. In particular he frequented La Iberia, on the Saint Jerome road, where peaceful gossip intermingled with the talk of the chess players. Journalists, poets, and politicians all met there and, among others Benavente knew Campoamor, Fernandez Bremón, Eusebio Blasco, Nuñez de Arce, and Luis Taboada. The young carefree Benavente was favorably received: he was always neatly and carefully dressed, something of a fashion-plate, and he always seemed well provided with money.

Benavente's leisure was thus divided among small Bohemian cafes and the Athenaeum library; but he was also to be seen in aristocratic drawing-rooms, at diplomatic receptions, and even at some middle-class gatherings. His small pointed beard and the enormous Havana cigars, or "chair-legs," which he always smoked, combined to make him a familiar figure. The rest of his time was spent traveling in France and Italy.

In about the year 1890, an English trapeze artist, "the beautiful Geraldine," made a sensation in Madrid at the Colon Theater. The gilded youths of the period took up this opulent blonde, who looked rather like a Rubens, and Benavente was the first to join the movement. Time and money were thrown to the winds and, fired by youthful enthusiasm, Benavente became her cavalier. He accompanied her on her professional tours around Spain, loading her with flowers and poems which were full of double meaning and were, in fact, rather mediocre. The romance, however, was short lived, and when Geraldine died in 1928, poor and abandoned, in a hospital in South America, Benavente had not seen her for thirty-five years.

However, the demon of the theater had made its mark on Benavente's mind, and about ten plays which he wrote during these frivolous years were submitted unsuccessfully to the famous actor, Emilio Mario, who was also director of the Comedy Theater. In 1894 Mario finally agreed to put on one of these plays, "the least bad," *El nido ajeno* (Another's Nest, 1894). It is a charming three-act comedy in which the author reveals some satiric verve not without depth, as well as a skeptical and pleasing wit. However, neither the public nor the critics appreciated this effort. Only one young writer, José Martinez Ruiz, whose magazine published theatrical criticism, spoke up for the young playwright. "I delight," he wrote, "in these subtle dialogues, in which from time to time there is a sparkle of wit like La Fontaine's or La Bruyère's. And when the curtain goes down, I say to myself: There is a cultured, elegant, and agreeable writer; his men are witty and his women attractive. I love the women and I respect the men because, now and then, when I have had enough of those who surround me here on earth, his men and women console me a little and give me the illusion that life is not as vulgar as we believe."

Four years later, the Spanish nation

went through a crucial time. It had to resign itself to the loss of its last overseas possessions, the Philippines and Cuba. Under the new order of things, there appeared what came to be known as "the generation of '98," which included men like Unamuno, Baroja, Valle-Inclan, Maetzu, Manuel Bueno, and Antonio Machado, who were poets and playwrights and great fermenters of new beliefs. Benavente became one of the flock, although with a certain amount of reserve. He was in fact in disagreement with the traditions rather than the ideals of the past, and his tastes drew him more particularly toward England and France.

At this time Benavente already had a certain literary output to his credit. Apart from *Another's Nest,* a volume of verse, *Cartes de Mujares* (Women's Letters, 1892–1893), an anthology *Teatro Faniastics* (The Fantastic Theater, 1892), he had written and seen performed *Gente Conôcide* (High Society, 1896), an adaptation of Molière's *Don Juan,* and *La farándula* (The Company of Comedians, 1897). By now his reputation was well established, and his thin face with its long drooping moustache and goatee was well known in the Spanish capital.

His success was rapidly increasing in part because of his talent, but also because the Spanish theater had now reached a critical moment in its evolution. The public was beginning to tire of Echegaray and his imitators, and it needed something new. Benavente had appeared like a meteor, sparkling, strange, and free, and he most nearly resembled the new face for which theatergoers were clamoring. He introduced methods that certainly were new to Spain, such as more directly expressed psychology of the characters, more exact analysis of passions, and a greater audacity of ideas. His phrases were more pointed, while the play on words was

witty, and irony came to the rescue of sentiment. In his plays he attacked both the middle class and the aristocracy. Such was the impression made by Benavente at the end of the nineteenth century, which was only the raising of the curtain for him.

Life continued for Benavente in much the same way as for many of his compatriots, even those who were strangers to the theater. He never went to bed before three in the morning, although bed played an important part in his life because he not only had breakfast in it, but lunch as well. In bed, he read all the newspapers and foreign reviews which he needed in order to keep in touch with current literary trends. He also wrote in bed—at what other time could he do it? He spent the rest of the day and the whole evening flitting in and out of the dressing rooms of well-known actresses, gossiping, relating anecdotes, making jokes, and sometimes playing chess with the actors. He used to wander the streets in a nonchalant way, crunching sweets and other tidbits which he bought from street vendors. Finally, like all self-respecting Madrilleños, he would haunt certain cafes, in particular the Café de Madrid, where he met his colleagues. Valle-Inclan was undoubtedly the noisiest and the most aggressive of the group, while Benavente always remained smiling and calm. From time to time between them a word would flash like lightning or a phrase sparkle like the blade of a knife. Sometimes the arguments became fierce and they nearly came to blows: then there was nothing for it but to move to new surroundings. Valle-Inclan would leave in the direction of the Horchateria Candelas, where syrups were served, and Benavente would go to the Brasserie Anglaise on the Saint Jerome road. It was during this time that Benavente succeeded Clarin as director of the famous review, *La Vida Literaria.*

During the next six years, various Madrid theaters staged Benavente's adaptation of *Love's Labour's Lost* (Cuento de amor, 1899), about twenty comedies including *Rosas de otoño* (Autumnal Roses, 1905), a vaudeville, four tragedies, a novel about the theater, and an adaptation of *Manon Lescaut* (1901), not to mention numerous one-act plays and playlets. This brought the number of his plays performed by the end of 1905 up to more than forty: the author had still not reached his fortieth year. Also in 1905, Benavente received the first of the public honors that were to become the landmarks in his long life: the Spanish theater put on a kind of Benavente festival during which a study of his work, written by the incomparable Galdós, was read aloud. Benavente improvised a few lines of verse by way of thanks.

In this batch of plays, there are some excellent ones. There is also *La comida de las fieras* (*The Wild Beasts' Meal*, 1913), a comedy in three acts. It is amusing to recall the polemics to which this play gave rise. At the time when it was first performed, Gomez Carrillo, a brilliant, Paris-based reporter, blasted Benavente in an article in which he claimed that *The Wild Beasts' Meal* was merely clever plagiarism of François de Curel's *The Lion's Meal*. Being thus accused of plagiarism, Benavente immediately denied Carrillo's charges, and Carrillo did in fact withdraw his accusation and generously admit the temerity of his first criticism. Shortly afterward, Benavente's innocence was officially recognized in a public lecture in which the two texts were compared and their disparity was proved.

In *Los malhechores del bien* (The Virtuous Evil-doers) Benavente gave free play to his satiric bent, mercilessly castigating the upper crust. He brought into the open all the selfishness, cowardice, hypocrisy, and even depravity in the frivolous lives of these privileged people. "Human society," he declared, "is democratic by nature: it has a tendency toward equality and it is only with great difficulty that anyone manages to stand out from the general mediocrity. Strength is needed to achieve this, also power, talent, beauty, and riches. Men struggle round this force like half-tamed wild animals: but finally the lion tamer thinks of feeding them, and the wild beasts seem satisfied until the day when the power crumbles, the money disappears, and the force is no longer there. And when that day comes—ah, don't we all know, the wild beasts' favorite meal is the lion tamer!"

In spite of his particular beliefs, Benavente never posed as a moralist. The reason he wanted to pinpoint the faults and blemishes of his contemporaries was that he saw these faults and blemishes as so many springs in the machinery of dramatic action.

Benavente had several strings to his bow, as can be seen in some of his other plays, which are more sentimental. They represent a kind of bourgeois comedy in which the characters give way to the nobler dictates of their hearts, breaking the bonds of convention binding them to society and rebelling against the tyranny of their oppressors. He turned to tragedy and poetry when he felt the need to escape from satirical comedy. *El dragon de fuego* (The Fire Dragon, 1912), a tragedy in three acts, *La noche del Sábado* (Saturday Night, 1913), a kind of novel about the theater in five tableaux, and *La princesa Bebé* (Princess Bebé, 1915) described by the author as "scenes of modern life divided into five acts," all belong to a group of plays that have an overwhelming kind of grandeur combined with an extreme profusion of ideas; will power which triumphs over fate in order to realize an ideal of justice, or revenge; human effort toward attaining a dreamed-of goal; realized ambition; attempts at a new way of life, even at the cost of daily disasters, to reach new truths. And in all this there is always the sound of laughter, either compassionate or sardonic, sometimes veiled by sorrow. Laughter remains Benavente's favorite weapon. "Laughter is the great grave digger," he assures us, "we weep over living things, which still trouble and still obsess us: when we laugh about something, it means it is truly dead. Shakespeare's clowns constitute the most tragic parts of the tragedies. Hamlet fades away in front of the grave diggers, who are singing and laughing among the graves. When they dig up the skull of Yorick with their spades, it jumps out of the grave still laughing with its clenched and grimacing jaws: everything dies, only laughter lives."

In 1906, for the first time, Benavente went to Latin America with the Manabuerro Company and Fernando Diaz de Mendoza. Both the writer and the actors were a great success. But the following year was to be an even greater one for Benavente as it saw the birth of his masterpiece *Los intereses creados* (The Bonds of Interest, 1907), a marionette comedy in two acts. It is a comedy of great human depth. It is like the barnstorming of ancient farce, very close to that of Molière, and because of this it is rich in lessons on life and men.

Many people think that *Los intereses creados* represents the peak of Benavente's success. He seems especially at ease and in full possession of his powers in this play form, which stems from the *commedia dell'arte* and from the Shakespeare of *A Midsummer Night's Dream* and *As You Like It*. His puppets, manipulated by the strings of selfish interests, teach us stern lessons; but the lessons are without bitterness, they do not preach morality and they do not give us too gloomy a view of life. The comedy is rich in wholesome gaiety from beginning to end, and the dialogue is subtle, sharp, and sensitive. The philosophy which emerges may seem to be a thoroughly cynical one, because vice is shown as being equal to virtue as a means of achieving the desired goal.

The Bonds of Interest had an enormous and unprecedented success which continued for many years. Benavente gave a part of his royalties to a fund to aid Spanish actors and he bought the Villa Rosario, near Toledo, some fifty miles from Madrid, where he subsequently spent long periods. Here he observed the local customs which inspired him to create the characters in *Señora Ama* (The Lady of the House) another of his more famous plays. Performed at the Princess Theater in 1908, it was his favorite among his own works.

In 1912, the Royal Spanish Academy "of the language" honored him with the award of the Piquer Prize.

The performance of *La Malquerida* (The Wrongly Loved) in 1913 was such a success that Benavente was carried home in triumph.

World War I provided Benavente with an opportunity to show himself as a merciless critic of an inhuman and bellicose world, in *La Ciadad alegre y confiada* (The Gay and Light-Hearted Town, 1916). This play had a mixed reception. It was generally considered to be a political gesture and some people were enthusiastic, others irritated. In any case, everyone knew that the character of the hero-exile was based on a real personage, Antonio Maura, then the prime minister. By the end of the war, Benavente had associated himself with Ricardo Calvo as impresario of the Spanish Theater. In 1919, he successfully presented an adaptation of Galdós's very fine novel, *The Audacious One,* a few days before the death of the great novelist and playwright.

Three years later, he was saddened by the loss of his mother, with whom he lived and of whom he always spoke as "the greatest love of my life." For a change of scene, he went to South America on a theatrical tour as artistic director of a company founded by the famous Argentinian actress Lola Membrives. In this way, he introduced a large part of his repertory to numerous countries. He took the opportunity to give a series of lectures in various theaters and universities where he expounded his artistic ideas. It was during the course of this journey that he belatedly heard the news that the Swedish Academy had awarded him the Nobel Prize for Literature.

From then on, honors came to Benavente in rapid succession. In March 1923, at Columbia University, the Institute "of the Spains" organized a reception in his honor, and he was made an honorary citizen of New York. The following year he was named "favorite son" of the city of Madrid in the presence of King Alfonso XIII, who gave him the Grand Cross of King Alfonso XII: the entire government and diplomatic corps were present, and General Primo de Rivera took part in the ceremony. A few days later, a banquet was given in his honor by the cast of his tragedy *Por una vida* (For a Lifetime), and finally, in the autumn of 1923 the Fontalba Theater opened with the first performance of *La virtud sos pechosa* (Suspect Virtue). Benavente then left for Egypt and the Middle East, having meanwhile produced a number of other plays.

But there is another side to Benavente's success story, for a succession of serious worries arose to disturb his peace and quiet and momentarily to tarnish his glory. While he was visiting the Middle East the municipality of Madrid suddenly seized his property as guarantee for payments due by Benavente and Calvo in their capacity as directors of the Spanish

Theater since 1921. On his return, Benavente paid his debts, but he was disgusted by the measures taken against him and returned his medal and Grand Cross to the mayor which, however, he later retrieved. His repertory of plays was nevertheless banned by the Spanish Theater, and the ban remained in force until 1931. Elsewhere, in the Esclava Theater, the government banned the performance of his play *Para el cielo y los altares* (Heaven and the Altars, 1928) because it contained pseudo-revolutionary suggestions which could be interpreted as being hostile to the government.

The public remained faithful to Benavente. In England, an important critic wrote in *The Observer*: "In the whole of Europe there is no more perfect or more proven dramatist. Others may be more human or more disquieting, such as Pirandello; or cause more passionate discussion, such as Shaw; but nobody, on the whole, can outdo Benavente."

However, his worries were not over. In 1931, he suffered his first attacks from Republican elements, as a result of which he reaffirmed his faith in a united Spain in an article published by the Madrid review *ABC*, and he refused to approve the political trends that were being forced on his country.

It seems, however, that politics were to be the bane of Benavente's existence. In 1935, when replying to a tribute paid to him in the Malaga Theater, he gave a somewhat violent speech against Republican ideals. A short time afterward, civil war broke out in Spain. Benavente was in Barcelona getting ready for a holiday. He was arrested at once and taken to the General Commissariat for Public Order but was allowed to go to Valencia, where he remained under house arrest for the duration of the war. Then in September 1936, the editor of a Marxist paper, *El Mercantil Valenciano*, extracted a declaration from him which was in principle favorable to the Republican people's cause: the article was at once reprinted and commented on by the Madrid and foreign press. On several occasions he was to make similar demonstrations: this doubtless explains his appointment as president of the Theater Commission, the advisory body of the Central Theater Council, on the very eve of General Franco's victory.

This kind of turnabout, of which there were many examples in Benavente's life, seems to be opportunism ever so slightly tinged with cynicism. Perhaps Benavente's veerings of opinion and tackings to and fro were simply the results of momentary enthusiasm, all the more keen if the subject was a new one, or of an impulse which was sincere at the time, but which he was unable to sustain for long.

According to Sainz de Robles "the most significant qualities of his theatrical work are irony, moral sense, psychological subtlety, a spontaneous and penetrating intelligence which lays bare the most secret motives, and a vein of skepticism which often rises to the surface: added to this is poetry which gently flows, emanating from a hidden source; an astonishing mastery of technique; and language which is noble, rich, and very evocative."

On July 14, 1954, he died in his house in Madrid at the age of eighty-eight. Many of his characters will survive him, because they are not phantoms, but real men and women integrated into daily life. And yet they preserve that poetic aura with which Benavente surrounded them by virtue of his secret and magic power. Ruben Dario wrote: "Penetrate his theater of dreams, and his theater of goodness. Let yourself be led by the hand that knows how to brush aside the dangerous branches. He will give you all the sweetness of poetry."

Luis Jaramillo is the permanent delegate from Ecuador to UNESCO.
Translated by Camilla Sykes.

THE 1922 PRIZE

By KJELL STRÖMBERG

THE Nobel Prize was awarded Jacinto Benavente "for the happy manner in which he has continued the illustrious traditions of the Spanish drama," according to the Swedish Academy, which likes to justify its choice in each case by publishing a brief report on its reasons for awarding the Prize.

Among the laureate's rivals was a compatriot among them, or a half-compatriot, Angel Guimera y Jorge, a Catalan poet and dramatic writer who had been proposed by the Royal Academy of Literature of Barcelona almost every other year since 1906.

Two Czech writers also entered the lists this year: one of them, Aloïs Jirasek, the creator of the historical novel in Bohemia, was proposed by the arts section of the Czech Academy of Science. The other, Otokar Brezina, "a poet who attained to the sublime in his magnificent mystic poetry," was proposed by the Academy of Brno.

The Swedes and the English insisted on putting forward once more the name of the great eighty-year-old poet and novelist Thomas Hardy, who in his own country, since the deaths of Meredith and Swinburne, who had both died without ever winning the Nobel Prize, was considered to be the most deserving candidate.

Benavente was the author of about a hundred plays which had found their way abroad, but the award caused general surprise mixed with disappointment almost everywhere in the world, except perhaps in Germany. The explanation is given in one of the big Hamburg newspapers, the *Hamburger Nachrichten,* which stated that not only was Benavente the best known and the most esteemed of all Spanish dramatic writers, a kind of "Spanish Shaw," but that he had played a first-class political role during World War I. Whereas a more or less hostile attitude toward Germany had shown itself in various neutral countries, a frankly pro-German popular movement had grown up in Spain, at the head of which Benavente is said to have been very active. He is even supposed to have paid homage to Germany's vocation in the world in a play which had had a certain success in a Frankfurt theater in 1918.

At the time when he won his Prize, Benavente had been living in South America for a year. He was seriously thinking of establishing himself in the Argentine, where his plays were beginning to have some success, and he did not go to Stockholm for the ceremony. Was it because he knew of the coolness with which the news of his award had been received by the literary world and most of the Swedish journalists? Or was it because he was afraid of having to play too obscure a part, overshadowed by those two world-famous giants of science, Albert Einstein and Niels Bohr, who were going there to collect their Prizes at the same time? However that may be, Benavente died in 1954, almost completely forgotten and without ever having set foot in the country of Nobel.

Translated by Camilla Sykes.

Henri Bergson

1927

"In recognition of his rich and
vitalizing ideas and the brilliant
skill with which they have been
presented"

Illustrated by KISCHKA

PRESENTATION ADDRESS

By *PER HALLSTRÖM*

PRESIDENT OF THE NOBEL COMMITTEE
OF THE SWEDISH ACADEMY

IN HIS *L'Évolution créatrice* (*Creative Evolution,* 1907), Henri Bergson has declared that the most lasting and most fruitful of all philosophical systems are those which originate in intuition. If one believes these words, it appears immediately with regard to Bergson's system how he has made fruitful the intuitive discovery that opens the gate to the world of his thought. This discovery is set forth in his doctoral thesis, *Essai sur les données immédiates de la conscience* (*Time and Free Will,* 1889), in which time is conceived not as something abstract or formal but as a reality, indissolubly connected with life and the human self. He gives it the name "duration," a concept that can be interpreted as "living time," by analogy with the life force. It is a dynamic stream, exposed to constant qualitative variations and perpetually increasing. It eludes reflection. It cannot be linked with any fixed point, for it would thereby be limited and no longer exist. It can be perceived and felt only by an introspective and concentrated consciousness that turns inward toward its origin.

What we usually call time, the time which is measured by the movement of a clock or the revolutions of the sun, is something quite different. It is only a form created by and for the mind and action. At the end of a most subtle analysis, Bergson concludes that it is nothing but an application of the form of space. Mathematical precision, certitude, and limitation prevail in its domain; cause is distinguished from effect and hence rises that edifice, a creation of the mind, whose intelligence has encircled the world, raising a wall around the most intimate aspirations of our minds toward freedom. These aspirations find satisfaction in "living time": cause and effect here are fused; nothing can be foreseen with certainty, for certainty resides in the act, simple in itself, and can be established only by this act. Living time is the realm of free choice and new creations, the realm in which something is produced only once and is never repeated in quite the same manner. The history of the personality originates in it. It is the realm where the mind, the soul, whatever one may call it, by casting off the forms and habits of intelligence becomes capable of perceiving in an inner vision the truth about its own essence and about the universal life which is a part of our self.

In his purely scientific account, the philosopher tells us nothing of the origin of this intuition, born perhaps of a personal experience skillfully seized upon and probed, or perhaps of a liberating crisis of the soul. One can only guess that this crisis was provoked by the heavy atmosphere of rationalistic biology that ruled toward the end of the last century. Bergson had been brought up and educated under the influence of this science, and when he decided to take up arms against it, he had a rare mastery of its own weapons and full knowledge of the necessity and grandeur it had in its own realm, the conceptual construction of the material world. Only when rationalism seeks to imprison life itself in its net does Bergson seek to prove that the dynamic and fluid nature of life passes without hindrance across its meshes.

Even if I were competent, it would still be impossible to give an account of the subtlety and scope of Bergson's thought in the few minutes at my disposal. The task is even more impossible for one who possesses only a very limited sense of philosophy and has never studied it.

At his starting point, the intuition of a living time, Bergson borrows in his analysis, in the development of his concepts, and in the sequence of his proofs, something of the dynamic, flowing, and almost irresistible essence of this intuition. One has to follow every movement; every moment introduces a new element. One has to follow the current, trying to breathe as best one can. There is scarcely time for reflection, for the moment one becomes static oneself, one loses all contact with the chain of reasoning.

In a singularly penetrating refutation of determinism our philosopher demonstrates that a universal intellect, which he calls Pierre, could not predict the life of another person, Paul, except in so far as he can follow Paul's experiences, sensations, and voluntary acts in all their manifestations, to the extent of becoming identical with him as completely as two equal triangles coincide. A reader who wants to understand Bergson completely must to a certain extent identify himself with the author and fulfill enormous requirements of power and flexibility of mind.

This is by no means to say that there is no point in following the author in his course, for good or ill. Imagination and intuition are sometimes capable of flights where intelligence lags behind. It is not always possible to decide whether the imagination is seduced or whether the intuition recognizes itself and lets itself be convinced. In any event, reading Bergson is always highly rewarding.

In the account, so far definitive, of his doctrine, *Creative Evolution,* the master has created a poem of striking grandeur, a cosmogony of great scope and unflagging power, without sacrificing a strictly scientific terminology. It may be difficult at times to profit from its penetrating analysis or from the profundity of its thought; but one always derives from it, without any difficulty, a strong esthetic impression.

The poem, if one looks at it in that way, presents a sort of drama. The world has been created by two conflicting tendencies. One of them represents matter which, in its own consciousness, tends downwards; the second is life with its innate sentiment of freedom and its perpetually creative force, which tends increasingly toward the light of knowledge and limitless horizons. These two elements are mingled, prisoners of each other, and the product of this union is ramified on different levels.

The first radical difference is found between the vegetable and the animal world, between immobile and mobile organic activity. With the help of the sun, the vegetable world stores up the energy it extracts from inert matter; the animal is exempt from this fundamental task because it can draw energy already stored up in the vegetables from which it frees the explosive force simultaneously and proportionately to its needs. At a higher level in the chain, the animal world lives at the expense of the animal world, being able, due to this concentration of energy, to accentuate its development. The evolutionary paths thus become more and more diverse and their choice is in no way blind: instinct is born at the same time as the organs that it utilizes. Intellect is also existent in an embryonic stage, but still mind is inferior to instinct.

At the top of the chain of being, in man, intelligence becomes predominant and instinct subsides, without however disappearing entirely;

it remains latent in the consciousness that unites all life in the current of "living time"; it comes into play in the intuitive vision. The beginnings of intelligence are modest and manifestly timid. Intelligence is expressed only by the tendency and the ability to replace organic instruments instinctively by instruments sprung from inert matter, and to make use of them by a free act. Instinct was more conscious of its goal, but this goal was, on the other hand, greatly limited; intelligence engaged itself, on the contrary, in greater risks, but tended also toward infinitely vaster goals, toward goals realized by the material and social culture of the human race. Inevitably a risk existed, however: intelligence, created to act in the spatial world, might distort the image of the world by the modality thus acquired from its concept of life and might remain deaf to its innermost dynamic essence and to the freedom that presides over its eternal variation. Hence the mechanistic and deterministic conception of an external world created by the conquests of intelligence in the natural sciences.

We will find ourselves, then, irremediably cornered in an impasse, without any consciousness of freedom of mind and cut off from the sources of life we carry within us, unless we also possess the gift of intuition when we trace ourselves back to our origin. Perhaps one can apply to this intuition, the central point of the Bergsonian doctrine, the brilliant expression that he uses about intelligence and instinct: the perilous way toward vaster possibilities. Within the limits of its knowledge, intelligence possesses logical certainty, but intuition, dynamic like everything that belongs to living time, must without doubt content itself with the intensity of its certainty.

This is the drama: creative evolution is disclosed, and man finds himself thrust on stage by the *élan vital* of universal life which pushes him irresistibly to act, once he has come to the knowledge of his own freedom, capable of divining and glimpsing the endless route that has been traveled with the perspective of a boundless field opening onto other paths. Which of these paths is man going to follow?

In reality we are only at the beginning of the drama, and it can scarcely be otherwise, especially if one considers Bergson's concept that the future is born only at the moment in which it is lived. However, something is lacking in this beginning itself. The author tells us nothing of the will inherent in the free personality, of the will that determines action and that has the power to trace straight lines across the unforeseeable curves of this personality. Furthermore, he tells us nothing about the problem of life dominated by will power, about the existence or non-existence of absolute values.

What is the essence of the irresistible *élan vital,* that onslaught of life against the inertia of matter, which, according to Bergson's audacious and magnificent expression, will one day triumph perhaps over death itself? What will it make of us when it places at our feet all earthly power?

However complicated they may be, one cannot escape these questions. Is the philosopher perhaps at this very moment on his way to the solution, certainly as tentative and audacious as his previous work has been and richer still in possibilities?

There still remain some points to clarify. Does he perhaps seek to put an end to the dualism of the image he gives of the world in seeking out a kind of *élan vital* that applies to matter? We know nothing in this regard, but Bergson has himself presented his system as constituting, on many points, only an outline that must be completed in its details by the collaboration of other thinkers.

We are indebted to him, nevertheless, for one achievement of importance: by a passage he has forced through the gates of rationalism, he has released a creative impulse of inestimable value, opening a large access to the waters of living time, to that atmosphere in which the human mind will be able to rediscover its freedom and thus be born anew.

If the outlines of his thought prove sound enough to serve as guides to the human spirit, Bergson can be assured, in the future, of an influence even greater than the influence he is already enjoying. As stylist and as poet, he yields place to none of his contemporaries; in their strictly objective search for truth, all his aspirations are animated by a spirit of freedom which, breaking the servitude that matter imposes, makes room for idealism.

ACCEPTANCE SPEECH

By *HENRI BERGSON*

I WISH I HAD BEEN ABLE to express my feelings in person. Permit me to do so through the French Minister, Mr. Armand Bernard, who has kindly consented to convey my message. I thank the Swedish Academy from the bottom of my heart. It has bestowed upon me an honor to which I should not have dared aspire. I recognize its value even more, and I am even more moved by it, when I consider that this distinction, given to a French writer, may be regarded as a sign of sympathy given to France.

The prestige of the Nobel Prize is due to many causes, but in particular to its twofold idealistic and international character: idealistic in that it has been designed for works of lofty inspiration; international in that it is awarded after the production of different countries has been minutely studied and the intellectual balance sheet of the whole world has been drawn up. Free from all other considerations and ignoring any but intellectual values, the judges have deliberately taken their place in what the philosophers have called a community of the mind. Thus they conform to the founder's explicit intention.

Alfred Bernhard Nobel declared in his will that he wanted to serve the causes of idealism and the brotherhood of nations. By establishing a Peace Prize alongside the high awards in arts and sciences, he marked his goal with precision. It was a great idea. Its originator was an inventive genius and yet he apparently did not share an illusion widespread in his century. If the nineteenth century made tremendous progress in mechanical inventions, it too often assumed that these inventions, by the sheer accumulation of their material effects, would raise the moral level of mankind. Increasing experience has proved, on the contrary, that the technological development of a society does not automatically result in the moral perfection of the men living in it, and that an increase in the material means at the disposal of humanity may even present dangers unless it is accompanied by a corresponding spiritual effort. The machines we build, being artificial organs that are added to our natural organs, extend their scope, and thus enlarge the body of humanity. If that body is to be kept entire and its movements regulated, the soul must expand in turn; otherwise its equilibrium will be threatened and grave difficulties will arise, social as well as political, which will reflect on another level the disproportion between the soul of mankind, hardly changed from its original state, and its enormously enlarged body. To take only the most striking example: one might have expected that the use of steam and electricity, by diminishing distances, would by itself bring about a moral *rapprochement* between peoples. Today we know that this was not the case and that antagonisms, far from disappearing, will risk being aggravated if a spiritual progress, a greater effort toward brotherhood, is not accomplished. To move toward such a *rapprochement* of souls is the natural tendency of a foundation with an international character and an idealistic outlook which implies that the entire civilized world is envisaged from a purely intellectual point of view as constituting one single and identical republic of minds. Such is the Nobel Foundation.

It is not surprising that this idea was conceived and realized in a country as highly intellectual as Sweden, among a people who have given so much attention to moral questions and have recognized that all others follow from them, and who, to cite only one example, have been the first to grasp that the political problem par excellence is the problem of education.

Thus the scope of the Nobel Foundation seems to widen as its significance is more deeply realized, and to have benefited from it becomes an honor all the more deeply appreciated. No one is more fully aware of this than I am. I wish to say so before this illustrious audience, and I conclude, as I began, with the expression of my profound gratitude.

CREATIVE EVOLUTION

By HENRI BERGSON

Translated by Arthur Mitchell

[Excerpt]

The history of the evolution of life, incomplete as it yet is, already reveals to us how the intellect has been formed, by an uninterrupted progress, along a line which ascends through the vertebrate series up to man. It shows us in the faculty of understanding an appendage of the faculty of acting, a more and more precise, more and more complex and supple adaptation of the consciousness of living beings to the conditions of existence that are made for them. Hence should result this consequence that our intellect, in the narrow sense of the word, is intended to secure the perfect fitting of our body to its environment, to represent the relations of external things among themselves—in short, to think matter. Such will indeed be one of the conclusions of the present essay. We shall see that the human intellect feels at home among inanimate objects, more especially among solids, where our action finds its fulcrum and our industry its tools; that our concepts have been formed on the model of solids; that our logic is, pre-eminently, the logic of solids; that, consequently, our intellect triumphs in geometry, wherein is revealed the kinship of logical thought with unorganized matter, and where the intellect has only to follow its natural movement, after the lightest possible contact with experience, in order to go from discovery to discovery, sure that experience is following behind it and will justify it invariably.

But from this it must also follow that our thought, in its purely logical form, is incapable of presenting the true nature of life, the full meaning of the evolutionary movement. Created by life, in definite circumstances, to act on definite things, how can it embrace life, of which it is only an emanation or an aspect? Deposited by the evolutionary movement in the course of its way, how can it be applied to the evolutionary movement itself? As well contend that the part is equal to the whole, that the effect can reabsorb its cause, or that the pebble left on the beach displays the form of the wave that brought it there. In fact, we do indeed feel that not one of the categories of our thought—unity, multiplicity, mechanical causality, intelligent finality, etc. —applies exactly to the things of life: who can say where individuality begins and ends, whether the living being is one or many, whether it is the cells which associate themselves into the organism or the organism which dissociates itself into cells? In vain we force the living into this or that one of our molds. All the molds crack. They are too narrow, above all too rigid, for what we try to put into them. Our reasoning, so sure of itself among things inert, feels ill at ease on this new ground. It would be difficult to cite a biological discovery due to pure reasoning. And most often, when experience has finally shown us how life goes to work to obtain a certain result, we find its way of working is just that of which we should never have thought.

Yet evolutionist philosophy does not hesitate to extend to the things of life the same methods of explanation which have succeeded in the case of unorganized matter. It begins by showing us in the intellect a local effect of evolution, a flame, perhaps accidental, which lights up the coming and going of living beings in the narrow passage open to their action; and lo! forgetting what it has just told us, it makes of this lantern glimmering in a tunnel a Sun which can illuminate the world. Boldly it proceeds, with the powers of conceptual thought alone, to the ideal reconstruction of all things, even of life. True, it hurtles in its course against such formidable difficulties, it sees its logic end in such strange contradictions, that it very speedily renounces its first ambition. "It is no longer reality itself," it says, "that it will reconstruct, but only an imitation of the real, or rather a symbolical image; the essence of things escapes us, and will escape us always; we move among relations; the absolute is not in our province; we are brought to a stand before the Unknowable."—But for the human intellect, after too much pride, this is really an excess of humility. If the intellectual form of the living being has been gradually modeled on the reciprocal actions and reactions of certain bodies and their material environment, how should it not reveal to us something of the very essence of which these bodies are made? Action cannot

move in the unreal. A mind born to speculate or to dream, I admit, might remain outside reality, might deform or transform the real, perhaps even create it—as we create the figures of men and animals that our imagination cuts out of the passing cloud. But an intellect bent upon the act to be performed and the reaction to follow, feeling its object so as to get its mobile impression at every instant, is an intellect that touches something of the absolute. Would the idea ever have occurred to us to doubt this absolute value of our knowledge if philosophy had not shown us what contradictions our speculation meets, what dead-locks it ends in? But these difficulties and contradictions all arise from trying to apply the usual forms of our thought to objects with which our industry has nothing to do, and for which, therefore, our molds are not made. Intellectual knowledge, in so far as it relates to a certain aspect of inert matter, ought, on the contrary, to give us a faithful imprint of it, having been stereotyped on this particular object. It becomes relative only if it claims, such as it is, to present to us life—that is to say, the maker of the stereotype-plate.

Must we then give up fathoming the depths of life? Must we keep to that mechanistic idea of it which the understanding will always give us—an idea necessarily artificial and symbolical, since it makes the total activity of life shrink to the form of a certain human activity which is only a partial and local manifestation of life, a result or by-product of the vital process? We should have to do so, indeed, if life had employed all the psychical potentialities it possesses in producing pure understandings—that is to say, in making geometricians. But the line of evolution that ends in man is not the only one. On other paths, divergent from it, other forms of consciousness have been developed, which have not been able to free themselves from external constraints or to regain control over themselves, as the human intellect has done, but which, none the less, also express something that is immanent and essential in the evolutionary movement. Suppose these other forms of consciousness brought together and amalgamated with intellect: would not the result be a consciousness as wide as life? And such a consciousness, turning around suddenly against the push of life which it feels behind, would have a vision of life complete—would it not?—even though the vision were fleeting.

It will be said that, even so, we do not transcend our intellect, for it is still with our intellect, and through our intellect, that we see the other forms of consciousness. And this would be right if we were pure intellects, if there did not remain, around our conceptual and logical thought, a vague nebulosity, made of the very substance out of which has been formed the luminous nucleus that we call the intellect. Therein reside certain powers that are complementary to the understanding, powers of which we have only an indistinct feeling when we remain shut up in ourselves, but which will become clear and distinct when they perceive themselves at work, so to speak, in the evolution of nature. They will thus learn what sort of effort they must make to be intensified and expanded in the very direction of life.

This amounts to saying that *theory of knowledge* and *theory of life* seem to us inseparable. A theory of life that is not accompanied by a criticism of knowledge is obliged to accept, as they stand, the concepts which the understanding puts at its disposal: it can but enclose the facts, willing or not, in pre-existing frames which it regards as ultimate. It thus obtains a symbolism which is convenient, perhaps even necessary to positive science, but not a direct vision of its object. On the other hand, a theory of knowledge which does not replace the intellect in the general evolution of life will teach us neither how the frames of knowledge have been constructed nor how we can enlarge or go beyond them. It is necessary that these two inquiries, theory of knowledge and theory of life, should join each other, and, by a circular process, push each other on unceasingly.

Together, they may solve by a method more sure, brought nearer to experience, the great problems that philosophy poses. For, if they should succeed in their common enterprise, they would show us the formation of the intellect, and thereby the genesis of that matter of which our intellect traces the general configuration. They would dig to the very root of nature and of mind. They would substitute for the false evolutionism of Spencer—which consists in cutting up present reality, already evolved, into little bits no less evolved, and then recomposing it with these fragments, thus positing in advance everything that is to be explained—a true evolutionism, in which reality would be followed in its generation and its growth.

But a philosophy of this kind will not be made in a day. Unlike the philosophical systems properly so called, each of which was the individual work of a man of genius and sprang up as a whole, to be taken or left, it will only be built up by the collective and progressive effort of many thinkers, of many observers also, completing, correcting and improving one another. So the present essay does not aim at resolving at once the greatest problems. It simply desires to define the method and to permit a glimpse, on some essential points, of the possibility of its application.

Its plan is traced by the subject itself. In the first chapter, we try on the evolutionary progress the two ready-made garments that our understanding puts at our disposal, mechanism and finality;[1] we show that they do not fit, neither the one nor the other, but that one of them might be recut and resewn, and in this new form fit less badly than the other. In order to transcend the point of view of the understanding, we try, in our second chapter, to reconstruct the main lines of evolution along which life has traveled by the side of that which has led to the human intellect. The intellect is thus brought back to its generating cause, which we then have to grasp in itself and follow in its movement. It is an effort of this kind that we attempt—incompletely indeed—in our third chapter. A fourth and last part is meant to show how our understanding itself, by submitting to a certain discipline, might prepare a philosophy which transcends it. For that, a glance over the history of systems became necessary, together with an analysis of the two great illusions to which, as soon as it speculates on reality in general, the human understanding is exposed.

---

[1] The idea of regarding life as transcending teleology as well as mechanism is far from being a new idea. Notably in three articles by Ch. Dunan on "Le problème de la vie" (*Revue philosophique,* 1892) it is profoundly treated. In the development of this idea, we agree with Ch. Dunan on more than one point. But the views we are presenting on this matter, as on the questions attaching to it, are those that we expressed long ago in our *Essai sur les données immédiates de la conscience* (Paris, 1889). One of the principal objects of that essay was, in fact, to show that the psychical life is neither unity nor multiplicity, that it transcends both the *mechanical* and the *intellectual,* mechanism and finalism having meaning only where there is "distinct multiplicity," "spatiality," and consequently assemblage of pre-existing parts: "real duration" signifies both undivided continuity and creation. In the present work we apply these same ideas to life in general, regarded, moreover, itself from the psychological point of view.

CHAPTER I

The Evolution of Life—Mechanism and Teleology

The existence of which we are most assured and which we know best is unquestionably our own, for of every other object we have notions which may be considered external and superficial, whereas, of ourselves, our perception is internal and profound. What, then, do we find? In this privileged case, what is the precise meaning of the word "exist"? Let us recall here briefly the conclusions of an earlier work.

I find, first of all, that I pass from state to state. I am warm or cold, I am merry or sad, I work or I do nothing, I look at what is around me or I think of something else. Sensations, feelings, volitions, ideas—such are the changes into which my existence is divided and which color it in turns. I change, then, without ceasing. But this is not saying enough. Change is far more radical than we are at first inclined to suppose.

For I speak of each of my states as if it formed a block and were a separate whole. I say indeed that I change, but the change seems to me to reside in the passage from one state to the next: of each state, taken separately, I am apt to think that it remains the same during all the time that it prevails. Nevertheless, a slight effort of attention would reveal to me that there is no feeling, no idea, no volition which is not undergoing change every moment: if a mental state ceased to vary, its duration would cease to flow. Let us take the most stable of internal states, the visual perception of a motionless external object. The object may remain the same, I may look at it from the same side, at the same angle, in the same light; nevertheless the vision I now have of it differs from that which I have just had, even if only because the one is an instant older than the other. My memory is there, which conveys something of the past into the present. My mental state, as it advances on the road of time, is continually swelling with the duration which it accumulates: it goes on increasing—rolling upon itself, as a snowball on the snow. Still more is this the case with states more deeply internal, such as sensations, feelings, desires, etc., which do not correspond, like a simple visual perception, to an unvarying external object. But it is expedient to disregard this uninterrupted change, and to notice it only when it becomes sufficient to impress a new attitude on the body, a new direction on the attention. Then, and then only, we find that our state has changed. The truth is that we change without ceasing, and that the state itself is nothing but change.

This amounts to saying that there is no essential difference between passing from one state to another and persisting in the same state. If the state which "remains the same" is more varied than we think, on the other hand the passing from one state to another resembles, more than we imagine, a single state being prolonged; the transition is continuous. But, just because we close our eyes to the unceasing variation of every psychical state, we are obliged, when the change has become so considerable as to force itself on our attention, to speak as if a new state were placed alongside the previous one. Of this new state we assume that it remains unvarying in its turn, and so on endlessly. The apparent discontinuity of the psychical life is then due to our attention being fixed on it by a series of separate acts: actually there is only a gentle slope; but in following the broken line of our acts of attention, we think we perceive separate steps. True, our psychic life is full of the unforeseen. A thousand incidents arise, which seem to be cut off from those which precede them, and to be disconnected from those which follow. Discontinuous though they appear, however, in point of fact they stand out against the continuity of a background on which they are designed, and to which indeed they owe the intervals that separate them; they are the beats of the drum which break forth here and there in the symphony. Our attention fixes on them because they interest it more, but each of them is borne by the fluid mass of our whole psychical existence. Each is only the best illuminated point of a moving zone which comprises all that we feel or think or will—all, in short, that we are at any given moment. It is this entire zone which in reality makes up our state. Now, states thus defined cannot be regarded as distinct elements. They continue each other in an endless flow.

But, as our attention has distinguished and separated them artificially, it is obliged next to reunite them by an artificial bond. It imagines, therefore, a formless *ego*, indifferent and unchangeable, on which it threads the psychic states which it has set up as independent entities. Instead of a flux of fleeting shades merging into each other, it perceives distinct and, so to speak, *solid* colors, set side by side like the beads of a necklace; it must perforce then suppose a thread, also itself solid, to hold the beads together. But if this colorless substratum is perpetually colored by that which covers it, it is for us, in its indeterminateness, as if it did not exist, since we only perceive what is colored, or, in other words, psychic states. As a matter of fact, this substratum has no reality; it is merely a symbol intended to recall unceasingly to our consciousness the artificial character of the process by which the attention places clean-cut states side by side, where actually there is a continuity which unfolds. If our existence were composed of separate states with an impassive ego to unite them, for us there would be no duration. For an ego which does not change does not *endure,* and a psychic state which remains the same so long as it is not replaced by the following state does not *endure* either. Vain, therefore, is the attempt to range such states beside each other on the ego supposed to sustain them: never can these solids strung upon a solid make up that duration which flows. What we actually obtain in this way is an artificial imitation of the internal life, a static equivalent which will lend itself better to the requirements of logic and language, just because we have eliminated from it the element of real time. But, as regards the psychical life unfolding beneath the symbols which conceal it, we readily perceive that time is just the stuff it is made of.

There is, moreover, no stuff more resistant nor more substantial. For our duration is not merely one instant replacing another; if it were, there would never be anything but the present—no prolonging of the past into the actual, no evolution, no concrete duration. Duration is the continuous progress of the past which gnaws into the future and which swells as it advances. And as the past grows without ceasing, so also there is no limit to its preservation. Memory, as we have tried to prove,[1] is not a faculty of putting away recollections in a drawer, or of inscribing them in a register. There is no register, no drawer; there is not even, properly speaking, a faculty, for a faculty works intermittently, when it will or when it can, while the piling up of the past upon the past goes on without relaxation. In reality, the past is preserved by itself, automatically. In its entirety, probably, it follows us at every instant; all that we have felt, thought and willed

from our earliest infancy is there, leaning over the present which is about to join it, pressing against the portals of consciousness that would fain leave it outside. The cerebral mechanism is arranged just so as to drive back into the unconscious almost the whole of this past, and to admit beyond the threshold only that which can cast light on the present situation or further the action now being prepared—in short, only that which can give *useful* work. At the most, a few superfluous recollections may succeed in smuggling themselves through the half-open door. These memories, messengers from the unconscious, remind us of what we are dragging behind us unawares. But, even though we may have no distinct idea of it, we feel vaguely that our past remains present to us. What are we, in fact, what is our *character,* if not the condensation of the history that we have lived from our birth—nay, even before our birth, since we bring with us prenatal dispositions? Doubtless we think with only a small part of our past, but it is with our entire past, including the original bent of our soul, that we desire, will and act. Our past, then, as a whole, is made manifest to us in its impulse; it is felt in the form of tendency, although a small part of it only is known in the form of idea.

From this survival of the past it follows that consciousness cannot go through the same state twice. The circumstances may still be the same, but they will act no longer on the same person, since they find him at a new moment of his history. Our personality, which is being built up each instant with its accumulated experience, changes without ceasing. By changing, it prevents any state, although superficially identical with another, from ever repeating it in its very depth. That is why our duration is irreversible. We could not live over again a single moment, for we should have to begin by effacing the memory of all that

---

[1] *Matière et mémoire,* Paris, 1896, chaps. ii. and iii.

had followed. Even could we erase this memory from our intellect, we could not from our will.

Thus our personality shoots, grows and ripens without ceasing. Each of its moments is something new added to what was before. We may go further: it is not only something new, but something unforeseeable. Doubtless, my present state is explained by what was in me and by what was acting on me a moment ago. In analyzing it I should find no other elements. But even a superhuman intelligence would not have been able to foresee the simple indivisible form which gives to these purely abstract elements their concrete organization. For to foresee consists of projecting into the future what has been perceived in the past, or of imagining for a later time a new grouping, in a new order, of elements already perceived. But that which has never been perceived, and which is at the same time simple, is necessarily unforeseeable. Now such is the case with each of our states, regarded as a moment in a history that is gradually unfolding: it is simple, and it cannot have been already perceived, since it concentrates in its indivisibility all that has been perceived and what the present is adding to it besides. It is an original moment of a no less original history.

The finished portrait is explained by the features of the model, by the nature of the artist, by the colors spread out on the palette; but, even with the knowledge of what explains it, no one, not even the artist, could have foreseen exactly what the portrait would be, for to predict it would have been to produce it before it was produced—an absurd hypothesis which is its own refutation. Even so with regard to the moments of our life, of which we are the artisans. Each of them is a kind of creation. And just as the talent of the painter is formed or deformed—in any case, is modified—under

the very influence of the works he produces, so each of our states, at the moment of its issue, modifies our personality, being indeed the new form that we are just assuming. It is then right to say that what we do depends on what we are; but it is necessary to add also that we are, to a certain extent, what we do, and that we are creating ourselves continually. This creation of self by self is the more complete, the more one reasons on what one does. For reason does not proceed in such matters as in geometry, where impersonal premises are given once for all, and an impersonal conclusion must perforce be drawn. Here, on the contrary, the same reasons may dictate to different persons, or to the same person at different moments, acts profoundly different, although equally reasonable. The truth is that they are not quite the same reasons, since they are not those of the same person, nor of the same moment. That is why we cannot deal with them in the abstract, from outside, as in geometry, nor solve for another the problems by which he is faced in life. Each must solve them from within, on his own account. But we need not go more deeply into this. We are seeking only the precise meaning that our consciousness gives to this word "exist," and we find that, for a conscious being, to exist is to change, to change is to mature, to mature is to go on creating oneself endlessly. Should the same be said of existence in general?

A material object, of whatever kind, presents opposite characters to those which we have just been describing. Either it remains as it is, or else, if it changes under the influence of an external force, our idea of this change is that of a displacement of parts which themselves do not change. If these parts took to changing, we should split them up in their turn. We should thus descend to the molecules of which the fragments are made, to the atoms that make up the molecules, to the corpuscles that generate the atoms, to the "imponderable" within which the corpuscle is perhaps a mere vortex. In short, we should push the division or analysis as far as necessary. But we should stop only before the unchangeable.

Now, we say that a composite object changes by the displacement of its parts. But when a part has left its position, there is nothing to prevent its return to it. A group of elements which has gone through a state can therefore always find its way back to that state, if not by itself, at least by means of an external cause able to restore everything to its place. This amounts to saying that any state of the group may be repeated as often as desired, and consequently that the group does not grow old. It has no history.

Thus nothing is created therein, neither form nor matter. What the group will be is already present in what it is, provided "what it is" includes all the points of the universe with which it is related. A superhuman intellect could calculate, for any moment of time, the position of any point of the system in space. And as there is nothing more in the form of the whole than the arrangement of its parts, the future forms of the system are theoretically visible in its present configuration.

All our belief in objects, all our operations on the systems that science isolates, rest in fact on the idea that time does not bite into them. We have touched on this question in an earlier work, and shall return to it in the course of the present study. For the moment, we will confine ourselves to pointing out that the abstract time t attributed by science to a material object or to an isolated system consists only in a certain number of simultaneities or more generally of correspondences, and that this number remains the same, whatever be the nature of the intervals between the correspondences. With these intervals we are never concerned when dealing with inert matter; or, if they are considered, it is in order to count therein fresh correspondences, between which again we shall not care what happens. Common sense, which is occupied with detached objects, and also science, which considers isolated systems, are concerned only with the ends of the intervals and not with the intervals themselves. Therefore the flow of time might assume an infinite rapidity, the entire past, present, and future of material objects or of isolated systems might be spread out all at once in space, without there being anything to change either in the formulae of the scientist or even in the language of common sense. The number t would always stand for the same thing; it would still count the same number of correspondences between the states of the objects or systems and the points of the line, ready drawn, which would be then the "course of time."

Yet succession is an undeniable fact, even in the material world. Though our reasoning on isolated systems may imply that their history, past, present and future, might be instantaneously unfurled like a fan, this history, in point of fact, unfolds itself gradually, as if it occupied a duration like our own. If I want to mix a glass of sugar and water, I must, willy-nilly, wait until the sugar melts. This little fact is big with meaning. For here the time I have to wait is not that mathematical time which would apply equally well to the entire history of the material world, even if that history were spread out instantaneously in space. It coincides with my impatience, that is to say, with a certain portion of my own duration, which I cannot protract or contract as I like. It is no longer something *thought*, it is something *lived*. It is no longer a relation, it is an absolute. What else can this mean than that the glass of water, the sugar, and the process of the sugar's melting in the water are abstractions, and that the Whole within which they have been cut out by my senses and understanding progresses, it may be in the manner of a consciousness?

Certainly, the operation by which science isolates and closes a system is not altogether artificial. If it had no objective foundation, we could not explain why it is clearly indicated in some cases and impossible in others. We shall see that matter has a tendency to constitute *isolable* systems, that can be treated geometrically. In fact, we shall define matter by just this tendency. But it is only a tendency. Matter does not go to the end, and the isolation is never complete. If science does go to the end and isolate completely, it is for convenience of study; it is understood that the so-called isolated system remains subject to certain external influences. Science merely leaves these alone, either because it finds them slight enough to be negligible, or because it intends to take them into account later on. It is none the less true that these influences are so many threads which bind up the system to another more extensive, and to this a third which includes both, and so on to the system most objectively isolated and most independent of all, the solar system complete. But, even here, the isolation is not absolute. Our sun radiates heat and light beyond the farthest planet. And, on the other hand, it moves in a certain fixed direction, drawing with it the planets and their satellites. The thread attaching it to the rest of the universe is doubtless very tenuous. Nevertheless it is along this thread that is transmitted down to the smallest particle of the world in which we live the duration immanent to the whole of the universe.

The universe *endures*. The more we study the nature of time, the more we shall comprehend that duration means invention, the creation of forms, the continual elaboration of the absolutely new. The systems marked off by science *endure* only because they are bound up inseparably with the rest of the universe. It is true that in the universe itself two opposite movements are to be distinguished, as we shall see later on, "descent" and "ascent." The first only unwinds a roll ready prepared. In principle, it might be accomplished almost instantaneously, like releasing a spring. But the ascending movement, which corresponds to an inner work of ripening or creating, *endures* essentially, and imposes its rhythm on the first, which is inseparable from it.

There is no reason, therefore, why a duration, and so a form of existence like our own, should not be attributed to the systems that science isolates, provided such systems are reintegrated into the Whole. But they must be so reintegrated. The same is even more obviously true of the objects cut out by our perception. The distinct outlines which we see in an object, and which give it its individuality, are only the design of a certain kind of *influence* that we might exert on a certain point of space: it is the plan of our eventual actions that is sent back to our eyes, as though by a mirror, when we see the surfaces and edges of things. Suppress this action, and with it consequently those main directions which by perception are traced out for it in the entanglement of the real, and the individuality of the body is reabsorbed in the universal interaction which, without doubt, is reality itself.

Now, we have considered material objects generally. Are there not some objects privileged? The bodies we perceive are, so to speak, cut out of the stuff of nature by our *perception,* and the scissors follow, in some way, the marking of lines along which *action* might be taken.

But the body which is to perform this action, the body which marks out upon matter the design of its eventual actions even before they are actual, the body that has only to point its sensory organs on the flow of the real in order to make that flow crystallize into definite forms and thus to create all the other bodies—in short, the *living* body—is this a body as others are?

Doubtless it, also, consists in a portion of extension bound up with the rest of extension, an intimate part of the Whole, subject to the same physical and chemical laws that govern any and every portion of matter. But, while the subdivision of matter into separate bodies is relative to our perception, while the building up of closed-off systems of material points is relative to our science, the living body has been separated and closed off by nature herself. It is composed of unlike parts that complete each other. It performs diverse functions that involve each other. It is an *individual,* and of no other object, not even of the crystal, can this be said, for a crystal has neither difference of parts nor diversity of functions. No doubt, it is hard to decide, even in the organized world, what is individual and what is not. The difficulty is great, even in the animal kingdom; with plants it is almost insurmountable. This difficulty is, moreover, due to profound causes, on which we shall dwell later. We shall see that individuality admits of any number of degrees, and that it is not fully realized anywhere, even in man. But that is no reason for thinking it is not a characteristic property of life. The biologist who proceeds as a geometrician is too ready to take advantage here of our inability to give a precise and general definition of individuality. A perfect definition applies only to a *completed* reality; now, vital properties are never entirely realized, though always on the way to become so; they are not so much *states* as *tendencies.* And a tendency achieves all that it aims at only if it is not thwarted by another tendency. How, then, could this occur in the domain of life, where, as we shall show, the interaction of antagonistic tendencies is always implied? In particular, it may be said of individuality that, while the tendency to individuate is everywhere present in the organized world, it is everywhere opposed by the tendency toward reproduction. For the individuality to be perfect, it would be necessary that no detached part of the organism could live separately. But then reproduction would be impossible. For what is reproduction, but the building up of a new organism with a detached fragment of the old? Individuality therefore harbors its enemy at home. Its very need of perpetuating itself in time condemns it never to be complete in space. The biologist must take due account of both tendencies in every instance, and it is therefore useless to ask him for a definition of individuality that shall fit all cases and work automatically.

But too often one reasons about the things of life in the same way as about the conditions of crude matter. Nowhere is the confusion so evident as in discussions about individuality. We are shown the stumps of a Lumbriculus, each regenerating its head and living thenceforward as an independent individual; a hydra whose pieces become so many fresh hydras; a sea-urchin's egg whose fragments develop complete embryos: where then, we are asked, was the individuality of the egg, the hydra, the worm?—But, because there are several individuals now, it does not follow that there was not a single individual just before. No doubt, when I have seen several drawers fall from a chest, I have no longer the right to say that the article was all of one piece. But the fact is that there can be nothing more in the present of the chest of drawers than there was in its past, and if it is made up of several different pieces now, it was so from the date of its manufacture. Generally speaking, unorganized bodies, which are what we have need of in order that we may act, and on which we have modeled our fashion of thinking, are regulated by this simple law: *the present contains nothing more than the past, and what is found in the effect was already in the cause.* But suppose that the distinctive feature of the organized body is that it grows and changes without ceasing, as indeed the most superficial observation testifies, there would be nothing astonishing in the fact that it was *one* in the first instance, and afterwards *many*. The reproduction of unicellular organisms consists in just this—the living being divides into two halves, of which each is a complete individual. True, in the more complex animals, nature localizes in the almost independent sexual cells the power of producing the whole anew. But something of its power may remain diffused in the rest of the organism, as the facts of regeneration prove, and it is conceivable that in certain privileged cases the faculty may persist integrally in a latent condition and manifest itself on the first opportunity. In truth, that I may have the right to speak of individuality, it is not necessary that the organism should be without the power to divide into fragments that are able to live. It is sufficient that it should have presented a certain systematization of parts before the division, and that the same systematization tends to be reproduced in each separate portion afterwards. Now, that is precisely what we observe in the organic world. We may conclude, then, that individuality is never perfect, and that it is often difficult, sometimes impossible, to tell what is an individual, and what is not, but that life nevertheless manifests a search for individuality, as if it strove to constitute systems naturally isolated, naturally closed.

By this is a living being distinguished from all that our perception or our science isolates or closes artificially. It would therefore be wrong to compare it to an *object*. Should we wish to find a term of comparison in the inorganic world, it is not to a determinate material object, but much rather to the totality of the material universe that we ought to compare the living organism. It is true that the comparison would not be worth much, for a living being is observable, while the whole of the universe is constructed or reconstructed by thought. But at least our attention would thus have been called to the essential character of organization. Like the universe as a whole, like each conscious being taken separately, the organism which lives is a thing that *endures*. Its past, in its entirety, is prolonged into its present, and abides there, actual and acting. How otherwise could we understand that it passes through distinct and well-marked phases, that it changes its age—in short, that it has a history? If I consider my body in particular, I find that, like my consciousness, it matures little by little from infancy to old age; like myself, it grows old. Indeed, maturity and old age are, properly speaking, attributes only of my body; it is only metaphorically that I apply the same names to the corresponding changes of my conscious self. Now, if I pass from the top to the bottom of the scale of living beings, from one of the most to one of the least differentiated, from the multicellular organism of man to the unicellular organism of the Infusorian, I find, even in this simple cell, the same process of growing old. The Infusorian is exhausted at the end of a certain number of divisions, and though it may be possible, by modifying the environment, to put off the moment when a rejuvenation by conjugation becomes necessary, this cannot be indefinitely postponed.[1] It is true that between these two extreme cases, in which the organism is completely individualized, there might be found a multitude of others in which the individuality is less well marked, and in which, although there is doubtless an aging somewhere, one cannot say exactly what it is that grows old. Once more, there is no universal biological law which applies precisely and automatically to every living thing. There are only *directions* in which life throws out species in general. Each particular species, in the very act by which it is constituted, affirms its independence, follows its caprice, deviates more or less from the straight line, sometimes even remounts the slope and seems to turn its back on its original direction. It is easy enough to argue that a tree never grows old, since the tips of its branches are always equally young, always equally capable of engendering new trees by budding. But in such an organism—which is, after all, a society rather than an individual—*something* ages, if only the leaves and the interior of the trunk. And each cell, considered separately, evolves in a specific way. *Wherever anything lives, there is, open somewhere, a register in which time is being inscribed.*

This, it will be said, is only a metaphor.—It is of the very essence of mechanism, in fact, to consider as metaphorical every expression which attributes to time an effective action and a reality of its own. In vain does immediate experience show us that the very basis of our conscious existence is memory, that is to say, the prolongation of the past into the present, or, in a word, *duration*, acting and irreversible. In vain does reason prove to us that the more we get away from the objects cut out and the systems isolated by common sense and by science and the deeper we dig beneath them, the more we have to do with a reality which changes as a whole in its inmost states, as if an accumulative memory of the past made it impossible to go back again. The mechanistic instinct of the mind is stronger than reason, stronger than immediate experience. The metaphysician that we each carry unconsciously within us, and the presence of which is explained, as we shall see later on, by the very place that man occupies among the living beings, has its fixed requirements, its ready-made explanations, its irreducible propositions: all unite in denying concrete duration. Change *must* be reducible to an arrangement or rearrangement of parts; the irreversibility of time *must* be an appearance relative to our ignorance; the impossibility of turning back *must* be only the inability of man to put things in place again. So growing old can be nothing more than the gradual gain or loss of certain substances, perhaps both together. Time is assumed to have just as much reality for a living being as for an hour-glass, in which the top part empties while the lower fills, and all goes where it was before when you turn the grass upside down.

True, biologists are not agreed on what is gained and what is lost between the day of birth and the day of death. There are those who hold to the continual growth in the volume of protoplasm from the birth of the cell right on to its death.[1]

---

[1] Calkins, *Studies on the Life History of Protozoa* (*Archiv f. Entwicklungsmechanik,* vol. xv., 1903, pp. 139–186).

[1] Sedgwick Minot, *On Certain Phenomena of Growing Old* (*Proc. Amer. Assoc. for the Advancement of Science,* 39th Meeting, Salem, 1891, pp. 271–288).

More probable and more profound is the theory according to which the diminution bears on the quantity of nutritive substance contained in that "inner environment" in which the organism is being renewed, and the increase on the quantity of unexcreted residual substances which, accumulating in the body, finally "crust it over."[1] Must we however—with an eminent bacteriologist—declare any explanation of growing old insufficient that does not take account of phagocytosis?[2] We do not feel qualified to settle the question. But the fact that the two theories agree in affirming the constant accumulation or loss of a certain kind of matter, even though they have little in common as to what is gained and lost, shows pretty well that the frame of the explanation has been furnished *a priori.* We shall see this more and more as we proceed with our study: it is not easy, in thinking of time, to escape the image of the hour-glass.

The cause of growing old must lie deeper. We hold that there is unbroken continuity between the evolution of the embryo and that of the complete organism. The impetus which causes a living being to grow larger, to develop and to age, is the same that has caused it to pass through the phases of the embryonic life. The development of the embryo is a perpetual change of form. Anyone who attempts to note all its successive aspects becomes lost in an infinity, as is inevitable in dealing with a continuum. Life does but prolong this prenatal evolution. The proof of this is that it is often impossible for us to say whether we are dealing with an organism growing old or with an embryo continuing to evolve;

such is the case, for example, with the larvae of insects and crustacea. On the other hand, in an organism such as our own, crises like puberty or the menopause, in which the individual is completely transformed, are quite comparable to changes in the course of larval or embryonic life—yet they are part and parcel of the process of our aging. Although they occur at a definite age and within a time that may be quite short, no one would maintain that they appear then *ex abrupto,* from without, simply because a certain age is reached, just as a legal right is granted to us on our one-and-twentieth birthday. It is evident that a change like that of puberty is in course of preparation at every instant from birth, and even before birth, and that the aging up to that crisis consists, in part at least, of this gradual preparation. In short, what is properly vital in growing old is the insensible, infinitely graduated, continuance of the change of form. Now, this change is undoubtedly accompanied by phenomena of organic destruction: to these, and to these alone, will a mechanistic explanation of aging be confined. It will note the facts of sclerosis, the gradual accumulation of residual substances, the growing hypertrophy of the protoplasm of the cell. But under these visible effects an inner cause lies hidden. The evolution of the living being, like that of the embryo, implies a continual recording of duration, a persistence of the past in the present, and so an appearance, at least, of organic memory.

The present state of an unorganized body depends exclusively on what happened at the previous instant; and likewise the position of the material points of a system defined and isolated by science is determined by the position of these same points at the moment immediately before. In other words, the laws that govern unorganized matter are expressible, in principle, by differential equa-

[1] Le Dantec, *L'Individualité et l'erreur individualiste,* Paris, 1905, pp. 84 ff.

[2] Metchnikoff, *La Dégénérescence sénile* (*Année biologique,* iii., 1897, pp. 249 ff.). Cf., by the same author, *La Nature humaine,* Paris, 1903, pp. 312 ff.

tions in which time (in the sense in which the mathematician takes this word) would play the role of independent variable. Is it so with the laws of life? Does the state of a living body find its complete explanation in the state immediately before? Yes, if it is agreed *a priori* to liken the living body to other bodies, and to identify it, for the sake of the argument, with the artificial systems on which the chemist, physicist and astronomer operate. But in astronomy, physics and chemistry the proposition has a perfectly definite meaning: it signifies that certain aspects of the present, important for science, are calculable as functions of the immediate past. Nothing of the sort in the domain of life. Here calculation touches, at most, certain phenomena of organic *destruction*. Organic *creation,* on the contrary, the evolutionary phenomena which properly constitute life, we cannot in any way subject to a mathematical treatment. It will be said that this impotence is due only to our ignorance. But it may equally well express the fact that the present moment of a living body does not find its explanation in the moment immediately before, that *all* the past of the organism must be added to that moment, its heredity—in fact, the whole of a very long history. In the second of these two hypotheses, not in the first, is really expressed the present state of the biological sciences, as well as their direction. As for the idea that the living body might be treated by some superhuman calculator in the same mathematical way as our solar system, this has gradually arisen from a metaphysic which has taken a more precise form since the physical discoveries of Galileo, but which, as we shall show, was always the natural metaphysic of the human mind. Its apparent clearness, our impatient desire to find it true, the enthusiasm with which so many excellent minds accept it without proof—all the

seductions, in short, that it exercises on our thought, should put us on our guard against it. The attraction it has for us proves well enough that it gives satisfaction to an innate inclination. But, as will be seen further on, the intellectual tendencies innate today, which life must have created in the course of its evolution, are not at all meant to supply us with an explanation of life: they have something else to do.

Any attempt to distinguish between an artificial and a natural system, between the dead and the living, runs counter to this tendency at once. Thus it happens that we find it equally difficult to imagine that the organized has duration and that the unorganized has not. When we say that the state of an artificial system depends exclusively on its state at the moment before, does it not seem as if we were bringing time in, as if the system had something to do with real duration? And, on the other hand, though the whole of the past goes into the making of the living being's present moment, does not organic memory press it into the moment immediately before the present, so that the moment immediately before becomes the sole cause of the present one?—To speak thus is to ignore the cardinal difference between *concrete* time, along which a real system develops, and that *abstract* time which enters into our speculations on artificial systems. What does it mean, to say that the state of an artificial system depends on what it was at the moment immediately before? There is no instant immediately before another instant; there could not be, any more than there could be one mathematical point touching another. The instant "immediately before" is, in reality, that which is connected with the present instant by the interval dt. All that you mean to say, therefore, is that the present state of the system is defined by equations into which differential coefficients enter, such as $ds/dt, dv/dt,$ that is to say, at bottom, *present* velocities and *present* accelerations. You are therefore really speaking only of the present—a present, it is true, considered along with its *tendency.* The systems science works with are, in fact, in an instantaneous present that is always being renewed; such systems are never in that real, concrete duration in which the past remains bound up with the present. When the mathematician calculates the future state of a system at the end of a time t, there is nothing to prevent him from supposing that the universe vanishes from this moment till that, and suddenly reappears. It is the t-th moment only that counts—and that will be a mere instant. What will flow on in the interval—that is to say, real time—does not count, and cannot enter into the calculation. If the mathematician says that he puts himself inside this interval he means that he is placing himself at a certain point, at a particular moment, therefore at the extremity again of a certain time t'; with the interval up to T' he is not concerned. If he divides the interval into infinitely small parts by considering the differential dt, he thereby expresses merely the fact that he will consider accelerations and velocities—that is to say, numbers which denote tendencies and enable him to calculate the state of the system at a given moment. But he is always speaking of a given moment—a static moment, that is—and not of flowing time. In short, *the world the mathematician deals with is a world that dies and is reborn at every instant—the world which Descartes was thinking of when he spoke of continued creation.* But, in time thus conceived, how could evolution, which is the very essence of life, ever take place? Evolution implies a real persistence of the past in the present, a duration which is, as it were, a hyphen, a connecting link. In other words, to know a living being or *natural system* is to get

at the very interval of duration, while the knowledge of an *artificial* or *mathematical system* applies only to the extremity.

Continuity of change, preservation of the past in the present, real duration—the living being seems, then, to share these attributes with consciousness. Can we go further and say that life, like conscious activity, is invention, is unceasing creation?

It does not enter into our plan to set down here the proofs of transformism. We wish only to explain in a word or two why we shall accept it, in the present work, as a sufficiently exact and precise expression of the facts actually known. The idea of transformism is already in germ in the natural classification of organized beings. The naturalist, in fact, brings together the organisms that are like each other, then divides the group into sub-groups within which the likeness is still greater, and so on: all through the operation, the characters of the group appear as general themes on which each of the sub-groups performs its particular variation. Now, such is just the relation we find, in the animal and in the vegetable world between the generator and the generated: on the canvas which the ancestor passes on, and which his descendants possess in common, each puts his own original embroidery. True, the differences between the descendant and the ancestor are slight, and it may be asked whether the same living matter presents enough plasticity to take in turn such different forms as those of a fish, a reptile and a bird. But, to this question, observation gives a peremptory answer. It shows that up to a certain period in its development the embryo of the bird is hardly distinguishable from that of the reptile, and that the individual develops, throughout the embryonic life in general, a series of transformations comparable to those through which, according to the theory of evolution, one species passes into another. A single cell, the result of the combination of two cells, male and female, accomplishes this work by dividing. Every day, before our eyes, the highest forms of life are springing from a very elementary form. Experience, then, shows that the most complex has been able to issue from the most simple by way of evolution. Now, has it arisen so, as a matter of fact? Paleontology, in spite of the insufficiency of its evidence, invites us to believe it has; for, where it makes out the order of succession of species with any precision, this order is just what considerations drawn from embryogeny and comparative anatomy would lead anyone to suppose, and each new paleontological discovery brings transformism a new confirmation. Thus, the proof drawn from mere observation is ever being strengthened, while, on the other hand, experiment is removing the objections one by one. The recent experiments of H. de Vries, for instance, by showing that important variations can be produced suddenly and transmitted regularly, have overthrown some of the greatest difficulties raised by the theory. They have enabled us greatly to shorten the time biological evolution seems to demand. They also render us less exacting toward paleontology. So that, all things considered, the transformist hypothesis looks more and more like a close approximation to the truth. It is not rigorously demonstrable; but, failing the certainty of theoretical or experimental demonstration, there is a probability which is continually growing, due to evidence which, while coming short of direct proof, seems to point persistently in its direction: such is the kind of probability that the theory of transformism offers.

Let us admit, however, that transformism may be wrong. Let us suppose that species are proved, by inference or by experiment, to have arisen by a discontinuous process, of which today we have no idea. Would the doctrine be affected in so far as it has a special interest or importance for us? Classification would probably remain, in its broad lines. The actual data of embryology would also remain. The correspondence between comparative embryogeny and comparative anatomy would remain too. Therefore biology could and would continue to establish between living forms the same relations and the same kinship as transformism supposes today. It would be, it is true, an *ideal* kinship, and no longer a *material* affiliation. But, as the actual data of paleontology would also remain, we should still have to admit that it is successively, not simultaneously, that the forms between which we find an ideal kinship have appeared. Now, the evolutionist theory, so far as it has any importance for philosophy, requires no more. It consists above all in establishing relations of ideal kinship, and in maintaining that wherever there is this relation of, so to speak, *logical* affiliation between forms, there is also a relation of *chronological* succession between the species in which these forms are materialized. Both arguments would hold in any case. And hence, an evolution *somewhere* would still have to be supposed, whether in a creative Thought in which the ideas of the different species are generated by each other exactly as transformism holds that species themselves are generated on the earth; or in a plan of vital organization immanent in nature, which gradually works itself out, in which the relations of logical and chronological affiliation between pure forms are just those which transformism presents as relations of real affiliation between living individuals; or, finally, in some unknown cause of life, which develops its effects *as if* they generated one another. Evolution would then simply have been *transposed,* made to pass from the visible to the invisible. Almost all that transformism tells us today would be preserved, open to interpretation in another way. Will it not, therefore, be better to stick to the letter of transformism as almost all scientists profess it? Apart from the question to what extent the theory of evolution describes the facts and to what extent it symbolizes them, there is nothing in it that is irreconcilable with the doctrines it has claimed to replace, even with that of special creations, to which it is usually opposed. For this reason we think the language of transformism forces itself now upon all philosophy, as the dogmatic affirmation of transformism forces itself upon science.

But then, we must no longer speak of *life in general* as an abstraction, or as a mere heading under which all living beings are inscribed. At a certain moment, in certain points of space, a visible current has taken rise; this current of life, traversing the bodies it has organized one after another, passing from generation to generation, has become divided among species and distributed among individuals without losing anything of its force, rather intensifying in proportion to its advance. It is well known that, on the theory of the "continuity of the germ-plasm," maintained by Weismann, the sexual elements of the generating organism pass on their properties directly to the sexual elements of the organism engendered. In this extreme form, the theory has seemed debatable, for it is only in exceptional cases that there are any signs of sexual glands at the time of segmentation of the fertilized egg. But, though the cells that engender the sexual elements do not generally appear at the beginning of the embryonic life, it is none the less true that they are always formed out of those tissues of the embryo which have not undergone any particular functional differentiation, and

whose cells are made of unmodified protoplasm.[1] In other words, the genetic power of the fertilized ovum weakens, the more it is spread over the growing mass of the tissues of the embryo; but, while it is being thus diluted, it is concentrating anew something of itself on a certain special point, to wit, the cells, from which the ova or spermatozoa will develop. It might therefore be said that, though the germ-plasm is not continuous, there is at least continuity of genetic energy, this energy being expended only at certain instants, for just enough time to give the requisite impulsion to the embryonic life, and being recouped as soon as possible in new sexual elements, in which, again, it bides its time. Regarded from this point of view, *life is like a current passing from germ to germ through the medium of a developed organism.* It is as if the organism itself were only an excrescence, a bud caused to sprout by the former germ endeavoring to continue itself in a new germ. The essential thing is the *continuous progress* indefinitely pursued, an invisible progress, on which each visible organism rides during the short interval of the time given it to live.

Now, the more we fix our attention on this continuity of life, the more we see that organic evolution resembles the evolution of a consciousness, in which the past presses against the present and causes the upspringing of a new form of consciousness, incommensurable with its antecedents. That the appearance of a vegetable or animal species is due to specific causes, nobody will gainsay. But this can only mean that if, after the fact, we could know these causes in detail, we could explain by them the form that has been produced; foreseeing the form is out

---

[1] Roule, *L'Embryologie générale,* Paris, 1893, p. 319.

of the question.[1] It may perhaps be said that the form could be foreseen if we could know, in all their details, the conditions under which it will be produced. But these conditions are built up into it and are part and parcel of its being; they are peculiar to that phase of its history in which life finds itself at the moment of producing the form: how could we know beforehand a situation that is unique of its kind, that has never yet occurred and will never occur again? Of the future, only that is foreseen which is like the past or can be made up again with elements like those of the past. Such is the case with astronomical, physical and chemical facts, with all facts which form part of a system in which elements supposed to be unchanging are merely put together, in which the only changes are changes of position, in which there is no theoretical absurdity in imagining that things are restored to their place; in which, consequently, the same total phenomenon, or at least the same elementary phenomena, can be repeated. But an original situation, which imparts something of its own originality to its elements, that is to say, to the partial views that are taken of it, how can such a situation be pictured as given before it is actually produced?[2] All that can be said is that, once produced, it will be explained by the elements that analysis will then carve out of it. Now, what is true of the production of a new species is also true of the production of a new individual, and, more generally, of any moment of any living form. For, though the variation must reach a certain importance and a certain generality in order to

give rise to a new species, it is being produced every moment, continuously and insensibly, in every living being. And it is evident that even the sudden "mutations" which we now hear of are possible only if a process of incubation, or rather of maturing, is going on throughout a series of generations that do not seem to change. In this sense it might be said of life, as of consciousness, that at every moment it is creating something.[1]

But against this idea of the absolute originality and unforeseeability of forms our whole intellect rises in revolt. The essential function of our intellect, as the evolution of life has fashioned it, is to be a light for our conduct, to make ready for our action on things, to foresee, for a given situation, the events, favorable or unfavorable, which may follow thereupon. Intellect therefore instinctively selects in a given situation whatever is like something already known; it seeks this out, in order that it may apply its principle that "like produces like." In just this does the prevision of the future by common sense consist. Science carries this faculty to the highest possible degree of exactitude and precision, but does not alter its essential character. Like ordinary

---

[1] The irreversibility of the series of living beings has been well set forth by Baldwin (*Development and Evolution*, New York, 1902; in particular p. 327).

[2] We have dwelt on this point and tried to make it clear in the *Essai sur les données immédiates de la conscience*, pp. 140–151.

[1] In his fine work on *Genius in Art* (*Le Génie dans l'art*), M. Séailles develops this twofold thesis, that art is a continuation of nature and that life is creation. We should willingly accept the second formula; but by creation must we understand, as the author does, a *synthesis* of elements? Where the elements pre-exist, the synthesis that will be made is virtually given, being only one of the possible arrangements. This arrangement a superhuman intellect could have perceived in advance among all the possible ones that surround it. We hold, on the contrary, that in the domain of life the elements have no real and separate existence. They are manifold mental views of an indivisible process. And for that reason there is radical contingency in progress, incommensurability between what goes before and what follows—in short duration.

knowledge, in dealing with things science is concerned only with the aspect of *repetition*. Though the whole be original, science will always manage to analyze it into elements or aspects which are approximately a reproduction of the past. Science can work only on what is supposed to repeat itself—that is to say, on what is withdrawn, by hypothesis, from the action of real time. Anything that is irreducible and irreversible in the successive moments of a history eludes science. To get a notion of this irreducibility and irreversibility, we must break with scientific habits which are adapted to the fundamental requirements of thought, we must do violence to the mind, go counter to the natural bent of the intellect. But that is just the function of philosophy.

In vain, therefore, does life evolve before our eyes as a continuous creation of unforeseeable form: the idea always persists that form, unforeseeability and continuity are mere appearance—the outward reflection of our own ignorance. What is presented to the senses as a continuous history would break up, we are told, into a series of successive states. "What gives you the impression of an original state resolves, upon analysis, into elementary facts, each of which is the repetition of a fact already known. What you call an unforeseeable form is only a new arrangement of old elements. The elementary causes, which in their totality have determined this arrangement, are themselves old causes repeated in a new order. Knowledge of the elements and of the elementary causes would have made it possible to foretell the living form which is their sum and their resultant. When we have resolved the biological aspect of phenomena into physico-chemical factors, we will leap, if necessary, over physics and chemistry themselves; we will go from masses to molecules, from molecules to atoms, from atoms to corpuscles: we must indeed at last come to something that can be treated as a kind of solar system, astronomically. If you deny it, you oppose the very principle of scientific mechanism, and you arbitrarily affirm that living matter is not made of the same elements as other matter."—We reply that we do not question the fundamental identity of inert matter and organized matter. The only question is whether the natural systems which we call living beings must be assimilated to the artificial systems that science cuts out within inert matter, or whether they must not rather be compared to that natural system which is the whole of the universe. That life is a kind of mechanism I cordially agree. But is it the mechanism of parts artificially isolated within the whole of the universe, or is it the mechanism of the real whole? The real whole might well be, we conceive, an indivisible continuity. The systems we cut out within it would, properly speaking, not then be *parts* at all; they would be *partial views* of the whole. And, with these partial views put end to end, you will not make even a beginning of the reconstruction of the whole, any more than, by multiplying photographs of an object in a thousand different aspects, you will reproduce the object itself. So of life and of the physico-chemical phenomena to which you endeavor to reduce it. Analysis will undoubtedly resolve the process of organic creation into an ever-growing number of physio-chemical phenomena, and chemists and physicists will have to do, of course, with nothing but these. But it does not follow that chemistry and physics will ever give us the key to life.

A very small element of a curve is very near being a straight line. And the smaller it is, the nearer. In the limit, it may be termed a part of the curve or a part of the straight line, as you please, for in each of its points a curve coincides with its tangent. So likewise "vitality" is tangent, at any and every point, to physical and chemical forces; but such points are, as a fact, only views taken by a mind which imagines stops at various moments of the movement that generates the curve. In reality, life is no more made of physico-chemical elements than a curve is composed of straight lines.

In a general way, the most radical progress a science can achieve is the working of the completed results into a new scheme of the whole, by relation to which they become instantaneous and motionless views taken at intervals along the continuity of a movement. Such, for example, is the relation of modern to ancient geometry. The latter, purely static, worked with figures drawn once for all; the former studies the varying of a function—that is, the continuous movement by which the figure is described. No doubt, for greater strictness, all considerations of motion may be eliminated from mathematical processes; but the introduction of motion into the genesis of figures is nevertheless the origin of modern mathematics. We believe that if biology could ever get as close to its object as mathematics does to its own, it would become, to the physics and chemistry of organized bodies, what the mathematics of the moderns has proved to be in relation to ancient geometry. The wholly superficial displacements of masses and molecules studied in physics and chemistry would become, by relation to that inner vital movement (which is transformation and not translation) what the position of a moving object is to the movement of that object in space. And, so far as we can see, the procedure by which we should then pass from the definition of a certain vital action to the system of physico-chemical facts which it implies would be like passing from the function to its derivative, from the equation of the curve (*i.e.* the law of the continuous movement by which the curve is generated) to the equation of the tangent giving its instantaneous direction. Such a science would be a *mechanics of transformation,* of which our *mechanics of translation* would become a particular case, a simplification, a projection on the plane of pure quantity. And just as an infinity of functions have the same differential, these functions differing from each other by a constant, so perhaps the integration of the physico-chemical elements of properly vital action might determine that action only in part—a part would be left to indetermination. But such an integration can be no more than dreamed of; we do not pretend that the dream will ever be realized. We are only trying, by carrying a certain comparison as far as possible, to show up to what point our theory goes along with pure mechanism, and where they part company.

Imitation of the living by the unorganized may, however, go a good way. Not only does chemistry make organic syntheses, but we have succeeded in reproducing artificially the external appearance of certain facts of organization, such as indirect cell-division and protoplasmic circulation. It is well known that the protoplasm of the cell effects various movements within its envelope; on the other hand, indirect cell-division is the outcome of very complex operations, some involving the nucleus and others the cytoplasm. These latter commence by the doubling of the centrosome, a small spherical body alongside the nucleus. The two centrosomes thus obtained draw apart, attract the broken and doubled ends of the filament of which the original nucleus mainly consisted, and join them to form two fresh nuclei about which the two new cells are constructed which will succeed the first. Now, in their broad lines and in their external appearance, some at least of these operations have been successfully imitated. If some sugar or table salt is pulverized and some very old oil is added, and a drop of the mixture is observed under the microscope, a froth of alveolar structure is seen whose configuration is like that of protoplasm, according to certain theories, and in which movements take place which are decidedly like those of protoplasmic circulation.[1] If, in a froth of the same kind, the air is extracted from an alveolus, a cone of attraction is seen to form, like those about the centrosomes which result in the division of the nucleus.[2] Even the external motions of a unicellular organism—of an amoeba, at any rate—are sometimes explained mechanically. The displacements of an amoeba in a drop of water would be comparable to the motion to and fro of a grain of dust in a drafty room. Its mass is all the time absorbing certain soluble matters contained in the surrounding water, and giving back to it certain others; these continual exchanges, like those between two vessels separated by a porous partition, would create an ever-changing vortex around the little organism. As for the temporary prolongations or pseudopodia which the amoeba seems to make, they would be not so much given out by it as attracted from it by a kind of inhalation or suction of the surrounding medium.[3] In the same way we may perhaps come to explain the more complex movements which the Infusorian makes with its vibratory cilia, which, moreover, are probably only fixed pseudopodia.

But scientists are far from agreed on the value of explanations and schemata of this sort. Chemists have pointed out that even in the organic—not to go so far as the organized—science has reconstructed hitherto nothing but waste products of vital activity; the peculiarly active plastic substances obstinately defy synthesis. One of the most notable naturalists of our time has insisted on the opposition of two orders of phenomena observed in living tissues, *anagenesis* and *katagenesis*. The role of the anagenetic energies is to raise the inferior energies to their own level by assimilating inorganic substances. They *construct* the tissues. On the other hand, the actual functioning of life (excepting, of course, assimilation, growth and reproduction) is of the katagenetic order, exhibiting the fall, not the rise, of energy. It is only with these facts of katagenetic order that physicochemistry deals—that is, in short, with the dead and not with the living.[1] The other kind of facts certainly seem to defy physico-chemical analysis, even if they are not anagenetic in the proper sense of the word. As for the artificial imitation of the outward appearance of protoplasm, should a real theoretic importance be attached to this when the question of the physical framework of protoplasm is not yet settled? We are still further from compounding protoplasm chemically. Finally, a physico-chemical explanation of the motions of the amoeba, and *a fortiori* of the behavior of the Infusoria, seems impossible to many of those who have closely observed these rudimentary organisms. Even in these humblest manifestations of life they discover traces of

[1] Bütschli, *Untersuchungen über mikroskopische Schäume und das Protoplasma,* Leipzig, 1892, First Part.

[2] Rhumbler, *Versuch einer mechanischen Erklärung der indirekten Zell- und Kernteilung (Roux's Archiv,* 1896).

[3] Berthold, *Studien über Protoplasmamechanik,* Leipzig, 1886, p. 102. Cf. the explanation proposed by Le Dantec, *Théorie nouvelle de la vie,* Paris, 1896, p. 60.

[1] Cope, *The Primary Factors of Organic Evolution,* Chicago, 1896, pp. 475–484.

an effective psychological activity.[1] But instructive above all is the fact that the tendency to explain everything by physics and chemistry is discouraged rather than strengthened by deep study of histological phenomena. Such is the conclusion of the truly admirable book which the histologist E. B. Wilson has devoted to the development of the cell: "The study of the cell has, on the whole, seemed to widen rather than to narrow the enormous gap that separates even the lowest forms of life from the inorganic world."[2]

To sum up, those who are concerned only with the functional activity of the living being are inclined to believe that physics and chemistry will give us the key to biological processes.[3] They have chiefly to do, as a fact, with phenomena that are *repeated* continually in the living being, as in a chemical retort. This explains, in some measure, the mechanistic tendencies of physiology. On the contrary, those whose attention is concentrated on the minute structure of living tissues, on their genesis and evolution, histologists and embryogenists on the one hand, naturalists on the other, are interested in the report itself, not merely in its contents. They find that this retort creates its own form through a *unique* series of acts that really constitute a *history*.

Thus, histologists, embryogenists, and naturalists believe far less readily than physiologists in the physico-chemical character of vital actions.

The fact is, neither one nor the other of these two theories, neither that which affirms nor that which denies the possibility of chemically producing an elementary organism, can claim the authority of experiment. They are both unverifiable, the former because science has not yet advanced a step toward the chemical synthesis of a living substance, the second because there is no conceivable way of proving experimentally the impossibility of a fact. But we have set forth the theoretical reasons which prevent us from likening the living being, a system closed off by nature, to the systems which our science isolates. These reasons have less force, we acknowledge, in the case of a rudimentary organism like the amoeba, which hardly evolves at all. But they acquire more when we consider a complex organism which goes through a regular cycle of transformations. The more duration marks the living being with its imprint, the more obviously the organism differs from a mere mechanism, over which duration glides without penetrating. And the demonstration has most force when it applies to the evolution of life as a whole, from its humblest origins to its highest forms, inasmuch as this evolution constitutes, through the unity and continuity of the animated matter which supports it, a single indivisible history. Thus viewed, the evolutionist hypothesis does not seem so closely akin to the mechanistic conception of life as it is generally supposed to be. Of this mechanistic conception we do not claim, of course, to furnish a mathematical and final refutation. But the refutation which we draw from the consideration of real time, and which is, in our opinion, the only refutation possible, becomes the

---

[1] Maupas, "Etude des infusoires ciliés" (*Arch. de zoologie expérimentale*, 1883, pp. 47, 491, 518, 549, in particular). P. Vignon, *Recherches de cytologie générale sur les épithéliums*, Paris, 1902, p. 655. A profound study of the motions of the Infusoria and a very penetrating criticism of the idea of tropism have been made recently by Jennings (*Contributions to the Study of the Behavior of Lower Organisms*, Washington, 1904). The "type of behavior" of these lower organisms, as Jennings defines it (pp. 237–252), is unquestionably of the psychological order.

[2] E. B. Wilson, *The Cell in Development and Inheritance*, New York, 1897, p. 330.

[3] Dastre, *La Vie et la mort*, p. 43.

more rigorous and cogent the more frankly the evolutionist hypothesis is assumed. We must dwell a good deal more on this point. But let us first show more clearly the notion of life to which we are leading up.

The mechanistic explanations, we said, hold good for the systems that our thought artificially detaches from the whole. But of the whole itself and of the systems which, within this whole, seem to take after it, we cannot admit *a priori* that they are mechanically explicable, for then time would be useless, and even unreal. The essence of mechanical explanation, in fact, is to regard the future and the past as calculable functions of the present, and thus to claim that *all is given*. On this hypothesis, past, present and future would be open at a glance to a superhuman intellect capable of making the calculation. Indeed, the scientists who have believed in the universality and perfect objectivity of mechanical explanations have, consciously or unconsciously, acted on a hypothesis of this kind. Laplace formulated it with the greatest precision: "An intellect which at a given instant knew all the forces with which nature is animated, and the respective situations of the beings that compose nature—supposing the said intellect were vast enough to subject these data to analysis—would embrace in the same formula the motions of the greatest bodies in the universe and those of the slightest atom: nothing would be uncertain for it, and the future, like the past, would be present to its eyes."[1] And Du Bois-Reymond: "We can imagine the knowledge of nature arrived at a point where the universal process of the world might be represented by a single mathematical formula, by one immense system of simultaneous differential equations, from which could be deduced, for each moment, the position, direction, and velocity of every atom of the world."[1] Huxley has expressed the same idea in a more concrete form: "If the fundamental proposition of evolution is true, that the entire world, living and not living, is the result of the mutual interaction, according to definite laws, of the forces possessed by the molecules of which the primitive nebulosity of the universe was composed, it is no less certain that the existing world lay, potentially, in the cosmic vapor, and that a sufficient intellect could, from a knowledge of the properties of the molecules of that vapor, have predicted, say the state of the Fauna of Great Britain in 1869, with as much certainty as one can say what will happen to the vapor of the breath in a cold winter's day." In such a doctrine, time is still spoken of: one pronounces the word, but one does not think of the thing. For time is here deprived of efficacy, and if it *does* nothing, it *is* nothing. Radical mechanism implies a metaphysic in which the totality of the real is postulated complete in eternity, and in which the apparent duration of things expresses merely the infirmity of a mind that cannot know everything at once. But duration is something very different from this for our consciousness, that is to say, for that which is most indisputable in our experience. We perceive duration as a stream against which we cannot go. It is the foundation of our being, and, as we feel, the very substance of the world in which we live. It is of no use to hold up before our eyes the dazzling prospect of a universal mathematic; we cannot sacrifice experience to the requirements of a system. That is why we reject radical mechanism.

---

[1] Laplace, *Introduction à la théorie analytique des probabilités* (*Œuvres complètes,* vol. vii., Paris, 1886, p. vi.).

[1] Du Bois-Reymond, *Über die Grenzen des Naturerkennens,* Leipzig, 1892.

But radical finalism is quite as unacceptable, and for the same reason. The doctrine of teleology, in its extreme form, as we find it in Leibniz for example, implies that things and beings merely realize a program previously arranged. But if there is nothing unforeseen, no invention or creation in the universe, time is useless again. As in the mechanistic hypothesis, here again it is supposed that *all is given*. Finalism thus understood is only inverted mechanism. It springs from the same postulate, with this sole difference, that in the movement of our finite intellects along successive things, whose successiveness is reduced to a mere appearance, it holds in front of us the light with which it claims to guide us, instead of putting it behind. It substitutes the attraction of the future for the impulsion of the past. But succession remains none the less a mere appearance, as indeed does movement itself. In the doctrine of Leibniz, time is reduced to a confused perception, relative to the human standpoint, a perception which would vanish, like a rising mist, for a mind seated at the center of things.

Yet finalism is not, like mechanism, a doctrine with fixed rigid outlines. It admits of as many inflections as we like. The mechanistic philosophy is to be taken or left: it must be left if the least grain of dust, by straying from the path foreseen by mechanics, should show the slightest trace of spontaneity. The doctrine of final causes, on the contrary, will never be definitively refuted. If one form of it be put aside, it will take another. Its principle, which is essentially psychological, is very flexible. It is so extensible, and thereby so comprehensive, that one accepts something of it as soon as one rejects pure mechanism. The theory we shall put forward in this book will therefore necessarily partake of finalism to a certain extent. For that reason it is important to intimate exactly what we are going to take of it, and what we mean to leave.

Let us say at once that to thin out the Leibnizian finalism by breaking it into an infinite number of pieces seems to us a step in the wrong direction. This is, however, the tendency of the doctrine of finality. It fully realizes that if the universe as a whole is the carrying out of a plan, this cannot be demonstrated empirically, and that even of the organized world alone it is hardly easier to prove all harmonious: facts would equally well testify to the contrary. Nature sets living beings at discord with one another. She everywhere presents disorder alongside of order, retrogression alongside of progress. But, though finality cannot be affirmed either of the whole of matter or of the whole of life, might it not yet be true, says the finalist, of each organism taken separately? Is there not a wonderful division of labor, a marvelous solidarity among the parts of an organism, perfect order in infinite complexity? Does not each living being thus realize a plan immanent in its substance?—This theory consists, at bottom, in breaking up the original notion of finality into bits. It does not accept, indeed it ridicules, the idea of an *external* finality, according to which living beings are ordered with regard to each other: to suppose the grass made for the cow, the lamb for the wolf—that is all acknowledged to be absurd. But there is, we are told, an *internal* finality: each being is made for itself, all its parts conspire for the greatest good of the whole and are intelligently organized in view of that end. Such is the notion of finality which has long been classic. Finalism has shrunk to the point of never embracing more than one living being at a time. By making itself smaller, it probably thought it would offer less surface for blows.

The truth is, it lay open to them a great deal more. Radical as our own theory may appear, finality is external or it is nothing at all.

Consider the most complex and the most harmonious organism. All the elements, we are told, conspire for the greatest good of the whole. Very well, but let us not forget that each of these elements may itself be an organism in certain cases, and that in subordinating the existence of this small organism to the life of the great one we accept the principle of an *external* finality. The idea of a finality that is *always* internal is therefore a self-destructive notion. An organism is composed of tissues, each of which lives for itself. The cells of which the tissues are made have also a certain independence. Strictly speaking, if the subordination of all the elements of the individual to the individual itself were complete, we might contend that they are not organisms, reserve the name organism for the individual, and recognize only internal finality. But every one knows that these elements may possess a true autonomy. To say nothing of phagocytes, which push independence to the point of attacking the organism that nourishes them, or of germinal cells, which have their own life alongside the somatic cells—the facts of regeneration are enough: here an element or a group of elements suddenly reveals that, however limited its normal space and function, it can transcend them occasionally; it may even, in certain cases, be regarded as the equivalent of the whole.

There lies the stumbling-block of the vitalistic theories. We shall not reproach them, as is ordinarily done, with replying to the question by the question itself: the "vital principle" may indeed not explain much, but it is at least a sort of label affixed to our ignorance, so as to remind us of this occasionally,[1] while mecha-

nism invites us to ignore that ignorance. But the position of vitalism is rendered very difficult by the fact that, in nature, there is neither purely internal finality nor absolutely distinct individuality. The organized elements composing the individual have themselves a certain individuality, and each will claim its vital principle if the individual pretends to have its own. But, on the other hand, the individual itself is not sufficiently independent, not sufficiently cut off from other things, for us to allow it a "vital principle" of its own. An organism such as a higher vertebrate is the most individuated of all organisms; yet, if we take into account that it is only the development of an ovum forming part of the body of its mother and of a spermatozoon belonging to the body of its father, that the egg (*i.e.* the ovum fertilized) is a connecting link between the two progenitors since it is common to their two substances, we shall realize that every individual organism, even that of a man, is merely a bud that has sprouted on the combined body of both its parents. Where, then, does the vital principle of the individual begin or end? Gradually we shall be carried further and further back, up to the individual's remotest ancestors: we shall find him solidary with

_____

[1] There are really two lines to follow in contemporary neo-vitalism: on the one hand, the assertion that pure mechanism is insufficient, which assumes great authority when made by such scientists as Driesch or Reinke, for example; and, on the other hand, the hypotheses which this vitalism superposes on mechanism (the "entelechies" of Driesch, and the "dominants" of Reinke, etc.). Of these two parts, the former is perhaps the more interesting. See the admirable studies of Driesch—*Die Lokalisation morphogenetischer Vorgänge,* Leipzig, 1899; *Die organischen Regulationen,* Leipzig, 1901; *Naturbegriffe und Natururteile,* Leipzig, 1904; *Der Vitalismus als Geschichte und als Lehre,* Leipzig, 1905; and of Reinke—*Die Welt als Tat,* Berlin, 1899; *Einleitung in die theoretische Biologie,* Berlin, 1901; *Philosophie der Botanik,* Leipzig, 1905.

each of them, solidary with that little mass of protoplasmic jelly which is probably at the root of the genealogical tree of life. Being, to a certain extent, one with this primitive ancestor, he is also solidary with all that descends from the ancestor in divergent directions. In this sense each individual may be said to remain united with the totality of living beings by invisible bonds. So it is of no use to try to restrict finality to the individuality of the living being. If there is finality in the world of life, it includes the whole of life in a single indivisible embrace. This life common to all the living undoubtedly presents many gaps and incoherences, and again it is not so mathematically *one* that it cannot allow each being to become individualized to a certain degree. But it forms a single whole, none the less; and we have to choose between the out-and-out negation of finality and the hypothesis which coordinates not only the parts of an organism with the organism itself, but also each living being with the collective whole of all others.

Finality will not go down any easier for being taken as a powder. Either the hypothesis of a finality immanent in life should be rejected as a whole, or it must undergo a treatment very different from pulverization.

The error of radical finalism, as also that of radical mechanism, is to extend too far the application of certain concepts that are natural to our intellect. Originally, we think only in order to act. Our intellect has been cast in the mold of action. Speculation is a luxury, while action is a necessity. Now, in order to act, we begin by proposing an end; we make a plan, then we go on to the detail of the mechanism which will bring it to pass. This latter operation is possible only if we know what we can reckon on. We must therefore have managed to extract resemblances from nature, which enable us to anticipate the future. Thus we must, consciously or unconsciously, have made use of the law of causality. Moreover, the more sharply the idea of efficient causality is defined in our mind, the more it takes the form of a *mechanical* causality. And this scheme, in its turn, is the more mathematical according as it expresses a more rigorous necessity. That is why we have only to follow the bent of our mind to become mathematicians. But, on the other hand, this natural mathematics is only the rigid unconscious skeleton beneath our conscious supple habit of linking the same causes to the same effects; and the usual object of this habit is to guide actions inspired by intentions, or, what comes to the same, to direct movements combined with a view to reproducing a pattern. We are born artisans as we are born geometricians, and indeed we are geometricians only because we are artisans. Thus the human intellect, inasmuch as it is fashioned for the needs of human action, is an intellect which proceeds at the same time by intention and by calculation, by adapting means to ends and by thinking out mechanisms of more and more geometrical form. Whether nature be conceived as an immense machine regulated by mathematical laws, or as the realization of a plan, these two ways of regarding it are only the consummation of two tendencies of mind which are complementary to each other, and which have their origin in the same vital necessities.

For that reason, radical finalism is very near radical mechanism on many points. Both doctrines are reluctant to see in the course of things generally, or even simply in the development of life, an unforeseeable creation of form. In considering reality, mechanism regards only the aspect of similarity or repetition. It is therefore dominated by this law, that in nature there is only *like* reproducing *like*.

The more the geometry in mechanism is emphasized, the less can mechanism admit that anything is ever created, even pure form. In so far as we are geometricians, then, we reject the unforeseeable. We might accept it, assuredly, in so far as we are artists, for art lives on creation and implies a latent belief in the spontaneity of nature. But disinterested art is a luxury, like pure speculation. Long before being artists, we are artisans; and all fabrication, however rudimentary, lives on likeness and repetition, like the natural geometry which serves as its fulcrum. Fabrication works on models which it sets out to reproduce; and even when it invents, it proceeds, or imagines itself to proceed, by a new arrangement of elements already known. Its principle is that "we must have like to produce like." In short, the strict application of the principle of finality, like that of the principle of mechanical causality, leads to the conclusion that "all is given." Both principles say the same thing in their respective languages, because they respond to the same need.

That is why again they agree in doing away with time. Real duration is that duration which gnaws on things, and leaves on them the mark of its tooth. If everything is in time, everything changes inwardly, and the same concrete reality never recurs. Repetition is therefore possible only in the abstract: what is repeated is some aspect that our senses, and especially our intellect, have singled out from reality, just because our action, upon which all the effort of our intellect is directed, can move only among repetitions. Thus, concentrated on that which repeats, solely preoccupied in welding the same to the same, intellect turns away from the vision of time. It dislikes what is fluid, and solidifies everything it touches. We do not *think* real time. But we *live* it, because life transcends intellect. The feeling we have of our evolution and of the evolution of all things in pure duration is there, forming around the intellectual concept properly so-called an indistinct fringe that fades off into darkness. Mechanism and finalism agree in taking account only of the bright nucleus shining in the center. They forget that this nucleus has been formed out of the rest by condensation, and that the whole must be used, the fluid as well as and more than the condensed, in order to grasp the inner movement of life.

Indeed, if the fringe exists, however delicate and indistinct, it should have more importance for philosophy than the bright nucleus it surrounds. For it is its presence that enables us to affirm that the nucleus is a nucleus, that pure intellect is a contraction, by condensation, of a more extensive power. And, just because this vague intuition is of no help in directing our action on things, which action takes place exclusively on the surface of reality, we may presume that it is to be exercised not merely on the surface, but below.

As soon as we go out of the encasings in which radical mechanism and radical finalism confine our thought, reality appears as a ceaseless upspringing of something new, which has no sooner arisen to make the present than it has already fallen back into the past; at this exact moment it falls under the glance of the intellect, whose eyes are ever turned to the rear. This is already the case with our inner life. For each of our acts we shall easily find antecedents of which it may in some sort be said to be the mechanical resultant. And it may equally well be said that each action is the realization of an intention. In this sense mechanism is everywhere, and finality everywhere, in the evolution of our conduct. But if our action be one that involves the whole of our person and is truly ours, it could not have been foreseen, even though its antecedents explain it when once it has been accomplished. And though it be the realizing of an intention, it differs, as a present and *new* reality, from the intention, which can never aim at anything but recommencing or rearranging the past. Mechanism and finalism are therefore, here, only external views of our conduct. They extract its intellectuality. But our conduct slips between them and extends much further. Once again, this does not mean that free action is capricious, unreasonable action. To behave according to caprice is to oscillate mechanically between two or more ready-made alternatives and at length to settle on one of them; it is no real maturing of an internal state, no real evolution; it is merely—however paradoxical the assertion may seem—bending the will to imitate the mechanism of the intellect. A conduct that is truly our own, on the contrary, is that of a will which does not try to counterfeit intellect, and which, remaining itself—that is to say, evolving—ripens gradually into acts which the intellect will be able to resolve indefinitely into intelligible elements without ever reaching its goal. The free act is incommensurable with the idea, and its "rationality" must be defined by this very incommensurability, which admits the discovery of as much intelligibility within it as we will. Such is the character of our own evolution; and such also, without doubt, that of the evolution of life.

Our reason, incorrigibly presumptuous, imagines itself possessed, by right of birth or by right of conquest, innate or acquired, of all the essential elements of the knowledge of truth. Even where it confesses that it does not know the object presented to it, it believes that its ignorance consists only in not knowing which one of its time-honored categories suits the new object. In what drawer, ready to open, shall we put it? In what garment, already cut out, shall we clothe it? Is it this, or that, or the other thing? And

"this," and "that," and "the other thing" are always something already conceived, already known. The idea that for a new object we might have to create a new concept, perhaps a new method of thinking, is deeply repugnant to us. The history of philosophy is there, however, and shows us the eternal conflict of systems, the impossibility of satisfactorily getting the real into the ready-made garments of our ready-made concepts, the necessity of making to measure. But, rather than go to this extremity, our reason prefers to announce once for all, with a proud modesty, that it has to do only with the relative, and that the absolute is not in its province. This preliminary declaration enables it to apply its habitual method of thought without any scruple, and thus, under pretense that it does not touch the absolute, to make absolute judgments upon everything. Plato was the first to set up the theory that to know the real consists in finding its Idea, that is to say, in forcing it into a pre-existing frame already at our disposal—as if we implicitly possessed universal knowledge. But this belief is natural to the human intellect, always engaged as it is in determining under what former heading it shall catalogue any new object; and it may be said that, in a certain sense, we are all born Platonists.

Nowhere is the inadequacy of this method so obvious as in theories of life. If, in evolving in the direction of the vertebrates in general, of man and intellect in particular, life has had to abandon by the way many elements incompatible with this particular mode of organization and consign them, as we shall show, to other lines of development, it is the totality of these elements that we must find again and rejoin to the intellect proper, in order to grasp the true nature of vital activity. And we shall probably be aided in this by the fringe of vague intuition that surrounds our distinct—that is, intellectual—representation. For what can this useless fringe be, if not that part of the evolving principle which has not shrunk to the peculiar form of our organization, but has settled around it unasked for, unwanted? It is there, accordingly, that we must look for hints to expand the intellectual form of our thought; from there shall we derive the impetus necessary to lift us above ourselves. To form an idea of the whole of life cannot consist in combining simple ideas that have been left behind in us by life itself in the course of its evolution. How could the part be equivalent to the whole, the content to the container, a by-product of the vital operation to the operation itself? Such, however, is our illusion when we define the evolution of life as a "passage from the homogeneous to the heterogeneous," or by any other concept obtained by putting fragments of intellect side by side. We place ourselves in one of the points where evolution comes to a head —the principal one, no doubt, but not the only one; and there we do not even take all we find, for of the intellect we keep only one or two of the concepts by which it expresses itself; and it is this part of a part that we declare representative of the whole, of something indeed which goes beyond the concrete whole, I mean of the evolution movement of which this "whole" is only the present stage! The truth is, that to represent this the entire intellect would not be too much—nay, it would not be enough. It would be necessary to add to it what we find in every other terminal point of evolution. And these diverse and divergent elements must be considered as so many extracts which are, or at least which were, in their humblest form, mutually complementary. Only then might we have an inkling of the real nature of the evolution movement; and even then we should fail to grasp it completely, for we should still be dealing only with the evolved, which is a result, and not with evolution itself, which is the act by which the result is obtained.

Such is the philosophy of life to which we are leading up. It claims to transcend both mechanism and finalism; but, as we announced at the beginning, it is nearer the second doctrine than the first. It will not be amiss to dwell on this point, and show more precisely how far this philosophy of life resembles finalism and wherein it is different.

Like radical finalism, although in a vaguer form, our philosophy represents the organized world as a harmonious whole. But this harmony is far from being as perfect as it has been claimed to be. It admits of much discord, because each species, each individual even, retains only a certain impetus from the universal vital impulsion and tends to use this energy in its own interest. In this consists *adaptation*. The species and the individual thus think only of themselves —whence arises a possible conflict with other forms of life. Harmony, therefore, does not exist in fact; it exists rather in principle; I mean that the original impetus is a *common* impetus, and the higher we ascend the stream of life the more do diverse tendencies appear complementary to each other. Thus the wind at a street corner divides into diverging currents which are all one and the same gust. Harmony, or rather "complementarity," is revealed only in the mass, in tendencies rather than in states. Especially (and this is the point on which finalism has been most seriously mistaken) harmony is rather behind us than before. It is due to an identity of impulsion and not to a common aspiration. It would be futile to try to assign to life an end, in the human sense of the word. To speak of an end is to think of a preexisting model which has only to be realized. It is to suppose, therefore, that all is given, and that the future can be read in the present. It is to believe that life, in its movement and in its entirety, goes to work like our intellect, which is only a motionless and fragmentary view of life, and which naturally takes its stand outside of time. Life, on the contrary, progresses and *endures* in time. Of course, when once the road has been traveled, we can glance over it, mark its direction, note this in psychological terms and speak as if there had been pursuit of an end. Thus shall we speak ourselves. But, of the road which was going to be traveled, the human mind could have nothing to say, for the road has been created *pari passu* with the act of traveling over it, being nothing but the direction of this act itself. At every instant, then, evolution must admit of a psychological interpretation which is, from our point of view, the best interpretation; but this explanation has neither value nor even significance except retrospectively. Never could the finalistic interpretation, such as we shall propose it, be taken for an anticipation of the future. It is a particular mode of viewing the past in the light of the present. In short, the classic conception of finality postulates at once too much and too little: it is both too wide and too narrow. In explaining life by intellect, it limits too much the meaning of life: intellect, such at least as we find it in ourselves, has been fashioned by evolution during the course of progress; it is cut out of something larger, or, rather, it is only the projection, necessarily on a plane, of a reality that possesses both relief and depth. It is this more comprehensive reality that true finalism ought to reconstruct, or, rather, if possible, embrace in one view. But, on the other hand, just because it goes beyond intellect—the faculty of connecting the same with the same, of perceiving and also of producing repetitions—this reality is undoubtedly creative, *i.e.* productive of effects in which it expands and tran-

scends its own being. These effects were therefore not given in it in advance, and so it could not take them for ends, although, when once produced, they admit of a rational interpretation, like that of the manufactured article that has reproduced a model. In short, the theory of final causes does not go far enough when it confines itself to ascribing some intelligence to nature, and it goes too far when it supposes a pre-existence of the future in the present in the form of idea. And the second theory, which sins by excess, is the outcome of the first, which sins by defect. In place of intellect proper must be substituted the more comprehensive reality of which intellect is only the contraction. The future then appears as expanding the present: it was not, therefore, contained in the present in the form of a represented end. And yet, once realized, it will explain the present as much as the present explains it, and even more; it must be viewed as an end as much as, and more than, a result. Our intellect has a right to consider the future abstractly from its habitual point of view, being itself an abstract view of the cause of its own being.

It is true that the cause may then seem beyond our grasp. Already the finalist theory of life eludes all precise verification. What if we go beyond it in one of its directions? Here, in fact, after a necessary digression, we are back at the question which we regard as essential: can the insufficiency of mechanism be proved by facts? We said that if this demonstration is possible, it is on condition of frankly accepting the evolutionist hypothesis. We must now show that if mechanism is insufficient to account for evolution, the way of proving this insufficiency is not to stop at the classic conception of finality, still less to contract or attenuate it, but, on the contrary, to go further.

Let us indicate at once the principle of

our demonstration. We said of life that, from its origin, it is the continuation of one and the same impetus, divided into divergent lines of evolution. Something has grown, something has developed by a series of additions which have been so many creations. This very development has brought about a dissociation of tendencies which were unable to grow beyond a certain point without becoming mutually incompatible. Strictly speaking, there is nothing to prevent our imagining that the evolution of life might have taken place in one single individual by means of a series of transformations spread over thousands of ages. Or, instead of a single individual, any number might be supposed, succeeding each other in a unilinear series. In both cases evolution would have had, so to speak, one dimension only. But evolution has actually taken place through millions of individuals, on divergent lines, each ending at a crossing from which new paths radiate, and so on indefinitely. If our hypothesis is justified, if the essential causes working along these diverse roads are of psychological nature, they must keep something in common in spite of the divergence of their effects, as school-fellows long separated keep the same memories of boyhood. Roads may fork or by-ways be opened along which dissociated elements may evolve in an independent manner, but nevertheless it is in virtue of the primitive impetus of the whole that the movement of the parts continues. Something of the whole, therefore, must abide in the parts; and this common element will be evident to us in some way, perhaps by the presence of identical organs in very different organisms. Suppose, for an instant, that the mechanistic explanation is the true one: evolution must then have occurred through a series of accidents added to one another, each new accident being preserved by selection if it is advan-

tageous to that sum of former advantageous accidents which the present form of the living being represents. What likelihood is there that, by two entirely different series of accidents being added together, two entirely different evolutions will arrive at similar results? The more two lines of evolution diverge, the less probability is there that accidental outer influences or accidental inner variations bring about the construction of the same apparatus upon them, especially if there was no trace of this apparatus at the moment of divergence. But such similarity of the two products would be natural, on the contrary, in a hypothesis like ours; even in the latest channel there would be something of the impulsion received at the source. *Pure mechanism, then, would be refutable, and finality, in the special sense in which we understand it, would be demonstrable in a certain aspect, if it could be proved that life may manufacture the like apparatus, by unlike means, on divergent lines of evolution; and the strength of the proof would be proportional both to the divergency between the lines of evolution thus chosen and to the complexity of the similar structures found in them.*

It will be said that resemblance of structure is due to sameness of the general conditions in which life has evolved, and that these permanent outer conditions may have imposed the same direction on the forces constructing this or that apparatus, in spite of the diversity of transient outer influences and accidental inner changes. We are not, of course, blind to the rôle which the concept of *adaptation* plays in the science of today. Biologists certainly do not all make the same use of it. Some think the outer conditions capable of causing change in organisms in a *direct* manner, in a definite direction, through physico-chemical alterations induced by them in the living substance; such is the hypothesis of

Eimer, for example. Others, more faithful to the spirit of Darwinism, believe the influence of conditions works *indirectly* only, through favoring, in the struggle for life, those representatives of a species which the chance of birth has best adapted to the environment. In other words, some attribute a *positive* influence to outer conditions, and say that they actually *give rise to* variations, while the others say these conditions have only a *negative* influence and merely *eliminate* variations. But, in both cases, the outer conditions are supposed to bring about a precise adjustment of the organism to its circumstances. Both parties, then, will attempt to explain mechanically, by adaptation to similar conditions, the similarities of structure which we think are the strongest argument against mechanism. So we must at once indicate in a general way, before passing to the detail, why explanations from "adaptation" seem to us insufficient.

Let us first remark that, of the two hypotheses just described, the latter is the only one which is not equivocal. The Darwinian idea of adaptation by automatic elimination of the unadapted is a simple and clear idea. But, just because it attributes to the outer cause which controls evolution a merely negative influence, it has great difficulty in accounting for the progressive and, so to say, rectilinear development of complex apparatus such as we are about to examine. How much greater will this difficulty be in the case of the similar structure of two extremely complex organs on two entirely different lines of evolution! An accidental variation, however minute, implies the working of a great number of small physical and chemical causes. An accumulation of accidental variations, such as would be necessary to produce a complex structure, requires therefore the concurrence of an almost infinite number of infinitesimal causes. Why should these

causes, entirely accidental, recur the same, and in the same order, at different points of space and time? No one will hold that this is the case, and the Darwinian himself will probably merely maintain that identical effects may arise from different causes, that more than one road leads to the same spot. But let us not be fooled by a metaphor. The place reached does not give the form of the road that leads there; while an organic structure is just the accumulation of those small differences which evolution has had to go through in order to achieve it. The struggle for life and natural selection can be of no use to us in solving this part of the problem, for we are not concerned here with what has perished, we have to do only with what has survived. Now, we see that identical structures have been formed on independent lines of evolution by a gradual accumulation of effects. How can accidental causes, occurring in an accidental order, be supposed to have repeatedly come to the same result, the causes being infinitely numerous and the effect infinitely complicated?

The principle of mechanism is that "the same causes produce the same effects." This principle, of course, does not always imply that the same effects must have the same causes; but it does involve this consequence in the particular case in which the causes remain visible in the effect that they produce and are indeed its constitutive elements. That two walkers starting from different points and wandering at random should finally meet, is no great wonder. But that, throughout their walk, they should describe two identical curves exactly superposable on each other, is altogether unlikely. The improbability will be the greater, the more complicated the routes; and it will become impossibility, if the zigzags are infinitely complicated. Now, what is this complexity of zigzags as compared with that of an organ in which thousands of different cells, each being itself a kind of organism, are arranged in a definite order?

Let us turn, then, to the other hypothesis, and see how it would solve the problem. Adaptation, it says, is not merely elimination of the unadapted; it is due to the positive influence of outer conditions that have molded the organism on their own form. This time, similarity of effects will be explained by similarity of cause. We shall remain, apparently, in pure mechanism. But if we look closely, we shall see that the explanation is merely verbal, that we are again the dupes of words, and that the trick of the solution consists in taking the term "adaptation" in two entirely different senses at the same time.

If I pour into the same glass, by turns, water and wine, the two liquids will take the same form, and the sameness in form will be due to the sameness in adaptation of content to container. Adaptation, here, really means mechanical adjustment. The reason is that the form to which the matter has adapted itself was there, ready-made, and has forced its own shape on the matter. But, in the adaptation of an organism to the circumstances it has to live in, where is the pre-existing form awaiting its matter? The circumstances are not a mold into which life is inserted and whose form life adopts: this is indeed to be fooled by a metaphor. There is no form yet, and the life must create a form for itself, suited to the circumstances which are made for it. It will have to make the best of these circumstances, neutralize their inconveniences and utilize their advantages—in short, respond to outer actions by building up a machine which has no resemblance to them. Such adapting is not *repeating,* but *replying,*—an entirely different thing. If there is still adaptation, it will be in the sense in which one may

say of the solution of a problem of geometry, for example, that it is adapted to the conditions. I grant indeed that adaptation so understood explains why different evolutionary processes result in similar forms: the same problem, of course, calls for the same solution. But it is necessary then to introduce, as for the solution of a problem of geometry, an intelligent activity, or at least a cause which behaves in the same way. This is to bring in finality again, and a finality this time more than ever charged with anthropomorphic elements. In a word, if the adaptation is passive, if it is mere repetition in the relief of what the conditions give in the mold, it will build up nothing that one tries to make it build; and if it is active, capable of responding by a calculated solution to the problem which is set out in the conditions, that is going further than we do—too far, indeed, in our opinion—in the direction we indicated in the beginning. But the truth is that there is a surreptitious passing from one of these two meanings to the other, a flight for refuge to the first whenever one is about to be caught *in flagrante delicto* of finalism by employing the second. It is really the second which serves the usual practice of science, but it is the first that generally provides its philosophy. In any *particular* case one talks as if the process of adaptation were an effort of the organism to build up a machine capable of turning external circumstances to the best possible account: then one speaks of adaptation *in general* as if it were the very impress of circumstances, passively received by an indifferent matter.

But let us come to the examples. It would be interesting first to institute here a general comparison between plants and animals. One cannot fail to be struck with the parallel progress which has been accomplished, on both sides, in the direction of sexuality. Not only is fecundation itself the same in higher plants and in animals, since it consists, in both, in the union of two nuclei that differ in their properties and structure before their union and immediately after become equivalent to each other; but the preparation of sexual elements goes on in both under like conditions: it consists essentially in the reduction of the number of chromosomes and the rejection of a certain quantity of chromatic substance.[1] Yet vegetables and animals have evolved on independent lines, favored by unlike circumstances, opposed by unlike obstacles. Here are two great series which have gone on diverging. On either line, thousands and thousands of causes have combined to determine the morphological and functional evolution. Yet these infinitely complicated causes have been consummated, in each series, in the same effect. And this effect could hardly be called a phenomenon of "adaptation": where is the adaptation, where is the pressure of external circumstances? There is no striking utility in sexual generation; it has been interpreted in the most diverse ways; and some very acute inquirers even regard the sexuality of the plant, at least, as a luxury which nature might have dispensed with.[2] But we do not wish to dwell on facts so disputed. The ambiguity of the term "adaptation," and the necessity of transcending both the point of view of mechanical causality and that of anthropomorphic finality, will stand out more clearly with simpler examples. At all times the doctrine of finality has laid much stress on the marvelous structure of the sense-organs, in order to liken the work of nature to that of an intelligent workman. Now, since these organs are found, in a rudimentary state, in the lower animals, and since nature offers us many intermediaries between the pigment-spot of the simplest organisms and the infinitely complex eye of the vertebrates, it may just as well be alleged that the result has been brought about by natural selection perfecting the organ automatically. In short, if there is a case in which it seems justifiable to invoke adaptation, it is this particular one. For there may be discussion about the function and meaning of such a thing as sexual generation, in so far as it is related to the conditions in which it occurs; but the relation of the eye to light is obvious, and when we call this relation an adaptation, we must know what we mean. If, then, we can show, in this privileged case, the insufficiency of the principles invoked on both sides, our demonstration will at once have reached a high degree of generality.

Let us consider the example on which the advocates of finality have always insisted: the structure of such an organ as the human eye. They have had no difficulty in showing that in this extremely complicated apparatus all the elements are marvelously co-ordinated. In order that vision shall operate, says the author of a well-known book on *Final Causes,* "the sclerotic membrane must become transparent in one point of its surface, so as to enable luminous rays to pierce it . . . ; the cornea must correspond exactly with the opening of the socket . . . ; behind this transparent opening there must be refracting media . . . ; there must be a retina[1] at the extremity of the dark chamber . . . ; perpendicular to the retina there must be an innu-

[1] P. Guérin, *Les Connaissances actuelles sur la fécondation chez les phanérogames,* Paris, 1904, pp. 144–148. Cf. Delage, *L'Hérédité,* 2nd edition, 1903, pp. 140 ff.

[2] Möbius, *Beiträge zur Lehre von der Fortpflanzung der Gewächse,* Jena, 1897, pp. 203–206 in particular. Cf. Hartog, "Sur les phénomènes de reproduction" (*Année biologique,* 1895, pp. 707–709).

[1] Paul Janet, *Les Causes finales,* Paris, 1876, p. 83.

merable quantity of transparent cones permitting only the light directed in the line of their axes to reach the nervous membrane,"[1] etc., etc. In reply, the advocate of final causes has been invited to assume the evolutionist hypothesis. Everything is marvelous, indeed, if one consider an eye like ours, in which thousands of elements are co-ordinated in a single function. But take the function at its origin, in the Infusorian, where it is reduced to the mere impressionability (almost purely chemical) of a pigment-spot to light: this function, possibly only an accidental fact in the beginning, may have brought about a slight complication of the organ, which again induced an improvement of the function. It may have done this either directly, through some unknown mechanism, or indirectly, merely through the effect of the advantages it brought to the living being and the hold it thus offered to natural selection. Thus the progressive formation of an eye as well contrived as ours would be explained by an almost infinite number of actions and reactions between the function and the organ, without the intervention of other than mechanical causes.

The question is hard to decide, indeed, when put directly between the function and the organ, as is done in the doctrine of finality, as also mechanism itself does. For organ and function are terms of different nature, and each conditions the other so closely that it is impossible to say *a priori* whether in expressing their relation we should begin with the first, as does mechanism, or with the second, as finalism requires. But the discussion would take an entirely different turn, we think, if we began by comparing together two terms of the same nature, an organ with an organ, instead of an organ with its function. In this case, it would be pos-

sible to proceed little by little to a solution more and more plausible, and there would be the more chance of a successful issue the more resolutely we assumed the evolutionist hypothesis.

Let us place side by side the eye of a vertebrate and that of a mollusk such as the common Pecten. We find the same essential parts in each, composed of analogous elements. The eye of the Pecten presents a retina, a cornea, a lens of cellular structure like our own. There is even that peculiar inversion of retinal elements which is not met with, in general, in the retina of the invertebrates. Now, the origin of mollusks may be a debated question, but, whatever opinion we hold, all are agreed that mollusks and vertebrates separated from their common parent-stem long before the appearance of an eye so complex as that of the Pecten. Whence, then, the stuctural analogy?

Let us question on this point the two opposed systems of evolutionist explanation in turn—the hypothesis of purely accidental variations, and that of a variation directed in a definite way under the influence of external conditions.

The first, as is well known, is presented today in two quite different forms. Darwin spoke of very slight variations being accumulated by natural selection. He was not ignorant of the facts of sudden variation; but he thought these "sports," as he called them, were only monstrosities incapable of perpetuating themselves; and he accounted for the genesis of species by an accumulation of *insensible* variations.[1] Such is still the opinion of many naturalists. It is tending, however, to give way to the opposite idea that a new species comes into being all at once by the simultaneous appearance of several new characters, all somewhat different from the previous ones. This latter hy-

[1] *Ibid.*, p. 80.

[1] Darwin, *Origin of Species*, chap. ii.

pothesis, already proposed by various authors, notably by Bateson in a remarkable book,[1] has become deeply significant and acquired great force since the striking experiments of Hugo De Vries. This botanist, working on the Œnothera Lamarckiana, obtained at the end of a few generations a certain number of new species. The theory he deduces from his experiments is of the highest interest. Species pass through alternate periods of stability and transformation. When the period of "mutability" occurs, unexpected forms spring forth in a great number of different directions.[2]—We will not attempt to take sides between this hypothesis and that of insensible variations. Indeed, perhaps both are partly true. We wish merely to point out that if the variations invoked are accidental, they do not, whether small or great, account for a similarity of structure such as we have cited.

Let us assume, to begin with, the Darwinian theory of insensible variations, and suppose the occurrence of small differences due to chance, and continually accumulating. It must not be forgotten that all the parts of an organism are necessarily co-ordinated. Whether the function be the effect of the organ or its cause, it matters little; one point is certain—the organ will be of no use and will not give selection a hold unless it functions. However the minute structure of the retina may develop, and however complicated it may become, such progress, instead of favoring vision, will probably hinder it if the visual centers do not develop at the same time, as well as several parts of the visual organ

itself. If the variations are accidental, how can they ever agree to arise in every part of the organ at the same time, in such way that the organ will continue to perform its function? Darwin quite understood this; it is one of the reasons why he regarded variation as insensible.[3] For a difference which arises accidentally at one point of the visual apparatus, if it be very slight, will not hinder the functioning of the organ; and hence this first accidental variation can, in a sense, wait for complementary variations to accumulate and raise vision to a higher degree of perfection. Granted; but while the insensible variation does not hinder the functioning of the eye, neither does it help it, so long as the variations that are complementary do not occur. How, in that case, can the variation be retained by natural selection? Unwittingly one will reason as if the slight variation were a toothing stone set up by the organism and reserved for a later construction. This hypothesis, so little conformable to the Darwinian principle, is difficult enough to avoid even in the case of an organ which has been developed along one single main line of evolution, e.g., the vertebrate eye. But it is absolutely forced upon us when we observe the likeness of structure of the vertebrate eye and that of the mollusks. How could the same small variations, incalculable in number, have ever occurred in the same order on two independent lines of evolution, if they were purely accidental? And how could they have been preserved by selection and accumulated in both cases, the same in the same order, when each of them, taken separately, was of no use?

Let us turn, then, to the hypothesis of sudden variations, and see whether it will solve the problem. It certainly lessens the difficulty on one point, but it makes it much worse on another. If the eye of the

---

[1] Bateson, Materials for the Study of Variation, London, 1894, especially pp. 567 ff. Cf. Scott, "Variations and Mutations" (American Journal of Science, Nov. 1894).

[2] De Vries, Die Mutationstheorie, Leipzig, 1901–1903. Cf., by the same author, Species and Varieties, Chicago, 1905.

[3] Darwin, Origin of Species, chap. vi.

mollusk and that of the vertebrate have both been raised to their present form by a relatively small number of sudden leaps, I have less difficulty in understanding the resemblance of the two organs than if this resemblance were due to an incalculable number of infinitesimal resemblances acquired successively: in both cases it is chance that operates, but in the first case chance is not required to work the miracle it would have to perform in the second. Not only is the number of resemblances to be added somewhat reduced, but I can also understand better how each could be preserved and added to the others; for the elementary variation is now considerable enough to be an advantage to the living being, and so to lend itself to the play of selection. But here there arises another problem, no less formidable, viz., how do all the parts of the visual apparatus, suddenly changed, remain so well co-ordinated that the eye continues to exercise its function? For the change of one part alone will make vision impossible, unless this change is absolutely infinitesmal. The parts must then all change at once, each consulting the others. I agree that a great number of unco-ordinated variations may indeed have arisen in less fortunate individuals, that natural selection may have eliminated these, and that only the combination fit to endure, capable of preserving and improving vision, has survived. Still, this combination had to be produced. And, supposing chance to have granted this favor once, can we admit that it repeats the self-same favor in the course of the history of a species, so as to give rise, every time, all at once, to new complications marvelously regulated with reference to each other, and so related to former complications as to go further on in the same direction? How, especially, can we suppose that by a series of mere "accidents" these sudden variations occur, the same, in the same

order—involving in each case a perfect harmony of elements more and more numerous and complex—along two independent lines of evolution?

The law of correlation will be invoked, of course; Darwin himself appealed to it.[1] It will be alleged that a change is not localized in a single point of the organism, but has its necessary recoil on other points. The examples cited by Darwin remain classic: white cats with blue eyes are generally deaf; hairless dogs have imperfect dentition, etc.—Granted; but let us not play now on the word "correlation." A collective whole of *solidary* changes is one thing, a system of *complementary* changes—changes so co-ordinated as to keep up and even improve the functioning of an organ under more complicated conditions—is another. That an anomaly of the pilous system should be accompanied by an anomaly of dentition is quite conceivable without our having to call for a special principle of explanation; for hair and teeth are similar formations,[2] and the same chemical change of the germ that hinders the formation of hair would probably obstruct that of teeth: it may be for the same sort of reason that white cats with blue eyes are deaf. In these different examples the "correlative" changes are only *solidary* changes (not to mention the fact that they are really *lesions,* namely, diminutions or suppressions, and not additions, which makes a great difference). But when we speak of "correlative" changes occurring suddenly in the different parts of the eye, we use the word in an entirely new sense: this time there is a whole set of changes not only simulta-

---

[1] Darwin, *Origin of Species,* chap. i.

[2] On this homology of hair and teeth, see Brandt, "Über . . . eine mutmassliche Homologie der Haare und Zahne" (*Biol. Centralblatt* vol. xviii., 1898, especially pp. 262 ff.).

neous, not only bound together by community of origin, but so co-ordinated that the organ keeps on performing the same simple function, and even performs it better. That a change in the germ, which influences the formation of the retina, may affect at the same time also the formation of the cornea, the iris, the lens, the visual centers, etc., I admit, if necessary, although they are formations that differ much more from one another in their original nature than do probably hair and teeth. But that all these simultaneous changes should occur in such a way as to improve or even merely maintain vision, this is what, in the hypothesis of sudden variation, I cannot admit, unless a mysterious principle is to come in, whose duty it is to watch over the interest of the function. But this would be to give up the idea of "accidental" variation. In reality, these two senses of the word "correlation" are often interchanged in the mind of the biologist, just like the two senses of the word "adaptation." And the confusion is almost legitimate in botany, that science in which the theory of the formation of species by sudden variation rests on the firmest experimental basis. In vegetables, function is far less narrowly bound to form than in animals. Even profound morphological differences, such as a change in the form of leaves, have no appreciable influence on the exercise of function, and so do not require a whole system of complementary changes for the plant to remain fit to survive. But it is not so in the animal, especially in the case of an organ like the eye, a very complex structure and very delicate function. Here it is impossible to identify changes that are simply solidary with changes which are also complementary. The two senses of the word "correlation" must be carefully distinguished; it would be a downright paralogism to adopt one of them in the premises of the reasoning, and the other in the conclusion. And this is just what is done when the principle of correlation is invoked in explanations of *detail* in order to account for complementary variations, and then correlation *in general* is spoken of as if it were any group of variations provoked by any variation of the germ. Thus, the notion of correlation is first used in current science as it might be used by an advocate of finality; it is understood that this is only a convenient way of expressing oneself, that one will correct it and fall back on pure mechanism when explaining the nature of the principles and turning from science to philosophy. And one does then come back to pure mechanism, but only by giving a new meaning to the word "correlation"—a meaning which would now make correlation inapplicable to the detail it is called upon to explain.

To sum up, if the accidental variations that bring about evolution are insensible variations, some good genius must be appealed to—the genius of the future species—in order to preserve and accumulate these variations, for selection will not look after this. If, on the other hand, the accidental variations are sudden, then, for the previous function to go on or for a new function to take its place, all the changes that have happened together must be complementary. So we have to fall back on the good genius again, this time to obtain the *convergence* of *simultaneous* changes, as before to be assured of the *continuity of direction* of *successive* variations. But in neither case can parallel development of the same complex structures on independent lines of evolution be due to a mere accumulation of accidental variations. So we come to the second of the two great hypotheses we have to examine. Suppose the variations are due, not to accidental and inner causes, but to the direct influence of outer circumstances. Let us see what line we should have to take, on this hypothesis, to account for the resemblance of eye-structure in two series that are independent of each other from the phylogenetic point of view.

Though mollusks and vertebrates have evolved separately, both have remained exposed to the influence of light. And light is a physical cause bringing forth certain definite effects. Acting in a continuous way, it has been able to produce a continuous variation in a constant direction. Of course it is unlikely that the eye of the vertebrate and that of the mollusk have been built up by a series of variations due to simple chance. Admitting even that light enters into the case as an instrument of selection, in order to allow only useful variations to persist, there is no possibility that the play of chance, even thus supervised from without, should bring about in both cases the same juxtaposition of elements co-ordinated in the same way. But it would be different supposing that light acted directly on the organized matter so as to change its structure and somehow adapt this structure to its own form. The resemblance of the two effects would then be explained by the identity of the cause. The more and more complex eye would be something like the deeper and deeper imprint of light on a matter which, being organized, possesses a special aptitude for receiving it.

But can an organic structure be likened to an imprint? We have already called attention to the ambiguity of the term "adaptation." The gradual complication of a form which is being better and better adapted to the mold of outward circumstances is one thing, the increasingly complex structure of an instrument which derives more and more advantage from these circumstances is another. In the former case, the matter merely receives an imprint; in the second, it reacts positively, it solves a problem. Obviously it is this second sense of the word "adapt" that is used when one says that the eye has become better and better adapted to the influence of light. But one passes more or less unconsciously from this sense to the other, and a purely mechanistic biology will strive to make the *passive* adaptation of an inert matter, which submits to the influence of its environment, mean the same as the *active* adaptation of an organism which derives from this influence an advantage it can appropriate. It must be owned, indeed, that Nature herself appears to invite our mind to confuse these two kinds of adaptation, for she usually begins by a passive adaptation where, later on, she will build up a mechanism for active response. Thus, in the case before us, it is unquestionable that the first rudiment of the eye is found in the pigment-spot of the lower organisms; this spot may indeed have been produced physically, by the mere action of light, and there are a great number of intermediaries between the simple spot of pigment and a complicated eye like that of the vertebrates.— But, from the fact that we pass from one thing to another by degrees, it does not follow that the two things are of the same nature. From the fact that an orator falls in, at first, with the passions of his audience in order to make himself master of them, it will not be concluded that to *follow* is the same as to *lead*. Now, living matter seems to have no other means of turning circumstances to good account than by adapting itself to them passively at the outset. Where it has to direct a movement, it begins by adopting it. Life proceeds by insinuation. The intermediate degrees between a pigment-spot and an eye are nothing to the point: however numerous the degrees, there will still be the same interval between the pigment-spot and the eye as between a photograph and a photographic apparatus. Certainly the photograph has been gradually turned into a photographic apparatus; but could light alone, a physical force, ever have provoked this change, and converted an impression left by it into a machine capable of using it?

It may be claimed that considerations of utility are out of place here; that the eye is not made to see; but that we see because we have eyes; that the organ is what it is, and "utility" is a word by which we designate the functional effects of the structure. But when I say that the eye "makes use of" light, I do not merely mean that the eye is capable of seeing; I allude to the very precise relations that exist between this organ and the apparatus of locomotion. The retina of vertebrates is prolonged in an optic nerve, which, again, is continued by cerebral centers connected with motor mechanisms. Our eye makes use of light in that it enables us to utilize, by movements of reaction, the objects that we see to be advantageous, and to avoid those which we see to be injurious. Now, of course, as light may have produced a pigment-spot by physical means, so it can physically determine the movements of certain organisms; ciliated Infusoria, for instance, react to light. But no one would hold that the influence of light has physically caused the formation of a nervous system, of a muscular system, of an osseous system, all things which are continuous with the apparatus of vision in vertebrate animals. The truth is, when one speaks of the gradual formation of the eye, and, still more, when one takes into account all that is inseparably connected with it, one brings in something entirely different from the direct action of light. One implicitly attributes to organized matter a certain capacity *sui generis,* the mysterious power of building up very complicated machines to utilize the simple excitation that it undergoes.

But this is just what is claimed to be unnecessary. Physics and chemistry are said to give us the key to everything.

Eimer's great work is instructive in this respect. It is well known what persevering effort this biologist has devoted to demonstrating that transformation is brought about by the influence of the external on the internal, continuously exerted in the same direction, and not, as Darwin held, by accidental variations. His theory rests on observations of the highest interest, of which the starting-point was the study of the course followed by the color variation of the skin in certain lizards. Before this, the already old experiments of Dorfmeister had shown that the same chrysalis, according as it was submitted to cold or heat, gave rise to very different butterflies, which had long been regarded as independent species, *Vanessa levana* and *Vanessa prorsa:* an intermediate temperature produces an intermediate form. We might class with these facts the important transformations observed in a little crustacean, *Artemia salina,* when the salt of the water it lives in is increased or diminished.[1] In these various experiments the external agent seems to act as a cause of transformation. But what does the word "cause" mean here? Without undertaking an exhaustive analysis of the idea of causality, we will merely remark that three very different meanings of this term are commonly confused. A cause may act by *impelling, releasing,* or *unwinding.* The billiard ball that strikes another determines its movement by *impelling.* The spark that explodes the powder acts by *releasing.* The gradual relaxing of the spring that makes the phonograph turn *unwinds* the melody inscribed on the cylinder: if the melody which is played

---

[1] It seems, from later observations, that the transformation of Artemia is a more complex phenomenon than was first supposed. See on this subject Samter and Heymons, "Die Variation bei Artemia Salina" (*Anhang zu den Abhandlungen der k. preussischen Akad. der Wissenschaften,* 1902).

be the effect, and the relaxing of the spring the cause, we must say that the cause acts by *unwinding*. What distinguishes these three cases from each other is the greater or less solidarity between the cause and the effect. In the first, the quantity and quality of the effect vary with the quantity and quality of the cause. In the second, neither quality nor quantity of the effect varies with quality and quantity of the cause: the effect is invariable. In the third, the quantity of the effect depends on the quantity of the cause, but the cause does not influence the quality of the effect: the longer the cylinder turns by the action of the spring, the more of the melody I shall hear, but the nature of the melody, or of the part heard, does not depend on the action of the spring. Only in the first case, really, does cause *explain* effect; in the others the effect is more or less given in advance, and the antecedent invoked is—in different degrees, of course—its occasion rather than its cause. Now, in saying that the saltness of the water is the cause of the transformations of Artemia, or that the degree of temperature determines the color and marks of the wings which a certain chrysalis will assume on becoming a butterfly, is the word "cause" used in the first sense? Obviously not: causality has here an intermediary sense between those of unwinding and releasing. Such, indeed, seems to be Eimer's own meaning when he speaks of the "kaleidoscopic" character of the variation,[1] or when he says that the variation of organized matter works in a definite way, just as inorganic matter crystallizes in definite directions.[2] And it may be granted, perhaps, that the process is a merely physical and chemical one in the case of the color-changes of the skin. But if this sort of explanation is extended to the case of the gradual formation of the eye of the vertebrate, for instance, it must be supposed that the physico-chemistry of living bodies is such that the influence of light has caused the organism to construct a progressive series of visual apparatus, all extremely complex, yet all capable of seeing, and of seeing better and better.[1] What more could the most confirmed finalist say, in order to mark out so exceptional a physico-chemistry? And will not the position of a mechanistic philosophy become still more difficult, when it is pointed out to it that the egg of a mollusk cannot have the same chemical composition as that of a vertebrate, that the organic substance which evolved toward the first of these two forms could not have been chemically identical with that of the substance which went in the other direction, and that, nevertheless, under the influence of light, the same organ has been constructed in the one case as in the other?

The more we reflect upon it, the more we shall see that this production of the same effect by two different accumulations of an enormous number of small causes is contrary to the principles of mechanistic philosophy. We have concentrated the full force of our discussion upon an example drawn from phylogenesis. But ontogenesis would have furnished us with facts no less cogent. Every moment, right before our eyes, nature arrives at identical results, in sometimes neighboring species, by entirely different embryogenic processes. Observations of "heteroblastia" have multiplied in late years,[2] and it has been necessary to re-

---

[1] Eimer, *Orthogenesis der Schmetterlinge,* Leipzig, 1897, p. 24. Cf. *Die Entstehung der Arten,* p. 53.

[2] Eimer, *Die Entstehung der Arten,* Jena, 1888, p. 25.

[1] *Ibid.,* pp. 165 ff.

[2] Salensky, "Heteroblastie" (*Proc. of the Fourth International Congress of Zoology,* London, 1899, pp. 111–118). Salensky has coined this word to designate the cases in which organs that are equivalent, but of dif-

ject the almost classical theory of the specificity of embryonic gills. Still keeping to our comparison between the eye of vertebrates and that of mollusks, we may point out that the retina of the vertebrate is produced by an expansion in the rudimentary brain of the young embryo. It is a regular nervous center which has moved toward the periphery. In the mollusk, on the contrary, the retina is derived from the ectoderm directly, and not indirectly by means of the embryonic encephalon. Quite different, therefore, are the evolutionary processes which lead, in man and in the Pecten, to the development of a like retina. But, without going so far as to compare two organisms so distant from each other, we might reach the same conclusion simply by looking at certain very curious facts of regeneration in one and the same organism. If the crystalline lens of a Triton be removed, it is regenerated by the iris.[1] Now, the original lens was built out of the ectoderm, while the iris is of mesodermic origin. What is more, in the *Salamandra maculata*, if the lens be removed and the iris left, the regeneration of the lens takes place at the upper part of the iris; but if this upper part of the iris itself be taken away, the regeneration takes place in the inner or retinal layer of the remaining region.[2] Thus, parts differently situated, differently constituted, meant normally for different functions, are capable of performing the same duties and even of manufacturing, when necessary, the same pieces of the machine. Here we have, indeed, the same

effect obtained by different combinations of causes.

Whether we will or no, we must appeal to some inner directing principle in order to account for this convergence of effects. Such convergence does not appear possible in the Darwinian, and especially the neo-Darwinian, theory of insensible accidental variations, nor in the hypothesis of sudden accidental variations, nor even in the theory that assigns definite directions to the evolution of the various organs by a kind of mechanical composition of the external with the internal forces. So we come to the only one of the present forms of evolution which remains for us to mention, viz., neo-Lamarckism.

It is well known that Lamarck attributed to the living being the power of varying by use or disuse of its organs, and also of passing on the variation so acquired to its descendants. A certain number of biologists hold a doctrine of this kind today. The variation that results in a new species is not, they believe, merely an accidental variation inherent in the germ itself, nor is it governed by a determinism *sui generis* which develops definite characters in a definite direction, apart from every consideration of utility. It springs from the very effort of the living being to adapt itself to the circumstances of its existence. The effort may indeed be only the mechanical exercise of certain organs, mechanically elicited by the pressure of external circumstances. But it may also imply consciousness and will, and it is in this sense that it appears to be understood by one of the most eminent representatives of the doctrine, the American naturalist Cope.[1] Neo-Lamarckism is therefore, of all the later

---

ferent embryological origin, are formed at the same points in animals related to each other.

[1] Wolff, "Die Regeneration der Urodelenlinse" (*Arch. f. Entwickelungsmechanik,* i., 1895, pp. 380 ff.).

[2] Fischel, "Über die Regeneration der Linse" (*Anat. Anzeiger,* xiv., 1898, pp. 373–380).

[1] Cope, *The Origin of the Fittest,* 1887; *The Primary Factors of Organic Evolution,* 1896.

forms of evolutionism, the only one capable of admitting an internal and psychological principle of development, although it is not bound to do so. And it is also the only evolutionism that seems to us to account for the building up of identical complex organs on independent lines of development. For it is quite conceivable that the same effort to turn the same circumstances to good account might have the same result, especially if the problem put by the circumstances is such as to admit of only one solution. But the question remains, whether the term "effort" must not then be taken in a deeper sense, a sense even more psychological than any neo-Lamarckian supposes.

For a mere variation of size is one thing, and a change of form is another. That an organ can be strengthened and grow by exercise, nobody will deny. But it is a long way from that to the progressive development of an eye like that of the mollusks and of the vertebrates. If this development be ascribed to the influence of light, long continued but passively received, we fall back on the theory we have just criticized. If, on the other hand, an internal activity is appealed to, then it must be something quite different from what we usually call an effort, for never has an effort been known to produce the slightest complication of an organ, and yet an enormous number of complications, all admirably co-ordinated, have been necessary to pass from the pigment-spot of the Infusorian to the eye of the vertebrate. But, even if we accept this notion of the evolutionary process in the case of animals, how can we apply it to plants? Here, variations of form do not seem to imply, nor always to lead to, functional changes; and even if the cause of the variation is of a psychological nature, we can hardly call it an effort, unless we give a very unusual extension to the meaning of the word.

The truth is, it is necessary to dig beneath the effort itself and look for a deeper cause.

This is especially necessary, we believe, if we wish to get at a cause of regular hereditary variations. We are not going to enter here into the controversies over the transmissibility of acquired characters; still less do we wish to take too definite a side on this question, which is not within our province. But we cannot remain completely indifferent to it. Nowhere is it clearer that philosophers cannot today content themselves with vague generalities, but must follow the scientists in experimental detail and discuss the results with them. If Spencer had begun by putting to himself the question of the hereditability of acquired characters, his evolutionism would no doubt have taken an altogether different form. If (as seems probable to us) a habit contracted by the individual were transmitted to its descendants only in very exceptional cases, all the Spencerian psychology would need remaking, and a large part of Spencer's philosophy would fall to pieces. Let us say, then, how the problem seems to us to present itself, and in what direction an attempt might be made to solve it.

After having been affirmed as a dogma, the transmissibility of acquired characters has been no less dogmatically denied, for reasons drawn *a priori* from the supposed nature of germinal cells. It is well known how Weismann was led, by his hypothesis of the continuity of the germ-plasm, to regard the germinal cells —ova and spermatozoa—as almost independent of the somatic cells. Starting from this, it has been claimed, and is still claimed by many, that the hereditary transmission of an acquired character is inconceivable. But if, perchance, experiment should show that acquired characters are transmissible, it would prove thereby that the germ-plasm is not so independent of the somatic envelope as has been contended, and the transmissibility of acquired characters would become *ipso facto* conceivable; which amounts to saying that conceivability and inconceivability have nothing to do with the case, and that experience alone must settle the matter. But it is just here that the difficulty begins. The acquired characters we are speaking of are generally habits or the effects of habit, and at the root of most habits there is a natural disposition. So that one can always ask whether it is really the habit acquired by the soma of the individual that is transmitted, or whether it is not rather a natural aptitude, which existed prior to the habit. This aptitude would have remained inherent in the germ-plasm which the individual bears within him, as it was in the individual himself and consequently in the germ whence he sprang. Thus, for instance, there is no proof that the mole has become blind because it has formed the habit of living underground; it is perhaps because its eyes were becoming atrophied that it condemned itself to a life underground.[1] If this is the case, the tendency to lose the power of vision has been transmitted from germ to germ without anything being acquired or lost by the soma of the mole itself. From the fact that the son of a fencing master has become a good fencer much more quickly than his father, we cannot infer that the habit of the parent has been transmitted to the child; for certain natural dispositions in course of growth may have passed from the plasma engendering the father to the plasma engendering the son, may have grown on the way by the effect of the primitive impetus, and thus assured to the son a greater suppleness

than the father had, without troubling, so to speak, about what the father did. So of many examples drawn from the progressive domestication of animals: it is hard to say whether it is the acquired habit that is transmitted or only a certain natural tendency—that, indeed, which has caused such and such a particular species or certain of its representatives to be specially chosen for domestication. The truth is, when every doubtful case, every fact open to more than one interpretation, has been eliminated, there remains hardly a single unquestionable example of acquired and transmitted peculiarities, beyond the famous experiments of Brown-Séquard, repeated and confirmed by other physiologists.[1] By cutting the spinal cord or the sciatic nerve of guinea pigs, Brown-Séquard brought about an epileptic state which was transmitted to the descendants. Lesions of the same sciatic nerve, of the restiform body, etc., provoked various troubles in the guinea pig which its progeny inherited sometimes in a quite different form: exophthalmia, loss of toes, etc. But it is not demonstrated that in these different cases of hereditary transmission there had been a real influence of the soma of the animal on its germ-plasm. Weismann at once objected that the operations of Brown-Séquard might have introduced certain special microbes into the body of the guinea pig, which had found their means of nutrition in the nervous tissues and transmitted the malady by penetrating into the sexual elements.[2] This objec-

---

[1] Cuénot, "La Nouvelle Théorie transformiste" (*Revue générale des sciences,* 1894). Cf. Morgan, *Evolution and Adaptation,* London, 1903, p. 357.

[1] Brown-Séquard, "Nouvelles recherches sur l'épilepsie due à certaines lésions de la moelle épinière et des nerfs rachidiens" (*Arch. de physiologie,* vol. ii., 1866, pp. 211, 422, and 497).

[2] Weismann, *Aufsätze über Vererbung,* Jena, 1892, pp. 376–378, and also *Vorträge über Descendenztheorie,* Jena, 1902, vol. ii., p. 76.

tion has been answered by Brown-Séquard himself;[1] but a more plausible one might be raised. Some experiments of Voisin and Peron have shown that fits of epilepsy are followed by the elimination of a toxic body which, when injected into animals,[2] is capable of producing convulsive symptoms. Perhaps the trophic disorders following the nerve lesions made by Brown-Séquard correspond to the formation of precisely this convulsion-causing poison. If so, the toxin passed from the guinea pig to its spermatozoon or ovum, and caused in the development of the embryo a general disturbance, which, however, had no visible effects except at one point or another of the organism when developed. In that case, what occurred would have been somewhat the same as in the experiments of Charrin, Delamare and Moussu, where guinea pigs in gestation, whose liver or kidney was injured, transmitted the lesion to their progeny, simply because the injury to the mother's organ had given rise to specific "cytotoxins" which acted on the corresponding organ of the foetus.[3] It is true that, in these experiments, as in a former observation of the same physiologists,[4] it was the already formed foetus that was influ-

enced by the toxins. But other researches of Charrin have resulted in showing that the same effect may be produced, by an analogous process, on the spermatozoa and the ova.[1] To conclude, then: the inheritance of an acquired peculiarity in the experiments of Brown-Séquard can be explained by the effect of a toxin on the germ. The lesion, however well localized it seems, is transmitted by the same process as, for instance, the taint of alcoholism. But may it not be the same in the case of every acquired peculiarity that has become hereditary?

There is, indeed, one point on which both those who affirm and those who deny the transmissibility of acquired characters are agreed, namely, that certain influences, such as that of alcohol, can affect at the same time both the living being and the germ-plasm it contains. In such case, there is inheritance of a defect, and the result is *as if* the soma of the parent had acted on the germ-plasm, although in reality soma and plasma have simply both suffered the action of the same cause. Now, suppose that the soma can influence the germ-plasm, as those believe who hold that acquired characters are transmissible. Is not the most natural hypothesis to suppose that things happen in this second case as in the first, and that the direct effect of the influence of the soma is a *general* alteration of the germ-plasm? If this is the case, it is by exception, and in some sort by accident, that the modification of the descendant is the same as that of the parent. It is like the hereditability of the alcoholic taint: it passes from father to children, but it may take a different form in each child, and in none of them be like what it was in the father. Let the letter C represent the change in the plasm, C being either posi-

[1] Brown-Séquard, "Hérédité d'une affection due à une cause accidentelle" (*Arch. de physiologie*, 1892, pp. 686 ff.).

[2] Voisin and Peron, "Recherches sur la toxicité urinaire chez les épileptiques" (*Arch. de neurologie*, vol. xxiv., 1892, and xxv., 1893. Cf. the work of Voisin, *L'Épilepsie*, Paris, 1897, pp. 125–133).

[3] Charrin, Delamare and Moussu, "Transmission expérimentale aux descendants de lésions développées chez les ascendants" (*C. R. de l'Acad. des sciences*, vol. cxxxv., 1902, p. 191). Cf. Morgan, *Evolution and Adaptation*, p. 257, and Delage, *L'Hérédité*, 2nd edition, p. 388.

[4] Charrin and Delamare, "Hérédité cellulaire" (*C. R. de l'Acad. des sciences*, vol. cxxxiii., 1901, pp. 69–71).

[1] Charrin, "L'Hérédité pathologique" (*Revue générale des sciences*, 15 janvier 1896).

tive or negative, that is to say, showing either the gain or loss of certain substances. The effect will not be an exact reproduction of the cause, nor will the change in the germ-plasm, provoked by a certain modification of a certain part of the soma, determine a similar modification of the corresponding part of the new organism in process of formation, unless all the other nascent parts of this organism enjoy a kind of immunity as regards C: the same part will then undergo alteration in the new organism, because it happens that the development of this part is alone subject to the new influence. And, even then, the part might be altered in an entirely different way from that in which the corresponding part was altered in the generating organism.

We should propose, then, to introduce a distinction between the hereditability of *deviation* and that of *character*. An individual which acquires a new character thereby *deviates* from the form it previously had, which form the germs, or oftener the half-germs, it contains would have reproduced in their development. If this modification does not involve the production of substances capable of changing the germ-plasm, or does not so affect nutrition as to deprive the germ-plasm of certain of its elements, it will have no effect on the offspring of the individual. This is probably the case as a rule. If, on the contrary, it has some effect, this is likely to be due to a chemical change which it has induced in the germ-plasm. This chemical change might, by exception, bring about the original modification again in the organism which the germ is about to develop, but there are as many and more chances that it will do something else. In this latter case, the generated organism will perhaps deviate from the normal type *as much as* the generating organism, but it will do so *differently*. It will have inherited deviation and not character. In general, there-

fore, the habits formed by an individual have probably no echo in its offspring; and when they have, the modification in the descendants may have no visible likeness to the original one. Such, at least, is the hypothesis which seems to us most likely. In any case, in default of proof to the contrary, and so long as the decisive experiments called for by an eminent biologist[1] have not been made, we must keep to the actual results of observation. Now, even if we take the most favorable view of the theory of the transmissibility of acquired characters, and assume that the ostensible acquired character is not, in most cases, the more or less tardy development of an innate character, facts show us that hereditary transmission is the exception and not the rule. How, then, shall we expect it to develop an organ such as the eye? When we think of the enormous number of variations, all in the same direction, that we must suppose to be accumulated before the passage from the pigment-spot of the Infusorian to the eye of the mollusk and of the vertebrate is possible, we do not see how heredity, as we observe it, could ever have determined this piling-up of differences, even supposing that individual efforts could have produced each of them singly. That is to say that neo-Lamarckism is no more able than any other form of evolutionism to solve the problem.

In thus submitting the various present forms of evolutionism to a common test, in showing that they all strike against the same insurmountable difficulty, we have in no wise the intention of rejecting them altogether. On the contrary, each of them, being supported by a considerable number of facts, must be true in its way. Each of them must correspond to a certain aspect of the process of evolution.

---

[1] Giard, *Controverses transformistes*, Paris, 1904, p. 147.

Perhaps even it is necessary that a theory should restrict itself exclusively to a particular point of view, in order to remain scientific, *i.e.* to give a precise direction to researches into detail. But the reality of which each of these theories takes a partial view must transcend them all. And this reality is the special object of philosophy, which is not constrained to scientific precision because it contemplates no practical application. Let us therefore indicate in a word or two the positive contribution that each of the three present forms of evolutionism seems to us to make toward the solution of the problem, what each of them leaves out, and on what point this threefold effort should, in our opinion, converge in order to obtain a more comprehensive, although thereby of necessity a less definite, idea of the evolutionary process.

The neo-Darwinians are probably right, we believe, when they teach that the essential causes of variation are the differences inherent in the germ borne by the individual, and not the experiences or behavior of the individual in the course of his career. Where we fail to follow these biologists, is in regarding the differences inherent in the germ as purely accidental and individual. We cannot help believing that these differences are the development of an impulse which passes from germ to germ across the individuals, that they are therefore not pure accidents, and that they might well appear at the same time, in the same form, in all the representatives of the same species, or at least in a certain number of them. Already, in fact, the theory of *mutations* is modifying Darwinism profoundly on this point. It asserts that at a given moment, after a long period, the entire species is beset with a tendency to change. The *tendency to change*, therefore, is not accidental. True, the change itself would be accidental, since the mutation works, accord-

ing to De Vries, in different directions in the different representatives of the species. But, first we must see if the theory is confirmed by many other vegetable species (De Vries has verified it only by the *Œnothera Lamarckiana*),[1] and then there is the possibility, as we shall explain further on, that the part played by chance is much greater in the variation of plants than in that of animals, because, in the vegetable world, function does not depend so strictly on form. Be that as it may, the neo-Darwinians are inclined to admit that the periods of mutation are determinate. The direction of the mutation may therefore be so as well, at least in animals, and to the extent we shall have to indicate.

We thus arrive at a hypothesis like Eimer's, according to which the variations of different characters continue from generation to generation in definite directions. This hypothesis seems plausible to us, within the limits in which Eimer himself retains it. Of course, the evolution of the organic world cannot be predetermined as a whole. We claim, on the contrary, that the spontaneity of life is manifested by a continual creation of new forms succeeding others. But this indetermination cannot be complete; it must leave a certain part to determination. An organ like the eye, for example, must have been formed by just a continual changing in a definite direction. Indeed, we do not see how otherwise to explain the likeness of structure of the eye in species that have not the same history. Where we differ from Eimer is in his claim that combinations of physical and chemical causes are enough to secure the result. We have tried to prove, on the

---

[1] Some analogous facts, however, have been noted, all in the vegetable world. See Blaringhem, "La Notion d'espèce et la théorie de la mutation" (*Année psychologique*, vol. xii., 1906, pp. 95 ff.), and De Vries, *Species and Varieties*, p. 655.

contrary, by the example of the eye, that if there is "orthogenesis" here, a psychological cause intervenes.

Certain neo-Lamarckians do indeed resort to a cause of a psychological nature. There, to our thinking, is one of the most solid positions of neo-Lamarckism. But if this cause is nothing but the conscious effort of the individual, it cannot operate in more than a restricted number of cases—at most in the animal world, and not at all in the vegetable kingdom. Even in animals, it will act only on points which are under the direct or indirect control of the will. And even where it does act, it is not clear how it could compass a change so profound as an increase of complexity: at most this would be conceivable if the acquired characters were regularly transmitted so as to be added together; but this transmission seems to be the exception rather than the rule. A hereditary change in a definite direction, which continues to accumulate and add to itself so as to build up a more and more complex machine, must certainly be related to some sort of effort, but to an effort of far greater depth than the individual effort, far more independent of circumstances, an effort common to most representatives of the same species, inherent in the germs they bear rather than in their substance alone, an effort thereby assured of being passed on to their descendants.

So we come back, by a somewhat roundabout way, to the idea we started from, that of an *original impetus* of life, passing from one generation of germs to the following generation of germs through the developed organisms which bridge the interval between the generations. This impetus, sustained right along the lines of evolution among which it gets divided, is the fundamental cause of variations, at least of those that are regularly passed on, that accumulate and create new species. In general, when species have begun to diverge from a common stock, they accentuate their divergence as they progress in their evolution. Yet, in certain definite points, they may evolve identically; in fact, they must do so if the hypothesis of a common impetus be accepted. This is just what we shall have to show now in a more precise way, by the same example we have chosen, the formation of the eye in mollusks and vertebrates. The idea of an "original impetus," moreover, will thus be made clearer.

Two points are equally striking in an organ like the eye: the complexity of its structure and the simplicity of its function. The eye is composed of distinct parts, such as the sclerotic, the cornea, the retina, the crystalline lens, etc. In each of these parts the detail is infinite. The retina alone comprises three layers of nervous elements—multipolar cells, bipolar cells, visual cells—each of which has its individuality and is undoubtedly a very complicated organism: so complicated, indeed, is the retinal membrane in its intimate structure, that no simple description can give an adequate idea of it. The mechanism of the eye is, in short, composed of an infinity of mechanisms, all of extreme complexity. Yet vision is one simple fact. As soon as the eye opens, the visual act is effected. Just because the act is simple, the slightest negligence on the part of nature in the building of the infinitely complex machine would have made vision impossible. This contrast between the complexity of the organ and the unity of the function is what gives us pause.

A mechanistic theory is one which means to show us the gradual building-up of the machine under the influence of external circumstances intervening either directly by action on the tissues or indirectly by the selection of better-adapted ones. But, whatever form this theory may take, supposing it avails at all to explain the detail of the parts, it throws no light on their correlation.

Then comes the doctrine of finality, which says that the parts have been brought together on a preconceived plan with a view to a certain end. In this it likens the labor of nature to that of the workman, who also proceeds by the assemblage of parts with a view to the realization of an idea or the imitation of a model. Mechanism, here, reproaches finalism with its anthropomorphic character, and rightly. But it fails to see that itself proceeds according to this method —somewhat mutilated! True, it has got rid of the end pursued or the ideal model. But it also holds that nature has worked like a human being by bringing parts together, while a mere glance at the development of an embryo shows that life goes to work in a very different way. *Life does not proceed by the association and addition of elements, but by dissociation and division.*

We must get beyond both points of view, both mechanism and finalism being, at bottom, only standpoints to which the human mind has been led by considering the work of man. But in what direction can we go beyond them? We have said that in analyzing the structure of an organ, we can go on decomposing forever, although the function of the whole is a simple thing. This contrast between the infinite complexity of the organ and the extreme simplicity of the function is what should open our eyes.

In general, when the same object appears in one aspect as simple and in another as infinitely complex, the two aspects have by no means the same importance, or rather the same degree of reality. In such cases, the simplicity belongs to the object itself, and the infinite complexity to the views we take in turning around it, to the symbols by which our senses or intellect represent it to us, or, more generally, to elements *of a different order,* with which we try to imitate it artificially, but with which it remains incommensurable, being of a different nature. An artist of genius has painted a figure on his canvas. We can imitate his picture with many-colored squares of mosaic. And we shall reproduce the curves and shades of the model so much the better as our squares are smaller, more numerous and more varied in tone. But an infinity of elements infinitely small, presenting an infinity of shades, would be necessary to obtain the exact equivalent of the figure that the artist has conceived as a simple thing, which he has wished to transport as a whole to the canvas, and which is the more complete the more it strikes us as the projection of an indivisible intuition. Now, suppose our eyes so made that they cannot help seeing in the work of the master a mosaic effect. Or suppose our intellect so made that it cannot explain the appearance of the figure on the canvas except as a work of mosaic. We should then be able to speak simply of a collection of little squares, and we should be under the mechanistic hypothesis. We might add that, besides the materiality of the collection, there must be a plan on which the artist worked; and then we should be expressing ourselves as finalists. But in neither case should we have got at the real process, for there are no squares brought together. It is the picture, *i.e.* the simple act, projected on the canvas, which, by the mere fact of entering into our perception, is *de*composed before our eyes into thousands and thousands of little squares which present, as *re*composed, a wonderful arrangement. So the eye, with its marvelous complexity of structure, may be only the simple act of vision, divided *for us* into a mosaic of cells, whose order seems marvelous to us because we have conceived the whole as an assemblage.

If I raise my hand from A to B, this

movement appears to me under two aspects at once. Felt from within, it is a simple, indivisible act. Perceived from without, it is the course of a certain curve, AB. In this curve I can distinguish as many positions as I please, and the line itself might be defined as a certain mutual co-ordination of these positions. But the positions, infinite in number, and the order in which they are connected, have sprung automatically from the indivisible act by which my hand has gone from A to B. Mechanism, here, would consist in seeing only the positions. Finalism would take their order into account. But both mechanism and finalism would leave on one side the movement, which is reality itself. In one sense, the movement is *more* than the positions and than their order; for it is sufficient to make it in its indivisible simplicity to secure that the infinity of the successive positions as also their order be given at once—with something else which is neither order nor position but which is essential, the mobility. But, in another sense, the movement is *less* than the series of positions and their connecting order: for, to arrange points in a certain order, it is necessary first to conceive the order and then to realize it with points; there must be the work of assemblage and there must be intelligence, whereas the simple movement of the hand contains nothing of either. It is not intelligent, in the human sense of the word, and it is not an assemblage, for it is not made up of elements. Just so with the relation of the eye to vision. There is in vision *more* than the component cells of the eye and their mutual co-ordination: in this sense, neither mechanism nor finalism go far enough. But, in another sense, mechanism and finalism both go too far, for they attribute to Nature the most formidable of the labors of Hercules in holding that she has exalted to the simple act of vision an infinity of infi-

nitely complex elements, whereas Nature has had no more trouble in making an eye than I have in lifting my hand. Nature's simple act has divided itself automatically into an infinity of elements which are then found to be co-ordinated to one idea, just as the movement of my hand has dropped an infinity of points which are then found to satisfy one equation.

We find it very hard to see things in that light, because we cannot help conceiving organization as manufacturing. But it is one thing to manufacture, and quite another to organize. Manufacturing is peculiar to man. It consists in assembling parts of matter which we have cut out in such manner that we can fit them together and obtain from them a common action. The parts are arranged, so to speak, around the action as an ideal center. To manufacture, therefore, is to work from the periphery to the center, or, as the philosophers say, from the many to the one. Organization, on the contrary, works from the center to the periphery. It begins in a point that is almost a mathematical point, and spreads around this point by concentric waves which go on enlarging. The work of manufacturing is the more effective, the greater the quantity of matter dealt with. It proceeds by concentration and compression. The organizing act, on the contrary, has something explosive about it: it needs at the beginning the smallest possible place, a minimum of matter, as if the organizing forces only entered space reluctantly. The spermatozoon, which sets in motion the evolutionary process of the embryonic life, is one of the smallest cells of the organism; and it is only a small part of the spermatozoon which really takes part in the operation.

But these are only superficial differences. Digging beneath them, we think, a deeper difference would be found.

A manufactured thing delineates exactly the form of the work of manufacturing it. I mean that the manufacturer finds in his product exactly what he has put into it. If he is going to make a machine, he cuts out its pieces one by one and then puts them together: the machine, when made, will show both the pieces and their assemblage. The whole of the result represents the whole of the work; and to each part of the work corresponds a part of the result.

Now I recognize that positive science can and should proceed as if organization was like making a machine. Only so will it have any hold on organized bodies. For its object is not to show us the essence of things, but to furnish us with the best means of acting on them. Physics and chemistry are well advanced sciences, and living matter lends itself to our action only so far as we can treat it by the processes of our physics and chemistry. Organization can therefore only be studied scientifically if the organized body has first been likened to a machine. The cells will be the pieces of the machine, the organism their assemblage, and the elementary labors which have organized the parts will be regarded as the real elements of the labor which has organized the whole. This is the standpoint of science. Quite different, in our opinion, is that of philosophy.

For us, the whole of an organized machine may, strictly speaking, represent the whole of the organizing work (this is, however, only approximately true), yet the parts of the machine do not correspond to parts of the work, because *the materiality of this machine does not represent a sum of means employed, but a sum of obstacles avoided:* it is a negation rather than a positive reality. So, as we have shown in a former study, vision is a power which should attain *by right* an infinity of things inaccessible to our eyes. But such a vision would not be continued into action; it might suit a phantom, but not a living being. The vision of a living being is an *effective* vision, limited to objects on which the being can act: it is a vision that is *canalized,* and the visual apparatus simply symbolizes the work of canalizing. Therefore the creation of the visual apparatus is no more explained by the assembling of its anatomic elements than the digging of a canal could be explained by the heaping-up of the earth which might have formed its banks. A mechanistic theory would maintain that the earth had been brought cart-load by cart-load; finalism would add that it had not been dumped down at random, that the carters had followed a plan. But both theories would be mistaken, for the canal has been made in another way.

With greater precision, we may compare the process by which nature constructs an eye to the simple act by which we raise the hand. But we supposed at first that the hand met with no resistance. Let us now imagine that, instead of moving in air, the hand has to pass through iron filings which are compressed and offer resistance to it in proportion as it goes forward. At a certain moment the hand will have exhausted its effort, and, at this very moment, the filings will be massed and co-ordinated in a certain definite form, to wit, that of the hand that is stopped and of a part of the arm. Now, suppose that the hand and arm are invisible. Lookers-on will seek the reason of the arrangement in the filings themselves and in forces within the mass. Some will account for the position of each filing by the action exerted upon it by the neighboring filings: these are the mechanists. Others will prefer to think that a plan of the whole has presided over the detail of these elementary actions: they are the finalists. But the truth is that there has been merely one indivisible act, that of the hand passing through the filings: the inexhaustible detail of the movement of the grains, as well as the order of their final arrangement, expresses negatively, in a way, this undivided movement, being the unitary form of a resistance, and not a synthesis of positive elementary actions. For this reason, if the arrangement of the grains is termed an "effect" and the movement of the hand a "cause," it may indeed be said that the whole of the effect is explained by the whole of the cause, but to parts of the cause parts of the effect will in no wise correspond. In other words, neither mechanism nor finalism will here be in place, and we must resort to an explanation of a different kind. Now, in the hypothesis we propose, the relation of vision to the visual apparatus would be very nearly that of the hand to the iron filings that follow, canalize and limit its motion.

The greater the effort of the hand, the farther it will go into the filings. But at whatever point it stops, instantaneously and automatically the filings co-ordinate and find their equilibrium. So with vision and its organ. According as the undivided act constituting vision advances more or less, the materiality of the organ is made of a more or less considerable number of mutually co-ordinated elements, but the order is necessarily complete and perfect. It could not be partial, because, once again, the real process which gives rise to it has no parts. That is what neither mechanism nor finalism takes into account, and it is what we also fail to consider when we wonder at the marvelous structure of an instrument such as the eye. At the bottom of our wondering is always this idea, that it would have been possible for *a part only* of this co-ordination to have been realized, that the complete realization is a kind of special favor. This favor the finalists consider as dispensed to them all at once, by the final cause; the mechanists claim to obtain it little by little, by the effect of natural selection; but both

see something positive in this co-ordination, and consequently something fractionable in its cause—something which admits of every possible degree of achievement. In reality, the cause, though more or less intense, cannot produce its effect except in one piece, and completely finished. According as it goes further and further in the direction of vision, it gives the simple pigmentary masses of a lower organism, or the rudimentary eye of a Serpula, or the slightly differentiated eye of the Alciope, or the marvelously perfected eye of the bird; but all these organs, unequal as is their complexity, necessarily present an equal co-ordination. For this reason, no matter how distant two animal species may be from each other, if the progress toward vision has gone equally far in both, there is the same visual organ in each case, for the form of the organ only expresses the degree in which the exercise of the function has been obtained.

But, in speaking of a progress toward vision, are we not coming back to the old notion of finality? It would be so, undoubtedly, if this progress required the conscious or unconscious idea of an end to be attained. But it is really effected in virtue of the original impetus of life; it is implied in this movement itself, and that is just why it is found in independent lines of evolution. If now we are asked why and how it is implied therein, we reply that life is, more than anything else, a tendency to act on inert matter. The direction of this action is not predetermined; hence the unforeseeable variety of forms which life, in evolving, sows along its path. But this action always presents, to some extent, the character of contingency; it implies at least a rudiment of choice. Now a choice involves the anticipatory idea of several possible actions. Possibilities of action must therefore be marked out for the living being before the action itself. Visual perception is nothing else:[1] the visible out-lines of bodies are the design of our eventual action on them. Vision will be found, therefore, in different degrees in the most diverse animals, and it will appear in the same complexity of struc-ture wherever it has reached the same degree of intensity.

We have dwelt on these resemblances of structure in general, and on the ex-ample of the eye in particular, because we had to define our attitude toward mechanism on the one hand and finalism on the other. It remains for us to de-scribe it more precisely in itself. This we shall now do by showing the divergent results of evolution not as presenting analogies, but as themselves mutually complementary.

CHAPTER II

The Divergent Directions of the Evolution of Life, Torpor, Intelligence, Instinct

The evolution movement would be a sim-ple one, and we should soon have been able to determine its direction, if life had described a single course, like that of a solid ball shot from a cannon. But it proceeds rather like a shell, which sud-denly bursts into fragments, which frag-ments, being themselves shells, burst in their turn into fragments destined to burst again, and so on for a time incom-mensurably long. We perceive only what is nearest to us, namely, the scattered movements of the pulverized explosions. From them we have to go back, stage by stage, to the original movement.

When a shell bursts, the particular way it breaks is explained both by the explo-sive force of the powder it contains and by the resistance of the metal. So of the way life breaks into individuals and species. It depends, we think, on two series of causes: the resistance life meets from inert matter, and the explosive force—due to an unstable balance of tendencies—which life bears within itself.

The resistance of inert matter was the obstacle that had first to be overcome. Life seems to have succeeded in this by dint of humility, by making itself very small and very insinuating, bending to physical and chemical forces, consenting even to go a part of the way with them, like the switch that adopts for a while the direction of the rail it is endeavoring to leave. Of phenomena in the simplest forms of life, it is hard to say whether they are still physical and chemical or whether they are already vital. Life had to enter thus into the habits of inert matter, in order to draw it little by little, magnetized, as it were, to another track. The animate forms that first appeared were therefore of extreme simplicity. They were probably tiny masses of scarcely differentiated protoplasm, out-wardly resembling the amoeba observable today, but possessed of the tremendous internal push that was to raise them even to the highest forms of life. That in virtue of this push the first organisms sought to grow as much as possible, seems likely. But organized matter has a limit of expansion that is very quickly reached; beyond a certain point it divides instead of growing. Ages of effort and prodigies of subtlety were probably nec-essary for life to get past this new ob-stacle. It succeeded in inducing an in-creasing number of elements, ready to divide, to remain united. By the division of labor it knotted between them an indissoluble bond. The complex and quasi-discontinuous organism is thus made to function as would a continuous living mass which had simply grown bigger.

___

[1] See, on this subject, *Matière et mémoire,* chap. i.

But the real and profound causes of division were those which life bore within its bosom. For life is tendency, and the essence of a tendency is to develop in the form of a sheaf, creating, by its very growth, divergent directions among which its impetus is divided. This we observe in ourselves, in the evolution of that special tendency which we call our character. Each of us, glancing back over his history, will find that his child-personality, though indivisible, united in itself divers persons, which could remain blended just because they were in their nascent state: this indecision, so charged with promise, is one of the greatest charms of childhood. But these inter-woven personalities become incompatible in course of growth, and, as each of us can live but one life, a choice must perforce be made. We choose in reality without ceasing; without ceasing, also, we abandon many things. The route we pursue in time is strewn with the remains of all that we began to be, of all that we might have become. But nature, which has at command an incalculable number of lives, is in no wise bound to make such sacrifices. She preserves the different tendencies that have bifurcated with their growth. She creates with them diverging series of species that will evolve separately.

These series may, moreover, be of unequal importance. The author who begins a novel puts into his hero many things which he is obliged to discard as he goes on. Perhaps he will take them up later in other books and make new characters with them, who will seem like extracts from, or rather like complements of, the first; but they will almost always appear somewhat poor and limited in comparison with the original character. So with regard to the evolution of life. The bifurcations on the way have been numerous, but there have been many blind alleys beside the two or three highways; and of these highways themselves, only one, that which leads through the vertebrates up to man, has been wide enough to allow free passage to the full breath of life. We get this impression when we compare the societies of bees and ants, for instance, with human societies. The former are admirably ordered and united, but stereotyped; the latter are open to every sort of progress, but divided, and incessantly at strife with themselves. The ideal would be a society always in progress and always in equilibrium, but this ideal is perhaps unrealizable: the two characteristics that would fain complete each other, which do complete each other in their embryonic state, can no longer abide together when they grow stronger. If one could speak, otherwise than metaphorically, of an impulse toward social life, it might be said that the brunt of the impulse was borne along the line of evolution ending at man, and that the rest of it was collected on the road leading to the hymenoptera: the societies of ants and bees would thus present the aspect complementary to ours. But this would be only a manner of expression. There has been no particular impulse toward social life; there is simply the general movement of life, which on divergent lines is creating forms ever new. If societies should appear on two of these lines, they ought to show divergence of paths at the same time as community of impetus. They will thus develop two classes of characteristics which we shall find vaguely complementary of each other.

So our study of the evolution movement will have to unravel a certain number of divergent directions, and to appreciate the importance of what has happened along each of them—in a word, to determine the nature of the dissociated tendencies and estimate their relative proportion. Combining these tendencies, then, we shall get an approximation, or rather an imitation, of the indivisible motor principle whence their impetus proceeds. Evolution will thus prove to be something entirely different from a series of adaptations to circumstances, as mechanism claims; entirely different also from the realization of a plan of the whole, as maintained by the doctrine of finality.

That adaptation to environment is the necessary condition of evolution we do not question for a moment. It is quite evident that a species would disappear, should it fail to bend to the conditions of existence which are imposed on it. But it is one thing to recognize that outer circumstances are forces evolution must reckon with, another to claim that they are the directing causes of evolution. This latter theory is that of mechanism. It excludes absolutely the hypothesis of an original impetus, I mean an internal push that has carried life, by more and more complex forms, to higher and higher destinies. Yet this impetus is evident, and a mere glance at fossil species shows us that life need not have evolved at all, or might have evolved only in very restricted limits, if it had chosen the alternative, much more convenient to itself, of becoming anchylosed in its primitive forms. Certain Foraminifera have not varied since the Silurian epoch. Unmoved witnesses of the innumerable revolutions that have upheaved our planet, the Lingulae are today what they were at the remotest times of the paleozoic era.

The truth is that adaptation explains the sinuosities of the movement of evolution, but not its general directions, still less the movement itself.[1] The road that leads to the town is obliged to follow the ups and downs of the hills; it *adapts itself* to the accidents of the ground; but the accidents of the ground are not the cause of the road, nor have they given it its direction. At every moment they furnish it with what is indispensable, namely, the soil on which it lies; but if we consider the whole of the road, instead of each of its parts, the accidents of the ground appear only as impediments or causes of delay, for the road aims simply at the town and would fain be a straight line. Just so as regards the evolution of life and the circumstances through which it passes—with this difference, that evolution does not mark out a solitary route, that it takes directions without aiming at ends, and that it remains inventive even in its adaptations.

But, if the evolution of life is something other than a series of adaptations to accidental circumstances, so also it is not the realization of a plan. A plan is given in advance. It is represented, or at least representable, before its realization. The complete execution of it may be put off to a distant future, or even indefinitely; but the idea is none the less formulable at the present time, in terms actually given. If, on the contrary, evolution is a creation unceasingly renewed, it creates, as it goes on, not only the forms of life, but the ideas that will enable the intellect to understand it, the terms which will serve to express it. That is to say that its future overflows its present, and cannot be sketched out therein in an idea.

There is the first error of finalism. It involves another, yet more serious.

If life realizes a plan, it ought to manifest a greater harmony the further it advances, just as the house shows better and better the idea of the architect as stone is set upon stone. If, on the contrary, the unity of life is to be found solely in the impetus that pushes it along

---

[1] This view of adaptation has been noted by M. F. Marin in a remarkable article on the origin of species, "L'Origine des espèces" (*Revue scientifique*, Nov. 1901, p. 580).

the road of time, the harmony is not in front, but behind. The unity is derived from a *vis a tergo:* it is given at the start as an impulsion, not placed at the end as an attraction. In communicating itself, the impetus splits up more and more. Life, in proportion to its progress, is scattered in manifestations which undoubtedly owe to their common origin the fact that they are complementary to each other in certain aspects, but which are none the less mutually incompatible and antagonistic. So the discord between species will go on increasing. Indeed, we have as yet only indicated the essential cause of it. We have supposed, for the sake of simplicity, that each species received the impulsion in order to pass it on to others, and that, in every direction in which life evolves, the propagation is in a straight line. But, as a matter of fact, there are species which are arrested; there are some that retrogress. Evolution is not only a movement forward; in many cases we observe a marking-time, and still more often a deviation or turning back. It must be so, as we shall show further on, and the same causes that divide the evolution movement often cause life to be diverted from itself, hypnotized by the form it has just brought forth. Thence results an increasing disorder. No doubt there is progress, if progress mean a continual advance in the general direction determined by a first impulsion; but this progress is accomplished only on the two or three great lines of evolution on which forms ever more and more complex, ever more and more high, appear; between these lines run a crowd of minor paths in which, on the contrary, deviations, arrests, and set-backs, are multiplied. The philosopher, who begins by laying down as a principle that each detail is connected with some general plan of the whole, goes from one disappointment to another as soon as he comes to examine the facts; and, as he had put everything in the same rank, he finds that, as the result of not allowing for accident, he must regard everything as accidental. For accident, then, an allowance must first be made, and a very liberal allowance. We must recognize that all is not coherent in nature. By so doing, we shall be led to ascertain the centers around which the incoherence crystallizes. This crystallization itself will clarify the rest; the main directions will appear, in which life is moving while developing the original impulse. True, we shall not witness the detailed accomplishment of a plan. Nature is more and better than a plan in course of realization. A plan is a term assigned to a labor: it closes the future whose form it indicates. Before the evolution of life, on the contrary, the portals of the future remain wide open. It is a creation that goes on forever in virtue of an initial movement. This movement constitutes the unity of the organized world—a prolific unity, of an infinite richness, superior to any that the intellect could dream of, for the intellect is only one of its aspects or products.

But it is easier to define the method than to apply it. The complete interpretation of the evolution movement in the past, as we conceive it, would be possible only if the history of the development of the organized world were entirely known. Such is far from being the case. The genealogies proposed for the different species are generally questionable. They vary with their authors, with the theoretic views inspiring them, and raise discussions to which the present state of science does not admit of a final settlement. But a comparison of the different solutions shows that the controversy bears less on the main lines of the movement than on matters of detail; and so, by following the main lines as closely as possible, we shall be sure of not going astray. Moreover, they alone are important to us; for we do not aim, like the naturalist, at finding the order of succession of different species, but only at defining the principal directions of their evolution. And not all of these directions have the same interest for us: what concerns us particularly is the path that leads to man. We shall therefore not lose sight of the fact, in following one direction and another, that our main business is to determine the relation of man to the animal kingdom, and the place of the animal kingdom itself in the organized world as a whole.

To begin with the second point, let us say that no definite characteristic distinguishes the plant from the animal. Attempts to define the two kingdoms strictly have always come to naught. There is not a single property of vegetable life that is not found, in some degree, in certain animals; not a single characteristic feature of the animal that has not been seen in certain species or at certain moments in the vegetable world. Naturally, therefore, biologists enamored of clean-cut concepts have regarded the distinction between the two kingdoms as artificial. They would be right, if definition in this case must be made, as in the mathematical and physical sciences, according to certain statical attributes which belong to the object defined and are not found in any other. Very different, in our opinion, is the kind of definition which befits the sciences of life. There is no manifestation of life which does not contain, in a rudimentary state —either latent or potential,—the essential characters of most other manifestations. The difference is in the proportions. But this very difference of proportion will suffice to define the group, if we can establish that it is not accidental, and that the group, as it evolves, tends more and more to emphasize these particular characters. In a word, *the group must*

not be defined by the possession of certain characters, but by its tendency to emphasize them. From this point of view, taking tendencies rather than states into account, we find that vegetables and animals may be precisely defined and distinguished, and that they correspond to two divergent developments of life.

This divergence is shown, first, in the method of alimentation. We know that the vegetable derives directly from the air and water and soil the elements necessary to maintain life, especially carbon and nitrogen, which it takes in mineral form. The animal, on the contrary, cannot assimilate these elements unless they have already been fixed for it in organic substances by plants, or by animals which directly or indirectly owe them to plants; so that ultimately the vegetable nourishes the animal. True, this law allows of many exceptions among vegetables. We do not hesitate to class among vegetables the Drosera, the Dionaea, the Pinguicula, which are insectivorous plants. On the other hand, the fungi, which occupy so considerable a place in the vegetable world, feed like animals: whether they are ferments, saprophytes or parasites, it is to already formed organic substances that they owe their nourishment. It is therefore impossible to draw from this difference any *static* definition such as would automatically settle in any particular case the question whether we are dealing with a plant or an animal. But the difference may provide the beginning of a *dynamic* definition of the two kingdoms, in that it marks the two divergent directions in which vegetables and animals have taken their course. It is a remarkable fact that the fungi, which nature has spread all over the earth in such extraordinary profusion, have not been able to evolve. Organically they do not rise above tissues which, in the higher vegetables, are formed in the embryonic sac of the

[331]

ovary, and precede the germinative development of the new individual.[1] They might be called the abortive children of the vegetable world. Their different species are like so many blind alleys, as if, by renouncing the mode of alimentation customary among vegetables, they had been brought to a standstill on the highway of vegetable evolution. As to the Drosera, the Dionaea, and insectivorous plants in general, they are fed by their roots, like other plants; they too fix, by their green parts, the carbon of the carbonic acid in the atmosphere. Their faculty of capturing, absorbing and digesting insects must have arisen late, in quite exceptional cases where the soil was too poor to furnish sufficient nourishment. In a general way, then, if we attach less importance to the presence of special characters than to their tendency to develop, and if we regard as essential that tendency along which evolution has been able to continue indefinitely, we may say that vegetables are distinguished from animals by their power of creating organic matter out of mineral elements which they draw directly from the air and earth and water. But now we come to another difference, deeper than this, though not unconnected with it.

The animal, being unable to fix directly the carbon and nitrogen which are everywhere to be found, has to seek for its nourishment vegetables which have already fixed these elements, or animals which have taken them from the vegetable kingdom. So the animal must be able to move. From the amoeba, which thrusts out its pseudopodia at random to seize the organic matter scattered in a drop of water, up to the higher animals which have sense-organs with which to recognize their prey, locomotor organs to go and seize it, and a nervous system to

co-ordinate their movements with their sensations, animal life is characterized, in its general direction, by mobility in space. In its most rudimentary form, the animal is a tiny mass of protoplasm enveloped at most in a thin albuminous pellicle which allows full freedom for change of shape and movement. The vegetable cell, on the contrary, is surrounded by a membrane of cellulose, which condemns it to immobility. And, from the bottom to the top of the vegetable kingdom, there are the same habits growing more and more sedentary, the plant having no need to move, and finding around it, in the air and water and soil in which it is placed, the mineral elements it can appropriate directly. It is true that phenomena of movement are seen in plants. Darwin has written a well-known work on the movements of climbing plants. He studied also the contrivances of certain insectivorous plants, such as the Drosera and the Dionaea, to seize their prey. The leaf-movements of the acacia, the sensitive plant, etc., are well known. Moreover, the circulation of the vegetable protoplasm within its sheath bears witness to its relationship to the protoplasm of animals, while in a large number of animal species (generally parasites) phenomena of fixation, analogous to those of vegetables, can be observed.[1] Here, again, it would be a mistake to claim that fixity and mobility are the two characters which enable us to decide, by simple inspection alone, whether we have before us a plant or an animal. But fixity, in the animal, generally seems like a torpor into which the species has fallen, a refusal to evolve further in a certain direction; it is closely akin to parasitism and is accompanied by features that recall those of vegetable

[1] De Saporta and Marion, *L'Évolution des cryptogames,* 1881, p. 37.

[1] On fixation and parasitism in general, see the work of Houssay, *La Forme et la vie,* Paris, 1900, pp. 721–807.

life. On the other hand, the movements of vegetables have neither the frequency nor the variety of those of animals. Generally, they involve only part of the organism and scarcely ever extend to the whole. In the exceptional cases in which a vague spontaneity appears in vegetables, it is as if we beheld the accidental awakening of an activity normally asleep. In short, although both mobility and fixity exist in the vegetable as in the animal world, the balance is clearly in favor of fixity in the one case and of mobility in the other. These two opposite tendencies are so plainly directive of the two evolutions that the two kingdoms might almost be defined by them. But fixity and mobility, again, are only superficial signs of tendencies that are still deeper.

Between mobility and consciousness there is an obvious relationship. No doubt, the consciousness of the higher organisms seems bound up with certain cerebral arrangements. The more the nervous system develops, the more numerous and more precise become the movements among which it can choose; the clearer, also, is the consciousness that accompanies them. But neither this mobility nor this choice nor consequently this consciousness involves as a necessary condition the presence of a nervous system; the latter has only canalized in definite directions, and brought up to a higher degree of intensity, a rudimentary and vague activity, diffused throughout the mass of the organized substance. The lower we descend in the animal series, the more the nervous centers are simplified, and the more, too, they separate from each other, till finally the nervous elements disappear, merged in the mass of a less-differentiated organism. But it is the same with all the other apparatus, with all the other anatomical elements; and it would be as absurd to refuse consciousness to an animal because it has no

brain as to declare it incapable of nourishing itself because it has no stomach. The truth is that the nervous system arises, like the other systems, from a division of labor. It does not create the function, it only brings it to a higher degree of intensity and precision by giving it the double form of reflex and voluntary activity. To accomplish a true reflex movement, a whole mechanism is necessary, set up in the spinal cord or the medulla. To choose voluntarily between several definite courses of action, cerebral centers are necessary, that is, crossways from which paths start, leading to motor mechanisms of diverse form but equal precision. But where nervous elements are not yet canalized, still less concentrated into a system, there is something from which, by a kind of splitting, both the reflex and the voluntary will arise, something which has neither the mechanical precision of the former nor the intelligent hesitations of the latter, but which, partaking of both, it may be infinitesimally, is a reaction simply undecided, and therefore vaguely conscious. This amounts to saying that the humblest organism is conscious in proportion to its power to move *freely*. Is consciousness here, in relation to movement, the effect or the cause? In one sense it is the cause, since it has to direct locomotion. But in another sense it is the effect, for it is the motor activity that maintains it, and, once this activity disappears, consciousness dies away or rather falls asleep. In crustaceans such as the rhizocephala, which must formerly have shown a more differentiated structure, fixity and parasitism accompany the degeneration and almost complete disappearance of the nervous system. Since, in such a case, the progress of organization must have localized all the conscious activity in nervous centers, we may conjecture that consciousness is even weaker in animals of this kind than in organisms much less differentiated, which have never had nervous centers but have remained mobile.

How then could the plant, which is fixed in the earth and finds its food on the spot, have developed in the direction of conscious activity? The membrane of cellulose, in which the protoplasm wraps itself up, not only prevents the simplest vegetable organism from moving, but screens it also, in some measure, from those outer stimuli which act on the sensibility of the animal as irritants and prevent it from going to sleep.[1] The plant is therefore unconscious. Here again, however, we must beware of radical distinctions. "Unconscious" and "conscious" are not two labels which can be mechanically fastened, the one on every vegetable cell, the other on all animals. While consciousness sleeps in the animal which has degenerated into a motionless parasite, it probably awakens in the vegetable that has regained liberty of movement, and awakens in just the degree to which the vegetable has reconquered this liberty. Nevertheless, consciousness and unconsciousness mark the directions in which the two kingdoms have developed, in this sense, that to find the best specimens of consciousness in the animal we must *ascend* to the highest representatives of the series, whereas, to find probable cases of vegetable consciousness, we must *descend* as low as possible in the scale of plants—down to the zoospores of the algae, for instance, and, more generally, to those unicellular organisms which may be said to hesitate between the vegetable form and animality. From this standpoint, and in this measure, we should define the animal by sensibility and awakened consciousness, the vegetable by consciousness asleep and by insensibility.

To sum up, the vegetable manufactures organic substances directly with mineral substances; as a rule, this aptitude enables it to dispense with movement and so with feeling. Animals, which are obliged to go in search of their food, have evolved in the direction of locomotor activity, and consequently of a consciousness more and more distinct, more and more ample.

Now, it seems to us most probable that the animal cell and the vegetable cell are derived from a common stock, and that the first living organisms oscillated between the vegetable and animal form, participating in both at once. Indeed, we have just seen that the characteristic tendencies of the evolution of the two kingdoms, although divergent, coexist even now, both in the plant and in the animal. The proportion alone differs. Ordinarily, one of the two tendencies covers or crushes down the other, but in exceptional circumstances the suppressed one starts up and regains the place it had lost. The mobility and consciousness of the vegetable cell are not so sound asleep that they cannot rouse themselves when circumstances permit or demand it; and, on the other hand, the evolution of the animal kingdom has always been retarded, or stopped, or dragged back, by the tendency it has kept toward the vegetative life. However full, however overflowing the activity of an animal species may appear, torpor and unconsciousness are always lying in wait for it. It keeps up its rôle only by effort, at the price of fatigue. Along the route on which the animal has evolved, there have been numberless shortcomings and cases of decay, generally associated with parasitic habits; they are so many shuntings on to the vegetative life. Thus, everything bears out the belief that vegetable and animal are descended from a common ancestor which united the tendencies of both in a rudimentary state.

But the two tendencies mutually im-

---

[1] Cope, *op. cit.*, p. 76.

plied in this rudimentary form became dissociated as they grew. Hence the world of plants with its fixity and insensibility, hence the animals with their mobility and consciousness. There is no need, in order to explain this dividing into two, to bring in any mysterious force. It is enough to point out that the living being leans naturally toward what is most convenient to it, and that vegetables and animals have chosen two different kinds of convenience in the way of procuring the carbon and nitrogen they need. Vegetables continually and mechanically draw these elements from an environment that continually provides it. Animals, by action that is discontinuous, concentrated in certain moments, and conscious, go to find these bodies in organisms that have already fixed them. They are two different ways of being industrious, or perhaps, we may prefer to say, of being idle. For this very reason we doubt whether nervous elements, however rudimentary, will ever be found in the plant. What corresponds in it to the directing will of the animal is, we believe, the direction in which it bends the energy of the solar radiation when it uses it to break the connection of the carbon with the oxygen in carbonic acid. What corresponds in it to the sensibility of the animal is the impressionability, quite of its kind, of its chlorophyll to light. Now, a nervous system being pre-eminently a mechanism which serves as intermediary between sensations and volitions, the true "nervous system" of the plant seems to be the mechanism of rather chemicism *sui generis* which serves as intermediary between the impressionability of its chlorophyll to light and the producing of starch: which amounts to saying that the plant can have no nervous elements, and that *the same impetus that has led the animal to give itself nerves and nerve centers must*

have ended, in the plant, in the chlorophyllian function.[1]

This first glance over the organized world will enable us to ascertain more precisely what unites the two kingdoms, and also what separates them.

Suppose, as we suggested in the preceding chapter, that at the root of life there is an effort to engraft on to the necessity of physical forces the largest possible amount of *indetermination*. This effort cannot result in the creation of energy, or, if it does, the quantity created does not belong to the order of magnitude apprehended by our senses and instruments of measurement, our experience and science. All that the effort can do, then, is to make the best of a pre-existing energy which it finds at its disposal. Now, it finds only one way of succeeding in this, namely, to secure such an accumulation of potential energy from matter, that it can get, at any moment, the amount of work it needs for its action, simply by pulling a trigger. The effort itself possesses only that power of releasing. But the work of releasing, although always the same and always smaller than any given quantity, will be the more effective the heavier the weight it makes fall and the greater the height— or, in other words, the greater the sum of

---

[1] Just as the plant, in certain cases, recovers the faculty of moving actively which slumbers in it, so the animal, in exceptional circumstances, can replace itself in the conditions of the vegetative life and develop in itself an equivalent of the chlorophyllian function. It appears, indeed, from recent experiments of Maria von Linden, that the chrysalides and the caterpillars of certain lepidoptera, under the influence of light, fix the carbon of the carbonic acid contained in the atmosphere (M. von Linden, "L'Assimilation de l'acide carbonique par les chrysalides de Lépidoptères," *C. R. de la Soc. de biologie*, 1905, pp. 692 ff.).

potential energy accumulated and disposable. As a matter of fact, the principal source of energy usable on the surface of our planet is the sun. So the problem was this: to obtain from the sun that it should partially and provisionally suspend, here and there, on the surface of the earth, its continual outpour of usable energy, and store a certain quantity of it, in the form of unused energy, in appropriate reservoirs, whence it could be drawn at the desired moment, at the desired spot, in the desired direction. The substances forming the food of animals are just such reservoirs. Made of very complex molecules holding a considerable amount of chemical energy in the potential state, they are like explosives which only need a spark to set free the energy stored within them. Now, it is probable that life tended at the beginning to compass at one and the same time both the manufacture of the explosive and the explosion by which it is utilized. In this case, the same organism that had directly stored the energy of the solar radiation would have expended it in free movements in space. And for that reason we must presume that the first living beings sought on the one hand to accumulate, without ceasing, energy borrowed from the sun, and on the other hand to expend it, in a discontinuous and explosive way, in movements of locomotion. Even today, perhaps, a chlorophyll-bearing Infusorian such as the Euglena may symbolize this primordial tendency of life, though in a mean form, incapable of evolving. Is the divergent development of the two kindgoms related to what one may call the oblivion of each kingdom as regards one of the two halves of the program? Or rather, which is more likely, was the very nature of the matter, that life found confronting it on our planet, opposed to the possibility of the two tendencies evolving very far together in the same organism? What is certain is that the vegetable has trended principally in the first direction and the animal in the second. But if, from the very first, in making the explosive, nature had for object the explosion, then it is the evolution of the animal, rather than that of the vegetable, that indicates, on the whole, the fundamental direction of life.

The "harmony" of the two kingdoms, the complementary characters they display, might then be due to the fact that they develop two tendencies which at first were fused in one. The more the single original tendency grows, the harder it finds it to keep united in the same living being those two elements which in the rudimentary state implied each other. Hence a parting in two, hence two divergent evolutions; hence also two series of characters opposed in certain points, complementary in others, but, whether opposed or complementary, always preserving an appearance of kinship. While the animal evolved, not without accidents along the way, toward a freer and freer expenditure of discontinuous energy, the plant perfected rather its system of accumulation without moving. We shall not dwell on this second point. Suffice it to say that the plant must have been greatly benefited, in its turn, by a new division, analogous to that between plants and animals. While the primitive vegetable cell had to fix by itself both its carbon and its nitrogen, it became able almost to give up the second of these two functions as soon as microscopic vegetables came forward which leaned in this direction exclusively, and even specialized diversely in this still-complicated business. The microbes that fix the nitrogen of the air and those which convert the ammoniacal compounds into nitrous ones, and these again into nitrates, have, by the same splitting up of a tendency primitively one, rendered to the whole vegetable world the same kind of service as the vegetables in general have rendered to animals. If a special kingdom were to be made for these microscopic vegetables, it might be said that in the microbes of the soil, the vegetables and the animals, we have before us the *analysis,* carried out by the matter that life found at its disposal on our planet, of all that life contained, at the outset, in a state of reciprocal implication. Is this, properly speaking, a "division of labor"? These words do not give the exact idea of evolution, such as we conceive it. Wherever there is division of labor, there is *association* and also *convergence* of effort. Now, the evolution we are speaking of is never achieved by means of association, but by *dissociation;* it never tends toward convergence, but toward *divergence* of efforts. The harmony between terms that are mutually complementary in certain points is not, in our opinion, produced, in course of progress, by a reciprocal adaptation; on the contrary, it is complete only at the start. It arises from an original identity, from the fact that the evolutionary process, splaying out like a sheaf, sunders, in proportion to their simultaneous growth, terms which at first completed each other so well that they coalesced.

Now, the elements into which a tendency splits up are far from possessing the same importance, or, above all, the same power to evolve. We have just distinguished three different kingdoms, if one may so express it, in the organized world. While the first comprises only microorganisms which have remained in the rudimentary state, animals and vegetables have taken their flight toward very lofty fortunes. Such, indeed, is generally the case when a tendency divides. Among the divergent developments to which it gives rise, some go on indefinitely, others come more or less quickly to the end of their tether. These latter do not issue directly from the primitive tendency, but from one of the elements into which it

has divided; they are residual developments made and left behind on the way by some truly elementary tendency which continues to evolve. Now, these truly elementary tendencies, we think, bear a mark by which they may be recognized.

This mark is like a trace, still visible in each, of what was in the original tendency of which they represent the elementary directions. The elements of a tendency are not like objects set beside each other in space and mutually exclusive, but rather like psychic states, each of which, although it be itself to begin with, yet partakes of others, and so virtually includes in itself the whole personality to which it belongs. There is no real manifestation of life, we said, that does not show us, in a rudimentary or latent state, the characters of other manifestations. Conversely, when we meet, on one line of evolution, a recollection, so to speak, of what is developed along other lines, we must conclude that we have before us dissociated elements of one and the same original tendency. In this sense, vegetables and animals represent the two great divergent developments of life. Though the plant is distinguished from the animal by fixity and insensibility, movement and consciousness sleep in it as recollections which may waken. But, beside these normally sleeping recollections, there are others awake and active, just those, namely, whose activity does not obstruct the development of the elementary tendency itself. We may then formulate this law: *When a tendency splits up in the course of its development, each of the special tendencies which thus arise tries to preserve and develop everything in the primitive tendency that is not incompatible with the work for which it is specialized.* This explains precisely the fact we dwelt on in the preceding chapter, viz., the formation of identical complex mechanisms on independent lines of evolution. Certain deep-seated analogies between the animal and the vegetable have probably no other cause: sexual generation is perhaps only a luxury for the plant, but to the animal it was a necessity, and the plant must have been driven to it by the same impetus which impelled the animal thereto, a primitive, original impetus, anterior to the separation of the two kingdoms. The same may be said of the tendency of the vegetable toward a growing complexity. This tendency is essential to the animal kingdom, ever tormented by the need of more and more extended and effective action. But the vegetable, condemned to fixity and insensibility, exhibits the same tendency only because it received at the outset the same impulsion. Recent experiments show that it varies at random when the period of "mutation" arrives; whereas the animal must have evolved, we believe, in much more definite directions. But we will not dwell further on this original doubling of the modes of life. Let us come to the evolution of animals, in which we are more particularly interested.

What constitutes animality, we said, is the faculty of utilizing a releasing mechanism for the conversion of as much stored-up potential energy as possible into "explosive" actions. In the beginning the explosion is haphazard, and does not choose its direction. Thus the amoeba thrusts out its pseudopodic prolongations in all directions at once. But, as we rise in the animal scale, the form of the body itself is observed to indicate a certain number of very definite directions along which the energy travels. These directions are marked by so many chains of nervous elements. Now, the nervous element has gradually emerged from the barely differentiated mass of organized tissue. It may, therefore, be surmised that in the nervous element, as soon as it appears, and also in its appendages, the faculty of suddenly freeing the gradually

stored-up energy is concentrated. No doubt, every living cell expends energy without ceasing, in order to maintain its equilibrium. The vegetable cell, torpid from the start, is entirely absorbed in this work of maintenance alone, as if it took for end what must at first have been only a means. But, in the animal, all points to action, that is, to the utilization of energy for movements from place to place. True, every animal cell expends a good deal—often the whole—of the energy at its disposal in keeping itself alive; but the organism as a whole tries to attract as much energy as possible to those points where the locomotive movements are effected. So that where a nervous system exists, with its complementary sense-organs and motor apparatus, everything should happen as if the rest of the body had, as its essential function, to prepare for these and pass on to them, at the moment required, that force which they are to liberate by a sort of explosion.

The part played by food among the higher animals is, indeed, extremely complex. In the first place it serves to repair tissues, then it provides the animal with the heat necessary to render it as independent as possible of changes in external temperature. Thus it preserves, supports and maintains the organism in which the nervous system is set and on which the nervous elements have to live. But these nervous elements would have no reason for existence if the organism did not pass to them, and especially to the muscles they control, a certain energy to expend; and it may even be conjectured that there, in the main, is the essential and ultimate destination of food. This does not mean that the greater part of the food is used in this work. A state may have to make enormous expenditure to secure the return of taxes, and the sum which it will have to dispose of, after deducting the cost of collection, will perhaps be very small: that sum is, none the less, the reason for the tax and for all that has been spent to obtain its return. So it is with the energy which the animal demands of its food.

Many facts seem to indicate that the nervous and muscular elements stand in this relation toward the rest of the organism. Glance first at the distribution of alimentary substances among the different elements of the living body. These substances fall into two classes, one the quaternary or albuminoid, the other the ternary, including the carbohydrates and the fats. The albuminoids are properly plastic, destined to repair the tissues—although, owing to the carbon they contain, they are capable of providing energy on occasion. But the function of supplying energy has developed more particularly on the second class of substances: these, being deposited in the cell rather than forming part of its substance, convey to it, in the form of chemical potential, an expansive energy that may be directly converted into either movement or heat. In short, the chief function of the albuminoids is to repair the machine, while the function of the other class of substances is to supply power. It is natural that the albuminoids should have no specially allotted destination, since every part of the machine has to be maintained. But not so with the other substances. The carbohydrates are distributed very unequally, and this inequality of distribution seems to us in the highest degree instructive.

Conveyed by the arterial blood in the form of glucose, these substances are deposited, in the form of glycogen, in the different cells forming the tissues. We know that one of the principal functions of the liver is to maintain at a constant level the quantity of glucose held by the blood, by means of the reserves of glycogen secreted by the hepatic cells. Now, in this circulation of glucose and accumulation of glycogen, it is easy to see that the effect is as if the whole effort of the organism were directed toward providing with potential energy the elements of both the muscular and the nervous tissues. The organism proceeds differently in the two cases, but it arrives at the same result. In the first case, it provides the muscle-cell with a large reserve deposited in advance: the quantity of glycogen contained in the muscles is, indeed, enormous in comparison with what is found in the other tissues. In the nervous tissue, on the contrary, the reserve is small (the nervous elements, whose function is merely to liberate the potential energy stored in the muscle, never have to furnish much work at one time); but the remarkable thing is that this reserve is restored by the blood at the very moment that it is expended, so that the nerve is instantly recharged with potential energy. Muscular tissue and nervous tissue are, therefore, both privileged, the one in that it is stocked with a large reserve of energy, the other in that it is always served at the instant it is in need and to the exact extent of its requirements.

More particularly, it is from the sensory-motor system that the call for glycogen, the potential energy, comes, as if the rest of the organism were simply there in order to transmit force to the nervous system and to the muscles which the nerves control. True, when we think of the part played by the nervous system (even the sensory-motor system) as regulator of the organic life, it may well be asked whether, in this exchange of good offices between it and the rest of the body, the nervous system is indeed a master that the body serves. But we shall already incline to this hypothesis when we consider, even in the static state only, the distribution of potential energy among the tissues; and we shall be entirely convinced of it when we reflect upon the conditions in which the energy is expended and restored. For suppose the sensory-motor system is a system like the others, of the same rank as the others. Borne by the whole of the organism, it will wait until an excess of chemical potential is supplied to it before it performs any work. In other words, it is the production of glycogen which will regulate the consumption by the nerves and muscles. On the contrary, if the sensory-motor system is the actual master, the duration and extent of its action will be independent, to a certain extent at least, of the reserve of glycogen that it holds, and even of that contained in the whole of the organism. It will perform work, and the other tissues will have to arrange as they can to supply it with potential energy. Now, this is precisely what does take place, as is shown in particular by the experiments of Morat and Dufourt.[1] While the glycogenic function of the liver depends on the action of the excitory nerves which control it, the action of these nerves is subordinated to the action of those which stimulate the locomotor muscles—in this sense, that the muscles begin by expending without calculation, thus consuming glycogen, impoverishing the blood of its glucose, and finally causing the liver, which has had to pour into the impoverished blood some of its reserve of glycogen, to manufacture a fresh supply. From the sensory-motor system, then, everything starts; on that system everything converges; and we may say, without metaphor, that the rest of the organism is at its service.

Consider again what happens in a prolonged fast. It is a remarkable fact that in animals that have died of hunger the brain is found to be almost unimpaired, while the other organs have lost more or less of their weight and their cells have

undergone profound changes.[1] It seems as though the rest of the body had sustained the nervous system to the last extremity, treating itself simply as the means of which the nervous system is the end.

To sum up: if we agree, in short, to understand by "the sensory-motor system" the cerebro-spinal nervous system together with the sensorial apparatus in which it is prolonged and the locomotor muscles it controls, we may say that a higher organism is essentially a sensory-motor system installed on systems of digestion, respiration, circulation, secretion, etc., whose function it is to repair, cleanse and protect it, to create an unvarying internal environment for it, and above all to pass it potential energy to convert into locomotive movement.[2] It is true that the more the nervous function is perfected, the more must the functions required to maintain it develop, and the more exacting, consequently, they become for themselves. As the nervous

---

1 De Manacéine, "Quelques observations expérimentales sur l'influence de l'insomnie absolue" (*Arch. ital. de biologie,* t. xxi., 1894, pp. 322 ff.). Recently, analogous observations have been made on a man who died of inanition after a fast of thirty-five days. See, on this subject, in the *Année biologique* of 1898, p. 338, the résumé of an article (in Russian) by Tarakevitch and Stchasny.

2 Cuvier said: "The nervous system is, at bottom, the whole animal; the other systems are there only to serve it." ("Sur un nouveau rapprochement à établir entre les classes qui composent le regne animal," *Arch. du Muséum d'histoire naturelle,* Paris, 1812, pp. 73–84.) Of course, it would be necessary to apply a great many restrictions to this formula—for example, to allow for the cases of degradation and retrogression in which the nervous system passes into the background. And, moreover, with the nervous system must be included the sensorial apparatus on the one hand and the motor on the other, between which it acts as intermediary. Cf. Foster, art. "Physiology," in the *Encyclopaedia Britannica,* Edinburgh, 1885, p. 17.

---

1 *Archives de physiologie,* 1892.

activity has emerged from the protoplasmic mass in which it was almost drowned, it has had to summon around itself activities of all kinds for its support. These could only be developed on other activities, which again implied others, and so on indefinitely. Thus it is that the complexity of functioning of the higher organisms goes on to infinity. The study of one of these organisms therefore takes us round in a circle, as if everything was a means to everything else. But the circle has a center, none the less, and that is the system of nervous elements stretching between the sensory organs and the motor apparatus.

We will not dwell here on a point we have treated at length in a former work. Let us merely recall that the progress of the nervous system has been effected both in the direction of a more precise adaptation of movements and in that of a greater latitude left to the living being to choose between them. These two tendencies may appear antagonistic, and indeed they are so; but a nervous chain, even in its most rudimentary form, successfully reconciles them. On the one hand, it marks a well-defined track between one point of the periphery and another, the one sensory, the other motor. It has therefore canalized an activity which was originally diffused in the protoplasmic mass. But, on the other hand, the elements that compose it are probably discontinuous; at any rate, even supposing they anastomose, they exhibit a *functional* discontinuity, for each of them ends in a kind of crossroad where probably the nervous current may choose its course. From the humblest Monera to the best-endowed insects, and up to the most intelligent vertebrates, the progress realized has been above all a progress of the nervous system, coupled at every stage with all the new constructions and complications of mechanism that this progress required. As we foreshadowed

in the beginning of this work, the rôle of life is to insert some *indetermination* into matter. Indeterminate, *i.e.* unforeseeable, are the forms it creates in the course of its evolution. More and more indeterminate also, more and more free, is the activity to which these forms serve as the vehicle. A nervous system, with neurones placed end to end in such wise that, at the extremity of each, manifold ways open in which manifold questions present themselves, is a veritable *reservoir of indetermination*. That the main energy of the vital impulse has been spent in creating apparatus of this kind is, we believe, what a glance over the organized world as a whole easily shows. But concerning the vital impulse itself a few explanations are necessary.

It must not be forgotten that the force which is evolving throughout the organized world is a limited force, which is always seeking to transcend itself and always remains inadequate to the work it would fain produce. The errors and puerilities of radical finalism are due to the misapprehension of this point. It has represented the whole of the living world as a construction, and a construction analogous to a human work. All the pieces have been arranged with a view to the best possible functioning of the machine. Each species has its reason for existence, its part to play, its allotted place; and all join together, as it were, in a musical concert, wherein the seeming discords are really meant to bring out a fundamental harmony. In short, all goes on in nature as in the works of human genius, where, though the result may be trifling, there is at least perfect adequacy between the object made and the work of making it.

Nothing of the kind in the evolution of life. There, the disproportion is striking between the work and the result. From the bottom to the top of the organized world we do indeed find one great effort; but most often this effort turns short, sometimes paralyzed by contrary forces, sometimes diverted from what it should do by what it does, absorbed by the form it is engaged in taking, hypnotized by it as by a mirror. Even in its most perfect works, though it seems to have triumphed over external resistances and also over its own, it is at the mercy of the materiality which it has had to assume. It is what each of us may experience in himself. Our freedom, in the very movements by which it is affirmed, creates the growing habits that will stifle it if it fails to renew itself by a constant effort: it is dogged by automatism. The most living thought becomes frigid in the formula that expresses it. The word turns against the idea.

The letter kills the spirit. And our most ardent enthusiasm, as soon as it is externalized into action, is so naturally congealed into the cold calculation of interest or vanity, the one takes so easily the shape of the other, that we might confuse them together, doubt our own sincerity, deny goodness and love, if we did not know that the dead retain for a time the features of the living.

The profound cause of this discordance lies in an irremediable difference of rhythm. Life in general is mobility itself; particular manifestations of life accept this mobility reluctantly, and constantly lag behind. It is always going ahead; they want to mark time. Evolution in general would fain go on in a straight line; each special evolution is a kind of circle. Like eddies of dust raised by the wind as it passes, the living turn upon themselves, borne up by the great blast of life. They are therefore relatively stable, and counterfeit immobility so well that we treat each of them as a *thing* rather than as a *progress,* forgetting that the very permanence of their form is only the outline of a movement. At times, however, in a fleeting vision, the invisible breath that bears them is materialized before our eyes. We have this sudden illumination before certain forms of maternal love, so striking, and in most animals so touching, observable even in the solicitude of the plant for its seed. This love, in which some have seen the great mystery of life, may possibly deliver us life's secret. It shows us each generation leaning over the generation that shall follow. It allows us a glimpse of the fact that the living being is above all a thoroughfare, and that the essence of life is in the movement by which life is transmitted.

This contrast between life in general, and the forms in which it is manifested, has everywhere the same character. It might be said that life tends toward the utmost possible action, but that each species prefers to contribute the slightest possible effort. Regarded in what constitutes its true essence, namely, as a transition from species to species, life is a continually growing action. But each of the species, through which life passes, aims only at its own convenience. It goes for that which demands the least labor. Absorbed in the form it is about to take, it falls into a partial sleep, in which it ignores almost all the rest of life; it fashions itself so as to take the greatest possible advantage of its immediate environment with the least possible trouble. Accordingly, the act by which life goes forward to the creation of a new form, and the act by which this form is shaped, are two different and often antagonistic movements. The first is continuous with the second, but cannot continue in it without being drawn aside from its direction, as would happen to a man leaping, if, in order to clear the obstacle, he had to turn his eyes from it and look at himself all the while.

Living forms are, by their very definition, forms that are able to live. In whatever way the adaptation of the organism to its circumstances is explained, it has necessarily been sufficient, since the species has subsisted. In this sense, each of the successive species that paleontology and zoology describe was a *success* carried off by life. But we get a very different impression when we refer each species to the movement that has left it behind on its way, instead of to the conditions into which it has been set. Often this movement has turned aside; very often, too, it has stopped short; what was to have been a thoroughfare has become a terminus. From this new point of view, failure seems the rule, success exceptional and always imperfect. We shall see that, of the four main directions along which animal life bent its course, two have led to blind alleys, and, in the other two, the effort has generally been out of proportion to the result.

Documents are lacking to reconstruct this history in detail, but we can make out its main lines. We have already said that animals and vegetables must have separated soon from their common stock, the vegetable falling asleep in immobility, the animal, on the contrary, becoming more and more awake and marching on to the conquest of a nervous system. Probably the effort of the animal kingdom resulted in creating organisms still very simple, but endowed with a certain freedom of action, and, above all, with a shape so undecided that it could lend itself to any future determination. These animals may have resembled some of our worms, but with this difference, however, that the worms living today, to which they could be compared, are but the empty and fixed examples of infinitely plastic forms, pregnant with an unlimited future, the common stock of the echinoderms, mollusks, arthropods and vertebrates.

One danger lay in wait for them, one obstacle which might have stopped the soaring course of animal life. There is one peculiarity with which we cannot help being struck when glancing over the fauna of primitive times, namely, the imprisonment of the animal in a more or less solid sheath, which must have obstructed and often even paralyzed its movements. The mollusks of that time had a shell more universally than those of today. The arthropods in general were provided with a carapace; most of them were crustaceans. The more ancient fishes had a bony sheath of extreme hardness.[1] The explanation of this general fact should be sought, we believe, in a tendency of soft organisms to defend themselves against one another by making themselves, as far as possible, undevourable. Each species, in the act by which it comes into being, trends toward that which is most expedient. Just as among primitive organisms there were some that turned toward animal life by refusing to manufacture organic out of inorganic material and taking organic substances ready made from organisms that had turned toward the vegetative life, so, among the animal species themselves, many contrived to live at the expense of other animals. For an organism that is animal, that is to say mobile, can avail itself of its mobility to go in search of defenseless animals, and feed on them quite as well as on vegetables. So, the more species became mobile, the more they became voracious and dangerous to one another. Hence a sudden arrest of the entire animal world in its progress toward higher and higher mobility; for the hard and calcareous skin of the echinoderm, the shell of the mollusk, the carapace of the crustacean and the

---

[1] See, on these different points, the work of Gaudry, *Essai de paléontogie philosophique,* Paris, 1896, pp. 14–16 and 78–79.

ganoid breast-plate of the ancient fishes probably all originated in a common effort of the animal species to protect themselves against hostile species. But this breast-plate, behind which the animal took shelter, constrained it in its movements and sometimes fixed it in one place. If the vegetable renounced consciousness in wrapping itself in a cellulose membrane, the animal that shut itself up in a citadel or in armor condemned itself to a partial slumber. In this torpor the echinoderms and even the mollusks live today. Probably arthropods and vertebrates were threatened with it too. They escaped, however, and to this fortunate circumstance is due the expansion of the highest forms of life.

In two directions, in fact, we see the impulse of life to movement getting the upper hand again. The fishes exchanged their ganoid breast-plates for scales. Long before that, the insects had appeared, also disencumbered of the breast-plate that had protected their ancestors. Both supplemented the insufficiency of their protective covering by an agility that enabled them to escape their enemies, and also to assume the offensive, to choose the place and the moment of encounter. We see a progress of the same kind in the evolution of human armaments. The first impulse is to seek shelter; the second, which is the better, is to become as supple as possible for flight and above all for attack—attack being the most effective means of defense. So the heavy hoplite was supplanted by the legionary; the knight, clad in armor, had to give place to the light free-moving infantryman; and in a general way, in the evolution of life, just as in the evolution of human societies and of individual destinies, the greatest successes have been for those who have accepted the heaviest risks.

Evidently, then, it was to the animal's interest to make itself more mobile. As we said when speaking of adaptation in general, any transformation of a species can be explained by its own particular interest. This will give the immediate cause of the variation, but often only the most superficial cause. The profound cause is the impulse which thrust life into the world, which made it divide into vegetables and animals, which shunted the animal on to suppleness of form, and which, at a certain moment, in the animal kingdom threatened with torpor, secured that, on some points at least, it should rouse itself up and move forward.

On the two paths along which the vertebrates and arthropods have separately evolved, development (apart from retrogressions connected with parasitism or any other cause) has consisted above all in the progress of the sensory-motor nervous system. Mobility and suppleness were sought for, and also—through many experimental attempts, and not without a tendency to excess of substance and brute force at the start— variety of movements. But this quest itself took place in divergent directions. A glance at the nervous system of the arthropods and that of the vertebrates shows us the difference. In the arthropods, the body is formed of a series more or less long of rings set together; motor activity is thus distributed amongst a varying—sometimes a considerable— number of appendages, each of which has its special function. In the vertebrates, activity is concentrated in two pairs of members only, and these organs perform functions which depend much less strictly on their form.[1] The independence becomes complete in man, whose hand is capable of any kind of work.

That, at least, is what we see. But behind what is seen there is what may be surmised—two powers, immanent in life and originally intermingled, which were

[1] See, on this subject, Shaler, *The Individual*, New York, 1900, pp. 118–125.

bound to part company in course of growth.

To define these powers, we must consider, in the evolution both of the arthropods and the vertebrates, the species which mark the culminating point of each. How is this point to be determined? Here again, to aim at geometrical precision will lead us astray. There is no single simple sign by which we can recognize that one species is more advanced than another on the same line of evolution. There are manifold characters, that must be compared and weighed in each particular case, in order to ascertain to what extent they are essential or accidental and how far they must be taken into account.

It is unquestionable, for example, that *success* is the most general criterion of superiority, the two terms being, up to a certain point, synonymous. By success must be understood, so far as the living being is concerned, an aptitude to develop in the most diverse environments, through the greatest possible variety of obstacles, so as to cover the widest possible extent of ground. A species which claims the entire earth for its domain is truly a dominating and consequently superior species. Such is the human species, which represents the culminating point of the evolution of the vertebrates. But such also are, in the series of the articulate, the insects and in particular certain hymenoptera. It has been said of the ants that, as man is lord of the soil, they are lords of the sub-soil.

On the other hand, a group of species that has appeared late may be a group of degenerates; but, for that, some special cause of retrogression must have intervened. By right, this group should be superior to the group from which it is derived, since it would correspond to a more advanced stage of evolution. Now man is probably the latest comer of the vertebrates;[1] and in the insect series no species is later than the hymenoptera, unless it be the lepidoptera, which are probably degenerates, living parasitically on flowering plants.

So, by different ways, we are led to the same conclusion. The evolution of the arthropods reaches its culminating point in the insect, and in particular in the hymenoptera, as that of the vertebrates in man. Now, since instinct is nowhere so developed as in the insect world, and in no group of insects so marvelously as in the hymenoptera, it may be said that the whole evolution of the animal kingdom, apart from retrogressions toward vegetative life, has taken place on two divergent paths, one of which led to instinct and the other to intelligence.

Vegetative torpor, instinct and intelligence—these, then, are the elements that coincided in the vital impulsion common to plants and animals, and which, in the course of a development in which they were made manifest in the most unforeseen forms, have been dissociated by the very fact of their growth. *The cardinal error which, from Aristotle onwards, has vitiated most of the philosophies of nature, is to see in vegetative, instinctive and rational life, three successive degrees of the development of one and the same tendency, whereas they are three divergent directions of an activity that has split up as it grew. The difference be-*

---

[1] This point is disputed by M. René Quinton, who regards the carnivorous and ruminant mammals, as well as certain birds, as subsequent to man (R. Quinton, *L'Eau de mer milieu organique*, Paris, 1904, p. 435). We may say here that our general conclusions, although very different from M. Quinton's, are not irreconcilible with them; for if evolution has really been such as we represent it, the vertebrates must have made an effort to maintain themselves in the most favorable conditions of activity—the very conditions, indeed, which life had chosen in the beginning.

tween them is not a difference of intensity, nor, more generally, of degree, but of kind.

It is important to investigate this point. We have seen in the case of vegetable and animal life how they are at once mutually complementary and mutually antagonistic. Now we must show that intelligence and instinct also are opposite and complementary. But let us first explain why we are generally led to regard them as activities of which one is superior to the other and based upon it, whereas in reality they are not things of the same order: they have not succeeded one another, nor can we assign to them different grades.

It is because intelligence and instinct, having originally been interpenetrating, retain something of their common origin. Neither is ever found in a pure state. We said that in the plant the consciousness and mobility of the animal, which lie dormant, can be awakened; and that the animal lives under the constant menace of being drawn aside to the vegetative life. The two tendencies—that of the plant and that of the animal—were so thoroughly interpenetrating, to begin with, that there has never been a complete severance between them: they haunt each other continually; everywhere we find them mingled; it is the proportion that differs. So with intelligence and instinct. There is no intelligence in which some traces of instinct are not to be discovered, more especially no instinct that is not surrounded with a fringe of intelligence. It is this fringe of intelligence that has been the cause of so many misunderstandings. From the fact that instinct is always more or less intelligent, it has been concluded that instinct and intelligence are things of the same kind, that there is only a difference of complexity or perfection between them, and, above all, that one of the two is expressible in terms of the other. In reality, they accompany each other only because they are complementary, and they are complementary only because they are different, what is instinctive in instinct being opposite to what is intelligent in intelligence.

We are bound to dwell on this point. It is one of the utmost importance.

Let us say at the outset that the distinctions we are going to make will be too sharply drawn, just because we wish to define in instinct what is instinctive, and in intelligence what is intelligent, whereas all concrete instinct is mingled with intelligence, as all real intelligence is penetrated by instinct. Moreover, neither intelligence nor instinct lends itself to rigid definition: they are tendencies, and not things. Also, it must not be forgotten that in the present chapter we are considering intelligence and instinct as going out of life which deposits them along its course. Now the life manifested by an organism is, in our view, a certain effort to obtain certain things from the material world. No wonder, therefore, if it is the diversity of this effort that strikes us in instinct and intelligence, and if we see in these two modes of psychical activity, above all else, two different methods of action on inert matter. This rather narrow view of them has the advantage of giving us an objective means of distinguishing them. In return, however, it gives us, of intelligence in general and of instinct in general, only the mean position above and below which both constantly oscillate. For that reason the reader must expect to see in what follows only a diagrammatic drawing, in which the respective outlines of intelligence and instinct are sharper than they should be, and in which the shading-off which comes from the indecision of each and from their reciprocal encroachment on one another is neglected. In a matter so obscure, we cannot strive too hard for

clearness. It will always be easy afterwards to soften the outlines and to correct what is too geometrical in the drawing—in short, to replace the rigidity of a diagram by the suppleness of life.

To what date is it agreed to ascribe the appearance of man on the earth? To the period when the first weapons, the first tools, were made. The memorable quarrel over the discovery of Boucher de Perthes in the quarry of Moulin-Quignon is not forgotten. The question was whether real hatchets had been found or merely bits of flint accidentally broken. But that, supposing they were hatchets, we were indeed in the presence of intelligence, and more particularly of *human* intelligence, no one doubted for an instant. Now let us open a collection of anecdotes on the intelligence of animals: we shall see that besides many acts explicable by imitation or by the automatic association of images, there are some that we do not hesitate to call intelligent: foremost among them are those that bear witness to some idea of manufacture, whether the animal life succeeds in fashioning a crude instrument or uses for its profit an object made by man. The animals that rank immediately after man in the matter of intelligence, the apes and elephants, are those that can use an artificial instrument occasionally. Below, but not very far from them, come those that *recognize* a constructed object: for example, the fox, which knows quite well that a trap is a trap. No doubt, there is intelligence wherever there is inference; but inference, which consists in an inflection of past experience in the direction of present experience, is already a beginning of invention. Invention becomes complete when it is materialized in a manufactured instrument. Toward that achievement the intelligence of animals tends as toward an ideal. And though, ordinarily, it does not yet succeed in fashioning artificial objects and in making use of them, it is preparing for this by the very variations which it performs on the instincts furnished by nature. As regards human intelligence, it has not been sufficiently noted that mechanical invention has been from the first its essential feature, that even today our social life gravitates around the manufacture and use of artificial instruments, that the inventions which strew the road of progress have also traced its direction. This we hardly realize, because it takes us longer to change ourselves than to change our tools. Our individual and even social habits survive a good while the circumstances for which they were made, so that the ultimate effects of an invention are not observed until its novelty is already out of sight. A century has elapsed since the invention of the steam engine, and we are only just beginning to feel the depths of the shock it gave us. But the revolution it has effected in industry has nevertheless upset human relations altogether. New ideas are arising, new feelings are on the way to flower. In thousands of years, when, seen from the distance, only the broad lines of the present age will still be visible, our wars and our revolutions will count for little, even supposing they are remembered at all; but the steam engine, and the procession of inventions of every kind that accompanied it, will perhaps be spoken of as we speak of the bronze or of the chipped stone of pre-historic times: it will serve to define an age.[1] If we could rid ourselves of all pride, if, to define our species, we kept strictly to what the historic and the prehistoric periods show us to be the constant char-

---

[1] M. Paul Lacombe has laid great stress on the important influence that great inventions have exercised on the evolution of humanity (P. Lacombe, *De l'histoire considérée comme science*, Paris, 1894. See, in particular, pp. 168–247).

acteristic of man and of intelligence, we should say not *Homo sapiens,* but *Homo faber.* In short, *intelligence, considered in what seems to be its original feature, is the faculty of manufacturing artificial objects, especially tools to make tools, and of indefinitely varying the manufacture.*

Now, does an unintelligent animal also possess tools or machines? Yes, certainly, but here the instrument forms a part of the body that uses it; and, corresponding to this instrument, there is an *instinct* that knows how to use it. True, it cannot be maintained that *all* instincts consist in a natural ability to use an inborn mechanism. Such a definition would not apply to the instincts which Romanes called "secondary"; and more than one "primary" instinct would not come under it. But this definition, like that which we have provisionally given of intelligence, determines at least the ideal limit toward which the very numerous forms of instinct are traveling. Indeed, it has often been pointed out that most instincts are only the continuance, or rather the consummation, of the work of organization itself. Where does the activity of instinct begin? And where does that of nature end? We cannot tell. In the metamorphoses of the larva into the nymph and into the perfect insect, metamorphoses that often require appropriate action and a kind of initiative on the part of the larva, there is no sharp line of demarcation between the instinct of the animal and the organizing work of living matter. We may say, as we will, either that instinct organizes the instruments it is about to use, or that the process of organization is continued in the instinct that has to use the organ. The most marvelous instincts of the insect do nothing but develop its special structure into movements: indeed, where social life divides the labor among different individuals, and thus allots them different instincts, a corresponding differ-

ence of structure is observed: the polymorphism of ants, bees, wasps and certain pseudoneuroptera is well known. Thus, if we consider only those typical cases in which the complete triumph of intelligence and of instinct is seen, we find this essential difference between them: *instinct perfected is a faculty of using and even of constructing organized instruments; intelligence perfected is the faculty of making and using unorganized instruments.*

The advantages and drawbacks of these two modes of activity are obvious. Instinct finds the appropriate instrument at hand: this instrument, which makes and repairs itself, which presents, like all the works of nature, an infinite complexity of detail combined with a marvelous simplicity of function, does at once, when required, what it is called upon to do, without difficulty and with a perfection that is often wonderful. In return, it retains an almost invariable structure, since a modification of it involves a modification of the species. Instinct is therefore necessarily specialized, being nothing but the utilization of a specific instrument for a specific object. The instrument constructed intelligently, on the contrary, is an imperfect instrument. It costs an effort. It is generally troublesome to handle. But, as it is made of unorganized matter, it can take any form whatsoever, serve any purpose, free the living being from every new difficulty that arises and bestow on it an unlimited number of powers. Whilst it is inferior to the natural instrument for the satisfaction of immediate wants, its advantage over it is the greater, the less urgent the need. Above all, it reacts on the nature of the being that constructs it; for in calling on him to exercise a new function, it confers on him, so to speak, a richer organization, being an artificial organ by which the natural organism is extended. For every need that it satisfies, it creates a new need; and so, instead of closing, like instinct, the round of action within which the animal tends to move automatically, it lays open to activity an unlimited field into which it is driven further and further, and made more and more free. But this advantage of intelligence over instinct only appears at a late stage, when intelligence, having raised construction to a higher degree, proceeds to construct constructive machinery. At the outset, the advantages and drawbacks of the artificial instrument and of the natural instrument balance so well that it is hard to foretell which of the two will secure to the living being the greater empire over nature.

We may surmise that they began by being implied in each other, that the original psychical activity included both at once, and that, if we went far enough back into the past, we should find instincts more nearly approaching intelligence than those of our insects, intelligence nearer to instinct than that of our vertebrates, intelligence and instinct being, in this elementary condition, prisoners of a matter which they are not yet able to control. If the force immanent in life were an unlimited force, it might perhaps have developed instinct and intelligence together, and to any extent, in the same organisms. But everything seems to indicate that this force is limited, and that it soon exhausts itself in its very manifestation. It is hard for it to go far in several directions at once: it must choose. Now, it has the choice between two modes of acting on the material world: it can either effect this action *directly* by creating an *organized* instrument to work with; or else it can effect it *indirectly* through an organism which, instead of possessing the required instrument naturally, will itself construct it by fashioning inorganic matter. Hence intelligence and instinct, which diverge more and more as they develop, but which

never entirely separate from each other. On the one hand, the most perfect instinct of the insect is accompanied by gleams of intelligence, if only in the choice of place, time and materials of construction: the bees, for example, when by exception they build in the open air, invent new and really intelligent arrangements to adapt themselves to such new conditions.[1] But, on the other hand, intelligence has even more need of instinct than instinct has of intelligence; for the power to give shape to crude matter involves already a superior degree of organization, a degree to which the animal could not have risen, save on the wings of instinct. So, while nature has frankly evolved in the direction of instinct in the arthropods, we observe in almost all the vertebrates the striving after rather than the expansion of intelligence. It is instinct still which forms the basis of their psychical activity; but intelligence is there, and would fain supersede it. Intelligence does not yet succeed in inventing instruments; but at least it tries to, by performing as many variations as possible on the instinct which it would like to dispense with. It gains complete self-possession only in man, and this triumph is attested by the very insufficiency of the natural means at man's disposal for defense against his enemies, against cold and hunger. This insufficiency, when we strive to fathom its significance, acquires the value of a prehistoric document; it is the final leave-taking between intelligence and instinct. But it is no less true that nature must have hesitated between two modes of psychical activity— one assured of immediate success, but limited in its effects; the other hazardous, but whose conquests, if it should reach independence, might be extended indefi-

---

[1] Bouvier, "La Nidification des abeilles à l'air libre" (*C. R. de l'Ac. des sciences,* 7 mai 1906).

nitely. Here again, then, the greatest success was achieved on the side of the greatest risk. *Instinct and intelligence therefore represent two divergent solutions, equally fitting, of one and the same problem.*

There ensue, it is true, profound differences of internal structure between instinct and intelligence. We shall dwell only on those that concern our present study. Let us say, then, that instinct and intelligence imply two radically different kinds of knowledge. But some explanations are first of all necessary on the subject of consciousness in general.

It has been asked how far instinct is conscious. Our reply is that there are a vast number of differences and degrees, that instinct is more or less conscious in certain cases, unconscious in others. The plant, as we shall see, has instincts; it is not likely that these are accompanied by feeling. Even in the animal there is hardly any complex instinct that is not unconscious in some part at least of its exercise. But here we must point out a difference, not often noticed, between two kinds of unconsciousness, viz., that in which consciousness is *absent,* and that in which consciousness is *nullified.* Both are equal to zero, but in one case the zero expresses the fact that there is nothing, in the other that we have two equal quantities of opposite sign which compensate and neutralize each other. The unconsciousness of a falling stone is of the former kind: the stone has no feeling of its fall. Is it the same with the unconsciousness of instinct, in the extreme cases in which instinct is unconscious? When we mechanically perform an habitual action, when the somnambulist automatically acts his dream, unconsciousness may be absolute; but this is merely due to the fact that the representation of the act is held in check by the performance of the act itself, which resembles the idea so perfectly, and fits it

so exactly, that consciousness is unable to find room between them. *Representation is stopped up by action.* The proof of this is, that if the accomplishment of the act is arrested or thwarted by an obstacle, consciousness may reappear. It was there, but neutralized by the action which fulfilled and thereby filled the representation. The obstacle creates nothing positive; it simply makes a void, removes a stopper. This inadequacy of act to representation is precisely what we here call consciousness.

If we examine this point more closely, we shall find that consciousness is the light that plays around the zone of possible actions or potential activity which surrounds the action really performed by the living being. It signifies hesitation or choice. Where many equally possible actions are indicated without there being any real action (as in a deliberation that has not come to an end), consciousness is intense. Where the action performed is the only action possible (as in activity of the somnambulistic or more generally automatic kind), consciousness is reduced to nothing. Representation and knowledge exist none the less in the case if we find a whole series of systematized movements the last of which is already prefigured in the first, and if, besides, consciousness can flash out at them at the shock of an obstacle. From this point of view, *the consciousness of a living being may be defined as an arithmetical difference between potential and real activity. It measures the interval between representation and action.*

It may be inferred from this that intelligence is likely to point toward consciousness, and instinct toward unconsciousness. For, where the implement to be used is organized by nature, the material furnished by nature, and the result to be obtained willed by nature, there is little left to choice; the consciousness inherent in the representation is therefore counterbalanced, whenever it tends to disengage itself, by the performance of the act, identical with the representation, which forms its counterweight. Where consciousness appears, it does not so much light up the instinct itself as the thwartings to which instinct is subject; it is the *deficit* of instinct, the distance, between the act and the idea, that becomes consciousness so that consciousness, here, is only an accident. Essentially, consciousness only emphasizes the starting-point of instinct, the point at which the whole series of automatic movements is released. Deficit, on the contrary, is the normal state of intelligence. Laboring under difficulties is its very essence. Its original function being to construct unorganized instruments, it must, in spite of numberless difficulties, choose for this work the place and the time, the form and the matter. And it can never satisfy itself entirely, because every new satisfaction creates new needs. In short, while instinct and intelligence both involve knowledge, this knowledge is rather *acted* and unconscious in the case of instinct, *thought* and conscious in the case of intelligence. But it is a difference rather of degree than of kind. So long as consciousness is all we are concerned with, we close our eyes to what is, from the psychological point of view, the cardinal difference between instinct and intelligence.

In order to get at this essential difference we must, without stopping at the more or less brilliant light which illumines these two modes of internal activity, go straight to the two *objects*, profoundly different from each other, upon which instinct and intelligence are directed.

When the horse-fly lays its eggs on the legs or shoulders of the horse, it acts as if it knew that its larva has to develop in the horse's stomach and that the horse, in licking itself, will convey the larva into its digestive tract. When a paralyzing wasp stings its victim on just those points where the nervous centers lie, so as to render it motionless without killing it, it acts like a learned entomologist and a skillful surgeon rolled into one. But what shall we say of the little beetle, the Sitaris, whose story is so often quoted? This insect lays its eggs at the entrance of the underground passages dug by a kind of bee, the Anthophora. Its larva, after long waiting, springs upon the male Anthophora as it goes out of the passage, clings to it, and remains attached until the "nuptial flight," when it seizes the opportunity to pass from the male to the female, and quietly waits until it lays its eggs. It then leaps on the egg, which serves as a support for it in the honey, devours the egg in a few days, and, resting on the shell, undergoes its first metamorphosis. Organized now to float on the honey, it consumes this provision of nourishment, and becomes a nymph, then a perfect insect. Everything happens *as if* the larva of the Sitaris, from the moment it was hatched, knew that the male Anthophora would first emerge from the passage; that the nuptial flight would give it the means of conveying itself to the female, who would take it to a store of honey sufficient to feed it after its transformation; that, until this transformation, it could gradually eat the egg of the Anthophora, in such a way that it could at the same time feed itself, maintain itself at the surface of the honey, and also suppress the rival that otherwise would have come out of the egg. And equally all this happens *as if* the Sitaris itself knew that its larva would know all these things. The knowledge, if knowledge there be, is only implicit. It is reflected outwardly in exact movements instead of being reflected inwardly in consciousness. It is none the less true that the behavior of the insect involves, or rather evolves, the idea of definite things existing or being produced in definite points of space and time, which the insect knows without having learned them.

Now, if we look at intelligence from the same point of view, we find that it also knows certain things without having learned them. But the knowledge in the two cases is of a very different order. We must be careful here not to revive again the old philosophical dispute on the subject of innate ideas. So we will confine ourselves to the point on which every one is agreed, to wit, that the young child understands immediately things that the animal will never understand, and that in this sense intelligence, like instinct, is an inherited function, therefore an innate one. But this innate intelligence, although it is a faculty of knowing, knows no object in particular. When the new-born babe seeks for the first time its mother's breast, so showing that it has knowledge (unconscious, no doubt) of a thing it has never seen, we say, just because the innate knowledge is in this case of a definite object, that it belongs to *instinct* and not to *intelligence*. Intelligence does not then imply the innate knowledge of any object. And yet, if intelligence knows nothing by nature, it has nothing innate. What, then, if it be ignorant of all things, can it know? Besides *things,* there are *relations.* The new-born child, so far as intelligent, knows neither definite objects nor a definite property of any object; but when, a little later on, he will hear an epithet being applied to a substantive, he will immediately understand what it means. The relation of attribute to subject is therefore seized by him naturally, and the same might be said of the general relation expressed by the verb, a relation so immediately conceived by the mind that language can leave it to be understood, as is instanced in rudimentary languages which have no verb. Intelligence, therefore, naturally makes use of rela-

tions of like with like, of content to container, of cause to effect, etc., which are implied in every phrase in which there is a subject, an attribute and a verb, expressed or understood. May one say that it has *innate* knowledge of each of these relations in particular? It is for logicians to discover whether they are so many irreducible relations, or whether they can be resolved into relations still more general. But, in whatever way we make the analysis of thought, we always end with one or several general categories, of which the mind possesses innate knowledge since it makes a natural use of them. Let us say, therefore, that *whatever, in instinct and intelligence, is innate knowledge, bears in the first case on* things *and in the second on* relations.

Philosophers distinguish between the matter of our knowledge and its form. The matter is what is given by the perceptive faculties taken in the elementary state. The form is the totality of the relations set up between these materials in order to constitute a systematic knowledge. Can the form, without matter, be an object of knowledge? Yes, without doubt, provided that this knowledge is not like a thing we possess so much as like a habit we have contracted—a direction rather than a state: it is, if we will, a certain natural bent of attention. The schoolboy, who knows that the master is going to dictate a fraction to him, draws a line before he knows what numerator and what denominator are to come; he therefore has present to his mind the general relation between the two terms although he does not know either of them; he knows the form without the matter. So is it, prior to experience, with the categories into which our experience comes to be inserted. Let us adopt then words sanctioned by usage, and give the distinction between intelligence and instinct this more precise formula: *Intelligence, in so far as it is innate, is the knowledge of a* form; *instinct implies the knowledge of a* matter.

From this second point of view, which is that of knowledge instead of action, the force immanent in life in general appears to us again as a limited principle, in which originally two different and even divergent modes of knowing coexisted and intermingled. The first gets at definite objects immediately, in their materiality itself. It says, "This is what is." The second gets at no object in particular; it is only a natural power of relating an object to an object, or a part to a part, or an aspect to an aspect—in short, of drawing conclusions when in possession of the premises, of proceeding from what has been learned to what is still unknown. It does not say, "This *is*"; it says only that *"if* the conditions are such, such will be the conditioned." In short, the first kind of knowledge, the instinctive, would be formulated in what philosophers call *categorical* propositions, while the second kind, the intellectual, would always be expressed *hypothetically.* Of these two faculties, the former seems, at first, much preferable to the other. And it would be so, in truth, if it extended to an endless number of objects. But, in fact, it applies only to one special object, and indeed only to a restricted part of that object. Of this, at least, its knowledge is intimate and full; not explicit, but implied in the accomplished action. The intellectual faculty, on the contrary, possesses naturally only an external and empty knowledge; but it has thereby the advantage of supplying a frame in which an infinity of objects may find room in turn. It is as if the force evolving in living forms, being a limited force, had had to choose between two kinds of limitation in the field of natural or innate knowledge, one applying to the *extension* of knowledge, the other to its *intension.* In the first case, the knowledge may be packed and full, but it will then be confined to one specific object; in the second, it is no longer limited by its object, but that is because it contains nothing, being only a form without matter. The two tendencies, at first implied in each other, had to separate in order to grow. They both went to seek their fortune in the world, and turned out to be instinct and intelligence.

Such, then, are the two divergent modes of knowledge by which intelligence and instinct must be defined, from the standpoint of knowledge rather than that of action. But knowledge and action are here only two aspects of one and the same faculty. It is easy to see, indeed, that the second definition is only a new form of the first.

If instinct is, above all, the faculty of using an organized natural instrument, it must involve innate knowledge (potential or unconscious, it is true), both of this instrument and of the object to which it is applied. Instinct is therefore innate knowledge of a *thing.* But intelligence is the faculty of constructing unorganized —that is to say artificial—instruments. If, on its account, nature gives up endowing the living being with the instruments that may serve him, it is in order that the living being may be able to vary his construction according to circumstances. The essential function of intelligence is therefore to see the way out of a difficulty in any circumstances whatever, to find what is most suitable, what answers best the question asked. Hence it bears essentially on the relations between a given situation and the means of utilizing it. What is innate in intellect, therefore, is the tendency to establish relations, and this tendency implies the natural knowledge of certain very general relations, a kind of stuff that the activity of each particular intellect will cut up into more special relations. Where activity is directed toward manufacture, therefore, knowledge necessarily bears on relations.

But this entirely *formal* knowledge of intelligence has an immense advantage over the *material* knowledge of instinct. A form, just because it is empty, may be filled at will with any number of things in turn, even with those that are of no use. So that a formal knowledge is not limited to what is practically useful, although it is in view of practical utility that it has made its appearance in the world. An intelligent being bears within himself the means to transcend his own nature.

He transcends himself, however, less than he wishes, less also than he imagines himself to do. The purely formal character of intelligence deprives it of the ballast necessary to enable it to settle itself on the objects that are of the most powerful interest to speculation. Instinct, on the contrary, has the desired materiality, but it is incapable of going so far in quest of its object; it does not speculate. Here we reach the point that most concerns our present inquiry. The difference that we shall now proceed to denote between instinct and intelligence is what the whole of this analysis was meant to bring out. We formulate it thus: *There are things that intelligence alone is able to seek, but which, by itself, it will never find. These things instinct alone could find; but it will never seek them.*

It is necessary here to consider some preliminary details that concern the mechanism of intelligence. We have said that the function of intelligence is to establish relations. Let us determine more precisely the nature of these relations. On this point we are bound to be either vague or arbitrary so long as we see in the intellect a faculty intended for pure speculation. We are then reduced to taking the general frames of the understanding for something absolute, irreducible and inexplicable. The understanding must have fallen from heaven with its form, as each of us is born with his face. This form may be defined, of course, but

that is all; there is no asking why it is what it is rather than anything else. Thus, it will be said that the function of the intellect is essentially unification, that the common object of all its operations is to introduce a certain unity into the diversity of phenomena, and so forth. But, in the first place, "unification" is a vague term, less clear than "relation" or even "thought," and says nothing more. And, moreover, it might be asked if the function of intelligence is not to divide even more than to unite. Finally, if the intellect proceeds as it does because it wishes to unite, and if it seeks unification simply because it has need of unifying, the whole of our knowledge becomes relative to certain requirements of the mind that probably might have been entirely different from what they are: for an intellect differently shaped, knowledge would have been different. Intellect being no longer dependent on anything, everything becomes dependent on it; and so, having placed the understanding too high, we end by putting too low the knowledge it gives us. Knowledge becomes relative, as soon as the intellect is made a kind of absolute.—We regard the human intellect, on the contrary, as relative to the needs of action. Postulate action, and the very form of the intellect can be deduced from it. This form is therefore neither irreducible nor inexplicable. And, precisely because it is not independent, knowledge cannot be said to depend on it: knowledge ceases to be a product of the intellect and becomes, in a certain sense, part and parcel of reality.

Philosophers will reply that action takes place in an *ordered* world, that this order is itself thought, and that we beg the question when we explain the intellect by action, which presupposes it. They would be right if our point of view in the present chapter was to be our final one. We should then be dupes of an illusion like that of Spencer, who believed that the intellect is sufficiently explained as the impression left on us by the general characters of matter: as if the order inherent in matter were not intelligence itself! But we reserve for the next chapter the question up to what point and with what method philosophy can attempt a real genesis of the intellect at the same time as of matter. For the moment, the problem that engages our attention is of a psychological order. We are asking what is the portion of the material world to which our intellect is specially adapted. To reply to this question, there is no need to choose a system of philosophy: it is enough to take up the point of view of common sense.

Let us start, then, from action, and lay down that the intellect aims, first of all, at constructing. This fabrication is exercised exclusively on inert matter, in this sense, that even if it makes use of organized material, it treats it as inert, without troubling about the life which animated it. And of inert matter itself, fabrication deals only with the solid; the rest escapes by its very fluidity. If, therefore, the tendency of the intellect is to fabricate, we may expect to find that whatever is fluid in the real will escape it in part, and whatever is life in the living will escape it altogether. *Our intelligence, as it leaves the hands of nature, has for its chief object the unorganized solid.*

When we pass in review the intellectual functions, we see that the intellect is never quite at its ease, never entirely at home, except when it is working upon inert matter, more particularly upon solids. What is the most general property of the material world? It is extended: it presents to us objects external to other objects, and, in these objects, parts external to parts. No doubt, it is useful to us, in view of our ulterior manipulation, to regard each object as divisible into parts arbitrarily cut up, each part being again divisible as we like, and so on *ad infini-*

tum. But it is above all necessary, for our present manipulation, to regard the real object in hand, or the real elements into which we have resolved it, as *provisionally final,* and to treat them as so many *units.* To this possibility of decomposing matter as much as we please, and in any way we please, we allude when we speak of the *continuity* of material extension; but this continuity, as we see it, is nothing else but our ability, an ability that matter allows to us to choose the mode of discontinuity we shall find in it. It is always, in fact, the mode of discontinuity once chosen that appears to us as the actually real one and that which fixes our attention, just because it rules our action. Thus discontinuity is thought for itself; it is thinkable in itself; we form an idea of it by a positive act of our mind; while the intellectual representation of continuity is negative, being, at bottom, only the refusal of our mind, before any actually given system of decomposition, to regard it as the only possible one. *Of the discontinuous alone does the intellect form a clear idea.*

On the other hand, the objects we act on are certainly mobile objects, but the important thing for us to know is *whither* the mobile object is going and *where* it is at any moment of its passage. In other words, our interest is directed, before all, to its actual or future positions, and not to the *progress* by which it passes from one position to another, progress which is the movement itself. In our actions, which are systematized movements, what we fix our mind on is the end or meaning of the movement, its design as a whole— in a word, the immobile plan of its execution. That which really moves in action interests us only so far as the whole can be advanced, retarded, or stopped by any incident that may happen on the way. From mobility itself our intellect turns aside, because it has nothing to gain in dealing with it. If the intellect were meant for pure theorizing, it would take its place within movement, for movement is reality itself, and immobility is always only apparent or relative. But the intellect is meant for something altogether different. Unless it does violence to itself, it takes the opposite course; it always starts from immobility, as if this were the ultimate reality: when it tries to form an idea of movement, it does so by constructing movement out of immobilities put together. This operation, whose illegitimacy and danger in the field of speculation we shall show later on (it leads to deadlocks, and creates artificially insoluble philosophical problems), is easily justified when we refer it to its proper goal. Intelligence, in its natural state, aims at a practically useful end. When it substitutes for movement immobilities put together, it does not pretend to reconstitute the movement such as it actually is; it merely replaces it with a practical equivalent. It is the philosophers who are mistaken when they import into the domain of speculation a method of thinking which is made for action. But of this more anon. Suffice it now to say that to the stable and unchangeable our intellect is attached by virtue of its natural disposition. *Of immobility alone does the intellect form a clear idea.*

Now, fabricating consists in carving out the form of an object in matter. What is the most important is the form to be obtained. As to the matter, we choose that which is most convenient; but, in order to choose it, that is to say, in order to go and seek it among many others, we must have tried, in imagination at least, to endow every kind of matter with the form of the object conceived. In other words, an intelligence which aims at fabricating is an intelligence which never stops at the actual form of things nor regards it as final, but, on the contrary, looks upon all matter as

if it were carvable at will. Plato compares the good dialectician to the skillful cook who carves the animal without breaking its bones, by following the articulations marked out by nature.[1] An intelligence which always proceeded thus would really be an intelligence turned toward speculation. But action, and in particular fabrication, requires the opposite mental tendency: it makes us consider every actual form of things, even the form of natural things, as artificial and provisional; it makes our thought efface from the object perceived, even though organized and living, the lines that outwardly mark its inward structure; in short, it makes us regard its matter as indifferent to its form. The whole of matter is made to appear to our thought as an immense piece of cloth in which we can cut out what we will and sew it together again as we please. Let us note, in passing, that it is this power that we affirm when we say that there is a *space,* that is to say, a homogeneous and empty medium, infinite and infinitely divisible, lending itself indifferently to any mode of decomposition whatsoever. A medium of this kind is never perceived; it is only conceived. What is perceived is extension colored, resistant, divided according to the lines which mark out the boundaries of real bodies or of their real elements. But when we think of our power over this matter, that is to say, of our faculty of decomposing and recomposing it as we please, we project the whole of these possible decompositions and recompositions behind real extension in the form of a homogeneous space, empty and indifferent, which is supposed to underlie it. This space is therefore, pre-eminently, the plan of our possible action on things, although, indeed, things have a natural tendency, as we shall explain further on, to enter into a frame of this kind. It is a

---

[1] Plato, *Phaedrus.*

view taken by mind. The animal has probably no idea of it, even when, like us, it perceives extended things. It is an idea that symbolizes the tendency of the human intellect to fabrication. But this point must not detain us now. Suffice it to say that *the intellect is characterized by the unlimited power of decomposing according to any law and of recomposing into any system.*

We have now enumerated a few of the essential features of human intelligence. But we have hitherto considered the individual in isolation, without taking account of social life. In reality, man is a being who lives in society. If it be true that the human intellect aims at fabrication, we must add that, for that as well as for other purposes, it is associated with other intellects. Now, it is difficult to imagine a society whose members do not communicate by signs. Insect societies probably have a language, and this language must be adapted, like that of man, to the necessities of life in common. By language community of action is made possible. But the requirements of joint action are not at all the same in a colony of ants and in a human society. In insect societies there is generally polymorphism, the subdivision of labor is natural, and each individual is riveted by its structure to the function it performs. In any case, these societies are based on instinct, and consequently on certain actions or fabrications that are more or less dependent on the form of the organs. So if the ants, for instance, have a language, the signs which compose it must be very limited in number, and each of them, once the species is formed, must remain invariably attached to a certain object or a certain operation: the sign is adherent to the thing signified. In human society, on the contrary, fabrication and action are of variable form, and, moreover, each individual must learn his part, because he is not preordained to it by his structure. So

a language is required which makes it possible to be always passing from what is known to what is yet to be known. There must be a language whose signs—which cannot be infinite in number—are extensible to an infinity of things. This tendency of the sign to transfer itself from one object to another is characteristic of human language. It is observable in the little child as soon as he begins to speak. Immediately and naturally he extends the meaning of the words he learns, availing himself of the most accidental connection or the most distant analogy to detach and transfer elsewhere the sign that had been associated in his hearing with a particular object. "Anything can designate anything"; such is the latent principle of infantine language. This tendency has been wrongly confused with the faculty of generalizing. The animals themselves generalize; and, moreover, a sign—even an instinctive sign—always to some degree represents a genus. But what characterizes the signs of human language is not so much their generality as their mobility. *The instinctive sign is* adherent, *the intelligent sign is* mobile.

Now, this mobility of words, that makes them able to pass from one thing to another, has enabled them to be extended from things to ideas. Certainly, language would not have given the faculty of reflecting to an intelligence entirely externalized and incapable of turning homeward. An intelligence which reflects is one that originally had a surplus of energy to spend, over and above practically useful efforts. It is a consciousness that has virtually reconquered itself. But still the virtual has to become actual. Without language, intelligence would probably have remained riveted to the material objects which it was interested in considering. It would have lived in a state of somnambulism, outside itself, hypnotized on its own work. Language has greatly contributed to its liberation. The word, made to pass from one thing to another, is, in fact, by nature transferable and free. It can therefore be extended, not only from one perceived thing to another, but even from a perceived thing to a recollection of that thing, from the precise recollection to a more fleeting image, and finally from an image fleeting, though still pictured, to the picturing of the act by which the image is pictured, that is to say, to the idea. Thus is revealed to the intelligence, hitherto always turned outwards, a whole internal world—the spectacle of its own workings. It required only this opportunity, at length offered by language. It profits by the fact that the word is an external thing, which the intelligence can catch hold of and cling to, and at the same time an immaterial thing, by means of which the intelligence can penetrate even to the inwardness of its own work. Its first business was indeed to make instruments, but this fabrication is possible only by the employment of certain means which are not cut to the exact measure of their object, but go beyond it and thus allow intelligence a supplementary—that is to say disinterested work. From the moment that the intellect, reflecting upon its own doings, perceives itself as a creator of ideas, as a faculty of representation in general, there is no object of which it may not wish to have the idea, even though that object be without direct relation to practical action. That is why we said there are things that intellect alone can seek. Intellect alone, indeed, troubles itself about theory; and its theory would fain embrace everything—not only inanimate matter, over which it has a natural hold, but even life and thought.

By what means, what instruments, in short by what method it will approach these problems, we can easily guess. Originally, it was fashioned to the form of matter. Language itself, which has enabled it to extend its field of operations, is made to designate things, and nought but things: it is only because the word is mobile, because it flies from one thing to another, that the intellect was sure to take it, sooner or later, on the wing, while it was not settled on anything, and apply it to an object which is not a thing and which, concealed till then, awaited the coming of the word to pass from darkness to light. But the word, by covering up this object, again converts it into a thing. So intelligence, even when it no longer operates upon its own object, follows habits it has contracted in that operation: it applies forms that are indeed those of unorganized matter. It is made for this kind of work. With this kind of work alone is it fully satisfied. And that is what intelligence expresses by saying that thus only it arrives at *distinctness* and *clearness*.

It must, therefore, in order to think itself clearly and distinctly, perceive itself under the form of discontinuity. Concepts, in fact, are outside each other, like objects in space; and they have the same stability as such objects, on which they have been modeled. Taken together, they constitute an "intelligible world," that resembles the world of solids in its essential characters, but whose elements are lighter, more diaphanous, easier for the intellect to deal with than the image of concrete things: they are not, indeed, the perception itself of things, but the representation of the act by which the intellect is fixed on them. They are, therefore, not images, but symbols. Our logic is the complete set of rules that must be followed in using symbols. As these symbols are derived from the consideration of solids, as the rules for combining these symbols hardly do more than express the most general relations among solids, our logic triumphs in that science which takes the solidity of bodies for its object, that is, in geometry. Logic and geometry engender each other, as we shall see a little further on. It is from the extension of a certain natural geometry, suggested by the most general and immediately perceived properties of solids, that natural logic has arisen; then from this natural logic, in its turn, has sprung scientific geometry, which extends further and further the knowledge of the external properties of solids.[1] Geometry and logic are strictly applicable to matter; in it they are at home, and in it they can proceed quite alone. But, outside this domain, pure reasoning needs to be supervised by common sense, which is an altogether different thing.

Thus, all the elementary forces of the intellect tend to transform matter into an instrument of action, that is, in the etymological sense of the word, into an *organ.* Life, not content with producing organisms, would fain give them as an appendage inorganic matter itself, converted into an immense organ by the industry of the living being. Such is the initial task it assigns to intelligence. That is why the intellect always behaves as if it were fascinated by the contemplation of inert matter. It is life looking outward, putting itself outside itself, adopting the ways of unorganized nature in principle, in order to direct them in fact. Hence its bewilderment when it turns to the living and is confronted with organization. It does what it can, it resolves the organized into the unorganized, for it cannot, without reversing its natural direction and twisting about on itself, think true continuity, real mobility, reciprocal penetration—in a word, that creative evolution which is life.

Consider continuity. The aspect of life that is accessible to our intellect—as in-

deed to our senses, of which our intellect is the extension—is that which offers a hold to our action. Now, to modify an object, we have to perceive it as divisible and discontinuous. From the point of view of positive science, an incomparable progress was realized when the organized tissues were resolved into cells. The study of the cell, in its turn, has shown it to be an organism whose complexity seems to grow, the more thoroughly it is examined. The more science advances, the more it sees the number grow of heterogeneous elements which are placed together, outside each other, to make up a living being. Does science thus get any nearer to life? Does it not, on the contrary, find that what is really life in the living seems to recede with every step by which it pushes further the detail of the parts combined? There is indeed already among scientists a tendency to regard the substance of the organism as continuous, and the cell as an artificial entity. But, supposing this view were finally to prevail, it could only lead, on deeper study, to some other mode of analyzing of the living being, and so to a new discontinuity—although less removed, perhaps, from the real continuity of life. The truth is that this continuity cannot be thought by the intellect while it follows its natural movement. It implies at once the multiplicity of elements and the interpenetration of all by all, two conditions that can hardly be reconciled in the field in which our industry, and consequently our intellect, is engaged.

Just as we separate in space, we fix in time. The intellect is not made to think *evolution,* in the proper sense of the word—that is to say, the continuity of a change that is pure mobility. We shall not dwell here on this point, which we propose to study in a special chapter. Suffice it to say that the intellect represents *becoming* as a series of *states,* each

---

[1] We return to these points in chapter ii.

of which is homogeneous with itself and consequently does not change. Is our attention called to the internal change of one of these states? At once we decompose it into another series of states which, reunited, will be supposed to make up this internal modification. Each of these new states must be invariable, or else their internal change, if we are forced to notice it, must be resolved again into a fresh series of invariable states, and so on to infinity. Here again, thinking consists in reconstituting, and, naturally, it is with *given* elements, and consequently with *stable* elements, that we reconstitute. So that, though we may do our best to imitate the mobility of becoming by an addition that is ever going on, becoming itself slips through our fingers just when we think we are holding it tight.

Precisely because it is always trying to reconstitute, and to reconstitute with what is given, the intellect lets what is *new* in each moment of a history escape. It does not admit the unforeseeable. It rejects all creation. That definite antecedents bring forth a definite consequent, calculable as a function of them, is what satisfies our intellect. That a definite end calls forth definite means to attain it, is what we also understand. In both cases we have to do with the known which is combined with the known, in short, with the old which is repeated. Our intellect is there at its ease; and, whatever be the object, it will abstract, separate, eliminate, so as to substitute for the object itself, if necessary, an approximate equivalent in which things will happen in this way. But that each instant is a fresh endowment, that the new is ever upspringing, that the form just come into existence (although, *when once produced,* it may be regarded as an effect determined by its causes) could never have been foreseen—because the causes here, unique in their kind, are part

of the effect, have come into existence with it, and are determined by it as much as they determine it—all this we can feel within ourselves and also divine, by sympathy, outside ourselves, but we cannot think it, in the strict sense of the word, nor express it in terms of pure understanding. No wonder at that: we must remember what our intellect is meant for. The causality it seeks and finds everywhere expresses the very mechanism of our industry, in which we go on recomposing the same whole with the same parts, repeating the same movements to obtain the same result. The finality it understands best is the finality of our industry, in which we work on a model given in advance, that is to say, old or composed of elements already known. As to invention properly so called, which is, however, the point of departure of industry itself, our intellect does not succeed in grasping it in its *upspringing,* that is to say, in its indivisibility, nor in its *fervor,* that is to say, in its creativeness. Explaining it always consists in resolving it, it the unforeseeable and new, into elements old or known, arranged in a different order. The intellect can no more admit complete novelty than real becoming; that is to say, here again it lets an essential aspect of life escape, as if it were not intended to think such an object.

All our analyses bring us to this conclusion. But it is hardly necessary to go into such long details concerning the mechanism of intellectual working; it is enough to consider the results. We see that the intellect, so skillful in dealing with the inert, is awkward the moment it touches the living. Whether it wants to treat the life of the body or the life of the mind, it proceeds with the rigor, the stiffness and the brutality of an instrument not designed for such use. The history of hygiene or of pedagogy teaches us much in this matter. When we think of the cardinal, urgent and constant need we have to preserve our bodies and to raise our souls, of the special facilities given to each of us, in this field, to experiment continually on ourselves and on others, of the palpable injury by which the wrongness of a medical or pedagogical practice is both made manifest and punished at once, we are amazed at the stupidity and especially at the persistence of errors. We may easily find their origin in the natural obstinacy with which we treat the living like the lifeless and think all reality, however fluid, under the form of the sharply defined solid. We are at ease only in the discontinuous, in the immobile, in the dead. *The intellect is characterized by a natural inability to comprehend life.*

Instinct, on the contrary, is molded on the very form of life. While intelligence treats everything mechanically, instinct proceeds, so to speak, organically. If the consciousness that slumbers in it should awake, if it were wound up into knowledge instead of being wound off into action, if we could ask and it could reply, it would give up to us the most intimate secrets of life. For it only carries out further the work by which life organizes matter—so that we cannot say, as has often been shown, where organization ends and where instinct begins. When the little chick is breaking its shell with a peck of its beak, it is acting by instinct, and yet it does but carry on the movement which has borne it through embryonic life. Inversely, in the course of embryonic life itself (especially when the embryo lives freely in the form of a larva), many of the acts accomplished must be referred to instinct. The most essential of the primary instincts are really, therefore, vital processes. The potential consciousness that accompanies them is generally actualized only at the outset of the act, and leaves the rest of the process to go on by itself.

It would only have to expand more widely, and then dive into its own depth completely, to be one with the generative force of life.

When we see in a living body thousands of cells working together to a common end, dividing the task between them, living each for itself at the same time as for the others, preserving itself, feeding itself, reproducing itself, responding to the menace of danger by appropriate defensive reactions, how can we help thinking of so many instincts? And yet these are the natural functions of the cell, the constitutive elements of its vitality. On the other hand, when we see the bees of a hive forming a system so strictly organized that no individual can live apart from the others beyond a certain time, even though furnished with food and shelter, how can we help recognizing that the hive is really, and not metaphorically, a single organism, of which each bee is a cell united to the others by invisible bonds? The instinct that animates the bee is indistinguishable, then, from the force that animates the cell, or is only a prolongation of that force. In extreme cases like this, instinct coincides with the work of organization.

Of course there are degrees of perfection in the same instinct. Between the bumble-bee, and the honey-bee, for instance, the distance is great; and we pass from one to the other through a great number of intermediaries, which correspond to so many complications of the social life. But the same diversity is found in the functioning of histological elements belonging to different tissues more or less akin. In both cases there are manifold variations on one and the same theme. The constancy of the theme is manifest, however, and the variations only fit it to the diversity of the circumstances.

Now, in both cases, in the instinct of the animal and in the vital properties of the cell, the same knowledge and the same ignorance are shown. All goes on as if the cell knew, of the other cells, what concerns itself; as if the animal knew, of the other animals, what it can utilize—all else remaining in shade. It seems as if life, as soon as it has become bound up in a species, is cut off from the rest of its own work, save at one or two points that are of vital concern to the species just arisen. Is it not plain that life goes to work here exactly like consciousness, exactly like memory? We trail behind us, unawares, the whole of our past; but our memory pours into the present only the odd recollection or two that in some way complete our present situation. Thus the instinctive knowledge which one species possesses of another on a certain particular point has its root in the very unity of life, which is, to use the expression of an ancient philosopher, a "whole sympathetic to itself." It is impossible to consider some of the special instincts of the animal and of the plant, evidently arisen in extraordinary circumstances, without relating them to those recollections, seemingly forgotten, which spring up suddenly under the pressure of an urgent need.

No doubt many secondary instincts, and also many varieties of primary instinct, admit of a scientific explanation. Yet it is doubtful whether science, with its present methods of explanation, will ever succeed in analyzing instinct completely. The reason is that instinct and intelligence are two divergent developments of one and the same principle, which in the one case remains within itself, in the other steps out of itself and becomes absorbed in the utilization of inert matter. This gradual divergence testifies to a radical incompatibility, and points to the fact that it is impossible for intelligence to re-absorb instinct. That which is instinctive in instinct cannot be expressed in terms of intelligence, nor, consequently, can it be analyzed.

A man born blind, who had lived among others born blind, could not be made to believe in the possibility of perceiving a distant object without first perceiving all the objects in between. Yet vision performs this miracle. In a certain sense the blind man is right, since vision, having its origin in the stimulation of the retina, by the vibrations of the light, is nothing else, in fact, but a retinal touch. Such is indeed the *scientific* explanation, for the function of science is just to express all perceptions in terms of touch. But we have shown elsewhere that the philosophical explanation of perception (if it may still be called an explanation) must be of another kind.[1] Now instinct also is a knowledge at a distance. It has the same relation to intelligence that vision has to touch. Science cannot do otherwise than express it in terms of intelligence; but in so doing it constructs an imitation of instinct rather than penetrates within it.

Anyone can convince himself of this by studying the ingenious theories of evolutionist biology. They may be reduced to two types, which are often intermingled. One type, following the principles of neo-Darwinism, regards instinct as a sum of accidental differences preserved by selection: such and such a useful behavior, naturally adopted by the individual in virtue of an accidental predisposition of the germ, has been transmitted from germ to germ, waiting for chance to add fresh improvements to it by the same method. The other type regards instinct as lapsed intelligence: the action, found useful by the species or by certain of its representatives, is supposed to have engendered a habit, which, by hereditary transmission, has become an

---

[1] *Matière et mémoire*, chap. i.

instinct. Of these two types of theory, the first has the advantage of being able to bring in hereditary transmission without raising grave objection; for the accidental modification which it places at the origin of the instinct is not supposed to have been acquired by the individual, but to have been inherent in the germ. But, on the other hand, it is absolutely incapable of explaining instincts as sagacious as those of most insects. These instincts surely could not have attained, all at once, their present degree of complexity; they have probably evolved; but, in a hypothesis like that of the neo-Darwinians, the evolution of instinct could have come to pass only by the progressive addition of new pieces which, in some way, by happy accidents, came to fit into the old. Now it is evident that, in most cases, instinct could not have perfected itself by simple accretion: each new piece really requires, if all is not to be spoiled, a complete recasting of the whole. How could mere chance work a recasting of the kind? I agree that an accidental modification of the germ may be passed on hereditarily, and may somehow wait for fresh accidental modifications to come and complicate it. I agree also that natural selection may eliminate all those of the more complicated forms of instinct that are not fit to survive. Still, in order that the life of the instinct may evolve, complications fit to survive have to be produced. Now they will be produced only if, in certain cases, the addition of a new element brings about the correlative change of all the old elements. No one will maintain that chance could perform such a miracle: in one form or another we shall appeal to intelligence. We shall suppose that it is by an effort, more or less conscious, that the living being develops a higher instinct. But then we shall have to admit that an acquired habit can become hereditary, and that it

does so regularly enough to insure an evolution. The thing is doubtful, to put it mildly. Even if we could refer the instincts of animals to habits intelligently acquired and hereditarily transmitted, it is not clear how this sort of explanation could be extended to the vegetable world, where effort is never intelligent, even supposing it is sometimes conscious. And yet, when we see with what sureness and precision climbing plants use their tendrils, what marvelously combined maneuvers the orchids perform to procure their fertilization by means of insects,[1] how can we help thinking that these are so many instincts?

This is not saying that the theory of the neo-Darwinians must be altogether rejected, any more than that of the neo-Lamarckians. The first are probably right in holding that evolution takes place from germ to germ rather than from individual to individual; the second are right in saying that at the origin of instinct there is an effort (although it is something quite different, we believe, from an *intelligent* effort). But the former are probably wrong when they make the evolution of instinct an *accidental* evolution, and the latter when they regard the effort from which instinct proceeds as an *individual* effort. The effort by which a species modifies its instinct, and modifies itself as well, must be a much deeper thing, dependent solely neither on circumstances nor on individuals. It is not purely accidental, although accident has a large place in it; and it does not depend solely on the initiative of individuals, although individuals collaborate in it.

Compare the different forms of the same instinct in different species of

_____

[1] See the two works of Darwin, *Climbing Plants* and *The Fertilization of Orchids by Insects.*

[363]

hymenoptera. The impression derived is not always that of an increasing complexity made of elements that have been added together one after the other. Nor does it suggest the idea of steps up a ladder. Rather do we think, in many cases at least, of the circumference of a circle, from different points of which these different varieties have started, all facing the same center, all making an effort in that direction but each approaching it only to the extent of its means, and to the extent also to which this central point has been illumined for it. In other words, instinct is everywhere complete, but it is more or less simplified, and, above all, simplified *differently*. On the other hand, in cases where we do get the impression of an ascending scale, as if one and the same instinct had gone on complicating itself more and more in one direction and along a straight line, the species which are thus arranged by their instincts into a linear series are by no means always akin. Thus, the comparative study, in recent years, of the social instinct in the different apidae proves that the instinct of the meliponines is intermediary in complexity between the still rudimentary tendency of the humble bees and the consummate science of the true bees; yet there can be no kinship between the bees and the meliponines.[1] Most likely, the degree of complexity of these different societies has nothing to do with any greater or smaller number of added elements. We seem rather to be before a *musical theme,* which had first been transposed, the theme as a whole, into a certain number of tones, and on which, still the whole theme, different variations had been played, some very simple, others very skillful. As to the original theme, it is everywhere and no-where. It is in vain that we try to express it in terms of any idea: it must have been, originally, *felt* rather than *thought.* We get the same impression before the paralyzing instinct of certain wasps. We know that the different species of hymenoptera that have this paralyzing instinct lay their eggs in spiders, bettles or caterpillars, which, having first been subjected by the wasp to a skillful surgical operation, will go on living motionless a certain number of days, and thus provide the larvae with fresh meat. In the sting which they give to the nerve-centers of their victim, in order to destroy its power of moving without killing it, these different species of hymenoptera take into account, so to speak, the different species of prey they respectively attack. The Scolia, which attacks a larva of the rose-beetle, stings it in one point only, but in this point the motor ganglia are concentrated, and those ganglia alone: the stinging of other ganglia might cause death and putrefaction, which it must avoid.[1] The yellow-winged Sphex, which has chosen the cricket for its victim, knows that the cricket has three nerve-centers which serve its three pairs of legs—or at least it acts as if it knew this. It stings the insect first under the neck, then behind the prothorax, and then where the thorax joins the abdomen.[2] The Ammophila Hirsuta gives nine successive strokes of its sting upon nine nerve-centers of its caterpillar, and then seizes the head and squeezes it in its mandibles, enough to cause paralysis without death.[3] The general theme is "the necessity of paralyzing without killing"; the variations are subordinated to the structure of the victim on which they are played. No doubt the

---

[1] Buttel-Reepen, "Die phylogenetische Entstehung des Bienenstaates" (*Biol. Centralblatt,* xxiii., 1903), p. 108 in particular.

[1] Fabre, *Souvenirs entomologiques,* 3e série, Paris, 1890, pp. 1–69.
[2] Fabre, *Souvenirs entomologiques,* 1re série, 3e édition, Paris, 1894, pp. 93 ff.
[3] Fabre, *Nouveaux souvenirs entomologiques,* Paris, 1882, pp. 14 ff.

operation is not always perfect. It has recently been shown that the Ammophila sometimes kills the caterpillar instead of paralyzing it, that sometimes also it paralyzes it incompletely.[1] But, because instinct is, like intelligence, fallible, because it also shows individual deviations, it does not at all follow that the instinct of the Ammophila has been acquired, as has been claimed, by tentative intelligent experiments. Even supposing that the Ammophila has come in course of time to recognize, one after another, by tentative experiment, the points of its victim which must be stung to render it motionless, and also the special treatment that must be inflicted on the head to bring about paralysis without death, how can we imagine that elements so special of a knowledge so precise have been regularly transmitted, one by one, by heredity? If, in all our present experience, there were a single indisputable example of a transmission of this kind, the inheritance of acquired characters would be questioned by no one. As a matter of fact, the hereditary transmission of a contracted habit is effected in an irregular and far from precise manner, supposing it is ever really effected at all.

But the whole difficulty comes from our desire to express the knowledge of the hymenoptera in terms of intelligence. It is this that compels us to compare the Ammophila with the entomologist, who knows the caterpillar as he knows everything else—from the outside, and without having on his part a special or vital interest. The Ammophila, we imagine, must learn, one by one, like the entomologist, the positions of the nerve-centers of the caterpillar—must acquire at least the practical knowledge of these positions by trying the effects of its sting. But there is no need for such a view if we

suppose a *sympathy* (in the etymological sense of the word) between the Ammophila and its victim, which teaches it from within, so to say, concerning the vulnerability of the caterpillar. This feeling of vulnerability might owe nothing to outward perception, but result from the mere presence together of the Ammophila and the caterpillar, considered no longer as two organisms, but as two activities. It would express, in a concrete form, the *relation* of the one to the other. Certainly, a scientific theory cannot appeal to considerations of this kind. It must not put action before organization, sympathy before perception and knowledge. But, once more, either philosophy has nothing to see here, or its rôle begins where that of science ends.

Whether it makes instinct a "compound reflex," or a habit formed intelligently that has become automatism, or a sum of small accidental advantages accumulated and fixed by selection, in every case science claims to resolve instinct completely either into *intelligent* actions, or into mechanisms built up piece by piece like those combined by our *intelligence*. I agree indeed that science is here within its function. It gives us, in default of a real analysis of the object, a translation of this object in terms of intelligence. But is it not plain that science itself invites philosophy to consider things in another way? If our biology was still that of Aristotle, if it regarded the series of living beings as unilinear, if it showed us the whole of life evolving toward intelligence and passing, to that end, through sensibility and instinct, we should be right, we, the intelligent beings, in turning back toward the earlier and consequently inferior manifestations of life and in claiming to fit them, without deforming them, into the molds of our understanding. But one of the clearest results of biology has been to show that evolution has taken place

[1] Peckham, *Wasps, Solitary and Social,* Westminster, 1905, pp. 28 ff.

along divergent lines. It is at the extremity of two of these lines—the two principal—that we find intelligence and instinct in forms almost pure. Why, then, should instinct be resolvable into intelligent elements? Why, even, into terms entirely intelligible? Is it not obvious that to think here of the intelligent, or of the absolutely intelligible, is to go back to the Aristotelian theory of nature? No doubt it is better to go back to that than to stop short before instinct as before an unfathomable mystery. But, though instinct is not within the domain of intelligence, it is not situated beyond the limits of mind. In the phenomena of feeling, in unreflecting sympathy and antipathy, we experience in ourselves—though under a much vaguer form, and one too much penetrated with intelligence—something of what must happen in the consciousness of an insect acting by instinct. Evolution does but sunder, in order to develop them to the end, elements which, at their origin, interpenetrated each other. More precisely, intelligence is, before anything else, the faculty of relating one point of space to another, one material object to another; it applies to all things, but remains outside them; and of a deep cause it perceives only the effects spread out side by side. Whatever be the force that is at work in the genesis of the nervous system of the caterpillar, to our eyes and our intelligence it is only a juxtaposition of nerves and nervous centers. It is true that we thus get the whole outer effect of it. The Ammophila, no doubt, discerns but a very little of that force, just what concerns itself; but at least it discerns it from within, quite otherwise than by a process of knowledge—by an intuition (*lived* rather than *represented*), which is probably like what we call divining sympathy.

A very significant fact is the swing to and fro of scientific theories of instinct, from regarding it as intelligent to regarding it as simply intelligible, or, shall I say, between likening it to an intelligence "lapsed" and reducing it to a pure mechanism.[1] Each of these systems of explanation triumphs in its criticism of the other, the first when it shows us that instinct cannot be a mere reflex, the other when it declares that instinct is something different from intelligence, even fallen into unconsciousness. What can this mean but that they are two symbolisms, equally acceptable in certain respects, and, in other respects, equally inadequate to their object? The concrete explanation, no longer scientific, but metaphysical, must be sought along quite another path, not in the direction of intelligence, but in that of "sympathy."

Instinct is sympathy. If this sympathy could extend its object and also reflect upon itself, it would give us the key to vital operations—just as intelligence, developed and disciplined, guides us into matter. For—we cannot too often repeat it—intelligence and instinct are turned in opposite directions, the former toward inert matter, the latter toward life. Intelligence, by means of science, which is its work, will deliver up to us more and more completely the secret of physical operations; of life it brings us, and moreover only claims to bring us, a translation in terms of inertia. It goes all round life, taking from outside the greatest possible number of views of it, drawing it into itself instead of entering into it. But it is to the very inwardness of life that *intuition* leads us—by intuition I mean instinct that has become disinterested, self-conscious, capable of reflecting upon its object and of enlarging it indefinitely.

That an effort of this kind is not im-

---

[1] See, in particular, among recent works, Bethe, "Dürfen wir den Ameisen und Bienen psychische Qualitäten zuschreiben?" (*Arch. f. d. ges. Physiologie*, 1898), and Forel, "Un Aperçu de psychologie comparée" (*Année psychologique*, 1895).

possible, is proved by the existence in man of an aesthetic faculty along with normal perception. Our eye perceives the features of the living being, merely as assembled, not as mutually organized. The intention of life, the simple movement that runs through the lines, that binds them together and gives them significance, escapes it. This intention is just what the artist tries to regain, in placing himself back within the object by a kind of sympathy, in breaking down, by an effort of intuition, the barrier that space puts up between him and his model. It is true that this aesthetic intuition, like external perception, only attains the individual. But we can conceive an inquiry turned in the same direction as art, which would take life *in general* for its object, just as physical science, in following to the end the direction pointed out by external perception, prolongs the individual facts into general laws. No doubt this philosophy will never obtain a knowledge of its object comparable to that which science has of its own. Intelligence remains the luminous nucleus around which instinct, even enlarged and purified into intuition, forms only a vague nebulosity. But, in default of knowledge properly so called, reserved to pure intelligence, intuition may enable us to grasp what it is that intelligence fails to give us, and indicate the means of supplementing it. On the one hand, it will utilize the mechanism of intelligence itself to show how intellectual molds cease to be strictly applicable; and on the other hand, by its own work, it will suggest to us the vague feeling, if nothing more, of what must take the place of intellectual molds. Thus, intuition may bring the intellect to recognize that life does not quite go into the category of the many nor yet into that of the one; that neither mechanical causality nor finality can give a sufficient interpretation of the vital process. Then, by the sympathetic communication which it establishes between us and the rest of the living, by the expansion of our consciousness which it brings about, it introduces us into life's own domain, which is reciprocal interpenetration, endlessly continued creation. But, though it thereby transcends intelligence, it is from intelligence that has come the push that has made it rise to the point it has reached. Without intelligence, it would have remained in the form of instinct, riveted to the special object of its practical interest, and turned outward by it into movements of locomotion.

How theory of knowledge must take account of these two faculties, intellect and intuition, and how also, for want of establishing a sufficiently clear distinction between them, it becomes involved in inextricable difficulties, creating phantoms of ideas to which there cling phantoms of problems, we shall endeavor to show a little further on. We shall see that the problem of knowledge, from this point of view, is one with the metaphysical problem, and that both one and the other depend upon experience. On the one hand, indeed, if intelligence is charged with matter and instinct with life, we must squeeze them both in order to get the double essence from them; metaphysics is therefore dependent upon theory of knowledge. But, on the other hand, if consciousness has thus split up into intuition and intelligence, it is because of the need it had to apply itself to matter at the same time as it had to follow the stream of life. The double form of consciousness is then due to the double form of the real, and theory of knowledge must be dependent upon metaphysics. In fact, each of these two lines of thought leads to the other; they form a circle, and there can be no other center to the circle but the empirical study of evolution. It is only in seeing consciousness run through matter, lose itself there and find itself there again, divide and reconstitute itself, that we shall form an idea of the mutual opposition of the two terms, as also, perhaps, of their common origin. But, on the other hand, by dwelling on this opposition of the two elements and on this identity of origin, perhaps we shall bring out more clearly the meaning of evolution itself.

Such will be the aim of our next chapter. But the facts that we have just noticed must have already suggested to us the idea that life is connected either with consciousness or with something that resembles it.

Throughout the whole extent of the animal kingdom, we have said, consciousness seems proportionate to the living being's power of choice. It lights up the zone of potentialities that surrounds the act. It fills the interval between what is done and what might be done. Looked at from without, we may regard it as a simple aid to action, a light that action kindles, a momentary spark flying up from the friction of real action against possible actions. But we must also point out that things would go on in just the same way if consciousness, instead of being the effect, were the cause. We might suppose that consciousness, even in the most rudimentary animal, covers by right an enormous field, but is compressed in fact in a kind of vise: each advance of the nervous centers, by giving the organism a choice between a larger number of actions, calls forth the potentialities that are capable of surrounding the real, thus opening the vise wider and allowing consciousness to pass more freely. In this second hypothesis, as in the first, consciousness is still the instrument of action; but it is even more true to say that action is the instrument of consciousness; for the complicating of action with action, and the opposing of action to action, are for the imprisoned consciousness the only possible means to set itself free. How, then, shall we choose

between the two hypotheses? If the first is true, consciousness must express exactly, at each instant, the state of the brain; there is strict parallelism (so far as intelligible) between the psychical and the cerebral state. On the second hypothesis, on the contrary, there is indeed solidarity and interdependence between the brain and consciousness, but not parallelism: the more complicated the brain becomes, thus giving the organism greater choice of possible actions, the more does consciousness outrun its physical concomitant. Thus, the recollection of the same spectacle probably modifies in the same way a dog's brain and a man's brain, if the perception has been the same; yet the recollection must be very different in the man's consciousness from what it is in the dog's. In the dog, the recollection remains the captive of perception; it is brought back to consciousness only when an analogous perception recalls it by reproducing the same spectacle, and then it is manifested by the recognition, *acted* rather than *thought,* of the present perception much more than by an actual reappearance of the recollection itself. Man, on the contrary, is capable of calling up the recollection at will, at any moment, independently of the present perception. He is not limited to *playing* his past life again; he *represents* and *dreams* it. The local modification of the brain to which the recollection is attached being the same in each case, the psychological difference between the two recollections cannot have its ground in a particular difference of detail between the two cerebral mechanisms, but in the difference between the two brains taken each as a whole. The more complex of the two, in putting a greater number of mechanisms in opposition to one another, has enabled consciousness to disengage itself from the restraint of one and all and to reach independence. That things do happen in this way, that the second of the two hypotheses is that which must be chosen, is what we have tried to prove, in a former work, by the study of facts that best bring into relief the relation of the conscious state to the cerebral state, the facts of normal and pathological recognition, in particular the forms of aphasia.[1] But it could have been proved by pure reasoning, before even it was evidenced by facts. We have shown on what self-contradictory postulate, on what confusion of two mutually incompatible symbolisms, the hypothesis of equivalence between the cerebral state and the psychic state rests.[2]

The evolution of life, looked at from this point, receives a clearer meaning, although it cannot be subsumed under any actual *idea*. It is as if a broad current of consciousness had penetrated matter, loaded, as all consciousness is, with an enormous multiplicity of interwoven potentialities. It has carried matter along to organization, but its movement has been at once infinitely retarded and infinitely divided. On the one hand, indeed, consciousness has had to fall asleep, like the chrysalis in the envelope in which it is preparing for itself wings; and, on the other hand, the manifold tendencies it contained have been distributed among divergent series of organisms which, moreover, express these tendencies outwardly in movements rather than internally in representations. In the course of this evolution, while some beings have fallen more and more asleep, others have more and more completely awakened, and the torpor of some has served the activity of others. But the waking could be effected in two different ways. Life, that is to say consciousness launched into matter, fixed its attention either on its own movement or on the matter it was passing through; and it has thus been turned either in the direction of intuition or in that of intellect. Intuition, at first sight, seems far preferable to intellect, since in it life and consciousness remain within themselves. But a glance at the evolution of living beings shows us that intuition could not go very far. On the side of intuition, consciousness found itself so restricted by its envelope that intuition had to shrink into instinct, that is, to embrace only the very small portion of life that interested it; and this it embraces only in the dark, touching it while hardly seeing it. On this side, the horizon was soon shut out. On the contrary, consciousness, in shaping itself into intelligence, that is to say in concentrating itself at first on matter, seems to externalize itself in relation to itself; but, just because it adapts itself thereby to objects from without, it succeeds in moving among them and in evading the barriers they oppose to it, thus opening to itself an unlimited field. Once freed, moreover, it can turn inwards on itself, and awaken the potentialities of intuition which still slumber within it.

From this point of view, not only does consciousness appear as the motive principle of evolution, but also, among conscious beings themselves, man comes to occupy a privileged place. Between him and the animals the difference is no longer one of degree, but of kind. We shall show how this conclusion is arrived at in our next chapter. Let us now show how the preceding analyses suggest it.

A noteworthy fact is the extraordinary disproportion between the consequences of an invention and the invention itself. We have said that intelligence is modeled on matter and that it aims in the first place at fabrication. But does it fabricate in order to fabricate or does it not pursue involuntarily, and even unconsciously, something entirely different? Fabricating

---

[1] *Matière et mémoire,* chaps. ii. and iii.
[2] "Le Paralogisme psycho-physiologique" (*Revue de métaphysique,* Nov. 1904).

consists in shaping matter, in making it supple and in bending it, in converting it into an instrument in order to become master of it. It is this *mastery* that profits humanity, much more even than the material result of the invention itself. Though we derive an immediate advantage from the thing made, as an intelligent animal might do, and though this advantage be all the inventor sought, it is a slight matter compared with the new ideas and new feelings that the invention may give rise to in every direction, as if the essential part of the effect were to raise us above ourselves and enlarge our horizon. Between the effect and the cause the disproportion is so great that it is difficult to regard the cause as *producer* of its effect. It releases it, while settling, indeed, its direction. Everything happens as though the grip of intelligence on matter were, in its main intention, to *let something pass* that matter is holding back.

The same impression arises when we compare the brain of man with that of the animals. The difference at first appears to be only a difference of size and complexity. But, judging by function, there must be something else besides. In the animal, the motor mechanisms that the brain succeeds in setting up, or, in other words, the habits contracted voluntarily, have no other object nor effect than the accomplishment of the movements marked out in these habits, stored in these mechanisms. But, in man, the motor habit may have a second result, out of proportion to the first: it can hold other motor habits in check, and thereby, in overcoming automatism, set consciousness free. We know what vast regions in the human brain language occupies. The cerebral mechanisms that correspond to the words have this in particular, that they can be made to grapple with other mechanisms, those, for instance, that correspond to the

things themselves, or even be made to grapple with one another. Meanwhile consciousness, which would have been dragged down and drowned in the accomplishment of the act, is restored and set free.[1]

The difference must therefore be more radical than a superficial examination would lead us to suppose. It is the difference between a mechanism which engages the attention and a mechanism from which it can be diverted. The primitive steam engine, as Newcomen conceived it, required the presence of a person exclusively employed to turn on and off the taps, either to let the steam into the cylinder or to throw the cold spray into it in order to condense the steam. It is said that a boy employed on this work, and very tired of having to do it, got the idea of tying the handles of the taps, with cords, to the beam of the engine. Then the machine opened and closed the taps itself; it worked all alone. Now, if an observer had compared the structure of this second machine with that of the first without taking into account the two boys left to watch over them, he would have found only a slight difference of complexity. That is, indeed, all we can perceive when we look only at the machines. But if we cast a glance at the two boys, we shall see that whilst one is wholly taken up by the watching, the other is free to go and play as he chooses, and that, from this point of view, the difference between the two machines is radical, the first holding the attention captive, the second setting it at liberty. A difference of the same kind, we think,

---

[1] A geologist whom we have already had occasion to cite, N. S. Shaler, well says that "when we come to man, it seems as if we find the ancient subjection of mind to body abolished, and the intellectual parts develop with an extraordinary rapidity, the structure of the body remaining identical in essentials" (Shaler, *The Interpretation of Nature*).

would be found between the brain of an animal and the human brain.

If, now, we should wish to express this in terms of finality, we should have to say that consciousness, after having been obliged, in order to set itself free, to divide organization into two complementary parts, vegetables on one hand and animals on the other, has sought an issue in the double direction of instinct and of intelligence. It has not found it with instinct, and it has not obtained it on the side of intelligence except by a sudden leap from the animal to man. So that, in the last analysis, man might be considered the reason for the existence of the entire organization of life on our planet. But this would be only a matter of speaking. There is, in reality, only a current of existence and the opposing current; thence proceeds the whole evolution of life. We must now grasp more closely the opposition of these two currents. Perhaps we shall thus discover for them a common source. By this we shall also, no doubt, penetrate the most obscure regions of metaphysics. However, as the two directions we have to follow are clearly marked, in intelligence on the one hand, in instinct and intuition on the other, we are not afraid of straying. A survey of the evolution of life suggests to us a certain conception of knowledge, and also a certain metaphysics, which imply each other. Once made clear, this metaphysics and this critique may throw some light, in their turn, on evolution as a whole.

THE LIFE AND WORKS OF
HENRI BERGSON

By JEAN GUITTON

GREAT PHILOSOPHERS are very rare, and it is difficult to judge whether a contemporary thinker is great. History is full of mistaken evaluations. In the 19th century, for instance, Victor Cousin, Caro, and Jules Simon were held in high esteem, but little was heard of Kierkegaard, Maine de Biran, or Jules Lequier. If Henri Bergson had been asked to evaluate one of his contemporaries, he would no doubt have replied that only time would tell. The true test of a philosopher lies in his influence. If his work inspires other thinkers, people will be able to say that he was great. Yet I have little doubt that in the case of Bergson, his contemporaries have made no mistake, and the Nobel Prize award was prophetic of a lasting fame.

Henri Bergson was born in 1859, the son of a Jewish musician and an Englishwoman. He was educated at the Lycée Condorcet and the Ecole Normale Supérieure. Here he showed an early interest in philosophy, and upon graduation he began to teach. After working in several secondary schools, he was appointed to the faculty of the Ecole Normale Supérieure in 1898. From 1900 to 1921, he held the chair in philosophy at the Collège de France. In 1914 he was elected to the Académie Française and from 1921 to 1926 he was president of the Commission for Intellectual Cooperation of the League of Nations.

Such are the highlights of Bergson's biography. In this tribute, I should like to consider some of his ideas, and sketch a few personal vignettes of the man himself.

I never heard Bergson give a lecture; I was too young at the time. But when I spoke with him alone, there was magic in it. He sculptured his thoughts. Laboriously but unhesitatingly, he sought for order, consistency, and proper sequence. In his flowing sustained discourse nothing was left to chance. Bergson did not chat as Montaigne did. He directed the conversation and logically marshaled his thoughts. Yet he seemed to chance upon new ideas by good fortune, and even appeared to be surprised at his discoveries. Then he smiled and contemplated them with a speculative eye. As I listened, I had no thought of the passing of time, of myself, or even of Bergson's presence. I was witnessing the emergence of thought, coming forth all armed like Pallas with her golden shield glinting in the sun.

I would surreptitiously watch his eyes; they were very gentle, but did not look directly at the person with whom he was conversing, perhaps out of modesty. His eyes had a hypnotic power. They were an untroubled blue, very deep-set, on watch beneath his shaggy eyebrows. The eyes of an owl, I thought, both meditative and gracious. Those true connoisseurs, the Greeks, chose the owl as a symbol of intelligence.

When Bergson spoke, his voice was restrained, warm, musical, and slow; it seemed to be disclosing a secret that he had just discovered and was confiding to you alone. And from time to time his eyes and his silences held points of suspension, or rather of surprise, which I have seen in no one else.

If modesty of the mind includes that sense of inviolability which constitutes modesty of the body, then Bergson had modesty in every fiber. The desire to avoid contact, to protect himself, to refrain from revealing himself too soon, to keep his past to himself—these instincts were deeply ingrained in his character. But he also had a true awareness of his original contribution to thought, a fear of seeing his ideas distorted by false friends or misinterpreted by true ones, a weary disinclination to reply to his critics, and an excessive benevolence toward those who praised him.

Bergson often spoke of emotion. He is one of the few moralists who maintained that men are more emotional than women. He did not mean those surface tremors in which, after a surprise of the mind or the senses, body and consciousness intertwine for a moment. For Bergson emotion was the herald of creation. It was in this sense that he nonchalantly said one day that brain work "arises out of a concentration of the mind with a pure emotion as its basis." He can have meant nothing else than the jolt which the mind receives when confronted with the innermost self, the trembling, obscure face of intuition.

Bergson recognized that in every man there is a point of intense sensitivity, the source of our anxieties and resentments, but also the mainspring of our hopes and achievements. He believed that the essence of understanding and friendship lay in finding this precise point. He defined politeness as "sparing other people's feelings and making them pleased with themselves and with us." Thus Bergson even applied intuition to ordinary human intercourse; he would no doubt have endorsed Pascal's view that "love and reason are one and the same thing."

There was within Bergson a conflict between two beliefs. At the root of most great systems of ideas lies a hidden conflict that the philosopher has had to overcome, a set of apparently contradictory principles that he has synthesized into a painful, glorious unity.

In an unpublished lecture that Bergson gave on Socrates, he showed the Greek philosopher divided between two fundamental ideas. One was the concept that nowadays might be called "scientific"; Socrates believed in the ideal of universal knowledge and was going to create a scientific system of knowledge that would apply to man. But at the same time Socrates was a religious man with an inner "demon" which drove him to become a missionary of knowledge in the Delphic world. Unity of these two vocations could only be achieved through the creation of a form of thought and life that was both scientific and religious. His task was to apply a scientific mode of thought to the shifting, changeable subjects of man, moral issues and the community—and in that way to gain self-knowledge.

Likewise, in Bergson's day, scholars, philosophers, positivists and scientists had propounded a system of knowledge, while psychologists, moralists, mystics, and poets were studying man subjectively and unsystematically. It remained for the exact and cautious scientific method to be applied to the study of man's inner being to create what Bergson sometimes called "positive metaphysics." Bergson was a true descendant of Socrates—a missionary of self-knowledge, a mystical free-thinker, a founder of "moral science."

Let us try to express the same view from another angle. We know how Greek philosopher Zeno mischievously argued that fleet-footed Achilles could never overtake the tortoise. Applying the logic of mathematics, which abhors continuity and always divides it into measurable units, Zeno argued that by the time Achilles reached the point from which the tortoise started, it would have moved on to another point; by the time he reaches that second point, it would have moved on again; and so on *ad infinitum*.

Zeno's argument seemed to Bergson to have a universal significance. Zeno was criticizing those who confused the spatial path of motion with the motion itself, and claimed that everything that is true of the path was also true of the motion. To be sure, if the path is divided an indefinite number of times, breaking Achilles's indivisible impetus, he will never catch up with the tortoise. But how can we understand motion by breaking it up into an infinite number of stops?

Is this not a constant tendency of the human mind? Doesn't the intellect always try to replace concrete, dynamic reality with abstract, static symbols? And does it not then proceed to handle these symbols with learned stupidity as though they were reality itself? And does it not end up in destroying the very essence of the reality that it thinks it has analyzed?

This is the illusion of the scientific mind when it applies itself to human affairs, and it was an illusion Bergson fought all his life. Everywhere he found the mask of the man whom Paul Valéry called "cruel Zeno."

He found Zeno first of all in Fechner and Stuart Mill, who zenonized on inten-sity and liberty, the two aspects of quality. They reduced it to a quantity! He saw Zeno, too, in Charcot, Ribot, and the psychologists of the Taine school, who more or less based memory on matter. Herbert Spencer was another Zeno. He was the first to excite Bergson's admiration, but he zenonized in the extreme. Just as a movie recreates movement from a series of still photographs (a preeminently zenonic device), Spencer studied evolution by placing side by side small fragments of its products, whereas evolution is in fact an indivisible impetus.

In Bergson's eyes, Einstein also zenonized in handling time as a fourth dimension of space. And, in the moral and religious sphere, Durkheim zenonized too, by reducing religions to a single, primitive element, such as the totem. This method of working by reduction from a higher level to a lower is a misuse of science; it purports to explain, but actually destroys the essence of what it is explaining, just as Zeno did. Laughter also zenonizes, for it carries life to its absurd extreme, substituting caricature for character. And in every one of us, habits and routines also zenonize; for inventive freshness they substitute a series of movements that take place without our volition.

At the end of his life Bergson turned to the problem of religion. Bergson never set out to prove anything, but only to analyze one aspect of experience. But he studied it with searching thoroughness.

In 1912, he said that his book on *Les Données immédiates de la conscience* (*Time and Free Will*) (1889) established the fact that freedom exists; *Matière et Mémoire* (*Matter and Memory*) (1896) gave positive proof of the reality of the mind; *L'Evolution créatrice* (*Creative Evolution*) (1907) presented creation as a fact. "From all this there clearly emerges the idea of a free, creative God, to whom both matter and life owe their existence and whose work of creation is continued, where life is concerned, by the evolution of the species and the formation of human personalities." Thus in his middle years, he saw both paths at once. *Les Deux Sources de la morale et de la religion* (*The Two Sources of Morality and Religion*) (1932) was an extension and, better still, a justification of *Creative Evolution*. The latter gives the immediate cause of the impetus that surges through the worlds. *The Two Sources* tells us of the conditions that are conducive to the appearance of the human personalities most capable of creative activity—mystics in particular, and above all the very few "complete mystics," "God's co-operators." Bergson found these among the Jewish prophets and the saints of Catholicism (which Bergson saw as the "fulfillment of Judaism"). This is the key to the closing words of Bergson's writings, which state that the world is the sum total of all the conditions conducive to the emergence of godly men—"a god-making machine."

In *The Two Sources,* Bergson does not dwell on the Christ of the Gospels (except once in an almost problematical way) any more than he mentions God in *Creative Evolution* (except for one discreet reference). In both these works we find evidence of his reticent modesty and the piety of silence. But Bergson came to think of Jesus as "the foremost among mystics"—the one in whom "man liberated the species and liberated himself from the species." These are the words of Henri Gouhier, the latest commentator on Bergson's works; and he adds "This is not the Christianity of the Passion or the Entombment, but that of the Ascension and the Assumption in which all mankind is borne aloft into a Venetian sky with Tintoretto's 'Resurrection' and Titian's 'Virgin'."

Creative Evolution is Bergson's most beautiful book. It is a stylistic masterpiece, both precise and musical in expression. Bergson told me that he wrote this book fairly quickly after several attempts, almost without rereading what he had written, like an epic poured forth in a state of lucid exaltation. There is, in fact, a rare degree of harmony between the flow of this work (which is astonishing both in its tempo and in its details) and the idea that inspires it. The author's purpose is to explain the inner impetus of the universe and of life, which bears the mark of a divine impulse and design. Bergson begins by denying the philosophy of materialism, which has so many close ties with Western man in Aristotelian and Stoic culture, and in the spurious metaphysics to which modern science has given rise. Matter, he says, is not a creative force. The impetus of life is directed toward freedom and spirituality (later on, Bergson would say toward mystical belief or, in other words, saintliness). This impetus encounters matter, the mere "fallout" of the mind, both as an obstacle and as an instrument. The plant and animal species are compromises in which life and consciousness are trapped together. But the primordial creative impetus refuses to be held captive forever. It partly sets itself free when humanity suddenly emerges from its animal world; then a being appears that is capable of indefinite progress, with the ability to create machines and machine-making machines through its intelligence while, through its intuition, it shares in the very source of creation.

Such is the main argument of this book. It is in effect the Judaeo-Christian answer to Lucretius's poem *De natura rerum,* which Bergson had annotated in his youth with veiled admiration.

Bergson's book is filled with subtle and fascinating conjections.

The ability to adapt to the world, for instance, which Bergson (wrongly perhaps) calls "intelligence," may have been copied from matter, where it is so successful. Intuition, on the other hand, may be our guide to the very core of reality. Perhaps philosophy—whether that of the Greeks, enamored of general ideas and classifications, or that of modern thinkers hallucinated by the "laws" of nature—has largely neglected the essentials: consciousness, freedom, inner life, duration, real time, history, individual existence.

Creative Evolution was a disturbing, poetic and revolutionary book. It jolted men's minds but was not understood either by the friends of science, who saw Bergson as a "romantic," or by the friends of tradition, who mistook him for a denier. After fifty years, it is easy to see that Bergson was less of an innovator than he thought. He revived the intuition of Plato, Plotinus, Saint Augustine, Saint Thomas, Descartes, and Leibniz, according to which a close, searching, complete study of either the cosmic or the psychic sphere reveals the existence of an impulse and an aspiration which it cannot have created itself. Bergson's book, furnished with observations drawn from science, based on a positive method and abounding in aesthetic, psychological, and mystical intuition, takes its place among the works on "the philosophy of nature" that link physics with metaphysics. It is Plato's *Timaeus* rethought by a modern philosopher who has read Genesis.

Jean Guitton is a literary critic and member of the Académie Française. Translated by Annie Jackson.

THE 1927 PRIZE

By KJELL STRÖMBERG

In 1928, the Swedish Academy awarded two Nobel Prizes for Literature. No award had been made in 1926, and the award made in 1927 was for 1926.

Although a good three dozen candidates were proposed, for once the choice must not have been very difficult. Among the candidates there were only three or four whose qualifications were more than sufficient and whose names would confer increased prestige on the Prize. Thus it came about that the 1927 Prize was awarded practically without discussion to the great French philosopher Henri Bergson, who was recommended by an impressive number of scholars and writers from his own country; and the 1928 Prize went to the Norwegian novelist Sigrid Undset, then at the peak of her fame in the Scandinavian countries and already translated into several foreign languages.

A year earlier, Thomas Mann had published his *Magic Mountain,* a masterpiece attempting a philosophical synthesis of the modern world, but Mann had to wait until 1929 to win the award. Maxim Gorki, also considered a sure winner, was turned down once again. Among the candidates who were also rejected were several French writers, including Paul Bourget, Countess Mathieu de Noailles, Edouard Estaunie, and J. H. Rosny, Sr.

The candidacy of Henri Bergson had first been proposed in 1912, by the British professor Andrew Lang, a member of the Royal Society of Literature. By this time Bergson had practically finished his life's work and was already famous throughout the world.

The Nobel Committee of the Swedish Academy acted on this candidacy by assigning two Scandinavian philosophers, Axel Herrlin and Vitalis Norström, to make a thorough study of his work. Norström, a member of the Academy, wrote additional reports on Bergson in 1913 and 1914. Perhaps he would have succeeded in having his choice ratified if war had not broken out, interrupting the awards for several years. Using the extensive reports of these two scholars as a point of departure, another Academician, the poet Werner von Heidenstam, who was to receive the Nobel Prize in 1916, resumed the reporting task in 1918 and 1921. In 1921, Bergson was seconded by a dozen members of the Parisian Académie des Sciences Morales et Politiques under the leadership of former Prime Minister Alexandre Ribot and former President of the Republic Paul Deschanel. Their action, however, had no practical effect. Anatole France took the Prize away from his distinguished compatriot, who was not again proposed until 1928. But by 1928, his candidacy was advanced with such power of persuasion that the Swedish Academy had nothing else to do but to give in gracefully.

Unfortunately, for a number of years Bergson had been confined to his home by a serious illness which paralyzed his legs and sometimes his hands as well. He was unable to go to Stockholm. France was being particularly honored that year because another great Frenchman, Dr. Charles Nicolle, conqueror of the typhus fever which had scourged North Africa, was to receive the Nobel Prize for Medicine for 1928. Dr. Nicolle was also prevented from attending because he had to preside over a bacteriological congress in Cairo. The French minister to Sweden, Armand Bernard, represented both his countrymen at the ceremony. Later, at the traditional Town Hall banquet following the ceremony, he read the messages of the two laureates.

These noble words were echoed almost immediately in Paris, beneath the dome of the Palais Mazarin, where Professor Lévy-Bruhl, presiding at the annual public meeting of the Académie des Sciences Morales et Politiques, delivered a ringing tribute to his illustrious colleague and to his Swedish judges:

This honor which comes to him from the North is echoed in the honor of unanimous agreement throughout the world. Whatever the merits of his competitors, no one could be surprised when the Swedish Academy chose Bergson. In awarding him the Prize for Literature, they were surely honoring first the philosopher, the original and profound genius whose irresistible influence has spread throughout the world and which has stamped an entire age with its imprint. If Bergson's philosophy had known adversaries, if it was even inevitable that it should meet with opposition, like any new doctrine which succeeds, there has never been anything but unanimity in regard to its *literary value*. His critics bow before the precision, the Greek elegance and perfection of his style which, seemingly without effort, succeeds in explaining the unexplainable.

Translated by Dale McAdoo.